The Infra-red Spectra of
Complex Molecules

The Infra-red Spectra
of
Complex Molecules

by

L. J. BELLAMY

B.Sc., Ph.D.

Senior Principal Scientific Officer,
Ministry of Supply

LONDON: METHUEN & CO LTD
NEW YORK: JOHN WILEY & SONS, INC.

First published July 15th, 1954
Reprinted, with minor corrections, 1956
Second edition, 1958
Reprinted four times
Reprinted 1964

2·6
CATALOGUE NO. 2/5480/11 (METHUEN)

*Printed in Great Britain by Richard Clay and Company, Ltd.,
Bungay, Suffolk*

PREFACE TO THE SECOND EDITION

THE justification for the issue of a revised edition of this book so soon after its first publication will, I hope, be apparent from the text. Although a good deal of material which has been superseded by later work has been deleted, the final product is considerably larger than before. Some indication of the volume of new work which has been included is given by the fact that over 700 new references have survived the screening process. I have, however, continued to aim to include all relevant references on the grounds that any unwanted ones are not difficult to skip.

I have adhered to my original intention of avoiding any theoretical discussion of the vibration-rotation spectra of small molecules, as this topic is well covered by a number of excellent texts. However, I have been unable to resist the temptation to include a final chapter on the origins and significance of group frequency shifts in large molecules. This subject has made appreciable advances in the past few years, and a beginning, at least, has been made on the task of introducing some kind of rational order into the mass of empirical data which exist on group frequencies in large molecules. Many problems remain to be solved in this field, and the reader should appreciate that some of the ideas discussed are still very much in the formative stage. Nevertheless, some of the spectral relationships which are derived from this work have already reached a stage of practical utility in structural diagnosis, whilst an understanding of the basic factors which underlie the sometimes apparently eccentric behaviour of individual group frequencies is essential if correlation work is to be properly carried out. In preparing this chapter I have tried to be as objective as possible, but the reader will do well to treat some small portions of it with the special degree of reserve we all accord to authors who are presenting an unbiased account of their own activities.

One serious problem in the preparation of this revision has been that of the presentation of intensity data. There is no doubt that the recognition of specific molecular groups will in the future be based as much on absolute intensities as on absolute frequencies, and in some cases the former can be a good deal more informative. At the present time, however, the variable quality of the data available and the lack of uniformity in the method of presenting the results make it impracticable for this data to be properly evaluated at this stage. I have not therefore attempted a separate review of this topic, but have followed the practice of the earlier edition and included such information as is available along with the discussion of the appropriate group frequency.

The task of collating the very considerable volume of literature in this field has been very greatly eased by the kindness of many authors who have sent me copies of reprints of their papers. To all of them, my very grateful thanks. In the hope that they—and others—will continue to help in this way I have hopefully included my address below. All books of this type must lean heavily on the work of their predecessors, and in both editions I have been much helped by the various correlation charts which have appeared in the literature from time to time and by the earlier texts of Randall, Fowler, Fuson and Dangl, and of Barnes, Gore, Liddel and van zandt Williams. For the purposes of this revision the excellent text by Jones and Sandorfy has also been of considerable assistance. I must also thank the Council of the Chemical Society for their kind permission to reproduce a number of illustrations which have appeared in their journal.

L. J. B.

E.R.D.E. Ministry of Supply,
  Waltham Abbey,   *July, 1957*
    Essex.

CONTENTS

Contents xi

Contents

PART V
Chapter 23. THE ORIGINS AND SIGNIFICANCE OF GROUP FREQUENCY SHIFTS

CORRELATION CHARTS

INFRA-RED SPECTRA

CHAPTER 1

Introduction

INFRA-RED spectroscopy is being employed to an ever-increasing extent in commerce and in organic chemistry for the recognition and the quantitative analysis of structural units in unknown compounds. Almost all the spectrometers employed in industry are used for this purpose, although, in the hands of theoretical physicists, the spectra can also be used to obtain fundamental data on the mechanics of simple molecules. The latter studies are extremely useful to the analyst, in that the particular motions associated with the various characteristic frequencies are determined, so that it is possible to assess to some extent the likelihood of frequency shifts occurring with changes in the local environment of the group. Nevertheless, these studies are necessarily restricted to simple molecules in which the frequencies associated with various structural units are often out of line with those found for more complex materials.

In the interpretation of spectra, therefore, the analyst must rely upon the empirical data which have been accumulated relating infra-red absorption bands with structural units. This involves a very complete knowledge of all the widely scattered work on this subject, and this is not easy to obtain. A number of correlation charts summarising this information have been published from time to time and, properly used, these are of great value. However, as their authors point out, the correlations are of unequal value and, in some cases, are based on the study of limited groups of compounds, so that their incautious use can lead to wholly misleading results. Furthermore, if the frequency ranges given for a specific grouping, such as the carbonyl vibration, were to be extended to cover all the known cases in which interference or interaction effects occur, the final range would be too wide to be of any value; whereas, in fact, the particular point at which a carbonyl absorption appears within this range will often throw a good deal of light on the nature of the adjoining structure.

The present work is, therefore, an attempt to present a critical review of the data on which infra-red spectral correlations are based, indicating the classes of compounds which have been studied in each case and the known factors which can influence the frequencies or intensities of the characteristic bands. In doing so, especial attention has been paid to publications dealing with the groups of compounds containing common structural units and although a considerable

1

number of fundamental studies on single molecules have been covered, no attempt has been made to provide a complete bibliography of these, as the absorption of structural units of very simple compounds are often not typical of those found in larger molecules. For ease of reference the chemical names given in the original publications have been retained throughout, although this has involved occasional departures from the accepted British nomenclature.

Many of the correlations discussed, particularly those in the high-frequency region, are capable of giving structural information of great value and precision, and the position and intensities of the absorption bands can be used to confirm the presence of a particular group and to obtain information as to its environment. Others, particularly in the region of skeletal vibrations, are subject to considerable frequency alterations with structural change. These can only be employed with caution and cannot safely be applied to structures widely different from those on which the correlations are based. Nevertheless, even these can be of value in indicating possible structures, whilst the absence of any bands in the appropriate region is usually a good indication of the absence of the particular grouping from the molecule. In any case, in work of this type, the spectroscopist is expected to indicate not only the presence of groupings of which he can be reasonably certain, but also to discuss the various structures which may be present but which cannot be identified with certainty. It is in assisting him to determine the proper weight which can be given to any particular identification that it is hoped this book will prove to be of value.

The subject-matter of this book has been strictly confined to the empirical interpretation of infra-red spectra, as this is the topic on which no adequate text has appeared. No attempt has been made to cover the many related aspects of practical spectroscopy, such as sample preparation, cell construction, quantitative analysis, instrumentation, etc. These topics have all been adequately discussed in a number of existing texts and in others which will be available shortly. Furthermore, very few workers in this field are so fortunate as to possess more than one type of instrument, and they rapidly learn by experience far more about its individual characteristics and peculiarities than can be covered in any general review of the subject.

In any book of this kind which deals with a mass of isolated empirical observations about a variety of different structural units, a purely arbitrary arrangement of subject-matter must be employed, and I have followed the general lines of the well-known correlation charts which have appeared in the literature from time to time.[1-8] The various types of linkage are roughly classified into four main classes:—

I. Carbon–carbon and carbon–hydrogen links. II. Carbon–oxygen and oxygen–hydrogen links. III. Carbon–nitrogen and nitrogen–hydrogen links. IV. Linkages involving other elements, or which are related to inorganic structures. This arrangement has not however been followed too rigidly. The discussion on amides, for example, cannot be divided between parts II and III; and it has been included at the head of part III, where it follows directly upon the discussion of carbonyl frequencies in part II. Similarly, the chapter on nitro-compounds and related structures heads part IV, where it follows the discussion of carbon–nitrogen linkages.

As regards the choice of units, I have employed wave-numbers throughout. In choosing to give frequencies rather than wave-lengths I have been influenced partly by the recent recommendations of the Royal Society Committee, and partly by my own view that the wave-number scale is the only really satisfactory one for correlation work. The use of this scale makes it much easier to identify overtone and combination bands, and it is especially valuable in enabling direct comparisons to be made with Raman spectra. Probably the most powerful argument which can be advanced for the wave-length scale is the fact that it is easier to construct an instrument which is linear on this basis. For the benefit of those who use such instruments a table of reciprocals is included at the end of the book.

At the beginning of each chapter a brief outline is given of the correlations to be discussed, together with a table giving the various frequency ranges, whilst at the end of this chapter a series of charts is given in which the correlations are summarised in the usual line drawing form. The first is intended to give the reader an outline of the particular correlations which exist before discussing any one of them in detail, whilst the second is designed to enable him to see readily any other structural units which might be expected to absorb in any specific region and which might therefore interfere. It cannot be too strongly emphasised that the indiscriminate use of either of these summaries for correlation work without reference to the detailed work on which they are based can only lead to error. An endeavour has been made to make the tables and discussion as complete as possible, and therefore they include many tentative, and even some rather dubious correlations which have not yet much experimental backing. They are, therefore, intended only for use in conjunction with the more detailed accounts of their origin and reliability. In both the charts and the tables a rough indication of the absorption intensity is given by the symbols (s)—strong; (m)—medium; (w)—weak and (v)—variable.

A small group of spectra have been included at the end of each of the four parts. These have been chosen to illustrate as far as possible some of the correlations which have been discussed, and the individual assignments for the various structural units involved have been indicated on them. As before, these include some doubtful correlations inserted for completeness, and the identifications are therefore not certain in all cases. Some particularly doubtful correlations are indicated by a question-mark on these spectra. These illustrations may also be of value to workers newly entering this field, for practice purposes.

These spectra were all obtained with a Perkin–Elmer 21B double beam spectrometer equipped with a rock-salt prism. The great majority of the spectra mentioned in the text as originating in our laboratories were also obtained with this instrument, although a few were obtained with a Hilger D.209 spectrometer working as a single beam instrument.

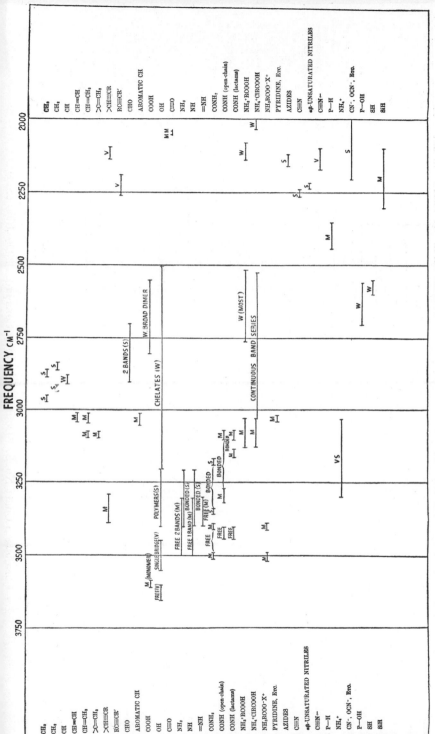

Correlation Chart No. 1.   Hydrogen stretching and triple-bond vibrations.   3750–2000 cm.$^{-1}$

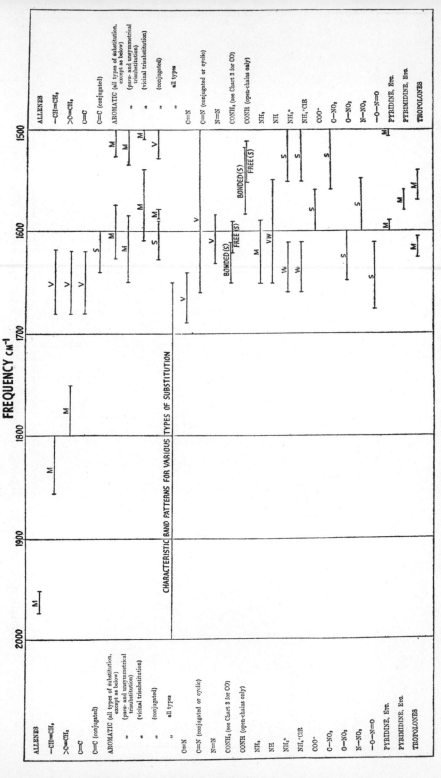

Correlation Chart No. 2.   Double-bond vibrations etc.   2000–1500 cm.⁻¹

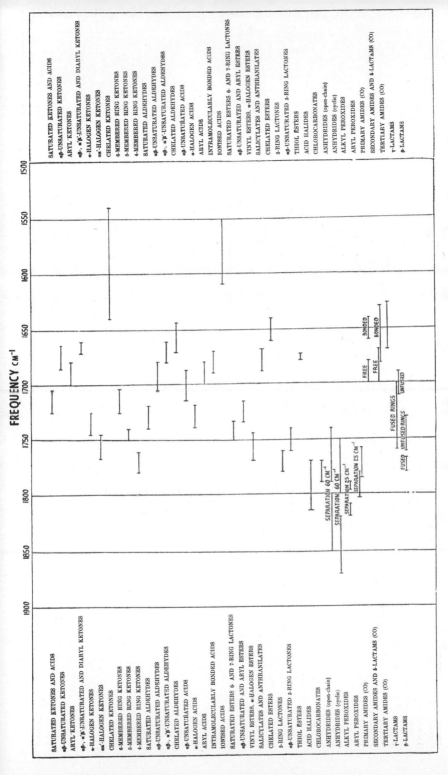

Correlation Chart No. 3.   Carbonyl vibrations (all strong bands).   1900–1500 cm.⁻¹

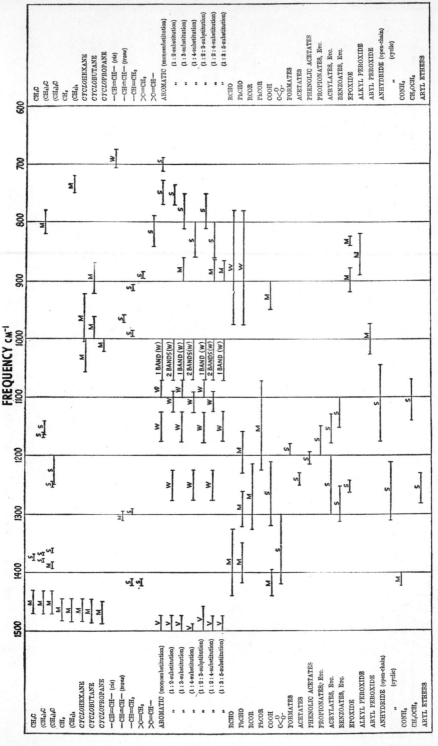

Correlation Chart No. 4. Single-bond vibrations etc. (I). 1500–650 cm.⁻¹

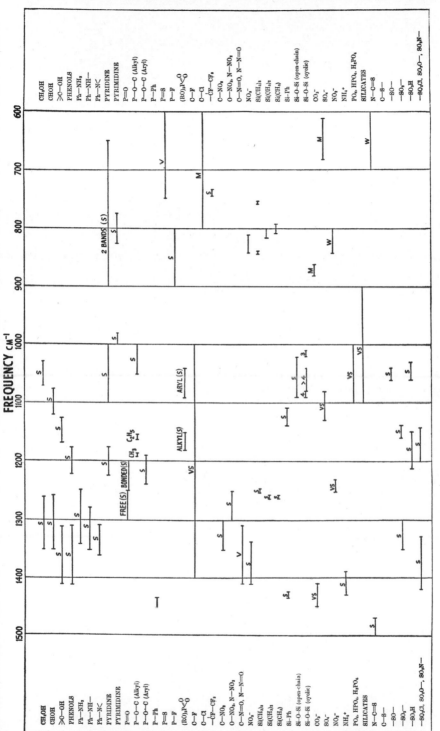

Correlation Chart No. 5. Single-bond vibrations etc. (II). 1500–650 cm.⁻¹

PART I

VIBRATIONS OF CARBON–CARBON AND CARBON–HYDROGEN LINKAGES

CHAPTER 2

Alkanes

2.1. INTRODUCTION AND TABLE

THE study of the characteristic absorption bands arising from various types of hydrocarbon structures has produced a number of reliable correlations between the band positions and the types of grouping present. Of these, the correlations involving C–H stretching and bending modes are the most specific, but correlations involving skeletal C–C frequencies are also available for certain types of branched-chain structures. The C–H stretching mode absorptions are especially useful in differentiating saturated and unsaturated materials and, when combined with a study of the deformation modes, it is also possible to obtain an approximate indication

TABLE 2

CH *Stretching Frequencies*		
CH_3	2962 and 2872 cm.$^{-1}$ ± 10 cm.$^{-1}$ (s)	
CH_2	2926 and 2853 cm.$^{-1}$ ± 10 cm.$^{-1}$ (s)	
CH (tertiary)	2890 ± 10 cm.$^{-1}$ (w)	
CH *Deformation Frequencies*		
C–CH_3	1450 ± 20 cm.$^{-1}$ (m) (asymmetrical)	
–CH_2–	1465 ± 20 cm.$^{-1}$ (m)	
C–CH_3	1380–1370 cm.$^{-1}$ (s) (symmetrical)	
–C–$(CH_3)_2$	1385–1380 (s) 1370–1365 cm.$^{-1}$ (s) (approx. equal intensity)	
–C–$(CH_3)_3$	1395–1385 (m) 1365 (s) cm.$^{-1}$	
–CH–	Near 1340 cm.$^{-1}$ (w)	
Skeletal Vibrations		
$(CH_3)_3$–C–R	1250 ± 5 cm.$^{-1}$ (s) 1250–1200 cm.$^{-1}$ (s) near 415 cm.$^{-1}$	
$(CH_3)_2$–C	1170 ± 5 cm.$^{-1}$ (s) 1170–1140 cm.$^{-1}$ (s) near 800 cm^{-1}	
–$(CH_2)_4$–	750–720 cm.$^{-1}$ (s)	
–$(CH_2)_4$–O– (or other functional group)	742–734 (s) (not applicable to hydrocarbons)	
Ring Systems		
*Cyclo*propane	1020–1000 cm.$^{-1}$ (m)	
*Cyclo*butane	920–866 cm.$^{-1}$ or 1000–960 cm.$^{-1}$	(m) All tentative
*Cyclo*pentane	Nil	(m) All tentative
*Cyclo*hexane	1005–925 cm.$^{-1}$ and 1055–1000 cm.$^{-1}$	(m) All tentative

of the proportions of CH_3, CH_2 and CH groups present in hydrocarbons.

The symmetrical CH_3 deformation is also valuable in diagnostic work in the recognition of both the $C-CH_3$ link and branched-chain structures, whilst assignments of the latter can be checked by reference to skeletal frequencies.

Correlations for the $-(CH_2)_4-$ group and for saturated cyclic hydrocarbons have also been considered in this section.

The correlations discussed are listed in Table 2.

2.2. C–H STRETCHING VIBRATIONS

2.2.(a). Position. In the region of 3000 cm.$^{-1}$ infra-red absorption bands arise from the C–H stretching modes of organic materials. This was recognised as early as 1905 by Coblentz,[1] whilst Bonino[2] in 1929 pointed out that the characteristic CH bands of aromatic and aliphatic compounds in this region occurred at different recognisable positions. The study of the nature of these bands and the correlation of their position with various types of structure is due to Fox and Martin.[3-6] In a series of papers between 1937 and 1940 they were able to show that, in hydrocarbons, the position of the absorption peaks from CH stretching modes is determined almost entirely by the nature of the linkage involved and is virtually independent of the rest of the structure. Thus, in saturated materials, a close group of absorption peaks arises from CH_3, CH_2 and CH groups; in aromatic compounds the presence of a double bond on the carbon atom to which the hydrogen atom is attached results in a shift to higher frequency, whilst full aliphatic unsaturation results in a further and bigger shift. Using the relatively low dispersion of a sodium chloride prism it is not possible to do more than recognise these main classes, but this is of considerable value, and Rasmussen and Brattain,[7] for example, have made use of this region in the recognition of unsaturation in olefines. With a lithium fluoride prism, however, the dispersion is sufficient to enable the differentiation of the various types of CH groups within the main classes, so that CH_3, CH_2 and CH groups can be recognised individually. The absorption peaks arising from unsaturated and aromatic vibrations are considered in Chapters 3 and 5, and this discussion is limited to the bands arising from CH stretching modes in compounds in which the carbon atom concerned is saturated.

CH_3 group. Fox and Martin[6] examined a large number of hydrocarbons containing methyl groups, and found that in all cases two strong bands occurred at 2962 cm.$^{-1}$ and 2872 cm.$^{-1}$, corresponding to asymmetrical and symmetrical stretching modes. In all the compounds examined, the variation from these values was not more than $+10$ cm.$^{-1}$. In addition, two weaker intermediate frequencies were

noted in some cases. The two main frequencies were not altered in position within the range given by the presence of a double bond adjacent to the methyl group, but in these cases the lower CH_3 frequency (2872 cm.$^{-1}$) was split into two by a resonance effect. The mean value of this pair, however, remained within a few wavenumbers of 2872 cm.$^{-1}$.

CH_2 group. This group gives rise to two characteristic bands at 2926 and 2853 cm.$^{-1}$ corresponding to the in-phase and out-of-phase vibrations of the hydrogen atoms [4, 6]. As before, the mean values are remarkably constant in position, being within ± 10 cm.$^{-1}$ over a range of hydrocarbon materials including not only aliphatic materials but also the CH_2 vibrations of compounds such as benzyl alcohol and diphenylmethane.

In the case of compounds containing the group $CH_2–C{=}C$, a resonance splitting effect, similar to that with CH_3 groups, is observed. In this case, also, the mean frequency is close to the normal value.

CH group. The absorption intensity of $\gtrless CH$ groups is extremely low in comparison with those of CH_2 and CH_3 groups, but a weak band, which Fox and Martin [6] believe to be characteristic, can be traced at 2890 cm.$^{-1}$ in such compounds as triphenylmethane. The assignment is, however, of very limited value. In certain cases when the group is directly linked to oxygen the intensity is considerably enhanced, but frequency shifts due to the presence of the oxygen atom complicate the picture, and Pozefsky and Coggeshall [50] were unable to identify any specific absorption from this cause in oxygenated materials.

All the above correlations have been fully substantiated by later workers,[8, 9] and no cases are known of true saturated hydrocarbons in which there is any significant departure from them. However, variations in the force field immediately around the C–H group will affect the stretching frequency, and it is because of this that the stretching frequency of $=C–H$ is different from that of $-\overset{|}{C}–H$. Similarly, substituents such as halogens which are directly joined to the C–H group, or the inclusion of CH_2 groups in strained rings, will affect the frequencies of the stretching modes and the correlations will not then apply.

The Region 2850–2500 *cm.*$^{-1}$. No correlations have been suggested for this region, but a number of hydrocarbons absorb in this range. No explanation of the bands is available. They are usually extremely weak in hydrocarbons, but compounds such as dioxan, tetrahydrofuran and cyclohexanone have somewhat stronger bands which could well be confused with the S–H stretching absorption which occurs in the same region and is of comparable intensity.

2.2(b). Factors Influencing the Characteristic C–H Stretching Frequency. As has been indicated above, the correlations

c

derived for C–H stretching frequencies are directly applicable only to unstrained hydrocarbons in which the groups concerned are linked to other carbon atoms. The influence of other substituents has not yet been worked out sufficiently to enable any precise statements to be made as to the degree of shift in all cases. The shift can be considerable, however, and methyl deuteride and the methyl halides (except methyl fluoride), for example, absorb close to 2970 cm.$^{-1}$ and 3060 cm.$^{-1}$, the frequency differences between corresponding bands being 87 and 86 cm.$^{-1}$. When the methyl group is attached to nitrogen, the 2872 cm.$^{-1}$ band generally shifts to a higher frequency,[10] whereas attachment to oxygen usually causes a shift to a higher frequency of the 2960 cm.$^{-1}$ band. However, a new band also appears in the range 2832–2815 cm.$^{-1}$, which is highly characteristic of the methoxy group.[113] When the methyl group is adjacent to a carbonyl, as in acetates, there is also some shift of all the bands.

Pozefsky and Coggeshall [50] have recently carried out an extensive investigation into the applicability of the C–H stretching correlations to compounds containing oxygen and sulphur. They have examined, in all, some twenty-four sulphur compounds and forty-five oxygen compounds using the high dispersion of a lithium fluoride prism. Their findings are below.

2962 *cm.*$^{-1}$ *(CH$_3$ vibrations)*. The assignment of the 2962 cm.$^{-1}$ band to the asymmetrical stretching mode of the methyl group has been confirmed by the fact that the relative intensity of this band is much greater in compounds with a higher proportion of branched chains. Excluding the first members of the series, which are often anomalous, they find that the inclusion of a sulphur atom makes little difference to this frequency and in such compounds the band occurs in the range 2969–2960 cm.$^{-1}$, except for ethyl sulphides, when it is between 2980 cm.$^{-1}$ and 2970 cm.$^{-1}$. Oxygen produces rather more perturbation, and in methyl *n*-butyrate two bands can be resolved at 2970 cm.$^{-1}$ and 2952 cm.$^{-1}$ corresponding to two different methyl groups. Most of the compounds with oxygen had this band between 2972 cm.$^{-1}$ and 2960 cm.$^{-1}$, but with Et–O links the frequency was raised to 2990–2980 cm.$^{-1}$ and to 2978–2973 cm.$^{-1}$ with *iso*-propyl, *sec.*-butyl and *tert.*-butyl groups.

In straight-chain compounds no difficulty was found in resolving these two bands but many branched-chain compounds gave only a single band in this region. The absence of a separate detectable CH$_2$ band does not, therefore, necessarily indicate the absence of CH$_2$ groups, but when two bands are present in this region it is reasonably strong evidence that both types are present.

One interesting feature of these spectra was the finding that, in oxygenated and sulphur-containing materials, the extinction coefficients of the CH stretching bands in this region are appreciably greater than Fox and Martin found them to be in hydrocarbons.

$2930\,cm.^{-1}\,(CH_3\ and\ CH_2\ vibrations)$. All the compounds examined[50] absorbed in the range 2948–2922 cm.$^{-1}$. In some cases separate bands due to CH_3 and CH_2 groups could be resolved, but this was not possible in all cases.

2890–$2850\ cm.^{-1}\ (CH_3\ and\ CH_2\ vibrations)$. In this region the CH_3 and CH_2 vibrations were found to agree reasonably well with the assignments of Fox and Martin,[6] and no appreciable shifts were produced following the introduction of oxygen or sulphur into the molecule. The average position of the methyl-group vibration was 2880 cm.$^{-1}$ for oxygenated materials and 2875 cm.$^{-1}$ for sulphur compounds. The CH_2 vibration occurred at an average value of 2861 cm.$^{-1}$ in both series.

These assignments for oxygenated compounds have been fully substantiated by Nolin and Jones,[79] who studied all the various partly deuterated diethyl ketones. Thus $C_2H_5COC_2H_5$ has bands at 2977 cm.$^{-1}$, 2936 cm.$^{-1}$, 2883 cm.$^{-1}$ and 2902 cm.$^{-1}$. The first three of these are absent from the spectrum of $CD_3CH_2COCH_2CD_3$, and must therefore be associated with the CH_3 group. The appearance of only one CH_2 stretching frequency in these compounds is probably due to the considerable intensity changes which occur when this group is adjacent to a carbonyl structure, and a second, very weak band is believed to occur at 2955 cm.$^{-1}$.

Another factor which can occasionally cause a shift in CH stretching frequencies is ring strain. The C–H stretching frequencies of unstrained rings are normal, and Plyler and Acquista [41] have shown that in nineteen *cyclo*pentane materials there is no very great shift of the CH_2 vibrations away from the normal value. With smaller rings, however, the effect of the ring size upon the bond lengths becomes apparent, and there are some frequency shifts. Roberts and Chambers [51] have shown that the frequencies of the CH_2 bands increase and the intensities decrease progressively as the ring size becomes smaller. They conclude, therefore, that the electrical character of the C–H bonds is a relatively continuous function of ring size. In this work they examined the CH_2 vibrations of three-, four-, five- and six-membered rings substituted with a single chlorine or bromine atom, and in each series they found that the values for six-membered rings were normal and for five-membered rings very nearly so; with further decrease in ring size, however, the frequency rose considerably, so that the CH_2 vibrations of bromo-*cyclo*propane were at 3077 cm.$^{-1}$ and 2985 cm.$^{-1}$ in contrast to the values of 2924 and 2841 cm.$^{-1}$ in bromo-*cyclo*hexane. In *cyclo*butane [80] the increase is still insufficient to raise the C–H stretching frequency above 3000 cm.$^{-1}$, but *cyclo*propane derivatives can be readily identified [62, 73] if unsaturation is absent. The methylene stretching frequency also remains high in steroids and triterpenes containing bridged structures, including a *cyclo*propane ring, and absorption in the 3060–3040-cm.$^{-1}$ region has been used for their identification.[74] Epoxy structures can be similarly identified,[114] provided they are not fully alkylated, and these absorb in the range 3056–2990 cm.$^{-1}$.

The high CH stretching frequencies of three-membered rings of this type reflects their well-known " unsaturated character ", and for the same reason they are sometimes difficult to differentiate from aromatic or olefinic absorptions.

Two minor factors which can cause small frequency shifts, remain to be mentioned. Fox and Martin [4] found that small frequency changes resulted from changes of state. These were always small and always in the same direction. Passing from the vapour to solution resulted in a fall in the frequency of about 7 cm.$^{-1}$, and a further fall of the same extent was found on passing from the solution to the pure liquid. The values quoted above refer to those obtained in carbon tetrachloride solution. A second factor which may result in small shifts in the characteristic frequencies is the occurrence of hydrogen bonding. CH stretching modes have been assumed to be free from such effects, but Sutherland [12] has recently pointed out that evidence is accumulating that they do, in fact, occur. In the case of chloroform it has been clearly established [81-82] that hydrogen bonding to oxygen atoms can occur, and nitroform $CH(NO_3)_3$ is such a strong proton donor that it can be titrated with alkali. Nevertheless, the frequency changes to be expected will usually be very small compared with those produced by intramolecular forces, so that this effect is not likely to introduce any great difficulty into correlation work.

2.2(c). Factors Influencing the Intensity. Rose [13] in 1938, in work on the overtones of the CH fundamentals, noted a considerable degree of constancy in the intensity of absorption of various molecular units, and this has been confirmed by Fox and Martin [6] working on the fundamentals themselves. Using the integrated absorption area as a measure of intensity they find that, in long-chain paraffins, the intensities of the CH_2 and CH_3 bands are directly related to the proportions of these groups present and the intensities of the CH_2 bands change by a steady increment for each unit increase in chain length. With branched chains the agreement was less good but, if account is taken of all the CH_3 bands in assessing the integrated absorption areas, it is reasonably satisfactory. With 2 : 3-dimethylbutane, 2 : 2 : 3-trimethylbutane and 2 : 3 : 4-trimethylbutane the ratios of CH_2 groups are found as 4·42 : 5 : 5·21, as against 4 : 5 : 5.

When a double bond is adjacent to the CH_3 group, the method fails if measurements are confined to the normal frequencies due to the band-splitting effect, but again, an integrated absorption area value based on all the methyl groups is reasonably good. For 1-butylene, *cis*- and *trans*-2-butylene and trimethylethylene they obtained values of $1 : 1·76 : 1·89 : 3·50$, as compared with $1 : 2 : 2 : 3$ for the ratio of the numbers of methyl groups in the molecules.

A similar degree of constancy was found for $=CH$ and $=CH_2$ group absorption intensities, and these authors quote the following relative intensity values based on the integrated absorption areas summed for all the bands associated with the group:

$$\rangle CH\ 410;\quad C=H_2\ 1800;\quad \rangle CH\ 120;\quad \rangle CH_2\ 2400;\quad \rangle C-CH_3\ 2230;$$
$$\rangle CH-CH_3\ 3800.$$

The reduction in intensity of CH_2 and CH_3 groups adjacent to double bonds is apparent from these values, as is the low relative intensity of the $-CH$ group absorption.

A somewhat similar study has been made by Francis,[9] although he has used the integrated intensities of the 2900 cm.$^{-1}$, 1460 cm.$^{-1}$ and 1375 cm.$^{-1}$ bands to obtain values for the unit structural group intensities of CH_3, $-CH_2-$ and $-CH-$ groups. He was able to show that the calculated absorption intensities of twelve aliphatic hydrocarbons at each of these frequencies generally stay close to the observed values and that it was only with very complex branched-chain materials that there was any significant departure from the additive values obtained by treating the hydrocarbon as a mixture of non-interacting CH_3, $-CH_2-$ and $-CH-$ units. In a subsequent paper [72] he proposes the use of integrated intensities between 790 and 685 cm.$^{-1}$ for the determination of paraffinic methylene groups. *cyclo*Pentyl and *cyclo*hexyl residues can be estimated separately using bands at 2957 cm.$^{-1}$ and 2926 cm.$^{-1}$ after these have been corrected for the interfering methyl and methylene absorptions.

Quantitative work in the 3000 cm.$^{-1}$ region therefore affords a method for the estimation of the relative numbers of CH_3, CH_2 and CH groups in hydrocarbons. Hastings *et al.*[61] have used a somewhat similar method, including also measurements in the 800–700 cm.$^{-1}$ region, for the determination of methyl and methylene groups in paraffin and methylene groups in substituted naphthalenes in complex mixtures.

It has already been noted, however, that Pozefsky and Coggeshall [50] find that extinction coefficients of the CH_3 and CH_2 groups in the 2890–2850 cm.$^{-1}$ region are not the same in oxygen-containing materials, so that these findings cannot be safely applied to non-hydrocarbons without supplementary basic work. This has been confirmed by Francis,[71] who finds a marked fall in the integrated absorption intensities of methyl or methylene groups adjacent to an oxygen atom or to a carbonyl group. Mirone and Fabbri [83] have also noted that the overall intensity of the CH_2 band in secondary alcohols and tertiary alcohols is lower than in the corresponding primary compounds. This is presumably due to the increase in the number of CH_2 groups adjacent to the oxygen atom.

Following the work of Rose,[13] similar estimations are possible in the overtone region; Hibbard and Cleaves [14] have used the second overtone region for this purpose, and Tuot and Barchewitz [15] have noted that the intensities of CH_3 and CH_2 bands in this region are functions of the number of groups present and have employed them for analysis. Gauthier [52] has employed a similar technique in the investigation of the proportion of branched chains in liquid hydrocarbons, working in the 8000–5000 cm.⁻¹ region. Evans, Hibbard and Powell [53] have also investigated this region extensively and have shown that it can be applied to relatively large molecules of molecular weight up to 500. They estimate that they are able to determine the various groups to within 0·40 group or less in paraffins, 1·2 group or less in naphthenes and 0·9 group or less in aromatics. Valuable reviews of characteristic frequencies and analyses in the overtone region has been given by Kaye [84] and others.[85]

This region has many advantages for this type of work, especially as normal optics can be employed and detectors of very high sensitivity are available.

2.3. CH_3–C AND CH_2 DEFORMATION VIBRATIONS

2.3(a). Position. It was recognised quite early in the study of infra-red spectra that CH_2 and CH_3 groupings give rise to absorption near 1460 cm.⁻¹ due to hydrogen bending vibrations.[16,17,18] Since that time the very large numbers of hydrocarbon spectra prepared under the A.P.I. project and the full mathematical analysis of many simple hydrocarbons have enabled this absorption to be defined with more precision. It is now accepted that CH_2 deformations give rise to absorption very close to 1465 cm.⁻¹ and asymmetrical CH_3 deformations to absorption at 1450 cm.⁻¹. Variations of more than 10–20 cm.⁻¹ from these values are extremely rare except in cases in which the presence of strongly electronegative atoms causes a change in the charge distribution on the carbon atom.

The data on which these assignments are based are primarily derived from the spectra of the relatively large number of simple hydrocarbons which have now been subjected to mathematical analysis by various workers, but the overall assignment of the CH_2 and CH_3 absorption to this region is supported by the data obtained from the A.P.I. project and from the fact that Raman evidence also assigns the CH_2 and CH_3 bending frequencies to this region.[19,34] In the case of the CH_3 group, two frequencies arise from the bending of the hydrogen atoms about the carbon atom, the asymmetrical mode giving rise to the 1460 cm.$^{-1}$ absorption, whilst the symmetrical mode is responsible for the band near 1375 cm.$^{-1}$. The corresponding –Ç–H bending band is less well defined. This is due to its inherently low intensity in comparison with the bands from CH_3 and CH_2 groups and also to the fact that less compounds in which this group occurs have been fully studied. It appears as a weak band close to 1340 cm.$^{-1}$ in hydrocarbons,[10, 63, 69] but is generally not sufficiently intense to be of much value in structural analysis although, in certain cases in which the attachment is to oxygen or nitrogen atoms, a considerable increase in intensity occurs.

The bands in the 1460 cm.$^{-1}$ region arising from CH_2 and CH_3 groups lie too close together to enable the two groupings to be readily differentiated, especially in view of the small shifts which may be induced by changes of state, but the overall intensity in the 1460 cm.$^{-1}$ region is directly proportional to the number of such groupings present and, as mentioned, has been employed by Francis [9] in conjunction with other bands for the calculation of the relative proportions of CH_3, CH_2 and CH groupings present in a molecule.

The symmetrical deformation mode of the hydrogen atoms of a methyl group results in an absorption band in the range 1385–1370 cm.$^{-1}$ which is extremely stable in position provided that the methyl group is attached to another carbon atom. This is a most valuable correlation, especially as splitting of the band, in certain circumstances, allows the identification of branched-chain systems. This correlation came into prominence as a result of the intensive study of hydrocarbons carried out during the World War II [16, 17, 38, 54] and was substantiated by Rasmussen in 1948.[28] As in the case of the methylene deformation absorptions, the correlation rests fundamentally upon the large number of hydrocarbon spectra which have been submitted to mathematical analysis, and also upon the large number in the A.P.I. series which are consistent with it.[60, 64]

The intensity of this band is considerably greater for each unit of structure than that for the corresponding methylene and asymmetrical methyl deformation and is directly proportional to the number of units present. Even when splitting of the band occurs, as in branched chains, Francis [9] has shown that the integrated absorption in the 1380 cm.$^{-1}$ region is still approximately related to the number of CH_3 groups and may be used in conjunction with the data from the other regions for the determination of the proportion of methyl groups present. This absorption has been similarly used by Freeman [65] in the determination of the degree of branching of fatty acids.

Luther and Czerwany [86] have carried out an extensive study of the integrated absorption areas of CH absorption bands in normal paraffins up to C_{32} and in many branched-chain materials. They quote values for the integrated absorption coefficients of CH_2 deformation and wagging modes, and for CH_3 asymmetric and symmetric deformations. As more data become available on the variations in such intensities with structural alterations, studies of this type will be a very valuable aid in correlation work.

2.3(b). Factors Influencing CH_2 and CH_3 Bending Frequencies and Intensities. As with the CH stretching frequencies, changes in the state of aggregation can lead to shifts of up to 10 cm.$^{-1}$. Richards and Thompson,[21] for example, found shifts of this order on examination of a number of hydrocarbons in the liquid and solid states. However, these shifts were accompanied by other changes, and they noted that bands obtained from the solids were sharper and that they doubled in many cases. This effect has been confirmed by Sutherland,[12] who finds the 1460 cm.$^{-1}$ absorptions to be double below the transition point in solid paraffins, but single above this and in the liquid state. This arises from the interaction between the CH_2 deformation frequencies in neighbouring hydrocarbon chains. Sheppard and Simpson [64] quote similar data for many other hydrocarbons.

Changes in these CH_2 deformation frequencies are also induced by the introduction of electro-negative groups in the immediate vicinity. Thus, in the case of unsaturated materials, the CH_2 deformation frequency of a vinyl type $=CH_2$ group is shifted to 1420–1410 cm.$^{-1}$, and this fact is of value in the identification of this type of double bond (Chapter 3). In allene,[22] the frequency falls further to 1389 cm.$^{-1}$. On the other hand the influence of unsaturated groups is mainly limited to the carbon atoms forming the bond, and adjacent CH_2 groups are relatively unaffected. However, when the unsaturated link occurs in a cyclic system a small shift to a lower frequency of the adjacent methylene vibration sometimes occurs. Thus in many sterols the CH_2 deformation frequency of the group $-C=C-CH_2-$ occurs [66] at 1438 cm.$^{-1}$. Changes which occur due to the substitution of halogens are again limited to the CH bending vibrations at the particular carbon atom to which they are attached. In methylene fluoride [23] the frequency is raised to 1508 cm.$^{-1}$, whilst it is 1429 cm.$^{-1}$ in the chloride; [24] similarly the asymmetrical deformation mode of methyl fluoride absorbs at 1471 cm.$^{-1}$ and the iodide [25] at 1441 cm.$^{-1}$. A typical illustration of the extent of such shifts is given by Brown and Sheppard [26] in discussing the spectra of some brominated hydrocarbons; 1 : 2-dibromoethane absorbed at 1435 cm.$^{-1}$, whereas *n*-butyl bromide and *n*-propyl bromide absorbed at 1435 cm.$^{-1}$ and also at 1460 cm.$^{-1}$; 1 : 4-dibromobutane gave two CH_2 deformation frequencies at 1433 and 1440 cm.$^{-1}$. Shifts also occur when the grouping is attached to other atoms such as nitrogen or sulphur, but the extent of these is not well defined and depends to some extent on the nature of the other attachments to these atoms.

With carbonyl substitution, the intensity of the CH_2 deformations of adjacent methylene groups is considerably increased and there is a shift towards lower frequency similar to that of vinyl groupings. Acetone for example absorbs at 1431 cm.$^{-1}$ and acetic acid at 1418 cm.$^{-1}$. Francis [71] has assigned the deformation frequency of a methylene group adjacent to a carbonyl at 1410 cm.$^{-1}$ and this has been confirmed by other workers for a variety of compounds. Thus in acids containing the group $-CH_2COOH$ Hadži and Sheppard [20] have observed a strong band at this point which is absent from other acids and which is quite distinct from the 1420 cm.$^{-1}$ band originating from the carboxyl group itself (Chapter 10), whilst studies of the ketones $CH_3\,CH_2\,CO\,CH_2\,CH_3$, $CH_3\,CD_2\,CO\,CD_2\,CH_3$ and $CD_3\,CH_2\,CO\,CH_2\,CD_3$ have indicated very clearly [67, 79] that the CH_2 deformation occurs at 1415 cm.$^{-1}$ and the CH_3 symmetrical deformation at 1380 cm.$^{-1}$. A very large number of steroids have also been examined from this point of view, and it has been found that in these, active methylene groups adjacent to carbonyls in the 3- or 17-position or in the side-chain absorb in the range 1418–1408 cm.$^{-1}$. However, a carbonyl group at the 4-, 6-, 7-, 11- or 12-position appears to have somewhat less influence on adjacent CH_2 groups which absorb at 1434 cm.$^{-1}$, close to the frequencies of cyclic methylene groups activated by a double bond.[66, 67, 87] These findings have been confirmed by deuteration studies.

In steroid acetates the influence of the CO grouping upon the CH_3 symmetrical mode is small, and although splitting into two bands at 1375 cm.$^{-1}$ and 1365 cm.$^{-1}$ has been found in 3- and 17-acetates, this is probably due to steric effects similar to those responsible for the splitting of the C–O stretching absorption (Chapter 11) rather than to any influence of the carbonyl group. When the methyl group is directly attached to the CO group, however, its influence is, of course, more pronounced,[66] and the symmetrical CH_3 deformation of sterols with a $COCH_3$ group in the side-chain has been assigned at 1356 cm.$^{-1}$.

Strained ring systems can also lead to small alterations in the charge distribution at methylene groups, with a corresponding alteration in the characteristic frequency. The CH_2 frequencies for ethylene oxide, imide and sulphide are 1500, 1475 and 1471 cm.$^{-1}$ respectively.[27] It will be seen that the effect is not large, and with larger rings with less strain, the CH_2 vibrations tend towards the normal values. In six-membered steroid rings this frequency falls between 1456 and 1448 cm.$^{-1}$, which is very slightly lower than the value for methylene groups in the side-chain (1468–1466 cm.$^{-1}$), so that in favourable cases it is possible to differentiate between the two types.[66, 67] When *cyclo*propane rings are included within larger systems, such as triterpenes, the CH deformation frequencies are not sufficiently distinctive to enable them to be identified directly.[74] However, the location and type of such rings can be found by a study of the changes in CH_3 and CH_2 deformation frequencies which take place when the rings are opened with hydrogen chloride and deuterium chloride.[88]

The shifts in the position of the symmetrical CH_3 absorption band due to changes of state have been investigated by Richards and Thompson,[21] who found that they were relatively small and rarely more than 10 cm.$^{-1}$. Changes in the type of substitution on the carbon atom to which the methyl group is attached also have very little influence upon the band position except in cases where a second methyl group is attached. This is illustrated by the following values assigned to the symmetrical CH_3 mode in molecules subjected to mathematical analysis: [29] acetaldehyde 1370 cm.$^{-1}$, methyl *iso*cyanate 1377 cm.$^{-1}$, methylacetylene 1379 cm.$^{-1}$, acetic acid 1381 cm.$^{-1}$ and methyl cyanide 1396 cm.$^{-1}$. In cases in which a second methyl group is attached to the same carbon atom, resonance splitting occurs and two separate bands appear.[17, 54, 64] The relative intensities of these bands are usually a direct indication of the extent of branching of the chain. The simplest case, ethane,[30] shows this effect and absorbs at 1374 and 1379 cm.$^{-1}$. With the *iso*propyl grouping $(CH_3)_2CH-$ or $(CH_3)_2-CR-$, the bands split further apart and appear at about an equal distance on each side of the mean value at 1385–1350 cm.$^{-1}$, with approximately equal intensities. This effect was first noted by Thompson and Torkington,[17] who found doubling of the CH_3 vibration in a number of 2 : 2-dimethyl-substituted hydrocarbons. With the tertiary butyl grouping $(CH_3)_3-C-$ the splitting appears to be very slightly farther apart, with bands at 1395 cm.$^{-1}$ and 1365 cm.$^{-1}$, whilst the intensity of the second band is about twice that of the first. The positions and relative intensities of bands in this region therefore afford a very valuable indication of the presence or absence of various types of branched chains in a molecule. These correlations have been very fully discussed by Sheppard and Simpson,[64] and by McMurry and Thornton.[60] A typical illustration of their use is the work of Sobotka and Stynler [31] in the identification of normal, *iso*- and *neo*-palmitic and stearic acids by studies in this region. It must be remembered, however, that the intensity pattern may be influenced by the presence of other methyl groups elsewhere in the molecule, which will contribute their own specific absorptions in this region. The characteristic skeletal absorptions of various types of branched chain should, therefore, also be sought in the identification of *iso*propyl and *tert.*-butyl groups. One other instance in which structural features influence the CH_3 symmetrical deformation frequency has been found in the steroid series.[66] A considerable number of sterols containing two re-entrant methyl groups situated between rings have been shown to absorb at 1384 cm.$^{-1}$ and 1378 cm.$^{-1}$, whereas thirteen other steroids in which only one such methyl group is present show only one of these bands. However, these frequencies may be influenced to some extent by stereochemical factors. Characteristic frequencies for methyl and methylene groups in various environments in steroids have been summarised by Jones and Herling.[111]

2.4. DEFORMATION VIBRATIONS OF METHYL GROUPS ATTACHED TO ELEMENTS OTHER THAN CARBON

The position of the CH_3 symmetrical deformation frequency when the methyl group is attached to an element other than carbon is determined largely by the electro-negativity of the element, and by its position in the periodic table.[89, 90] The magnitude of the resulting shifts can be very considerable. The methyl halides, fluoride, chloride, bromide and iodide absorb at 1475, 1355, 1305 and 1255 cm.$^{-1}$ respectively.[29] Examples of other frequencies with different elements are given by methanol (1456 cm.$^{-1}$) and dimethyl ether (1466 cm.$^{-1}$) for the CH_3–O group, dimethyl sulphide (1323 cm.$^{-1}$) for the CH_3–S group, and methylamine (1418 cm.$^{-1}$) for the CH_3–N group. Similarly, silicones with the CH_3–Si group absorb constantly at 1250 cm.$^{-1}$ and phosphorus compounds with the CH_3–P link may absorb near 1280 cm.$^{-1}$. When the methyl group is attached to an aromatic ring it shows a very specific rocking frequency [91] near 1042 cm.$^{-1}$. This correlation must be used with caution, however, as *meta*-substituted compounds have a ring frequency near this point, and some interactions can occur in *ortho*-substituted materials.

Bellamy and Williams [89] have pointed out that in any CH_3X compound the individual CH frequencies are all directly related to one another and to the HX-stretching frequency. This is more fully discussed in Chapter 23.

2·5. SKELETAL VIBRATIONS

2.5(a). *iso*Propyl and *tert.*-Butyl Structures. Skeletal vibrations are usually very sensitive to changes in the immediate environment of the vibrating group and hence considerable frequency shifts can be caused. However, these considerations do not apply to branched units such as the structures $\begin{matrix} CH_3 \\ \diagdown \\ C \\ \diagup \\ CH_3 \end{matrix}\begin{matrix} CH_3 \\ \diagup \\ \diagdown \\ C \end{matrix}$ and $\begin{matrix} CH_3 \\ \diagdown \\ CH—C, \\ \diagup \\ CH_3 \end{matrix}$ each of which might be expected to exhibit characteristic frequencies of their own. Simpson and Sutherland [32, 33] have been able to calculate the expected frequencies ν_2 and ν_3 of these groupings on the basis of a relatively simple force field. For 2 : 2-dimethyl-substituted paraffins containing the group $(CH_3)_3CR$, they were able to show that no great variation in either of these frequencies is to be expected from alteration in the mass of the R group from methyl (15) up to heptyl (99), Throughout this series the ν_2 frequency would be expected to decrease slowly by only 37 cm.$^{-1}$ and the ν_3 frequency by only 97 cm.$^{-1}$.

Experimentally they have found that in paraffins up to and including the nonanes, strong absorption bands occur near 1250 cm.$^{-1}$ and 1200 cm.$^{-1}$ whenever the 2 : 2-dimethyl group is present. The former is almost constant in position and does not vary by more than a few wave-numbers throughout the series, whilst the second band coincides with the first in *neo*pentane, and then falls steadily throughout the series to 1200 cm.$^{-1}$. The greater consistency in the position of the 1250 cm.$^{-1}$ band is to be expected as this arises from the ν_2 vibration, which is a perpendicular mode of the $(CH_3)_3C$ group and so will be much less affected than the ν_3 parallel vibration when the rest of the hydrocarbon chain varies. The C–C skeletal modes can sometimes be differentiated from the various CH_2 wagging modes by a comparison of the spectra of hydrocarbons with those of corresponding compounds with polar substituents. The CH_2 modes often become intensified in the second cases, and in this way further support has been obtained for the skeletal assignments quoted above.[92]

Similar calculations by the same authors for the *iso*propyl type skeletons indicate that the ν_2 and ν_3 frequencies should occur near 1170 and 1145 cm.$^{-1}$ and experimental evidence again confirms this. In the series 2-methylpropane to 2-methylnonane, they find one frequency to be constant in the range 1170–1167 cm.$^{-1}$, whilst the second falls steadily from 1170 cm.$^{-1}$ in the first to 1142 cm.$^{-1}$ in the last. The structure $(CH_3)_2C{<}$ with no free hydrogen atom on the central carbon gives only a single band in this region [54] at 1195 cm.$^{-1}$. A second band near 1210 cm.$^{-1}$ has been observed in some cases, but it is more variable in position.[64]

These correlations have also been fully substantiated by the observations of Rasmussen.[28] Whilst differing in the interpretation of these bands, he has given empirical data obtained on a large number of branched-chain paraffins which confirm that bands at the positions indicated can be associated with these different types of branched-chain structure. These correlations appear to hold, also, for many non hydrocarbons provided no oxygen atoms are attached

near the chain branching. The structure $\begin{matrix} C & & C \\ & \diagdown C \diagup & \\ C \diagup & & \diagdown O \end{matrix}$ absorbs near 900

cm.$^{-1}$ (Chapter 7).

In addition to these correlations, Simpson and Sutherland have pointed out that a third skeletal vibration (v_4) can also be predicted for each of the branched structures discussed. For *tert.*-butyl compounds this occurs at 415 cm.$^{-1}$ and for *iso*propyl compounds near 850 cm.$^{-1}$. These are, however, less valuable than the others. Very little information is available as regards the first of these, whilst the second is variable within the range 840–793 cm.$^{-1}$ in the series of 2-methyl compounds quoted.

A considerable number of correlations have also been worked out for a series of highly specialised hydrocarbon structures. These have been developed by Sheppard and Simpson [64] and by McMurry and Thornton [60] on the basis of the A.P.I. spectra, and they include correlations for CH_2 wagging, rocking and twisting modes, and for C–C stretching vibrations as well as for various patterns of methyl-group substitution. As they are not generally applicable they have not been included here and the original publications must be consulted for them. In many cases they include details of the number of compounds on which any particular correlation is based, together with some indication of the intrinsic intensity of the bands in question.

2.5(b). Paraffinic Chains. As has been mentioned above, correlations for open-chain skeletal vibrations are frequently unreliable and cover a wide range of frequencies. Correlations involving single bond stretchings of ethyl and *n*-propyl groups have been developed by Kohlrausch [34] and by Sheppard and Simpson,[64] and are included in Colthup's frequency-correlation chart,[10] and in the chart issued by the Spectroscopic Group of the Institute of Petroleum.[55] However, the bands are frequently weak and cover such a wide frequency range as to be of little practical value for work on complex molecules. There is, however, one correlation arising from an open-chain vibration which has proved to be extremely valuable in practice. This is that concerned with a long chain of the type $-(CH_2)_n-$ ($n = 4$ or more) which gives rise to a strong absorption band near 720 cm.$^{-1}$. This band arises from a rocking mode of the (CH_2) groups and is not strictly a skeletal mode, but it can conveniently be considered here, as it arises from a structural group rather than from a single unit.

Tuot and Lecomte [35] in 1943 gave data on a series of thirty alcohols in which they noted the appearance of a band near 720 cm.$^{-1}$ when at least four adjacent straight-chain methylene groups were present, and Thompson and Torkington [17] assigned the doublet at 721 and 732 cm.$^{-1}$ in polythene to this cause. The vibration has been shown to be due to a rocking mode of the CH_2 groups by Sheppard and Sutherland [36] working on fully deuterated paraffins and by Sutherland and Vallence Jones,[37] who used polarised radiation to show that the vibrations were at right angles to the hydrocarbon chains. The former workers suggested the range 760–720 cm.$^{-1}$ for this vibration in hydrocarbons.

It is clear, therefore, that a number of directly linked $-CH_2-$ groups will give rise to absorption in this region, but it is not to be expected that any very clear-cut line of demarcation will be possible as regards the number of CH_2 groups necessary for its production. Generally the number is given as four, and no hydrocarbon containing four or more CH_2 groups, directly linked, has been reported in which this band is not present in the spectra. On the other hand it appears in some, but not all, compounds in which only three (CH_2) groups are linked, and there is a suggestion of a gradual shift towards higher frequency as the number of groups is reduced.[38, 60] The correlation can, therefore, be used positively for recognising the absence of the $-(CH_2)_4-$ group but must be interpreted with caution when the band is present.

Recently Wiberley and Bassett [39] have suggested a more precise correlation for the *n*-butyl group itself. In a series of eighteen *n*-butyl derivatives in which the butyl group is attached to oxygen, nitrogen or some other functional group, this frequency was found to fall always within the range 742–734 cm.$^{-1}$. They would, therefore, restrict this correlation to compounds of this type and they point out that with this restricted frequency range it is not applicable to hydrocarbons. In this connection they quote Smith as having pointed out to them that of seven hundred A.P.I. hydrocarbon spectra, two hundred and twenty absorb in the range 750–720 cm.$^{-1}$; of these, thirty-four lie in the 742–734 cm.$^{-1}$ range, of which only six contain butyl groups, whilst seventeen contain propyl groups. Similarly six compounds containing the *n*-butyl group absorb between 728 and 730 cm.$^{-1}$, whilst others absorb above 742 cm.$^{-1}$. This analysis is confirmed by McMurry and Thornton [60] and emphasises the need for caution in the use of this band for diagnostic purposes. A useful discussion of this band has also been given by Bomstein.[93]

One factor, which is of value in identifying a band in the 750–720 cm.$^{-1}$ region as being due to this type of methylene-group vibration, is its behaviour when the material is examined in different states. Like the CH_2 deformation frequency, this band is always double below the transition point and in the solid state, and single in the liquid state and in solution,[12, 68] and this property will enable this band to be recognised among others in the same spectral region which arise from other causes and do not show this behaviour. This phenomenon has been extensively studied by many workers [77, 94–100] using such techniques as polarised radiation, temperature dependance, etc. It is now certain that the doubling of this band in the crystalline material arises from interactions between neighbouring molecules in the crystalline phase. Studies of the relative intensities of these bands therefore afford a convenient method for the determination of the crystalline/amorphous ratio. It may also be possible to obtain some tentative confirmation of the presence of long-chain methylene groups by the examination of the 1300–1200 cm.$^{-1}$ region of the spectrum. Brown, Sheppard and Simpson [40] have found weak bands near 1300 cm.$^{-1}$ and near 1240 cm.$^{-1}$ in a number of long-chain paraffins which they attribute to CH_2 wagging vibrations. This region is complicated by the presence of C–C stretching modes coupled with CH_2 wagging frequencies, but in the compounds examined the 1300 cm.$^{-1}$ band appeared in all the even-numbered carbon atom paraffins from four to fourteen carbon atoms, and the 1240 cm.$^{-1}$ vibration in all from six carbon atoms upwards. A number of workers have studied this region in detail, [75,100-104,112] and the various frequencies can be disentangled and assigned in many simple hydrocarbons. The number of bands increases progressively with the chain length, and is reduced by the introduction of substituents which lowers the number of adjacent methylene groups. However, these absorptions are weak in normal hydrocarbons, and it is only in compounds with polar end groups that they become sufficiently intense to be identified without difficulty. There are, however, possibilities at least for the use of this region in the determination of chain lengths, and some success in this direction has been achieved in the fatty acid series (Chapter 10).

2.5(c). Cyclic Systems. The saturated cyclic compounds form another group from which characteristic frequencies arising from ring deformations might be expected, and a number of papers have been published in this field.[41, 51, 54] These will be considered under individual ring systems, but it should be appreciated that, for the larger systems at least, the correlations quoted are not of much practical value. The most characteristic of the vibrations of cyclic systems is the ring-breathing frequency, which is unfortunately inactive in the infra-red but is readily identified in Raman spectra.[105]

Cyclopropane. Bartleson, Burk and Lankelma [42] in 1946 noted that *cyclo*propane derivatives appeared to absorb near 1026 cm.$^{-1}$ and 866 cm.$^{-1}$. This observation was followed up by Derfer, Pickett and Boord,[43] who examined fourteen different *cyclo*propane derivatives. They found that a strong band at 866 cm.$^{-1}$ was not consistently present, but that in all cases there was a band at 1020–1000 cm.$^{-1}$. The only exception to this was *cyclo*propane itself, which absorbs just outside this region. In three hundred other hydrocarbon spectra this band was not present more often than it would be expected to occur by chance. They, therefore, regarded this band as being typical of the *cyclo*propane structure and suggested that it arises from a ring deformation mode. The band was present in the spectra of the compounds of Bartleson *et al.*, and Marrison [44] has since pointed out that it is also present in the spectrum of vinyl *cyclo*propane.[45] Slabey [58] has confirmed this and found the band also in di*cyclo*propyl. In later papers [59, 73] he reports results of studies on large numbers of *cyclo*propane derivatives. Thus thirty-four compounds with this structure absorbed in the range 1048–1017 cm.$^{-1}$, of which twenty-nine absorbed within 5 cm.$^{-1}$ of 1021 cm.$^{-1}$. Wiberley and Bunce [62] also confirm this frequency in nine *cyclo*-propane compounds, and Bridson-Jones *et al.*[69, 70] have observed it in seven other cases. The occurrence of this band within a very narrow frequency range is not confined to simple structures and it appears, for example, in the spectrum of *i*-cholestane [46] in which the *cyclo*propane ring is part of a bridged-ring system of a six-membered ring, and also in carene [47] and car.3.-ene, in which one side of the *cyclo*propane ring is supplied by a side of another six-membered ring. The occurrence of a similar band in the spectrum of artenol, a triterpenoid ketone, has been used by Barton [46] as evidence for the presence of a *cyclo*propane ring system. How-ever, as Cole has pointed out,[74] it is necessary to be very cautious in the use of this correlation in oxygenated compounds. Whilst he observes a band near 1010 cm.$^{-1}$ in a number of triterpenes con-taining *cyclo*propane rings, he does not consider it sufficiently characteristic without reference also to the CH stretching region. This correlation is also supported by Sheppard's work on naphthene hydrocarbons.[54]

Cyclobutane. The position of *cyclo*butane correlations is less clear cut than is the case with *cyclo*propane partly because the charac-teristic bands are considerably less intense. Wilson [48] assigned bands at 920 and 903 cm.$^{-1}$ in *cyclo*butane to two CH_2 rocking frequencies, and Derfer *et al.*[43] followed this by the observation that seven sub-stituted *cyclo*butanes all absorbed in the narrow range 920–910 cm.$^{-1}$. They pointed out, however, that if the assignment to CH_2 modes was correct, this band would not be expected to appear in fully substi-tuted materials. Reid and Sack [49] later examined a series of eight substituted *cyclo*butanes in which all the carbon atoms were sub-stituted. Their samples were examined as solids and all absorbed between 888 and 868 cm.$^{-1}$ and none between 920 and 910 cm.$^{-1}$. Marrison [44] has pointed out that neither methylene nor octafluoro *cyclo*butane absorbs in the 920–910 cm.$^{-1}$ region but that all the *cyclo*-butanes in the A.P.I. series absorb between 1000 and 960 cm.$^{-1}$ The value of this latter correlation is partly discounted by the additional observation that many *cyclo*pentane derivatives also absorb in this region. Sheppard [54] supports the 910 cm.$^{-1}$ correlation but does not state the compounds studied. A band near this position occurs in the spectra of a number of *cyclo*butane derivatives described by Roberts and Chambers [51, 56] and by Roberts and Simmons.[57]

Cyclopentane. As stated, Marrison [44] has noted that the spectra of *cyclo*pentane derivatives contain a band whose average position is 977 cm.$^{-1}$. The variation from compound to compound is, however, too wide to afford this observation any significance. Sheppard [54] regards bands near 930 and 890 cm.$^{-1}$ as being characteristic but does not indicate the compounds he examined.

Cyclohexane. Marrison [44] has noted that the published spectra of all *cyclo*hexane derivatives (with two exceptions) show bands in the ranges 1005–952 cm.$^{-1}$ and 1055–1000 cm.$^{-1}$. This relates to fifty published spectra, and the two exceptions (*cyclo*hexane and β-gammexane) each show one of these bands. In addition, he quotes a further nine materials he has examined which absorb in these regions. These tentative correlations do not, however, apply to *cyclo*hexanone derivatives in which the introduction of the carbonyl group would be expected to alter any characteristic ring deformation frequencies. Sheppard [54] quotes values near 1260 cm.$^{-1}$ and 890 cm.$^{-1}$ for *cyclo*hexanes but again gives no data.

2.5(d). Low-frequency Absorptions

Hydrocarbons have a number of weak absorption bands due to skeletal vibrations in the region below 650 cm.$^{-1}$. These are usually extremely weak, and can be studied only in relatively thick films. Plyler [106] has given data on a number of such materials over the range 650–400 cm.$^{-1}$, and Borello and Mussa [107] have suggested there is a characteristic methyl-group frequency in this region which can be used in the estimation of CH_3 groups in polyethylene.

Studies at lower frequencies have been made by Gates,[108] and more recently Donneaud [109, 110] has found some interesting differences between straight- and branched-chain compounds in this region and discussed their possible analytical applications.

2.6. BIBLIOGRAPHY

1. Coblentz, *Investigations of Infra-red Spectra* (Carnegie Institute, Washington, Part 1, 1905).
2. Bonino, *Trans. Faraday Soc.*, 1929, **25**, 876.
3. Fox and Martin, *Proc. Roy. Soc.*, 1937, **A162**, 419.
4. Fox and Martin, *ibid.*, 1938, **A167**, 257.
5. Fox and Martin, *J. Chem. Soc.*, 1939, 318.
6. Fox and Martin, *Proc. Roy. Soc.*, 1940, **A175**, 208, 234.
7. Rasmussen and Brattain, *J. Chem. Phys.*, 1947, **15**, 120, 131, 135.
8. Saier and Coggeshall, *Analyt. Chem.*, 1948, **20**, 812.
9. Francis, *J. Chem. Phys.*, 1950, **18**, 861.
10. Colthup, *J. Opt. Soc. Amer.*, 1950, **40**, 397.
11. Jones, McKay and Sinclair, *J. Amer. Chem. Soc.*, 1952, **74**, 2575.
12. Sutherland, *Discuss. Faraday Soc.*, 1950, **9**, 274.

13. Rose, *J. Res. Nat. Bur. Stand.*, 1938, **20**, 129.
14. Hibbard and Cleaves, *Analyt. Chem.*, 1949, **21**, 486.
15. Tuot and Barchewitz, *Bull. Soc. Chim.*, 1950, 851.
16. Barnes, Gore, Liddel and Van Zandt Williams, *Infra-red Spectroscopy* (Reinhold, 1944).
17. Thompson and Torkington, *Proc. Roy. Soc.*, 1945, **A184**, 3.
18. Thompson and Torkington, *Trans. Faraday Soc.*, 1945, **41**, 246.
19. Crawford, Avery and Linnett, *J. Chem. Phys.*, 1938, **6**, 682.
20. Hadži and Sheppard, *Proc. Roy. Soc.*, 1953, **A216**, 247.
21. Richards and Thompson, *Proc. Roy. Soc.*, 1948, **A195**, 1.
22. Herzberg, *Infra-red and Raman Spectra of Polyatomic Molecules* (Van Nostrand, 1945), p. 339.
23. Pitzer, *J. Chem. Phys.*, 1944, **12**, 310.
24. Herzberg, *op. cit.*, p. 317.
25. Herzberg, *op. cit.*, p. 314.
26. Brown and Sheppard, *Discuss. Faraday Soc.*, 1950, **9**, 144.
27. Thompson and Cave, *Trans. Faraday Soc.*, 1951, **47**, 946, 951.
28. Rasmussen, *J. Chem. Phys.*, 1948, **16**, 712.
29. Cf. Randall, Fowler, Fuson and Dangl, *Infra-red Determination of Organic Structures* (Van Nostrand, 1949).
30. Herzberg, *op. cit.*, p. 344.
31. Sobotka and Stynler, *J. Amer. Chem. Soc.*, 1950, **72**, 5139.
32. Sutherland and Simpson, *J. Chem. Phys.*, 1947, **15**, 153.
33. Simpson and Sutherland, *Proc. Roy. Soc.*, 1949, **A199**, 169.
34. Kohlrausch, *Ramanspektren* (Akad. Verlags. Becker-Erler, Leipzig, 1943).
35. Tuot and Lecomte, *C.R. Acad. Sci. Paris*, 1943, **216**, 339.
36. Sheppard and Sutherland, *Nature*, 1947, **159**, 739.
37. Sutherland and Vallence Jones, *Nature*, 1947, **160**, 567.
38. Fellgett, Harris, Simpson, Sutherland, Thompson, Whiffen and Willis, *Inst. Petroleum Reports*, XI, 1946.
39. Wiberley and Bassett, *Analyt. Chem.*, 1950, **22**, 841.
40. Brown, Sheppard and Simpson, *Discuss. Faraday Soc.*, 1950, **9**, 261.
41. Plyler and Acquista, *J. Res. Nat. Bur. Stand.*, 1949, **43**, 37.
42. Bartleson, Burk and Lankelma, *J. Amer. Chem. Soc.*, 1946, **68**, 2513.
43. Derfer, Pickett and Boord, *J. Amer. Chem. Soc.*, 1949, **71**, 2482.
44. Marrison, *J. Chem. Soc.*, 1951, 1614.
45. Van Volkenburgh, Greenlee, Derfer and Boord, *J. Amer. Chem. Soc.*, 1949, **71**, 3595.
46. Barton, *J. Chem. Soc.*, 1951, 1444.
47. Pliva and Herout, *Coll. Trav. Chim. Tchécosl.*, 1950, **15**, 160.
48. Wilson, *J. Chem. Phys.*, 1943, **11**, 369.
49. Reid and Sack, *J. Amer. Chem. Soc.*, 1951, **73**, 1985.
50. Pozefsky and Coggeshall, *Analyt. Chem.*, 1951, **23**, 1611.
51. Roberts and Chambers, *J. Amer. Chem. Soc.*, 1951, **73**, 5030.
52. Gauthier, *C.R. Acad. Sci. Paris*, 1950, **231**, 837.
53. Evans, Hibbard and Powell, *Analyt. Chem.*, 1951, **23**, 1604.
54. Sheppard, *J. Inst. Pet.*, 1951, **37**, 95.
55. "The Spectroscopic Panel of the Hydrocarbon Research Group," *J. Inst. Pet.*, 1951, **37**, 109.
56. Roberts and Chambers, *J. Amer. Chem. Soc.*, 1951, **73**, 5034.
57. Roberts and Simmons, *J. Amer. Chem. Soc.*, 1951, **73**, 5487.
58. Slabey, *J. Amer. Chem. Soc.*, 1952, **74**, 4930.
59. Slabey, *ibid.*, p. 4928.
60. McMurry and Thornton, *Analyt. Chem.*, 1952, **24**, 318.
61. Hastings, Watson, Williams and Anderson, *Analyt. Chem.*, 1952, **24**, 611.
62. Wiberley and Bunce, *Analyt. Chem.*, 1952, **24**, 623.
63. Pitzer and Kilpatrick, *Chem. Reviews*, 1946, **39**, 435.
64. Sheppard and Simpson, *Quarterly Reviews*, 1953, **7**, 19.
65. Freeman, *J. Amer. Chem. Soc.*, 1953, **75**, 1859.
66. Jones and Cole, *J. Amer. Chem. Soc.*, 1952, **74**, 5648.
67. Jones, Cole and Nolin, *ibid.*, p. 5662.
68. Robert and Favre, *C.R. Acad. Sci. (Paris)*, 1952, **234**, 2270.

69. Bridson-Jones, Buckley, Cross and Driver, *J. Chem. Soc.*, 1951, 2999.
70. Bridson-Jones and Buckley, *ibid.*, p. 3009.
71. Francis, *J. Chem. Phys.*, 1951, **19**, 942.
72. Francis, *Analyt. Chem.*, 1953, **25**, 1466.
73. Slabey, *J. Amer. Chem. Soc.*, 1954, **76**, 3604.
74. Cole, *J. Chem. Soc.*, 1954, 3807, 3810.
75. Tschamler, *J. Chem. Phys.*, 1954, **22**, 1845.
76. Keller and Sandeman, *J. Polymer. Sci.*, 1955, **15**, 133.
77. Tobin and Carrano, *J. Polymer. Sci.*, 1957, **24**, 93.
78. Stein and Sutherland, *ibid.*, 1953, **12**, 370.
79. Nolin and Jones, *J. Amer. Chem. Soc.*, 1953, **75**, 5626.
80. Rathgens, Freeman, Gwinn and Pitzer, *ibid.*, 1953, **75**, 5634.
81. Lord, Nolin and Stidham, *ibid.*, 1955, **77**, 1365.
82. Huggins, Pimentel and Schoolery, *J. Chem. Phys.*, 1955, **23**, 1244.
83. Mirone and Fabbri, *Gazz. chim.*, 1954, **84**, 187.
84. Kaye, *Spectrochim. Acta*, 1954, **6**, 257.
85. Lauer and Rosenbaum, *App. Spectroscopy*, 1952, **6**, 29.
86. Luther and Czerwany, *Z. Phys. Chem.*, 1956, **6**, 286.
87. Jones, Nolin and Roberts, *J. Amer. Chem. Soc.*, 1955. **77**, 6331.
88. Barton, Page and Warnhoff, *J. Chem. Soc.*, 1954, 2715.
89. Bellamy and Williams, *ibid.*, 1956, 2753.
90. Sheppard, *Trans. Faraday Soc.*, 1955, **51**, 1465.
91. Randle and Whiffen, *J. Chem. Soc.*, 1955, 3497.
92. Sheppard and Simpson, *J. Chem. Phys.*, 1955, **23**, 582.
93. Bomstein, *Analyt. Chem.*, 1953, **25**, 512.
94. Keller and Sandeman, *J. Polymer. Sci.*, 1954, **13**, 511.
95. Stein and Sutherland, *J. Chem. Phys.*, 1954, **22**, 1993.
96. Krimm, *ibid.*, 1054, **22**, 567.
97. *Idem, Phys. Rev.*, 1954, **94**, 1426.
98. Novak, *Zhur. Tekh Fiz.*, 1954, **24**, 18.
99. Nikitin and Pokrovskiy, *Doklady, Akad Nauk, S.S.S.R.*, 1954, **95**, 109.
100. Krimm, Liang and Sutherland, *J. Chem. Phys.*, 1956, **25**, 549.
101. Primas and Günthard, *Helv. Chim. Acta*, 1953, **36**, 1791; 1956, **39**, 1182.
102. Brown, Sheppard and Simpson, *Phil. Trans.*, 1954, **A247**, 35.
103. *Idem, J. Phys. Radium*, 1954, **15**, 593.
104. Mizushima, *The Structure of Molecules* (Academic Press, 1954), pp. 98 et seq.
105. Bateuv, *Izvest Akad. Nauk. S.S.S.R. Otdel Khim Nauk*, 1947, **1**, 3.
106. Plyler, *J. Opt. Soc. Amer.*, 1947, **37**, 746.
107. Borello and Mussa, *J. Polymer. Sci.*, 1954, **13**, 402.
108. Gates, *J. Chem. Phys.*, 1949, **17**, 393.
109. Donneaud, *Compt. Rend. Acad. Sci. Paris*, 1954, **239**, 1480.
110. *Idem, Rev. Inst. Franc. Petrole*, 1955, **10**, 1525.
111. Jones and Herling, *J. Org. Chem.*, 1954, **19**, 1252.
112. Brini, *Bull. Soc. Chim. Fr.*, 1955, 996.
113. Henbest, Meakins, Nicholls and Wagland, *J. Chem. Soc.*, 1957, 1462.
114. Henbest, Meakins, Nicholls and Taylor, *ibid.*, 1459.

CHAPTER 3

Alkenes

3.1. INTRODUCTION AND TABLE

INFRA-RED absorption bands associated with the various types of double bond have been extensively studied, so that recognition of the presence and type of unsaturation in an unknown compound is usually possible with reasonable certainty, although this depends to some extent on the amount of substitution at the double bond. This is due to the fact that the most characteristic frequencies available for identification arise from CH stretching and deformation vibrations,

TABLE 3

C=C *Stretching Vibrations*

Non-conjugated	. .	1680–1620 cm.$^{-1}$ (intensity very variable)
Phenyl conjugated .	.	Near 1625 cm.$^{-1}$ (intensity enhanced)
CO or C=C conjugated	.	Near 1600 cm.$^{-1}$ (intensity enhanced)

C–H *Stretching and Deformation Vibrations*

–CH=CH– (*trans*)	3040–3010 cm.$^{-1}$ (m.)	CH stretching
	970–960 cm.$^{-1}$ (s.)	CH out-of-plane deformation
	1310–1295 cm.$^{-1}$ (s.-w.)	CH in-plane deformation
–CH=CH– (*cis*) .	3040–3010 cm.$^{-1}$ (m.)	CH stretching
	Near 690 cm.$^{-1}$	CH out-of-plane deformation (correlation uncertain)
CH=CH$_2$ (Vinyl)	3040–3010 cm.$^{-1}$ (m.)	CH stretching
	3095–3075 cm.$^{-1}$ (m.)	CH stretching
	995–985 cm.$^{-1}$ (s.)	CH out-of-plane deformation
	915–905 cm.$^{-1}$ (s.)	CH$_2$ out-of-plane deformation
	1856–1800 cm.$^{-1}$ (m.)	Possible overtone of the above
	1420–1410 cm.$^{-1}$ (s.)	CH$_2$ in-plane deformation
	1300–1290 cm.$^{-1}$ (s.-w.)	CH in-plane deformation
CR$_1$R$_2$=CH$_2$.	3095–3075 cm.$^{-1}$ (m.)	CH stretching
	895–885 cm.$^{-1}$ (s.)	Out-of-plane deformation
	1800–1750 cm.$^{-1}$ (m.)	Possible overtone of the above
	1420–1410 cm.$^{-1}$ (s.)	CH$_2$ in-plane deformation
CR$_1$R$_2$=CHR$_3$.	3040–3010 cm.$^{-1}$ (m.)	CH stretching
	840–790 cm.$^{-1}$ (s.)	CH out-of-plane deformation

so that in materials of the type $R_1R_2C=CHR_3$ the number of characteristic frequencies is reduced. Unsaturation in compounds of the type $R_1R_2C=CR_3R_4$ is extremely difficult to detect, as the only remaining characteristic frequency is the $C=C$ stretching mode, the intensity of which is considerably reduced by the symmetry around the bond. A very full review of fundamental work on simple molecules in this field has been given by Sheppard and Simpson.[47] Other useful reviews are those of Lecomte and Naves,[80] Gruzdev [81] and O'Connor.[82]

Many of the characteristic frequencies of double bonds occur in the region of C–O and C–C stretching bands, so that the occurrence of an absorption band at a specific frequency can not alone be taken as evidence for the presence of a certain type of double bond, although from the absence of a band we may conclude the absence of the group with fair confidence.

On the other hand, examination of all the regions in which specific absorption frequencies occur usually allows a fairly certain identification of the double bond and its type, at least for the less heavily substituted materials. The relatively constant intensity of the specific bands arising from CH stretching and CH out-of-plane deformations in relation to the molecular weight has also resulted in the development of numerous quantitative methods for the analysis of complex hydrocarbons and polymers. It has been suggested by some workers that a statistical relationship connects the $C=C$ and CH frequencies of olefines.[83] This may well hold good for any limited series of related hydrocarbons, but is unlikely to apply very widely, as the $C=C$ stretching frequencies are more sensitive to changes of mass than are the deformation modes.

The correlations relating bond structure and frequencies are listed in Table 3.

3.2. $C=C$ STRETCHING VIBRATIONS

3.2(a). Position and Intensity. In contrast to the strong $C=O$ absorption the $C=C$ stretching vibration gives rise only to weak bands in the infra-red in non-conjugated compounds. The position of the absorption peak is modified to some extent by the nature of the substituents on the two carbon atoms, but the main factors influencing both the frequency and the intensity are symmetry considerations, conjugation and fluorine substitution. The influence of each of these factors is discussed below.

In compounds which contain only an isolated double bond the absorption peak normally occurs within the range 1680–1620 cm.$^{-1}$, with the majority absorbing in the 1660–1640 cm.$^{-1}$ region. Barnes *et al.*[1] list about twenty compounds in which the absorption appears in the 1660–1640 cm.$^{-1}$ range, whilst numerous fundamental studies on hydrocarbons and small molecules have also resulted in the assignment of the $C=C$ stretching vibration to this region. Thus, Sheppard [2] finds a band at 1645 cm.$^{-1}$ in butene-1, which he assigns to this mode, and Thompson and Torkington [3] have reported a band near 1650 cm.$^{-1}$ in a series of allyl halides and allyl alcohol. Randall *et al.*[4] also include a number of examples of structural assignments of the $C=C$ in this region, such as *iso*butylene at 1637 cm.$^{-1}$ and propylene and butene-2 at 1647 cm.$^{-1}$.

This correlation has been further studied by Sheppard and Sutherland,[5] and, as a result of studies on hydrocarbons, they have suggested that it is possible to differentiate between the double-bond types $RR_1C=CH_2$ and $RR_1C=CHR_2$ by means of the position of the absorption peak in this region. They quote ranges of 1655–1645 cm.$^{-1}$ and 1680–1670 cm.$^{-1}$, respectively, for these two types of linkage. These two linkages can also be differentiated by the intensity in this region, as the terminal double bond gives rise to a considerably more intense band than that from a double bond included in the chain. This differentiation has been supported by Thompson and Whiffen,[6] who point out that it is also in line with the results of Raman spectra of similar compounds,[7] and it has also been applied by Thompson and Torkington [8] in assigning the 1645 and 1690 cm.$^{-1}$ bands of polymerised 2 : 3-dimethylbutadiene to the two types of double bond. No characteristic band has been assigned to the $R_1R_2C=CR_3R_4$ linkage, but from Raman data it is probable that this will also absorb in the 1690–1680 cm.$^{-1}$ region.[47,58] The intensity of this band in the infra-red will, however, always be low, and often it will not be observed at all. The classified studies of the A.P.I. spectra by McMurry and Thornton [58] support this assignment, as do the summaries of Sheppard [55] and of Sheppard and Simpson,[47] of the results of studies of simple olefinic compounds. The latter workers quote the following average values for the $C=C$ vibration in simple olefines of the type studied:

$CHR=CH_2$, 1643 cm.$^{-1}$; $CHR^1=CHR^2$ (*trans*), 1673 cm.$^{-1}$;
$CHR^1=CHR^2$ (*cis*), 1657 cm.$^{-1}$; $CR^1R^2=CH_2$, 1653 cm.$^{-1}$;
$CR^1R^2=CHR^3$, 1670 cm.$^{-1}$; $CR^1R^2=CR^3R^4$, 1670 cm.$^{-1}$

This division of the correlation into groups has been valuable in hydrocarbon studies and in work with relatively simple molecules. However, it is not intended for use with oxygenated or other olefines with polar groupings, as minor disturbances of the $C=C$ modes then occur. Vinyl compounds [74] with an oxygen or a carbonyl group at the double bond absorb between 1652 and 1611 cm.$^{-1}$, and the corresponding vinylidene derivatives between 1670 and 1632 cm.$^{-1}$. Similarly, small differences in $C=C$ frequencies occur even with the minor differences in strain which occur in the various steroid rings.

Jones *et al.*[9] have studied a large number of such materials and have found that the position of the C=C absorption band is closely related to the relative position of the unsaturated unit in the ring system. Thus ten different Δ^5-unsaturated steroids absorbed in the range 1672–1664 cm.$^{-1}$, whereas a number of Δ^{11}-steroids absorbed between 1628 cm.$^{-1}$ and 1624 cm.$^{-1}$. Similar correlations were found for other positions of the double bond, and they concluded that the peak frequency was dependent on the double-bond position and that it was relatively unaffected by other structural features. In all these steroids the absorption was uniformly weak. In none of the unconjugated materials (twenty-nine in all), however, did the absorption fall outside the overall range 1680–1620 cm.$^{-1}$. Henbest *et al.*[77, 108] and Cole and Thornton[109] have obtained similar data for *cis* double bonds in steroids and triterpenes. Studies of the influence of greater degrees of ring strain have been made by Lord and Walker.[75] As the size of the ring diminishes and strain is increased, the C–H stretching frequency rises and the –C=C– frequency falls. The C=C frequency of *cyclo*heptene is 1651 cm.$^{-1}$ and *cyclo*butene 1566 cm.$^{-1}$. The fusion of an additional ring increases the degree of strain, so that the five-membered rings of *biscyclo*(2-2-1)-hept-2-ene absorb at 1568 cm.$^{-1}$ close to *cyclo*butene. The comparable bridged system with a six-membered ring likewise absorbs close to *cyclo*pentene. Supporting evidence that fusion of a second ring does in fact increase the ring strain is given by reactivity studies,[106] which show a similar effect. On the other hand, the substitution of a methyl group on the olefinic carbons appears to reduce the strain and the C=C frequencies rise (1-methyl*cyclo*heptene 1673 cm.$^{-1}$). The origins and significance of these effects have been discussed by Lord and Miller.[84] With exocyclic double bonds the effect of strain is in the opposite direction, leading to rises in the C=C frequencies as the ring strain is increased. Methylene groups attached to four-, five- and six-membered ring systems absorb respectively[84] at 1678 cm.$^{-1}$, 1657 cm.$^{-1}$ and 1651 cm.$^{-1}$. In 1 : 2-dimethylene*cyclo*pentane[110] conjugation lowers this frequency to 1626 cm.$^{-1}$, but it is interesting to note that this does not occur with 1-2-dimethylene*cyclo*butane,[111] which absorbs at the same frequency as the 1-methylene compound. The effects of ring strain on C=C intensities have not been studied in detail, but it is noteworthy that some bridged-ring *cyclo*heptene compounds[108] studied by Henbest *et al.*, in which the high C–H frequencies indicate considerable strain, did not show any detectable C=C absorptions.

In general, therefore, the C=C absorption will be found as a weak band in the range 1680–1620 cm.$^{-1}$. In simple hydrocarbons and in steroids[85, 108] furthercorrelations are available within this range which will give valuable additional information, but considerable caution is necessary in their application to complex molecules. Reference to the other regions of the spectrum in which CH vibrations occur and a consideration of the relative intensities of all the bands connected with double-bond structure are essential in the recognition of the type of linkage involved, especially in symmetrical non-conjugated C=C compounds in which the C=C frequency may not appear. In cases of doubt the changes following hydrogenation, bromination or other chemical attack upon the double bond can be studied. One such application by Leonard and Gash [78] is valuable in the identification of αβ-unsaturated tertiary amines. These compounds epimerise to the partial structure $\rangle\overset{-}{C}H{-}C{=}\overset{+}{N}\langle$ on treatment with perchloric acid, with a consequent shift of the double-bond absorption of 20–50 cm.$^{-1}$ towards higher frequencies. βγ-Unsaturated amines, on the other hand, are not affected and continue to show absorption in the original 1665–1640-cm.$^{-1}$ range.

As indicated below, C=C absorptions vary considerably in intensity, depending upon the symmetry of the bond and on factors such as conjugation, etc. No detailed studies of absolute intensities have been made, but Jones and Sandorfy [86] have compiled a useful summary of intensity data in the A.P.I. series, and Davison and Bates [74] report extinction coefficients for a variety of oxygenated olefines.

3.2(b). The Influence of Symmetry. It can be predicted from theoretical considerations that no C=C stretching vibration will appear in the infra-red from compounds with a *trans* double bond at a centre of symmetry. This arises from the fact that infra-red absorption takes place only when there is a change of dipole moment, and there is no appreciable change involved in the C=C stretching vibration of a *trans* symmetrical molecule. On the other hand, some change will occur in the dipole moment in the case of compounds with *cis* double bonds, whilst both types will be active in Raman spectra.[47, 55] The intensity of the C=C double bond in the infra-red would therefore be expected to diminish when it is moved from the end of a chain towards the centre and the molecule becomes more symmetrical. This affords a ready explanation of the enhanced intensity of this group absorption in terminal $R_1R_2C{=}CH_2$ structures as against compounds of the type $R_1R_2C{=}CHR_3$.

Numerous examples of this effect are known. Thus, ethylene and *trans*-dichloroethylene are both inactive in the infra-red in this region, but emit strongly at 1623 cm.$^{-1}$ and 1577 cm.$^{-1}$, respectively, in their Raman spectra.[10] *cis*-Dichloroethylene,[11] on the other hand, shows a strong infra-red absorption at 1590 cm.$^{-1}$. Similarly, Flett [12] has found no C=C absorption in fumaric acid, and this is, again, associated with the presence of a centre of symmetry.

Many cases have been reported in which the intensity of the $C=C$ band falls as the tendency to symmetry increases. Kletz and Sumner[13] drew attention to the fall in intensity of this band in a series of trimethylpentenes in which the symmetry was gradually increased, and they have suggested that observations on the relative intensity may give an indication of the type of linkage involved. Thus $2:4:4$-trimethylpent-1-ene with a terminal $=CH_2$ link shows the strongest absorption of this series. Assigning this an arbitrary value of 1, the value for the optical density of the corresponding $2:4:4$-trimethylpent-2-ene is only 0·35. The same value is given by $3:4:4$-trimethylpent-2-ene, which also has the $R_1R_2C=CHR_3$ structure, and there is a further decrease in intensity with increase of symmetry in $2:3:4$-trimethylpentene to 0·14 when the double bond is of the type $R_1R_2C=CR_3R_4$. Shreve *et al.*[14] have been unable to detect the $C=C$ stretching vibration in *trans* long-chain unsaturated fatty acids and alcohols in which the double bond is situated towards the centre of the chain. On the other hand, weak indications of this link could be found with comparable *cis*-compounds. In contrast, Δ^{10}-undecenoic acid and its methyl ester both show relatively strong $C=C$ absorption due to the terminal vinyl grouping.

Intensity studies on the $C=C$ linkage will therefore yield some indication of the nature of the double bond involved, and in cases where this is known they can be used for the study of *cis–trans* isomerism. A typical example of the latter use is that of Bernstein and Powling [15] in studies on *cis-* and *trans-*1 : 2-dichloro-1-propene and their deutero-derivatives. After separation of the two isomers they could be readily identified by the relatively high intensity of the $C=C$ absorption at 1606 cm.$^{-1}$ (D) and 1614 cm.$^{-1}$ (H) in the *cis*-compound, against the low intensity of the bands at 1605 cm.$^{-1}$ (D) and 1615 cm.$^{-1}$ (H) in the *trans*-compound. Additional evidence in these cases can also be obtained from the overall number of bands in the spectrum. These are considerably fewer in the more symmetrical isomer, and in the case quoted only about half the number of absorption bands appear in the *trans-* as compared with the *cis*-compound. It is also a general—but obviously not invariable—rule that the $C=C$ absorption of *cis*-isomers is a little lower than that of the corresponding *trans*-compounds.[47, 112-114] The small but significant shifts which occur in this way are well illustrated in the various isomers of the compound $CH_3CH=CH–CH=CH–COOCH_3$ which have been studied by Allan, Meakins and Whiting.[87] The *trans–trans*-compound absorbs at 1642 and 1614 cm.$^{-1}$, and the *cis–cis-* at 1623 and 1587 cm.$^{-1}$, whilst the mixed isomers show intermediate values. This effect has been used, for example, in the differentiation of *cis*- and *trans*-propenylbenzenes.[73]

3.2(c). The Influence of Conjugation. *Aliphatic Conjugation.*

When aliphatic conjugation of C=C bonds occurs, splitting of the two double-bond absorption bands usually results.[16,17] This arises partly by mechanical interaction and partly because the nature of the normal modes has been altered, and, for two identical bonds, the modes of the in-phase and opposite-phase simultaneous vibration of the two bonds will come into play. Nevertheless, in simple conjugated systems one band is usually stronger than the other, and this usually occurs at about 30 cm.$^{-1}$ lower frequency than the corresponding non-conjugated material. Barnes *et al.*[1] quote a number of examples of absorption near 1600 cm.$^{-1}$ arising from conjugated C=C systems, and 1 : 3-butadiene (1597 cm.$^{-1}$) [18] and vinyl acetylene [2] (1600 cm.$^{-1}$) are other instances. In all cases a very considerable enhancement of the intensity is observed in the infrared.

The fullest investigation of the effects of a number of conjugated double links upon each other is due to Blout, Fields and Karplus.[19] They examined a series of long-chain conjugated materials, including polyenes containing two, three, four and five conjugated C=C linkages. As they expected, the absorption pattern was complex in the 1650–1600 cm.$^{-1}$ region, but they noted that the diene had two, the triene three, and the tetræne four double bands in this region. The strongest band in all cases remained near 1650 cm.$^{-1}$ throughout the series. They also examined polyene azides and polyene aldehydes containing two, four, six, eight and ten conjugated double linkages. In these cases, in which conjugation with a different type of unsaturated link is also involved, the assignment becomes even more complicated, but the C=C vibrations appeared to shift progressively towards lower frequencies as the number of bonds in conjugation was increased. They point out that their results cannot be properly interpreted without mathematical analysis, but their findings confirm the general statement that conjugation results in a shift of the main C=C absorption band towards lower frequencies. The extent and occurrence of this shift will, however, be conditioned by many other factors which are not yet fully understood.

Conjugation with acetylenic links has been studied by Allan *et al.*[87] The frequency effects are similar, except that doubling of the –C=C– band does not, of course, occur. The intensity of the absorption is also increased, but the effect is smaller than that arising from conjugation with a carbonyl group. Thus the two compounds

CH_3–C=C–CH≡CH–COOCH$_3$ and CH_3–CH=CH–C≡C–COOCH$_3$

can be readily differentiated by the reversal of the relative intensities of the C=C and C≡C absorptions, depending upon which is adjacent to the carbonyl group. Conjugation effects in olefines have also been discussed by Scrocco and Salvetti,[92] and other examples are available in papers by Sörensen and Sörensen [115] and by Bohlmann and Mannhardt.[116]

In the sterol series Jones *et al.*[9] have examined a limited number of conjugated dienes, all of which give two maxima in the C=C stretching region. A $\Delta^{3:5}$-sterol, for example, absorbs at 1618 and 1578 cm.[-1] However, marked interaction effects appear to arise when ester groups are also present in the molecule, and two $\Delta^{3:5}$ esters absorb at 1670 and 1639 cm.[-1], although the ester group is not close to the double bonds. In this connection it should be noted that doubling of the C=C absorption is a common feature both of vinyl ethers and of acrylates.[74] This is probably associated with the appearance of an overtone frequency or results from rotational isomerism, but the presence of more than one C=C absorption does not necessarily imply that more than one olefinic group is present. Conjugation effects in steroids and triterpenes have also been studied by Henbest *et al.*[108] and by Cole and Thornton.[109]

Aromatic Conjugation. When double bond is conjugated with an aromatic ring the C=C frequency shift is generally less than that occurring in full aliphatic conjugation. This is to be expected from the weaker nature of the double bond of the aromatic system. Absorption therefore appears in the neighbourhood of 1625 cm.[-1]. Barnes *et al.*[1] quote several examples of this shift occurring with absorption close to 1625 cm.[-1]. Cinnamic acid, as a typical example, has its main C=C absorption near 1626 cm.[-1]. Bearing in mind, however, the overall frequency range of 1680–1620 cm.[-1] of the unconjugated C=C link, it will be seen that absorption near 1625 cm.[-1] does not necessarily indicate conjugation with an aryl group. However, consideration of the relative intensity of this band and of those of the aromatic ring, which also become enhanced on conjugation, will frequently give a useful lead as to whether this type of conjugation is present. There is, also, a third aromatic C=C vibration which appears near 1590 cm.[-1] when the ring is in conjugation, which is also of considerable assistance in interpretation (see Chapter 5).

$\alpha\beta$ *Unsaturated ketones, etc.* Conjugation of a double bond with a carbonyl grouping results in a low-frequency shift of the C=C absorption which is similar to, but smaller than, that arising from a normal pair of conjugate double bonds. Thus Rasmussen *et al.*[20] place the C=C absorption of isophorone at 1639 cm.[-1], and state that other unpublished studies on this type of conjugated ketone show that the C=C band falls in the range 1647–1621 cm.[-1]. Similarly, they find acetyl acetone acetate absorbs strongly at 1633 cm.[-1], and Blout *et al.*[19] find the strongest bands in the C=C region for crotonaldehyde and 2 : 4-hexadienal at 1638 cm.[-1] and 1642 cm.[-1] in solution. In the solid state these compounds give values about 10 cm.[-1] higher. Raman data give essentially similar results for such systems.[21] As in the case of conjugated dienes, however, the degree of shift can be considerably influenced by other factors, such as inclusion in ring systems. In unsaturated keto-steroids, for example, the frequency in some cases falls as low as 1588 cm.$^{-1}$, its actual value being determined almost entirely by its position in the system. Jones *et al.*[9] and also Furchgott *et al.*[22] have examined numbers of such compounds and have been able to correlate the observed frequencies with ring position; $\Delta^{16 \cdot 20}$ ketones, for example, absorb at 1592–1588 cm.^{1}, whilst $\Delta^{4 \cdot 3}$ ketones absorb at 1617 cm.$^{-1}$. The C=C frequency is only slightly reduced in $\alpha\beta$ unsaturated acids. Freeman [37] quotes 1653–1631 cm.$^{-1}$ for this vibration in a series of 2-hexenoic acids. Data on the molecular extinction coefficients of a number of compounds of this type are now available in the literature.[74, 87]

The exact position of the C=C absorption cannot therefore be predicted accurately for complex molecules, except in the few cases, such as the steroid systems, in which a number of closely related materials have already been examined.

3.2(d). Influence of Fluorine Substitution.

Thompson and Torkington [23] have drawn attention to the remarkable increase in the C=C stretching frequency which occurs when the fluorine atoms are substituted on one of the carbon atoms constituting the double bond. The C=C absorption of ethylene at 1626 cm.$^{-1}$ shows only a small frequency shift to 1650–1645 cm.$^{-1}$ with a single fluorine substituent, but rises to 1730 cm.$^{-1}$ in $CH_2=CF_2$ and $CCl_2=CF_2$. The ethylene frequency quoted is, of course, derived from Raman data, but the remainder show sufficient asymmetry for this vibration to be active in the infra-red. The reasons for this shift are not known, but must indicate a shortening of the double bond under the influence of the fluorine substitution. These findings have been confirmed by Hatcher and Yost,[64] and by others,[65, 66] and cases of a greater frequency shift on further fluorine substitution are known. Edgell [24] finds the C=C stretching absorption of fully fluorinated propene at 1798 cm.$^{-1}$, and Park, Lycan and Lacher [25] have published a spectrum of trifluoroethylene in which a strong band is shown near 1780 cm.$^{-1}$. The latter workers do not make any specific assignment for this absorption, but it is significant that the band is absent from the corresponding saturated dichloride CF_2Cl–CFClH and also from the dibromide. Perfluorobutene-1 also absorbs [88] at 1792 cm.$^{-1}$, and it is significant that the frequency falls to 1733 cm.$^{-1}$ in perfluorobutene-2. Other comparable cases have been discussed by Brice *et al.*[88] and by Weiblen.[118] Haszeldine [67] has tabulated the C=C frequencies for variously substituted ethylenes and has shown that when the fluorine is not directly attached to the double bond, as in the group –CH=CH–CF$_3$, its influence is virtually negligible.

3.3. =CH STRETCHING VIBRATIONS

One of the most valuable means of detection of double bonds through infra-red spectra is the examination of the region near 3000 cm.$^{-1}$ with a high-dispersion lithium fluoride prism. The C–H valence stretching absorptions occur in this region, and these are virtually independent of the nature of the associated structure apart from the valency state of the carbon atom. The groupings =CH$_2$ and =CRH therefore exhibit characteristic CH stretching frequencies which can be recognised and which are easily distinguished from the –CH$_2$ and –CH$_3$ frequencies occurring at longer wave-lengths. Fox and Martin [26] have shown that the C–H stretching frequencies of a number of hydrocarbons containing the =CH$_2$ group occur in the range 3092–3077 cm.$^{-1}$. All of these, except ethylene, showed a second band in the region 3025–3012 cm.$^{-1}$, which is also shown by five other unsaturated hydrocarbons, and is ascribed to the =CH– vibration. By the use of these bands it is therefore possible to differentiate the structures –CH=CH$_2$ (both bands), –C̦=CH$_2$ (3079 cm.$^{-1}$ only), and –Ċ=CH– (3019 cm.$^{-1}$ only). Sheppard and Simpson,[47] for example, record the CH stretching absorptions for a considerable number of substituted ethylenes. The =CH$_2$ absorption is found in the range 3095–3075 cm.$^{-1}$ (thirteen examples) and the =CH absorption in the range 3030–3000 cm.$^{-1}$ (sixteen examples). The normal CH vibrations of saturated structures occur at frequencies below 3000 cm.$^{-1}$, and do not interfere. In the case of some of the higher hydrocarbons, however, the methyl-group absorption band can result in masking of the lower frequency =CH band.

These findings have been confirmed for hydrocarbons by Saunders and Smith [63] and applied by Saier and Coggeshall [27] to the quantitative estimation of complex hydrocarbon mixtures. They have analysed successfully mixtures of the isomers 2 : 4 : 4-trimethyl 1- and 2-pentenes, using the =CH$_2$ band of the former near 3090 cm.$^{-1}$ and mixtures of *n*-octane, 2-octene and 1-octene, using bands at 3067, 3012 and 2857 cm.$^{-1}$. The =C–H stretching vibrations of aromatic rings occur near 3030 cm.$^{-1}$, and these also have been used in quantitative studies such as in the analysis of benzene *n*-heptane mixtures and in the determination of benzyl alcohol in *n*-octanol and methyl ethyl ketone. Several other instances are given [27] of this type of analysis, all of which give recovery figures within 1·0 per cent of the theoretical amounts. These absorptions can also be used in kinetic studies, as in the thermal polymerisation of styrene.[90]

The identification of double-bond types in sterols and triterpenes has also been carried out by Jones *et al.*[9,28] and others [108,109] using the high-frequency region. They found that in saturated steroids the first absorption maximum in this region was at 2970 cm.$^{-1}$, whereas steroids containing an ethylenic double bond show a band in the 3040–3030 cm.$^{-1}$ range. In some cases the insolubility of the material made the observation of the absorption peak difficult in solution, but a band in the appropriate region has been found in a considerable number of unsaturated steroids, and appears to show little change of position with ring structure or with ketonic conjugation. Vinyl testosterone also shows a weak band near 3085 cm.$^{-1}$, arising from the terminal vinyl grouping, whilst four ethynyl derivatives absorb at 3310 cm.$^{-1}$ due to the C≡C–H group. Meakins [87] has recently noticed that the CH stretching frequency of some vinylidene ethers is as high as 3120 cm.$^{-1}$. This is some 40 cm.$^{-1}$ above the usual value, and if it proves to be generally applicable it will be a useful diagnostic pointer.

It is therefore clear that valuable data can be obtained from the study of this region and, with the greater availability of lithium fluoride prisms, the use of this spectral range will probably be considerably extended. In the meantime, it should be remembered that the correlation has been worked out for hydrocarbons, and that the introduction of new groupings, such as halogens to the same carbon atom as the hydrogen atom giving rise to the vibration, will almost certainly give rise to frequency changes. Thus, a number of saturated halogenated hydrocarbons absorb in the 3090–3010 cm.$^{-1}$ region due to displacement of the CH frequencies under the influence of the halogen atom. For example, although *cis*- and *trans*-dichloroethylene absorb at 3085 cm.$^{-1}$, methyl bromide and iodide absorb at 3058 cm.$^{-1}$ and methylene chloride at 3049 cm.$^{-1}$. Even with normal hydrocarbons, Fox and Martin [26] emphasise the necessity of studying molecules closely related to those being analysed. The changes in the =CH absorption in passing from aliphatic to aromatic systems have already been noted, and will be dealt with more fully in the section on ring structures. Nevertheless, the possibility of absorption in the 3090–3000 cm.$^{-1}$ region arising from such structures or from saturated halogenated hydrocarbons must be borne in mind when this region is used for making assignments, and confirmation of the double-bond types suspected must be sought elsewhere in the spectrum.

The C–H stretching bands give rise to a first harmonic in the 8000–5000 cm.$^{-1}$ region, and these have been employed in a similar way by Rose [29] in the identification of structural units.

3.4. OUT-OF-PLANE =CH DEFORMATION VIBRATIONS

One of the most widely studied methods of detecting carbon–carbon double bonds and of differentiating the various types is through a study of the out-of-plane deformation of the attached hydrogen atoms. These gave rise to highly characteristic absorptions in the region 1000–800 cm.[-1] which are very largely independent of the nature of the surrounding structure, and they have been employed for qualitative and quantitative work in a wide variety of fields.

The first correlation of these absorptions as arising from unsaturated centres was due to Lambert and Lecomte,[30,31] but more precise rules were later formulated by Thompson and Torkington,[8] Gore and Johnson,[32] Rasmussen and Brattain,[16,33] and Sheppard.[55] The detailed assignment of the various vibrational modes producing these characteristic bands has been described by Sheppard and Sutherland,[34] and by Sheppard and Simpson,[47] and Torkington[45] has given a mathematical treatment which enables observed frequency shifts to be correlated with the electronegativity of other substituents.

3.4(a). Di-substituted Ethylenes. –CH=CH– (*trans*).

trans-Ethylenic double bonds give rise to a medium to strong band at 990–965 cm.[-1]. This has been shown by Kilpatrick and Pitzer[35] to be due to the hydrogen atoms which are out of plane at the double bond. In consequence, alteration in the weight of either of the substituents on the carbon atoms has very little effect on the position of the band, and the intensity varies inversely with the molecular weight. This follows from the fact that the absolute intensity from each double bond is constant, but the proportion of double bonds per unit volume falls as the chain length is increased. Rasmussen and Brattain[33] have shown that this absorption band appears only with *trans* double bonds, and this is valuable in elucidating problems of *cis*- and *trans*-structure.

So many examples of this specific absorption are available that only a few examples can be given, together with some illustrations of its use in analyses. However, it can be stated that apart from halogenated products which might be expected to interfere no case has yet been found of any departure from this correlation, despite the large numbers of spectra of hydrocarbons now available in the A.P.I. series, and that, although developed for hydrocarbons, it appears to hold equally well for a variety of other materials, such as acids, aromatic compounds, polymers, etc.

Typical cases of absorption within the 980–965 cm.[-1] range are listed by Sheppard and Sutherland,[34] by Sheppard[55] and by Sheppard and Simpson[47] for a number of olefines and ethylenes, and Hampton[36] lists another series of hydrocarbons with additional data. In almost all these cases the frequency lies close to 965 cm.[-1]. Long-chain *trans*-unsaturated fatty acids and alcohols all absorb[38] at 965 cm.[-1], but if the double bond is αβ to the carbonyl group, some small displacement to higher frequencies occurs. Crotonic, cinnamic, o-coumaric and acrylic acids[12] absorb in the range 980–974 cm.[-1], and many other examples are known.[70,71,87,93,112] This effect is a general one for all types of carbonyl groups, including amides and similar materials. Substitution as the α-carbon atom of CN, OH or OR groups has no effect upon this frequency,[76,87,93] but a rise to 978 cm.$^{-1}$ occurs in some methyl-substituted ethylenes. The presence of an α-chlorine atom in an olefine cannot therefore be detected directly from this frequency, but a new characteristic band of unknown origin is found near 1250 cm.$^{-1}$ in such materials.[76,87] The direct substitution of a halogen on to the double bond has a more pronounced effect. Haszeldine[67] quotes values of 935 cm.$^{-1}$ for the CH deformation of –CH=CHBr and –CH=CHCl, and Kitson[76] confirms this. *trans*-1 : 2-Dialkylvinyl ethers also absorb about 30 cm.$^{-1}$ below the normal level.[93]

The influence of conjugation upon this frequency has been extensively studied, particularly in relation to multiple conjugations such as occur in vegetable oils, etc., and the available data have been very well reviewed by O'Connor,[82] who has a very full bibliography. The effects are again small, but there is usually a shift towards higher frequencies, particularly in long conjugated chains. Allan *et al.*[87] describe many such compounds in which a steady increase in frequency occurs as the conjugated chain is lengthened, and in which the frequency reaches a limiting value of about 1000 cm.$^{-1}$ when the chain is also conjugated with acid or ester groups. Some attempts have been made [82,94,107] to subdivide the 1000–965 cm.$^{-1}$ range into regions characteristic of various steric patterns, in long-chain fatty acids. Thus, *trans–trans*-compounds absorb near 980 cm.$^{-1}$, *cis–trans*- near 984 cm.$^{-1}$, *trans–trans–trans*- near 995 cm.$^{-1}$, etc. However, whilst this approach may be useful within the fatty acid series, it cannot be indiscriminately used elsewhere. For example, Chapman and Taylor[96] instance a number of cases, such as β-carotene with eleven conjugated double bonds, in which the CH deformation frequency is essentially unaltered at 968 cm.$^{-1}$

Conjugation with aromatic rings, as in the stilbenes,[39,97] does not influence the position of the 965 cm.$^{-1}$ band, but it is displaced to slightly lower frequency when conjugated with acetylenic links.[87] The intensity of this absorption in other substituted stilbenes has been studied by Orr,[119] who finds significant alterations in band width where steric effects are likely.

The extinction coefficient of this band has been measured by a number of workers, and despite the difficulty in comparing values obtained on different instruments, it is clear that it has a fairly consistent value. This is also of value in confirming that an absorption band at 965 cm.$^{-1}$ is due to the –CH=CH– (*trans*) structure. As the band is situated in a spectral region in which very many other vibrations occur, its absence can be regarded as conclusive evidence for the absence of this type of linkage, but when the band is present, confirmation must be sought from intensity measurements and from other spectral regions, such as the C–H stretching and C=C vibrations.

Anderson and Seyfried [40] have given a value for the extinction coefficient of the *trans*-ethylenic double-bond absorption at 967 cm.$^{-1}$ in terms of a functional group absorption coefficient. The value agrees reasonably well with those quoted by Hampton [36] and with those from the A.P.I. series. The latter (on the basis of the whole molecular weight of the compounds) range from 132 to 141, whilst Shreve *et al.*[38] give 140–156 for elaidic acid and related materials. The variation from compound to compound is appreciable, but is small in relation to other materials, such as, for example, methyl oleate and triolein, for which Shreve gives values of 12·2 and 74·4, respectively.

The relative stability of the intensity of this band in relation to the proportion of double bonds has been used by many workers for quantitative studies. In the fatty acid series the intensity of this band appears to remain roughly additive even in conjugated materials,[94, 98] but Allan *et al.*[87] note considerate variations when conjugation is with COOR or with acetylenic links. The work of Shreve already mentioned was designed to give a method for the determination of *trans*-octadecenoic acids, esters and alcohols in complex mixtures, and similar methods have been used for the estimation of *trans*-olefines in lubricating oils [41, 68, 95] and in gasoline.[42] An especially valuable application has been in the quantitative and qualitative study of polymerisation reactions. These include applications to low-temperature polymers of butadiene and styrene,[36, 43] natural and synthetic rubbers [44, 60, 69] and to the vulcanisation of natural rubber.[59] In the terpene field,[46] and in sterols [48, 61] also, studies on the absorption at 965 cm.$^{-1}$ coupled with work on the hydrogen deformations of other double-bond types have given valuable structural information. All these applications provide further evidence for the constancy of this frequency in a wide range of different materials.

The evidence that this band is specific for *trans* types of ethylenic links rests, of course, upon its absence in comparable materials of the *cis* series.[16] The corresponding *cis*-compounds are often difficult to obtain completely free from the *trans*-isomer, but the band at 965 cm.$^{-1}$ has been effectively eliminated in many cases. In others the intensity at 965 cm.$^{-1}$ is extremely low—as in oleic acid, for example —and differentiation between the two isomers has frequently been made on this basis. Typical cases of such a differentiation are those between *cis*- and *trans*-phenylbutadiene,[49] polyurethanes,[50] long-chain unsaturated enols,[51] and the isomers of crotonyl chloride.[52] It is, however, necessary to exercise some caution in dealing with

E

this assignment. For example, the group $-CH=C(CH_3)-$ in the *trans*-configuration can also give rise to an absorption in the 1000–980 cm.$^{-1}$ region when conjugated with a carbonyl group.[80]

3.4(b). Di-substituted Ethylenes (*cis*).

Owing to the relatively small numbers of *cis*-isomers available in pure form, much less information is available on the out-of-plane hydrogen deformations [34] of *cis*-di-substituted ethylenes. Several spectra of such compounds are available in the American Petroleum Institute series and elsewhere,[47,55] and these suggest that the absorption peak due to this vibration lies near 690 cm.$^{-1}$, although it appears to be much more variable in position than the corresponding band from the *trans* form. Thus, *cis*-2-pentene absorbs at 698 cm.$^{-1}$ and 4-methyl-*cis*-2-pentene at 719 cm.$^{-1}$. Sheppard and Simpson [47] quote a range of 728–675 cm.$^{-1}$ for a number of simple ethylene derivatives, but even with these some of the assignments are uncertain. Support for this assignment has been forthcoming from many workers.[76,79,87,99,112,120] In hydrocarbons the frequency usually falls near 730 cm.$^{-1}$, but it is very much more sensitive to the nature of the surrounding structure than is the corresponding 965 cm.$^{-1}$ *trans* band. The substitution of chlorine,[76] methyl [76,79,99] or an oxygenated group [87] at the α-position results in a marked shift to higher frequencies. 1-Chloro-2-butene (*cis*) absorbs [76] at 769 cm.$^{-1}$ and 1 : 4-dichloro-2-butene (*cis*) at 787 cm.$^{-1}$, and the shifts from the other substituents listed are of the same order of magnitude.

Conjugation of the double bond also causes an upward frequency shift, the extent of which depends upon whether or not conjugation is on both sides, and on the number of double bonds involved; [79] and shifts up to 780 cm.$^{-1}$ are known.[100,101] On the other hand, acetylenic conjugation results in only a small frequency shift to slightly lower frequency, and a fairly stable value of 720 cm.$^{-1}$ is found.[87] Conjugation with carbonyl groups has a very marked effect, and the group $-CH=CH-COOR$ (*cis*) absorbs near 820 cm.$^{-1}$ with sufficient regularity for this to be a useful assignment, especially as this value is not altered significantly by further conjugation. This absorption is usually much weaker in intensity than that from the *trans*-series, but it is usually considerably enhanced on conjugation.

In complex systems, such as the steroids and triterpenes, etc., *cis*-olefines of this type give rise to a multiple series of bands in the 800–650 cm.$^{-1}$ region. Useful information can be obtained from the study of these patterns in relation to the substitution arrangements of the rings,[77,108,109] but it is usually not possible to identify any particular band of the series with the $-CH=CH-$ *cis*-absorption, and considerable disturbances result from the introduction of conjugated substituents. This emphasises the caution which is necessary in the identification of *cis*-olefines in this region, and it should not be forgotten that many other structures, including even some *trans*-olefines, absorb here also. *trans*-Phenylpropenyl carbinol [54] and *trans*-crotonyl chloride,[53] for example, absorb in the 690 cm.[-1] region.

3.4(c). Mono-substituted Ethylenes. The vinyl type double bond gives rise to two strong bands near 990 cm.[-1] and 910 cm.[-1]. The first of these is connected with the hydrogen deformation mode of the $-CH=C-$ structure,[34] and is absent from asymmetrically di-substituted ethylenes. The second band arises from out-of-plane deformations of the hydrogens of the $=CH_2$ group and occurs in both types of linkage.

As with the $-CH=CH-$ link, these frequencies are remarkably constant in position and many spectra are available in support of these assignments, both in the A.P.I. series and elsewhere. Anderson and Seyfried,[40] for example, report twelve vinyl compounds as absorbing at 995 ± 2 cm.[-1] and 910 ± 2 cm.[-1], and Hampton[36] lists a further nine materials taken from the A.P.I. series, in which the frequency range for the second band is 912–909 cm.[-1]. McMurry and Thornton[58] list fifteen such compounds, whilst Sheppard and Sutherland,[34] and Sheppard and Simpson[47] also quote numbers of vinyl compounds absorbing in the frequency ranges 995–985 cm.[-1] and 915–905 cm.[-1]. Small shifts, however, occur in certain circumstances. Thus, in structures $RCH=CH_2$, in which the α carbon atom of the R grouping is fully substituted, the frequency moves to 1005–995 cm.[-1] and if one of the substituents on this saturated carbon is a functional grouping, the 910 cm.[-1] band shifts to 930–918 cm.[-1].[54, 55] The compound linalool, for example, absorbs at 925 cm[-].[1] and 997 cm.[-1]. These effects have recently been studied in some detail by a number of workers,[74, 76, 93, 102] and the influence on both bands of various substituents is generally well known. The attachment of polar groups at the α-carbon atom to the double bond, as in CH_2Cl[76], CH_2CN[76], $-CH_2OR$[74, 93], is CH_2SR[62] and CH_2OH, has only a small effect, and the higher frequency remains unchanged whilst the lower one is displaced upwards by about 12 cm.[-1]. With the group CH_2OCOR this effect is more marked,[74] and the two frequencies move together and appear at 985 cm.[-1] and 932 cm.[-1], and a slightly greater effect is produced by carbonyl groups directly attached to the double bond. The higher frequency then occurs at 982 cm.[-1] and the lower in the range 965–950 cm.[-1], depending upon the nature of the carbonyl group.[74, 93]

The most marked changes, however, result from the direct attachment of oxygen atoms, as in vinyl ethers, etc. The 990-cm.[-1] absorption moves down to 962 cm.[-1] in vinyl ethers and to 948 cm.[-1] in vinyl esters.[74, 89, 93] The position of the original 910-cm.[-1] band in these compounds is less certain. Davison[74] originally assigned this tentatively at 942 cm.$^{-1}$ in vinyl ethers and at 870 cm.$^{-1}$ in vinyl esters. However, Meakins [89] has identified this band as falling near 810 cm.$^{-1}$ in vinyl ethers, and this has been supported by the more extensive studies of Philpotts.[93] This correlation is also supported by the observation that the 890-cm.$^{-1}$ band of compounds $CH_2{=}CR_2$ is shifted by about twice this amount when both the R groups are alkoxy residues.[93] On the other hand, in vinyl nitrate, which might be expected to parallel the oxygenated compounds, these bands are assigned [103] at 965 and 940 cm.$^{-1}$.

Halogen substituents, again, show some interference when substituted on one of the carbon atoms of the double bond, but possibilities are limited in this case to vinyl fluoride, chloride and iodide. These have been examined by Thompson and Torkington,[56] who found the expected lowering in frequencies with absorptions at 860, 895 and 902 cm.$^{-1}$, respectively, corresponding to the 910 cm.$^{-1}$ band in alkyl compounds.

Both of the bands of this correlation show the same consistency in intensity in relation to molecular weight, which is a feature of out-of-plane hydrogen deformations at a double bond. For quantitative work the 910 cm.$^{-1}$ band has generally been employed, as it is the more useful of the two for the analysis of olefine contents of polymers and hydrocarbons. Anderson [40] finds a constant value for the intensity of the 910 cm.$^{-1}$ band within about 7 per cent, after allowance for molecular weight, and the A.P.I. series, quoted by Hampton,[36] all show extinction coefficients within the range 143–153 on a molecular weight basis. The most detailed study is due to Johansen,[121] who showed the integrated area of this band was reasonably constant although the band width varied considerably. Variations in the observed extinction coefficients with various polar substituents are also recorded by Davison.[74]

Applications of these frequencies to qualitative and quantitative analysis are, of course, included in the studies referred to under the discussion of the –CH=CH– link, as they were all primarily concerned with the detection and estimation of the various double-bond types in mixtures.[36, 38, 40–46] This correlation, also, is probably applicable within rather wider limits to non-hydrocarbons.

In addition to this pair of characteristic frequencies, vinyl compounds nearly always show a medium intensity band in the range 1850–1800 cm.$^{-1}$ which may be an overtone associated in some way with the bands at 910 and 990 cm.$^{-1}$. The suggestion is supported by the fact that with the double-bond types $R_1R_2C{=}CH_2$ in which the out-of-plane hydrogen deformations occur at a lower frequency than 900 cm.$^{-1}$, the possible overtone band is also observed at a lower frequency (near 1800–1750 cm.$^{-1}$). On the other hand, the intensity of these "overtone" bands is often considerably greater than would be expected. Their origin is therefore not entirely clear, but they afford a useful confirmation of the presence of the $=CH_2$ grouping in many cases.

3.4(d). Asymmetric Di-substituted Ethylenes. $R_1R_2C=CH_2$. The hydrogen out-of-plane deformations in compounds of the type $R_1R_2C=CH_2$ occur at 890 cm.$^{-1}$. The consistency of frequency is of the same order as with the double-bond types already described. Sheppard and Simpson,[47] for example, quote a range of 892–887 cm.$^{-1}$ for seven different compounds with this group. The influences of polar groups are essentially the same as with the corresponding frequency of vinyl compounds. The groups Cl, CN, OR and OH substituted on an α-carbon atom usually give a small shift [74,76,93] to 900 cm.$^{-1}$, but this does not always occur, and 2 : 3-dichloro-1 : 3-butadiene, for example, absorbs in the normal position [105] at 892 cm.$^{-1}$. Carbonyl groups directly on the double bond [74,76,93,104] raise the frequency to 930–945 cm.$^{-1}$, and similar values are given with a directly attached nitro group.[103] The direct attachment of oxygen, as before, leads to a major shift [89,93] to 795 cm.$^{-1}$, with a further fall to 710 cm.$^{-1}$ in diethoxy compounds.[93] Conjugation with an olefinic group raises this frequency slightly in some cases,[104] but the effect is more marked with acetylenic conjugation (908 cm.$^{-1}$) or with the direct attachment of a nitrile group (934 cm.$^{-1}$). With halogen substitution, the frequency falls as before. Thompson and Torkington [56] quote shifts of 5, 11 and 71 cm.$^{-1}$ for this frequency in vinylidene bromide, chloride and fluoride respectively. The intensity of this band is a little more variable, and Anderson [40] quotes deviations from the average of up to 30 per cent. Nevertheless, absorption intensity analyses based on this frequency can be made with reasonable accuracy in many cases. Typical illustrations of the utilisation of absorption in analysis have already been quoted.[36,38,40-46]

As with the vinyl compounds, a band also occurs in the range 1800–1750 cm.$^{-1}$, which may be due to an overtone of the 890 cm.$^{-1}$ frequency and which is often useful in providing confirmation of the presence of the asymmetric ethylene linkage.

3.4(e). Tri-substituted Ethylenes. $R_1R_2C=CHR_3$. With trisubstitution at the double bond the specificity of the CH out-of-plane deformation is much reduced, and the frequency shows more variation with the nature of the substituents. These changes are probably connected with the nature of the substituents R_1, R_2 and R_3, which can now cause a greater proportional variation in the force constants than in the mono- and di-substituted ethylenes. The general frequency range for this structure is 840–800 cm.$^{-1}$, although a few cases have been reported with absorptions as low as 790 cm.$^{-1}$. As before, the bulk of the data on which this assignment is based are to be found in the A.P.I. series of spectra,[58] but a number of examples are quoted by Sheppard and Sutherland,[34] Thompson and Torkington [3] and others. The variation in frequency of this band renders it of less use for analytical purposes than those from other types of double bond, but it has, nevertheless, been successfully employed for qualitative identifications in hydrocarbons and for quantitative estimations of olefine mixtures. One example of a suitable application is that of Ruzicka *et al.*,[57] who have used the presence or absence of a band in the 840–800 cm.$^{-1}$ region to differentiate between sesquiterpenes containing the $R_1R_2C{=}CHR_3$ group and the fully substituted types $R_1R_2C{=}CR_3R_4$, in which no band can arise from hydrogen deformations about the double bond. Hirschmann [72] has found this band near 800 cm.$^{-1}$ in a large number of unsaturated sterols and has noted a second band near 812 cm.$^{-1}$ which appears to occur only in Δ^5-3β-acetoxy compounds. The influence of halogen substitution at the double bond has not been fully studied, but would be expected to cause reduction in the frequency; neoprene, which contains the structure $R_1ClC{=}CHR_2$, absorbs at 826 cm.$^{-1}$. However, this frequency is not a particularly trustworthy one, and it can be used only with great caution. A band in the 1000–980 cm.$^{-1}$ region has been identified with the group $\diagdown C{=}CH-$ (*trans*) $\overset{|}{\underset{}{CH_3}}$

in certain irones by Lecomte and Naves,[80] this may be a CH_3–C stretching frequency, and a somewhat similar correlation has been suggested by Gunzler *et al.*[117] for fully substituted ethylenes carrying a methyl substituent. In these cases a reasonably constant absorption occurs near 1155 cm.$^{-1}$.

3.5. IN-PLANE $=$CH DEFORMATION VIBRATIONS

The in-plane deformation frequencies of hydrogen atoms about a double bond have been less used for analytical work and have not been so extensively studied. This is principally due to the fact that symmetry considerations either forbid the appearance of the normal vibration in certain cases or result in a weakening of the intensity. Nevertheless, these frequencies have a similar precision to those arising from out-of-plane deformations, and in double-bond types, which give rise to strong bands, the detection of the in-plane frequencies can provide useful confirmation of the presence of the double bond, despite the fact that the bands normally occur in the region associated also with C–C stretching modes and with saturated –CH deformations.

3.5(a). Di-substituted Ethylenes (*trans*). The ν_1 in-plane hydrogen deformation in symmetrically substituted ethylenes should appear only in the Raman spectrum and is forbidden in the infra-red.

Sheppard and Sutherland [34] have shown that, in fact, a strong band appears in the region 1310–1290 cm.$^{-1}$ in both the Raman and infrared spectra of a series of hydrocarbons of this type. They have assigned these to the two in-plane deformations ν_1 and ν_2 with different symmetry classes. A band in this region can be traced in the infra-red spectrum of all hydrocarbons of this type, but the intensity appears to be somewhat variable and the band is occasionally weak in intensity.[34,47,55]

3.5(b). Di-substituted Ethylenes (*cis*). *cis*-Di-substituted ethylenes show a strong Raman line near 1260 cm.$^{-1}$ which is assigned to the ν_1 vibration.[47,55] This band would be permitted by symmetry considerations to appear also in the infra-red spectrum, but no consistent absorption can be found in this region in the infra-red. However, a medium intensity band is found near 1405 cm.$^{-1}$ in many cases. This is also attributed to a CH in-plane deformation.[47]

3.5(c). Mono-substituted Ethylenes. As in the case of the out-of-plane hydrogen deformations, the vinyl-type compounds give rise to two frequencies from the corresponding planar modes. The ν_1 frequency arises from deformations of the hydrogen of the $=CH_2$ structure, whilst ν_2 rises, chiefly, from the $-CH=C-$ structure. Two bands are found in both the infra-red and Raman spectra, in the ranges 1420–1410 cm.$^{-1}$ and 1300–1290 cm.$^{-1}$. The higher frequency band has been assigned to the $=CH_2$ deformations [34,47,55] in analogy with $R_1R_2C=CH_2$ structures in which it is also present, and with the corresponding CH_2 deformation near 1450 cm.$^{-1}$ in saturated hydrocarbons. The lower-frequency band is in the expected region and is found also in *trans*-symmetrically di-substituted ethylenes.

The high-frequency band near 1415 cm.$^{-1}$ is usually strong in the infra-red and is very stable in position, so that it serves as a useful guide in analysis. The substitution of CH_2OR and CH_2OCOR groups has little or no effect upon this frequency, but in the case of acrylates and methylacrylates it shows a slight fall [74] to 1405 cm.$^{-1}$. The lower-frequency band is also relatively stable in position, but appears to be more variable in intensity.

3.5(d). Asymmetric Di-substituted Ethylenes. This type of structure would be expected, from the above, to show strong absorption in the range 1420–1410 cm.$^{-1}$ in both Raman and infrared spectra, due to the planar deformation of the $=CH_2$ group. This is found experimentally and the frequency shows the expected degree of consistency of position within a few cm.$^{-1}$.[34,47,55]

3.5(e). Tri-substituted Ethylenes. The in-plane deformation of the single hydrogen atom of these structures gives rise to a strong Raman line in the region 1390–1375 cm.$^{-1}$ Although allowed in the infra-red, the corresponding band is weak in most cases and, as such, is of little value for work on structural analysis.

3.6. BIBLIOGRAPHY

1. Barnes, Gore, Liddel and Williams, *Infra-red Spectroscopy* (Reinhold, 1944).
2. Sheppard, *J. Chem. Phys.*, 1949, **17**, 74.
3. Thompson and Torkington, *Trans. Faraday Soc.*, 1946, **42**, 432.
4. Randall, Fowler, Fuson and Dangl, *Infra-red Determination of Organic Structures* (Van Nostrand, 1949).
5. Sheppard and Sutherland, *J. Chem. Soc.*, 1947, 1540.
6. Thompson and Whiffen, *ibid.*, 1948, 1412.
7. Hibben, *The Raman Effect and its Chemical Applications* (Reinhold, 1939), p. 166.
8. Thompson and Torkington, *Trans. Faraday Soc.*, 1945, **41**, 246.
9. Jones, Humphries, Packard and Dobriner, *J. Amer. Chem. Soc.*, 1950, **72**, 86.
10. Herzberg, *Infra-red and Raman Spectra of Polyatomic Molecules* (Van Nostrand, 1945), p. 325.
11. *Idem, ibid.*, p. 329.
12. Flett, *J. Chem. Soc.*, 1951, 962.
13. Kletz and Sumner, *ibid.*, 1948, 1456.
14. Shreve, Heether, Knight and Swern, *Analyt. Chem.*, 1950, **22**, 1498.
15. Bernstein and Powling, *J. Amer. Chem. Soc.*, 1951, **73**, 1843.
16. Rasmussen and Brattain, *J. Chem. Phys.*, 1947, **15**, 120.
17. Bradacs and Kahovec, *Z. physikal. Chem.*, 1940, **B48**, 63.
18. Rasmussen, Tunnicliff and Brattain, *J. Chem. Phys.*, 1943, **11**, 432.
19. Blout, Fields and Karplus, *J. Amer. Chem. Soc.*, 1948, **70**, 194.
20. Rasmussen, Tunnicliff and Brattain, *ibid.*, 1949, **71**, 1068.
21. Kohlrausch and Pongratz, *Z. Chem. Phys.*, 1934, **B27**, 176.
22. Furchgott, Rosenkrantz, Harris and Shorr, *J. Biol. Chem.*, 1946, **163**, 375.
23. Torkington and Thompson, *Trans. Faraday Soc.*, 1945, **41**, 236.
24. Edgell, *J. Amer. Chem. Soc.*, 1948, **70**, 2816.
25. Park, Lycan and Lacher, *ibid.*, 1951, **73**, 711.
26. Fox and Martin, *Proc. Roy. Soc.*, 1940, **A175**, 208.
27. Saier and Coggeshall, *Analyt. Chem.*, 1948, **20**, 812.
28. Jones, Williams, Whalen and Dobriner, *J. Amer. Chem. Soc.*, 1948, **70**, 2024.
29. Rose, *J. Res. Nat. Bur. Stand.*, 1938, **20**, 129.
30. Lambert and Lecomte, *Compt. rend. Acad. Sci. Paris*, 1938, **206**, 1007.
31. *Idem, Ann. Phys.*, 1938, **10**, 503.
32. Gore and Johnson, *Phys. Rev.*, 1945, **68**, 283.
33. Rasmussen and Brattain, *J. Chem. Phys.*, 1947, **15**, 131, 135.
34. Sheppard and Sutherland, *Proc. Roy. Soc.*, 1949, **A196**, 195.
35. Kilpatrick and Pitzer, *J. Res. Nat. Bur. Stand.*, 1947, **38**, 191.
36. Hampton, *Analyt. Chem.*, 1949, **21**, 923.
37. Freeman, *J. Amer. Chem. Soc.*, 1953, **75**, 1859.
38. Shreve, Heether, Knight, and Swern, *Analyt. Chem.*, 1950, **22**, 1261.
39. Thompson, Vago, Corfield and Orr, *J. Chem. Soc.*, 1950, 214.
40. Anderson and Seyfried, *Analyt. Chem.*, 1948, **20**, 998.
41. Fred and Putscher, *ibid.*, 1949, **21**, 900.
42. Johnston, Appleby and Baker, *ibid.*, 1948, **20**, 805.
43. Treumann and Wall, *ibid.*, 1949, **21**, 1161.
44. Dinsmore and Smith, *ibid.*, 1948, **20**, 11.
45. Torkington, *Proc. Roy. Soc.*, 1951, **A206**, 17.
46. Bateman, Cunneen, Fabian and Koch, *J. Chem. Soc.*, 1950, 936.
47. Sheppard and Simpson, *Quart. Rev.*, 1952, **6**, 1.
48. Jones, *J. Amer. Chem. Soc.*, 1950, **72**, 5332.
49. Grummit and Christoph, *ibid.*, 1951, **73**, 3479.
50. Marvel and Young, *ibid.*, p. 1066.
51. Crombie and Harper, *J. Chem. Soc.*, 1950, 1707, 1714.
52. Hatch and Nesbitt, *J. Amer. Chem. Soc.*, 1950, **72**, 727.
53. Philpotts and Thain, *Nature*, 1950, **166**, 1028.
54. Barnard, Bateman, Harding, Koch, Sheppard and Sutherland, *J. Chem. Soc.*, 1950, 915.

55. Sheppard, *J. Inst. Pet.*, 1951, **37**, 95.
56. Thompson and Torkington, *Proc. Roy. Soc.*, 1945, **A184**, 21.
57. Ruzicka, Jeger *et al.*, *Helv. Chim. Acta*, 1950, **33**, 672, 711, 1050.
58. McMurry and Thornton, *Analyt. Chem.*, 1952, **24**, 318.
59. Sheppard and Sutherland, *Trans. Faraday Soc.*, 1945, **41**, 261.
60. Salomon, Van der Schee, Ketelaar and Van Eyk., *Discuss. Faraday Soc.*, 1950, **9**, 291.
61. Bladon, Fabian, Henbest, Koch and Wood, *J. Chem. Soc.*, 1951, 2402.
62. Tarbell and McCall, *J. Amer. Chem. Soc.*, 1952, **74**, 48.
63. Saunders and Smith, *J. Applied Phys.*, 1949, **20**, 953.
64. Hatcher and Yost, *J. Chem. Phys.*, 1937, **5**, 992.
65. Morino, Kuchitsu and Shimanouchi, *ibid.*, 1952, **20**, 726.
66. Nielsen, Liang and Smith, *ibid.*, 1090.
67. Haszeldine, *Nature*, 1951, **168**, 1028.
68. Putscher, *Analyt. Chem.*, 1952, **24**, 1551.
69. Richardson and Sacher, *J. Polymer Sci.*, 1953, **10**, 353.
70. Crombie, *J. Chem. Soc.*, 1952, 2997, 4338.
71. Sinclair, McKay, Myers and Jones, *J. Amer. Chem. Soc.*, 1952, **74**, 2578.
72. Hirschmann, *ibid.*, 5357.
73. Mixer, Heck, Winstein and Young, *ibid.*, 1953, **75**, 4098.
74. Davison and Bates, *J. Chem. Soc.*, 1953, 2607.
75. Lord and Walker, *J. Amer. Chem. Soc.*, 1954, **76**, 2518.
76. Kitson, *Analyt. Chem.*, 1953, **25**, 1470.
77. Henbest, Meakins and Wood, *J. Chem. Soc.*, 1954, 800.
78. Leonard and Gash, *J. Amer. Chem. Soc.*, 1954, **76**, 2781.
79. Oroshnik and Mebane, *ibid.*, 5719.
80. Lecomte and Naves, *J. Chim. Phys.*, 1956, 462.
81. Gruzdev, *Zhur, Fiz, Khim.*, 1954, **28**, 507.
82. O'Connor, *J. Amer. Oil. Chem. Soc.*, 1956, **33**, 1.
83. Werner and Lark, *J. Chem. Soc.*, 1954, 1152.
84. Lord and Miller, *Applied Spectroscopy*, 1956, **10**, 115.
85. Jones and Herling, *J. Org. Chem.*, 1954, **19**, 1252.
86. Jones and Sandorfy, *Chemical Applications of Spectroscopy* (Interscience, 1956), p. 370.
87. Allan, Meakins and Whiting, *J. Chem. Soc.*, 1955, 1874.
88. Brice, Lazerte, Hals and Petersen, *J. Amer. Chem. Soc.*, 1953, **75**, 2698.
89. Meakins, *J. Chem. Soc.*, 1953, 4170.
90. Slowinski, Emil and Claver, *J. Polymer. Sci.*, 1955, **17**, 269.
91. Bellamy, *J. Chem. Soc.*, 1955, 4221.
92. Scrocco and Salvetti, *Bull. Sci. della Fac. Chim. Bologna*, 1954, **12**, 1.
93. Philpotts, *private communication.*
94. Ahlers, Brett and McTaggart, *J. App. Chem.*, 1953, **3**, 433.
95. Francis, *Analyt. Chem.*, 1956, **28**, 1171.
96. Chapman and Taylor, *Nature*, 1954, **174**, 1011.
97. DeTar and Carpino, *J. Amer. Chem. Soc.*, 1956, **78**, 475.
98. Bickford, DuPré, Mack and O'Connor, *J. Amer. Oil. Chem. Soc.*, 1953, **30**, 379.
99. Hall and Mikos, *Analyt. Chem.*, 1949, **21**, 422.
100. Kuhn, Inhoffen, Staab and Otting, *Chem. Ber.*, 1953, **86**, 965.
101. Zechmeister, *Experimentia*, 1954, **10**, 9.
102. Kirmann and Chancel, *Bull. Soc. Chim. Fr.*, 1954, 1338.
103. Brown, *J. Amer. Chem. Soc.*, 1955, **77**, 6341.
104. Brügel, *Angew. Chem.*, 1956, **68**, 441.
105. Sheppard and Szasz, *Trans. Faraday Soc.*, 1953, **49**, 358.
106. Traynham and Sehnert, *J. Amer. Chem. Soc.*, 1956, **78**, 4024.
107. Jackson, Paschke, Tolberg, Boyd and Wheeler, *J. Amer. Oil. Chem. Soc.*, 1952, **29**, 229.
108. Henbest, Meakins, Nicholls and Wilson, *J. Chem. Soc.*, 1957, 997.
109. Cole and Thornton, *ibid.*, 1332.
110. Blomquist, Wolinsky, Meinwald and Longone, *J. Amer. Chem. Soc.*, 1956, **78**, 6057.
111. Blomquist and Verdol, *ibid.*, 1955, **77**, 1806.

112. Heilmann, Gaudemaris and Arnaud. *Bull. Soc. Chim. Fr.*, 1957, **112**, 119.
113. Gamboni, Theus and Schinz, *Helv. Chim. Acta*, 1955, **38**, 255.
114. Theus, Surber, Colombi and Schinz, *ibid.*, 239.
115. Sörensen and Sörensen, *Acta Chem. Scand.*, 1954, **8**, 1741, 1763.
116. Bohlmann and Mannhardt, *Chem. Ber.*, 1955, **88**, 429, 1336.
117. Gunzler, Kienitz and Neuhaus, *Naturwiss.*, 1956, **43**, 299.
118. Weiblen, *Fluorine Chemistry.* Ed. Simons. Vol. 2 (Academic Press, New York, 1954), p. 449.
119. Orr, *Spectrochim. Acta*, 1956, **8**, 218.
120. Jones, Mansfield and Whiting, *J. Chem. Soc.*, 1956, 4073.
121. Johansen, *Bull. Acad. Sci. U.S.S.R.*, 1954, **18**, 708.

CHAPTER 4

Alkynes and Allenes

4.1. INTRODUCTION AND TABLE

THE possibilities of detection of acetylenic links in unknown materials depend largely on the degree of substitution at the triple bond. Mono-substituted acetylenes can be readily identified by the highly characteristic $\equiv$C–H stretching vibration and also by the C$\equiv$C vibration, which gives a strong band when the triple bond is situated at the end of the chain. In di-substituted materials the former band is, of course, absent, whilst the second is very variable in intensity, depending on the position of the triple bond. In symmetrical structures the C$\equiv$C absorption is often too weak to be detectable, and in these circumstances there is no sure way of recognising this type of bond. On the other hand, when the C$\equiv$C stretching band is present, its position is highly characteristic, whilst the usual shifts arising from conjugation and from aromatic substitution are also very informative.

The only other regions from which information might be sought are, in the case of mono-substituted materials, the $\equiv$CH bending and combination frequencies. Deformation vibrations occur near 650 cm.$^{-1}$ and a combination frequency near 1250 cm.$^{-1}$ has been described in some cases. However, insufficient data are available at present to allow the unequivocal identification of bands at either of these positions as being due to this cause.

A review of the absorption bands found in simple alkynes has been given by Sheppard and Simpson,[20] who have also summarised the observed frequencies for the C$\equiv$C and $\equiv$CH absorptions in these materials. An extensive study of conjugated acetylenes has been made by Allan, Meakins and Whiting.[25]

Allenic materials are not common, and relatively few have been studied. They appear to behave as though the bonds were more nearly triple and single, rather than as two double bonds, and characteristic absorption bands arise near 1950 cm.$^{-1}$ and 1060 cm.$^{-1}$, due to the stretching modes of the C$\equiv$C$\equiv$C structure. It is interesting to note that absorption in the 2000 cm.$^{-1}$ region also arises from other similar structures,[1] such as HN=C=O (2274 cm.$^{-1}$), O=C=O (2349 cm.$^{-1}$), HN=N$\equiv$N (2140 cm.$^{-1}$), O=N$\equiv$N (2223 cm.$^{-1}$), NH=C=S (1963 cm.$^{-1}$) and O=C=S (2050 cm.$^{-1}$).

The correlations discussed are listed in Table 4.

TABLE 4

Acetylenic Materials

$\equiv$CH stretching absorptions .   .   .   3300 cm.$^{-1}$ (s.)

C$\equiv$C stretching absorptions, mono-substi-
tuted .   .   .   .   2140–2100 cm.$^{-1}$ (s.)

C$\equiv$C stretching absorptions, di-substituted   2260–2190 cm.$^{-1}$, very
                                                      variable intensity

Absorptions in the regions 1250 and 650 cm.$^{-1}$ are also discussed.

Allenic Materials

C=C=C, stretching absorptions 1950 and 1060 cm.$^{-1}$ (m.)

4.2. $\equiv$CH STRETCHING VIBRATIONS

The work of Fox and Martin [2] and others on hydrogenic stretching vibrations has already been described in relation to alkanes and alkenes. In the light of these results, an absorption is to be expected somewhere above 3000 cm.$^{-1}$ which is due to the stretching of the hydrogen atom attached to a triply-bonded carbon atom in a mono-substituted acetylenic material. Furthermore, this band can be expected to be reasonably strong and to be largely free from inter-ference from the remainder of the molecule, especially as in this case it is not possible for any other substituents to be directly joined to the same carbon atom as the single hydrogen. This expectation is, of course, realised in practice; Randall *et al.*[3] quote data for a number of mathematically analysed molecules in which the $\equiv$C–H stretching absorption occurs in the range 3390–3290 cm.$^{-1}$, whilst Sheppard [4] gives values of 3300 cm.$^{-1}$ for 1-butyne and 3305 cm.$^{-1}$ for vinyl acetylene (Raman). Wotiz and co-workers [5,6] have examined about a dozen mono-substituted acetylenes, in all of which this band appears near 3270 cm.$^{-1}$. They note, however, that owing to the poor dis-persion of rock-salt in this region their values are 20–40 cm.$^{-1}$ lower than known Raman values for a few of these products, and this correction would bring their findings into line with the others. It is interesting to note that the CH stretching absorption of HCN [7] also occurs at 3311 cm.$^{-1}$, indicating that the nature of the attachment of the triple bond does not exert any marked influence on the absorp-tion frequency.

Mono-substituted acetylenes can therefore be readily differentiated from double-bonded and saturated materials by the examination of this region. The only other groupings likely to absorb in the same region are bonded OH and NH groups. These can be readily differ-entiated by their broad appearance, and in any case confirmation of the acetylenic structure can be obtained by reference to the C$\equiv$C stretching region.

4.3. C≡C STRETCHING VIBRATIONS

4.3(a). Position. The C≡C stretching vibration is known, from fundamental studies on simple molecules,[3, 4, 8, 20] to occur near 2100 cm.[-1]. Wotiz and co-workers [5, 6] have examined twenty-eight variously substituted acetylenes and studied the position and intensity of this absorption band. Their findings are in line with earlier Raman data [8] and show that the position depends on the number of substituents. For the series CH≡CR the band always occurred in the range 2140–2100 cm.[-1], whilst in the series CR≡CR¹ it was in the range 2260–2190 cm.[-1]. These ranges relate to non-conjugated materials in which R is saturated and either aliphatic or a halogen. In a further series of sixteen other acetylenes their results were confirmed,[6] although variations in the substituents on the α-carbon atom resulted in slight shifts away from these ranges in some cases. For example, the compounds $C_4H_9CHX-C≡CH$, where X is OH and Br, were found to absorb at 2080 and 2090 cm.[-1], respectively. On the other hand, the C≡C frequency of $CF_3C≡CH$ is normal [26] and α-chlorine substitution has no effect upon it in di-substituted acetylenes. This particular substitution pattern can, however, be readily identified in the latter materials, as the group $-C≡CCH_2Cl$ has a characteristic frequency near 1250 cm.[-1] similar to that shown by the related olefines.[25] The attachment of polar groups does not therefore always result in a frequency shift, and even $CH_3C≡C-Cl$ shows a normal band [33] despite the direct attachment of the chlorine to the triple bond. Similarly, although phenyl substitution in compounds $R-C≡C-CH_2-X$ lowers the frequency from 2260 cm.[-1] (saturated) to 2210 cm.[-1] (aromatic), the results still fall within the range quoted for di-substituted products. Sheppard and Simpson [20] quote values for seventeen variously substituted acetylenes which agree with this correlation, as do the values recently obtained by Blomquist [21] for the C≡C vibration in *cyclo*decyne and *cyclo*nonyne.

4.3(b). The Influence of Conjugation. There has recently been a good deal of interest in the chemistry of conjugated acetylenes, and a certain amount of infra-red data are now available.[25, 27–31, 35] Conjugation with acetylenic or olefinic groups usually causes some intensification of the absorption, together with a small shift towards lower frequencies. The changes are, however, much smaller than those which occur in the olefines. Conjugation with carbonyl groups does not alter the frequency appreciably [25, 37–39] in most cases, but a few α-carbonyl compounds show shifts to 2170 cm.[-1] although others do not.

Similarly, in an extensive series of conjugated acids and esters studied by Allan *et al.*[25] the main C≡C frequency occurred in the region 2260–2235 cm.[-1], which is towards the top of the normal region. Wotiz and Miller [5] find the $C\equiv C$ stretching absorption of $C_5H_{11}C\equiv CCN$ at 2120 cm.[-1], which is below the normal range for di-substituted acetylenes, whilst diacetylene [9] and vinyl acetylene [4] absorb at 2024 and 2099 cm.[-1], respectively. This frequency shift is not shown by $\alpha\beta-\alpha'\beta'$-conjugated alkynes in which the individual conjugation effects appear to cancel each other. Dicyanoacetylene,[22] for example, absorbs at 2267 cm.[-1]. This effect has been observed also in conjugated acids and esters $R(-C\equiv C-)_nCOOR$, where N is greater than 1. In some cases three bands are observed although only two triple bonds are present. 1 : 4-Nonadiyne and 5 : 8-tridecadiyne, for example, give three bands in the 2000 cm.[-1] region.[34] Doubling of the $C\equiv C$ frequency is also found in fluorinated compounds, such as trifluoro-propyne [10] and perfluoro-dimethylacetylene.[32]

The origin of these additional bands is unknown. They have been attributed by some authors to mechanical coupling effects and by others to the appearance of overtone or combination bands. One other feature of interest, in connection with this correlation, is the observation of Wotiz and Miller [5] that the $C\equiv C$ stretching band in mono-substituted products appears as a single absorption, whereas with di-substituted materials there are two or more bands in this region. These bands were observable only in cases in which the fundamental was of good intensity, but their appearance is in line with earlier findings from Raman spectra.[8] In general, in solution, the higher-frequency band is appreciably more intense than the other, but instances have been reported in which the relative intensities are reversed when the sample is examined in a disc or in a mull.

Duplication of bands in this region is also shown by trifluoropropyne [10] and perfluoro-2-butyne, both of which show a band at 1960 cm.[-1] in addition to the main fundamental at 2128 cm.[-1].

4.3(c). Intensity. The intensity of the fundamental $C\equiv C$ stretching vibration is extremely variable and is directly related to the position of the triple bond in the molecule. Wotiz and Miller [5] found the band to be strong in compounds in which the triple bond terminated the chain, and that the intensity diminished progressively in compounds in which the triple bond was situated farther and farther away from the end. This arises from the establishment of a pseudo centre of symmetry about which the stretching of the triple bond is symmetrical and, therefore, inactive in the infra-red. A strictly comparable phenomenon exists with the $C=C$ linkage, and it has been fully discussed in Chapter 3. The consequence is that the $C\equiv C$ fundamental is not detectable in a compound such as $C_3H_7-C\equiv C-(CH_2)_2Cl$, and the absence of an absorption band in the triple-bond region cannot therefore be taken as evidence for the absence of such a bond. In contrast, this band is, of course, always strong in Raman spectra. Conjugation usually increases the intensity a little, but in di-substituted materials it is necessary to have as many as four conjugated C≡C groups to bring up a band of medium intensity.[27] In $CH_3(C{\equiv}C)_3CH_3$, for example, the absorption at 2222 cm.$^{-1}$ is weak, whilst $CH_3(C{\equiv}C)_4CH_3$ has a medium-strength band at 2237 cm.$^{-1}$.

Conjugation with carbonyl groups also increases the intensity, and extinction coefficient data for a number of such materials have been given by Allan *et al.*[25]

4.4. ≡CH BENDING VIBRATIONS

These absorptions have not been systematically studied except in the case of a few mathematically analysed materials. By analogy with double-bond vibrations, the vibrations involving ≡C–H bending modes should give rise to bands which are reasonably constant in position, but they fall in the 700–600 cm.$^{-1}$ range, which is largely beyond the rock-salt region, and have not therefore been studied in any large number of materials. However, in a number of single mono-substituted alkynes this band appears [20] strongly between 642 cm.$^{-1}$ and 615 cm.$^{-1}$. In a number of cases a strong combination band in the 1300–1200 cm.$^{-1}$ range has been recorded as being due to these bands,[4,11,12,20] but so many different types of structure give rise to absorption in this region that this observation is not likely to be of much value for structural diagnosis, unless later work should show a selective narrowing of this range for various structural types.

4.5. ALLENIC STRUCTURES

The allenic structure C=C=C is rare in organic chemistry, and the spectra of very few compounds containing this group are available. It is known, however, that the normal C=C stretching mode does not appear near 1600 cm.$^{-1}$, but that strong interactions occur to give two bands more closely corresponding to triple- and single-bond frequencies. Allene is the simplest compound of this type, and it has been investigated by Linnett and Avery,[13] and by Thompson and Harris,[14] who assigned the two bands near 1965 and 1070 cm.$^{-1}$ to this vibration. On the other hand, the =C–H stretching vibrations correspond more closely with those from a double-bond, rather than a triple-bond structure. 1 : 2-Butadiene has been studied by Rasmussen and Brattain,[15] who found a similar effect with C=C bands at 1970 cm.$^{-1}$ and 1064 cm.$^{-1}$. Wotiz [16] reports 1 : 2-heptadiene as absorbing at 1950 cm.$^{-1}$, and has employed this band for the estimation of this compound in admixture with 2-heptyne and with 1-heptyne. As has already been noted, this behaviour is paralleled by many different types of compound containing the structure $=C=$, and in ketens, for example, there are bands at 2160 cm.$^{-1}$ and 1130 cm.$^{-1}$ whilst diphenyl keten [17,18] has a band at 2130 cm.$^{-1}$. Whilst, therefore, the identification of allenic-type structures is possible, with reasonable certainty, from the infra-red spectra, the degree of overlap is such that it is not possible, using these bands alone, to differentiate between, for example, allenes and *iso*cyanates ; the most which can be derived from the infra-red spectrum being the identification of the skeleton $X=C=X$ as being correlated with the appearance of a medium intensity absorption band near 1950 cm.$^{-1}$.

A review of allenic structures, whose spectra have been mathematically analysed, has been given by Sheppard and Simpson.[20] Wotiz and Celmer [19] have examined eleven different allenes, seven of which contained COOH, $CONH_2$ or COOR groups directly attached to a terminal allenic bond. In all the latter cases a doublet at 1950 and 1930 cm.$^{-1}$ was observed, whereas in the four cases in which such substituents were absent or the allenic bond was further inside the chain, only a single absorption was shown. Some differentiation is possible on this basis. Conjugated allenes are very uncommon, but in the few cases examined,[23, 24] such as mycomycin, the characteristic frequency is lowered to 1900 cm.$^{-1}$. As with alkynes, the effect appears to be reduced when conjugation is on both sides of the allenic structure and the band appears near 1930 cm.$^{-1}$

Insufficient information is available on the $=C-H$ stretching modes of these compounds to permit the use of the 3000 cm.$^{-1}$ region for structural analysis. In this connection, Rasmussen and Brattain,[15] using a rock-salt prism, were unable to identify any $=C-H$ band in 1 : 2-butadiene which was separate from the main CH bands between 3030 cm.$^{-1}$ and 2940 cm.$^{-1}$.

4.6. BIBLIOGRAPHY

1. Herzberg and Reid, *Discuss. Faraday Soc.*, 1950, **9**, 92.
2. Fox and Martin, *Proc. Roy. Soc.*, 1940, **A175**, 208.
3. Randall, Fowler, Fuson and Dangl, *Infra-red Determination of Organic Structures* (Van Nostrand, 1949).
4. Sheppard, *J. Chem. Phys.*, 1949, **17**, 74.
5. Wotiz and Miller, *J. Amer. Chem. Soc.*, 1949, **71**, 3441.
6. Wotiz, Miller and Palchak, *ibid.*, 1950, **72**, 5055.
7. Herzberg, *Molecular Spectra and Molecular Structure : Diatomic Molecules* (Van Nostrand, 1950), p. 279.
8. Hibben, *The Raman Effect and its Chemical Application* (Reinhold, 1939), pp. 200 ff.
9. Herzberg, *Infra-red and Raman Spectra of Polyatomic Molecules* (Van Nostrand, 1945), p. 323.
10. Henne and Nager, *J. Amer. Chem. Soc.*, 1951, **73**, 1042.
11. Wu, *Vibrational Spectra and Structure of Polyatomic Molecules* (Edwards, 1946), p. 176.
12. Crawford, *J. Chem. Phys.*, 1940, **8**, 526.
13. Linnett and Avery, *ibid.*, 1938, **6**, 686; cf. also Herzberg, *op. cit.*, p. 339.
14. Thompson and Harris, *Trans. Faraday Soc.*, 1944, **40**, 295.

15. Rasmussen and Brattain, *J. Chem. Phys.*, 1947, **15**, 120–135.
16. Wotiz, *J. Amer. Chem. Soc.*, 1951, **73**, 693.
17. Whiffen and Thompson, *J. Chem. Soc.*, 1946, 1005.
18. Drayton and Thompson, *ibid.*, 1948, 1416.
19. Wotiz and Celmer, *J. Amer. Chem. Soc.*, 1952, **74**, 1860.
20. Sheppard and Simpson, *Quarterly Reviews*, 1952, **6**, 1.
21. Blomquist, Burge, Huang Liu, Bohrer, Sucry and Kleis, *J. Amer. Chem. Soc.*, 1951, **73**, 5510.
22. Miller and Hannan, *J. Chem. Phys.*, 1953, **21**, 110
23. Oroshnik, Mebane and Karmas, *J. Amer. Chem. Soc.*, 1953, **75**, 1050.
24. Celmer and Solomons, *ibid.*, 1372.
25. Allan, Meakins and Whiting, *J. Chem. Soc.*, 1955, 1874.
26. Haszeldine and Leedham, *ibid.*, 1952, 2150.
27. Cook, Jones and Whiting, *ibid.*, 1952, 2883.
28. Bohlmann, *Chem. Ber.*, 1955 **88**, 1755.
29. Bohlmann and Viehe, *ibid.*, 1955, **88**, 1017, 1245.
30. Schubach and Trautschold, *Annalen*, 1955, **594**, 67.
31. Georgieff, Cave and Blakie, *J. Amer. Chem. Soc.*, 1954, **76**, 5494.
32. Henne and Finnegan, *ibid.*, 1949, **71**, 298.
33. Davidson and Bernstein, *Can. J. Chem.*, 1955, **33**, 1226.
34. Gensler, Mahadeven and Casella, *J. Amer. Chem. Soc.*, 1956, **78**, 163.
35. Sörensen and Sörensen, *Acta Chem. Scand.*, 1954, **8**, 1741, 1763.
36. Bohlmann and Mannhardt, *Chem. Ber.*, 1955, **88**, 1330.
37. Theus, Surber, Colombi and Schinz, *Helv. Chim. Acta*, 1955, **38**, 239.
38. Gamboni, Theus and Schinz, *ibid.*, 255.
39. Grob and Fischer, *ibid.*, 1794.

CHAPTER 5

Aromatic Compounds

5.1. INTRODUCTION AND TABLE

AROMATIC-TYPE compounds give rise to a large number of very sharp, characteristic bands, so that their identification by infra-red methods is usually straightforward; furthermore, the changes in certain regions which result from substitution are largely independent of the nature of the substituents, so that it is usually possible to determine, also, the degree and type of substitution present.

In a molecule as complex as benzene a very considerable number of normal vibrational modes are possible, but infra-red studies have contributed largely to the demonstration of the planar nature of the ring,[1] and a number of workers have studied the normal vibrations and enabled many of them to be identified.[2-8] The origin of many of the bands used in correlation work is therefore known so that it is often possible to assess the extent of any changes which are likely to result from structural modifications. Studies on the correlation of spectral changes following upon substitution of various types were initiated by Lecomte [9, 10, 11] in a considerable series of papers between 1937 and 1946, and these have been further developed by later workers.

The presence of an aromatic-type structure is best recognised by the presence of the =C–H stretching vibrations near 3030 cm.$^{-1}$ and the C=C vibrations in the 1600–1500 cm.$^{-1}$ region. In these regions the absorption bands are very little affected by the substitution pattern, although a study of the C=C region can also throw light on the nature of substitution in certain cases, and on the presence of conjugation with the double bonds of the ring.

Once the presence of an aromatic ring is established, the presence and relative positions of substituents can be studied in the regions 2000–1660 cm.$^{-1}$, 1250–1000 cm.$^{-1}$ and 1000–650 cm.$^{-1}$. Of these regions, the first is generally the most definite, and usually gives a clear indication of the type of substitution. Confirmation of this can then be sought in the low-frequency region and, to a lesser extent, in the 1250–1000 cm.$^{-1}$ region. The presence of groupings absorbing or giving overtones in the 2000–1660 cm.$^{-1}$ region complicates the interpretation in some cases, whilst strong electron attracting or donating substituents, such as nitro-groups, exert a profound influence on all these three regions. The interpretation of the spectrum is then rendered much less precise.

The regions of absorption to be discussed are listed in Table 5.

TABLE 5

=C–H *Stretching Modes*
Sharp absorption near 3030 cm.$^{-1}$.

2000–1660 cm.$^{-1}$
Absorption patterns typical of the substitution type (see Fig. 6)

C=C *Skeletal In-plane Vibrations*
Near 1600 cm.$^{-1}$ (v.)
   „   1500 cm.$^{-1}$ (v.)
   „   1580 cm.$^{-1}$ (m.) (conjugated rings)
   „   1450 cm.$^{-1}$ (m.)

CH *Out-of-plane Deformations*

Five adjacent free hydrogen atoms	770–730 cm.$^{-1}$ (v.s.) and 710–690 cm.$^{-1}$ (s.)
Four „ „	770–735 cm.$^{-1}$ (v.s.)
Three „ „	810–750 cm.$^{-1}$ (v.s.)
Two „ „	860–800 cm.$^{-1}$ (v.s.)
One free hydrogen atom . .	900–860 cm.$^{-1}$ (m.)

The Region 1225–950 cm.$^{-1}$

1 : 2-, 1 : 4- and 1 : 2 : 4-substitution	1225–1175 cm.$^{-1}$, 1125–1090 cm.$^{-1}$, 1070–1000 cm.$^{-1}$ (2 bands) (all w.)
Mono-, 1 : 3-, 1 : 2 : 3- and 1 : 3 : 5-substitution	1175–1125 cm.$^{-1}$, 1110–1070 cm.$^{-1}$ (not 1 : 3 : 5-), 1070–1000 cm.$^{-1}$ (1 band) (all w.)
1:2-, 1:2:3- and 1:2:4-substitution	1000–960 cm.$^{-1}$ (w.)
Tropolones	1630–1600 cm.$^{-1}$, 1570–1535 cm.$^{-1}$ (v.)

5.2. =CH STRETCHING VIBRATIONS

Studies on the CH stretching absorptions of saturated and unsaturated compounds have already been discussed fairly fully (Chapter 3), and the same considerations as to stability of position apply in the aromatic series. Fox and Martin [12, 13, 14] have examined many aromatic materials in the 3000 cm.$^{-1}$ region using the high dispersion of a grating, including polycyclic materials such as naphthalene and quinoline. They find that the CH aromatic stretching vibrations produce bands close to 3038 cm.$^{-1}$ which are generally three in number. Many mono-substituted aromatics give a characteristic triplet of this type about 3058 cm.$^{-1}$ in carbon tetrachloride solution, but there are sometimes more bands than this, and in multiple-ring systems very complex patterns are produced. In nearly all cases, however, one of the bands in this region is considerably more intense than the others. This region has been studied in some detail at high resolution by Josien and Lebas [61] using mono-substituted aromatics. They have shown very clearly that in these cases the multiple-band systems can be explained very simply in terms of a single fundamental absorption accompanied by a series of weaker absorptions arising from combinations of the various bands in the 1600–1400 cm.$^{-1}$ region. The fundamentals themselves fall within the range 3079 cm.$^{-1}$: (nitrobenzene) to 3030 cm.$^{-1}$ (toluene).

These workers have also discussed the relationships which these frequencies may have to the electron withdrawing or donating powers of the substituent,[62, 68] and to such properties as dipole moments, electron densities as calculated by molecular diagrams, and reactivities. It is interesting to note, for example, that with the exception of the halogen atoms, which are anomalous, an approximately linear relationship connects the C–H stretching frequency and the percentage of *m*-substituted material obtained on nitration.

The CH_3 stretching frequencies of multiple-ring systems have been studied by Fox and Martin,[14] and by Fuson and Josien,[63] who have paid particular attention to substituted benzanthracenes. In the latter case some possible correlations between the CH frequencies and the carcinogenic activities of the compound have been discussed.

In general, therefore, there is very little difficulty, in practice, in identifying the CH absorption in aromatic compounds and usually, using a rock-salt prism, it appears as a sharp, relatively weak band about 3030 cm.$^{-1}$ on the side of the main, much stronger, CH_2 and CH_3 absorption bands below 3000 cm.$^{-1}$. The intensity is appreciably less than the saturated CH_2 vibrations, but increases in proportion to the amount of aromatic residues present.

Changes of state cause small shifts of the order of 10–15 cm.$^{-1}$ but, except where a lithium fluoride prism is used, this is negligible in the wave-length region in question.

These aromatic CH stretching vibrations have been successfully employed in quantitative analysis by Saier and Coggeshall [15] in the estimation of benzyl alcohol in *n*-octanol and methyl ethyl ketone, of benzene in *n*-hexane, of ethylbenzene in mixtures with *n*-octane, 2-octene and carbitol, and of the components of several other such mixtures.

Other factors which can cause absorption above 3000 cm.$^{-1}$ are CH stretching absorptions of normal double bonds of various types and of CHX groups, where X is a halogen. The former can usually be identified by their position using lithium fluoride, and also by the characteristic bands they show elsewhere in the spectrum. The differentiation from halogenated materials is less easy, but confirmation of an aromatic structure is usually obtainable from the 1600–

1500 cm.$^{-1}$ region. Interferences arising from hydrogen-bonded OH and NH groups are usually eliminated by the use of dilute solutions, but in some cases where intramolecular bonds are involved the $=$CH aromatic stretching region may be masked.

These stretching vibrations show overtones in the 8000–5000 cm.$^{-1}$ region which are also characteristic of the aromatic structure,[66] and Rose [16] has employed this region for the analysis of the aromatic components of hydrocarbons.

5.3. ABSORPTIONS IN THE REGION 2000–1650 CM.$^{-1}$

Studies of the absorption patterns produced by substituted aromatics in the 2000–1650 cm.$^{-1}$ range afford one of the best and most selective methods for the identification of benzene-ring substitution. This method is due to Young, Duvall and Wright,[17] who have shown that each of the various types of substitution gives rise to a typical absorption pattern which, within limits, is independent of the nature of the substituents.

Aromatic compounds, generally, give a much richer absorption pattern in this region than most other materials, and a series of overtone and combination bands is obtained. They are relatively weak compared with the fundamentals, and for studying this region fairly thick cells (0·1 mm. for liquids and 1·0 mm. for 10 per cent solutions of solids) are employed. In the latter case double-beam operation, with solvent cancellation of the small carbon tetrachloride absorptions in this region, is desirable.

Whiffen [64] has recently been able to show that all the bands in this region can be assigned with reasonably high precision to summation bands of the CH out-of-plane fundamentals which occur between 1000 and 700 cm.$^{-1}$. This accounts for the variations in characteristic pattern with alterations in the positions of substitution and explains why the general shapes are more important in this case than the absolute frequencies. This also explains the simplification of the bands with more symmetrical structures in which a smaller number of out-of-plane CH fundamentals occur.

Young *et al.*[17] state that they have employed this spectral region for a number of years in the characterisation of benzene-ring substitution and that it has stood the test of experience with a large number and variety of compounds. Since their publication we have used this region in our own laboratories, with considerable success, on a wide range of aromatic compounds without encountering any difficulties other than the occasional production of an irregular pattern when certain limited substituents are present. This last fact had been noted by the original authors, and is discussed below.

The essential difference between analysis in this region and normal infra-red techniques lies in the fact that the intensities and numbers of the bands are relatively more significant than the precise wavelengths at which they occur. It is therefore desirable that workers in this field should have a set of reference patterns readily available for comparison. Typical patterns are illustrated by Young et al.,[17] but it is a relatively simple matter to obtain a typical set by the examination of the various toluenes, xylenes, etc., on the instrument being used, and this is to be preferred.

These patterns are sufficiently distinctive to permit small variations in intensity and position to occur without seriously complicating the recognition of the characteristic type. Thus, mono-substituted materials generally produce a series of four bands of gradually diminishing intensity towards the long wave-length region. In the case of chloro- and bromo-benzenes the intensity of the first of these is actually a little less than that of the second, whilst in phenol the fourth band is stronger than the second and third, and all bands show a shift towards longer wave-lengths. Nevertheless, the patterns are all sufficiently different from those produced by other types of substitution, and sufficiently similar to the standard, to allow the ready identification of these materials as mono-substituted aromatics.

Di-, tri- and tetra-substituted materials show even more regularity with respect to the appropriate typical patterns. Young et al.[17] note that occasionally there is a more marked splitting of doublets than is usual, but state that they have had no serious trouble in their identification. Patterns are also given for penta- and hexa-substituted materials, but these must be treated with more caution, partly because the pattern is less characteristic as substitution is increased, and partly because the original authors do not consider they have yet examined enough samples of these types to be statistically significant. Whiffen [64] has pointed out that 1 : 2 : 3 : 4- and 1 : 2 : 3 : 5-tetra-substituted aromatics have only two out-of-plane CH frequencies, and so can give rise to only three summation bands ($a + a$, $a + b$ and $b + b$), of which only two will fall in the 2000–1650 cm.$^{-1}$ range. In the former case they will be well separated, but in the latter they will be close together and may sometimes appear as a single band. In 1 : 2 : 4 : 5- and in penta-substituted aromatics only one fundamental CH is permitted. This normally falls near 870 cm.$^{-1}$, so that a strong single band near 1740 cm.$^{-1}$ is to be expected.

Interference with these typical patterns can arise from two causes: the occurrence of a fundamental or some other overtone band in the same region, and the presence of certain substituents which alter appreciably the original fundamental frequencies.

Fundamentals and overtones of other bands in this region are not difficult to recognise, and appear simply as an additional band superimposed upon the original pattern. In styrene, for example, a band appears at 1818 cm.[1] which is the overtone of the double-bond vibration at 910 cm.[-1], and this is superimposed on the normal mono-substituted pattern which appears on either side.

When carbonyl groups are present, the intensity of the CO funda-mental, at the cell thickness required, usually blots out a considerable proportion of the region and reduces the possibilities of the identi-fication.

The presence of fluorine, ether or nitro-substituents in mono-substituted compounds causes considerable alterations in the general pattern. In the first two instances the spectrum is very similar to the normal, but has an additional band above 2000 cm.[-1], which is a little confusing. This can be shown to be also due to a summation band,[64] and it can be safely ignored in making a diagnosis. The pattern derived from nitrobenzene is markedly different from the others, because, as will be indicated later, the fundamental CH out-of-plane frequencies are themselves considerably displaced in this compound. It is a general rule that if the pattern for a com-pound differs from the normal one for that specific configuration, the pattern so obtained will not resemble any of the others, so that only in occasional rare cases is it not possible to obtain any useful information from this region. With further substitution the pat-terns become normal in most cases, and the nitrotoluenes and nitroxylenes, for example, show normal or near normal patterns. However, we find that heavy nitro-group substitution can still result in atypical patterns in some cases.

Little data are available on the applicability of these absorptions to naphthenic and polycyclic hydrocarbons, but it is to be expected that the patterns resulting from the combined effects of two or more rings, each differently substituted, will invalidate the use of this region for identifications. The A.P.I. series of spectra includes a number of variously substituted naphthalenes which would not be classifiable from the patterns in this region, but, as in earlier cases, the patterns obtained are quite distinct from any standard pattern. This has been confirmed by Fuson and Josien [63] in studies on sub-stituted benzanthracenes. Whilst they do not regard the absorption pattern in this region as being indicative of the substitution pattern, they have noted a number of regularities in this region which may be helpful in the subdivision of these compounds into different classes.

5.4. C=C STRETCHING VIBRATIONS

The fundamental studies on benzene vibrations, referred to above,[2-7] have shown that the characteristic skeletal stretching modes of the semi-unsaturated carbon–carbon bonds lead to the appearance of a group of four bands between 1650 and 1450 cm.[-1]; of these, those near 1600 cm.[-1] and 1500 cm.[-1] are highly characteristic of the aromatic ring itself and, taken in conjunction with the C–H stretching bands near 3030 cm.[-1], they afford a ready means of recognition for this structure. The actual positions of the bands are influenced to some extent by the nature of substituent groups, but depend, to a rather greater degree, on the way in which the latter are arranged round the ring, so that in some cases it is possible to obtain a certain amount of confirmatory evidence as to the type of substitution. It will be seen, however, that the amount of overlapping between the ranges for various kinds of substitution is such that the number of cases in which such a differentiation is possible is limited.

Until recently very little information has been available in the literature on the positions of these bands for any large number of compounds, but Barnes *et al.*[18] have given a table indicating the positions of the two major bands for a number of mono- and disubstituted materials, whilst there are now a considerable number of aromatics available in the A.P.I. series of hydrocarbon spectra. The latter give a good illustration of the relative shifts produced by changes in mass and relative positions of the substituents round the ring, but, being nearly all of one type, they do not fully reflect the overall ranges to be expected for any single type with different sorts of functional substituent groups. Randall *et al.*[19] have quoted the approximate ranges of 1613–1600 cm.[-1] and 1504–1493 cm.[-1] for over fifty aromatic compounds examined in their laboratory, whilst Colthup[20] has given more detailed correlations based on the very large number of aromatic materials examined in the laboratories of the American Cyanamide Company. Cannon and Sutherland[42] have also discussed aromatic correlation and published the spectra of over a hundred aromatics of various types.

A valuable contribution towards the understanding of this region has been made by Randle and Whiffen,[65] who have summarised a good deal of the available data on variously substituted aromatics and assigned the various group frequencies. In agreement with earlier work of Lecomte[66] they attribute four bands in the 1650–1450 cm.[-1] region to C–C skeletal modes. One of these (near 1580 cm.[-1]) is often very weak, however, whilst another near 1450 cm.[-1] is close to a deformation mode of CH_2 groups, and is therefore often obscured. These assignments have been fully supported by further detailed studies on mono-substituted aromatics by Josien and Lebas.[61] Altogether, these correlations can be regarded as being very firmly established in so far as the recognition of aromatic structures is concerned. However, as will be seen, the intensities of these bands are extremely variable, so that in some cases they appear only as weak shoulders on the sides of other bands, and their recognition is then correspondingly more difficult.

5.4(a). The 1600 cm.⁻¹ Band. Colthup [20] shows this band as occurring within the range 1625–1575 cm.⁻¹ for most aromatic materials. With *para*-substitution there is a small shift towards higher frequencies (1650–1585 cm.⁻¹), and this applies also, to a lesser extent, to unsymmetrical tri-substituted materials. With vicinal tri-substituted materials, on the other hand, the shift is towards lower frequencies (1610–1560 cm.⁻¹).

These limits are fully substantiated by our own findings, by the A.P.I. series of spectra and by the work of Whiffen [65,67] and of Josien. [61] In the great majority of mono-substituted materials the band lies within ±5 cm.⁻¹ of 1600 cm.⁻¹, but in compounds such as chlorobenzene, bromobenzene and thiophenol it lies close to the lower limit, whilst the frequency is higher than the average in nitrobenzene. This would suggest that the band position is determined, to some extent, by the electronegativity of the substituent groups, but this is only one of a number of factors operating, and the introduction of further electronegative groups does not result in any further reduction in the frequency. Furthermore, these shifts are considerably less than those which can be produced by alterations in the positions of the substituents. The position of this band therefore affords little or no evidence as to the nature of the substituents, and only in favourable circumstances, in which the absorption is appreciably above or below 1600 cm.⁻¹, does it give any reliable indication of the type of substitution. However, corresponding shifts also occur in the position of the 1500 cm.⁻¹ band (see below), so that the two bands taken together will give an indication, at least, of certain types of substitution which is occasionally useful in confirmation of data obtained from other regions of the spectrum. Cannon and Sutherland [42] have shown this correlation to be applicable to a wide range of polycyclic aromatics as well as to simpler materials.

5.4(b). The 1600–1560 cm.⁻¹ Region. There is a certain amount of confusion in the literature as to the occurrence and significance of this band. Barnes *et al.* [18] show this second band close to the first in a limited number of cases, and make no comment upon it. Colthup [20] includes it as a definite medium intensity band occurring generally in the range quoted above, whilst Randall *et al.* [19] regard a band in the range 1587–1575 cm.⁻¹ as a positive indication of conjugation of a double bond with the aromatic ring. Rasmussen, Tunnicliff and Brattain [21] have made the more limited suggestion that absorption at 1600 cm.⁻¹ and at 1585 cm.⁻¹ may be indicative of the presence of the benzoyl group, whilst Cannon and Sutherland [42] have noted the double nature of the 1600 cm.⁻¹ band in diphenyl, naphthalenes, phenanthrenes and other compounds.

This confusion probably arises from two causes: first, the fact that this band occurs in the water-vapour region in which the detection of small bands is difficult with single-beam instruments, and secondly, because of the variation from one laboratory to another in the choice of film thickness to be examined. In normal circumstances, with no conjugation of the ring, we find, with a double-beam instrument, that this second band shows as a weak shoulder adjoining the main 1600 cm.$^{-1}$ band when the sample is examined in capillary film thicknesses or in thin nujol pastes. In some cases it is so weak as to be practically undetectable, although it can be intensified by the use of thicker cells. In all cases in which a sufficiently thick film has been examined the band has been found in the position indicated by Colthup. In a few cases the relative intensities of the 1600 and 1580 cm.$^{-1}$ bands are reversed, so that *ortho*-dichlorobenzene and certain xylenols have the weak band on the short wave-length side of the main band. Owing to the overlapping of the ranges in which these bands occur, however, this does not involve any departure from the correlations quoted. Josien and Lebas [61] and Randle and Whiffen [65] have confirmed the presence of a weak subsidiary C–C fundamental in this region.

Where a carbonyl group or any unsaturated group is directly attached to the ring, however, the intensity of this second 1580 cm.$^{-1}$ band is very considerably enhanced, and it becomes much more prominent in the spectrum; this accounts for the suggestions that this band can be used for the detection of conjugation with the ring. In all the cases which we have examined, the enhancement in the intensity of this band is sufficient to enable conjugation to be recognised after a certain amount of experience. The conflict in the literature can therefore be reconciled by the view that the 1580 cm.$^{-1}$ band is a normal aromatic vibration, but that it is always weak and difficult to detect unless it is made stronger by external conjugation, when it becomes a readily recognisable band of medium intensity, but the identification of such conjugation must clearly be made with caution after consideration of the film thickness employed and the relative intensity of the band in relation to that at 1600 cm.$^{-1}$.

5.4(c). The 1525–1475 cm.$^{-1}$ Band. The behaviour of this band, with alterations in the positions of substituents around the ring, is exactly parallel to that of the 1600 cm.$^{-1}$ band. In agreement with Colthup and with the A.P.I. spectra, we find that the band always occurs in the range 1525–1475 cm.$^{-1}$ and usually close to 1500 cm.$^{-1}$, except where *para*-substitution or unsymmetrical tri-substitution causes a small shift towards higher frequencies, or vicinal tri-substitution a shift towards lower frequencies. These findings have again been fully substantiated by the detailed studies of Whiffen [65] and of Josien.[61]

5.4(d). The 1450 cm.$^{-1}$ Band. The existence of a fourth skeletal C–C frequency in the region of 1450 cm.$^{-1}$ was suggested by Lecomte,[66] and has been fully substantiated by later workers.[61,65] In a series of mono-substituted aromatics studied by Josien and Lebas [61] it fell in the range 1470–1439 cm.$^{-1}$, and was usually of moderate to strong intensity. In some cases, however, as with aniline and nitrobenzene, the intensity was relatively weak. This band is frequently overlaid by strong CH_2 deformations, and its utility for identification purposes is therefore reduced, but it can be readily identified in compounds, such as the halogenated benzenes and similar materials, as well as in polynuclear compounds.[63]

5.4(e). Polycyclic Compounds. On theoretical grounds the main 1600 and 1500 cm.$^{-1}$ bands of the phenyl ring can be expected to occur also in polycyclic materials although, as bond fixation occurs in such materials and not all the bonds are of equal length,[22] it is to be expected that there may be some broadening of the overall ranges in which they can occur. This is reflected in Colthup's [20] findings, as he indicates a shift towards shorter wave-lengths of the 1600 cm.$^{-1}$ band (1650–1600 cm.$^{-1}$) and a broadening of the range of its subsidiary band to 1630–1575 cm.$^{-1}$ for α- and β-substituted naphthalenes. The third and fourth bands remain unchanged in the 1525–1450 cm.$^{-1}$ range. We ourselves have not a sufficiently large number of spectra of polycyclic aromatics to be able to comment on the limits of these ranges, but we have never had any difficulty, in practice, in recognising the aromatic character of such compounds, or of substituted quinolines and similar materials. Similarly, these bands can be recognised without difficulty in the spectra of a number of polynuclear hydrocarbons illustrated by Orr and Thompson,[23] in stilbene derivatives by Thompson, Vago, Corfield and Orr,[24] in substituted naphthalenes [60,69] and in the polynuclear hydrocarbon spectra of Cannon and Sutherland [42] and of Fuson and Josien.[63] Absorptions in the 1640–1600 cm.$^{-1}$ range have also been successfully used in the recognition of the phenyl group in alkaloids [25] and in aromatic steroids.[26,71]

5.4(f). Absorption Intensities of the Aromatic Bands 1600–1450 cm.$^{-1}$. The absorption bands due to aromatic structures in the 1600–1500 cm.$^{-1}$ region are notorious for the very wide fluctuations in intensity which are encountered. Frequently the bands are weak in unconjugated structures, and are often shown only as shoulders on other bands. In general, the 1500 cm.$^{-1}$ band appears to be a little stronger than the 1600 cm.$^{-1}$ band. Conjugation of the ring with any double bond such as CO, C=C, NO_2, etc., produces in most cases a very marked enhancement of the intensity of all bands, including the 1600–1560 cm.$^{-1}$ band, which has already been discussed. In a limited number of cases the enhancement of the intensity of the first pair of bands appears to be at the expense of the third, which is reduced in intensity. In mercaptobenzthiazole, for example, the 1500 cm.$^{-1}$ band is readily detected in the unconjugated thioketo form, but is extremely weak in derivatives of the conjugated mercaptan form. This behaviour is not, however, general, and in most conjugated aromatics the 1500 cm.$^{-1}$ band can be identified without difficulty, although its intensity is often somewhat diminished. The intensity of the band near 1450 cm.$^{-1}$ is usually fairly constant, but alters markedly with certain substituents.

The intensity of these bands appears also to be related to the relative positions of substituents, as alterations in these can produce marked changes. In some instances the 1600 cm.$^{-1}$ band becomes so strong as to have a greater intensity than that of a carbonyl group with which it is conjugated. This occurs, for example, in the spectra of solutions of *p*-hydroxyacetophenone and of *o*-hydroxybenzaldehyde. In certain cases in which the carbonyl absorption is capable of shifting towards the 1600 cm.$^{-1}$ region under the influence of strong hydrogen bonds, this sometimes makes it difficult to differentiate between the two, and so decide the extent of the carbonyl absorption shift.

5.4(g). Identification of Aromatic Structures in the Presence of other Groupings. In the great majority of cases the three 1600–1500 cm.$^{-1}$ bands of an aromatic structure can be recognised without difficulty, provided sufficient attention is paid to the preparation of films of suitable thickness; and, coupled with data from the 3000 cm.$^{-1}$ region, this is usually sufficient for the positive identification of this group. However, heterocyclic aromatics such as pyridine and pyrimidines also give a somewhat similar set of bands in the 1600 cm.$^{-1}$ region.[27] *cyclo*Octatetraene also gives similar absorption bands in the 1600 cm.$^{-1}$ region, and the spectrum closely resembles that of styrene, in which a normal C=C link is conjugated with the ring.[28]

Other factors which can complicate the identification of aromatics in this region are the presence of CO–NH, C=C, NO_2 and NH_2 groupings. Occasionally these will mask one or other of the main regions. The bands from a normal C=C link near 1640 cm.$^{-1}$ are usually just above the 1600 cm.$^{-1}$ phenyl band, but when conjugated with the ring the C=C frequency often falls within the same absorption region. The second C=C band arising from resonance splitting of two non-aromatic C=C vibrations is, however, at an appreciably higher frequency than the aromatic band at 1500 cm.$^{-1}$. Difficulties are also encountered in the identification of the 1600 cm.$^{-1}$ band in certain aromatic β-diketones and other structures in which the carbonyl band is shifted into the same region of absorption. Certain quinones and similar materials, in which bond fixation occurs, are also somewhat less easy to recognise, as the aromatic bands occur towards the extremes of the normal range.

In general, there is little difficulty in this identification, and the correlations can be applied to the spectra of samples examined in solution or as pastes in paraffin oil, as the shifts produced by changes of state are very small [29] and well within the limits of the ranges quoted.

5.5. OUT-OF-PLANE CH DEFORMATION VIBRATIONS

Strong bands appear in the region 1000–650 cm.$^{-1}$ in the spectra of aromatic materials due to the out-of-plane deformation vibrations of the hydrogen atoms remaining on the ring. Their position is determined almost wholly by the positions rather than the nature of the substituents and, with certain limitations, they provide an excellent method for the recognition of the type of substitution. The numbers and positions of these bands in variously substituted aromatics have been discussed by Randle and Whiffen.[65] However, although they are all relatively stable in position, most of them are weak, and attention has been directed almost exclusively at the one or two strong bands of the series. The very high intensity of these bands makes them particularly well suited for quantitative work, and very many applications have been described for the estimation of the relative proportions of *ortho*, *meta*- and *para*-substituted isomers and for certain tri-substituted products. Whiffen and Thompson,[31] for example, have given a method for the quantitative analysis of cresylic acid based on these bands, and have also worked out the basis for a similar analysis of mixed xylenols. Friedel, Peirce and McGovern [38] have studied this analysis further and described a method for the analysis of phenols, cresols, xylenols and ethyl phenols. Other typical examples are Ferguson and Levant's [39] method for the analysis of the four component mixture of chlorobenzene with *ortho*-, *meta*- and *para*-chlorobromobenzenes; Hales' [40] method for the analysis of mixed *tert.*-butylphenols, and Perry's [41] estimation of mixtures of five C_{10} aromatics.

The occurrence of these bands and their correlation with *ortho*-, *meta*- and *para*-substitution was noted by Barnes *et al.*,[18] and was developed and amplified by Whiffen, Torkington and Thompson [30] and by Whiffen and Thompson,[31] who determined their position in a number of mono- and di-substituted materials and in a lesser number of tri- and tetra-substituted products. Their findings were later amplified by further data by Richards and Thompson [32] working on substituted phenols, by Thompson, Vago, Corfield and Orr [24] working on substituted stilbenes, by Orr and Thompson [23] working on polynuclear hydrocarbons, and by Kamada,[52] and by Cannon and Sutherland [42] working on a wide range of aromatic materials.

This correlation has been included in the various charts issued by different workers,[20,33,34] with a gradual increase in the proposed limiting ranges as greater numbers of compounds were examined. The band positions, in relation to the various types of substitution, have been neatly summarised by Colthup [20] in terms of the numbers of adjacent hydrogen atoms remaining round the ring, and they will be considered below under this classification. Finally, Cole and Thompson [35] have supplied a mathematical basis for this empirical correlation and have been able to calculate the expected position of the principal CH out-of-plane frequencies for the various types of substitution, using a simple force system with only two force constants. Their results are in good agreement with the experimental values which they have determined for a considerable series of halogenated benzenes. The correlations even hold good for *ortho-*, *meta-* and *para-*dideuterobenzenes, although the characteristic bands appear about 20 cm.$^{-1}$ above the normal values.[53]

These correlations therefore derive from a very considerable volume of data in the literature, which is fully sufficient to substantiate them in respect of di- and tri-substituted products. With tetra- and penta-substituted materials, naphthalenes [69] and polycyclic compounds the correlations appear to apply with slightly greater deviations. Thus in *cyclo*pentenophenanthrenes [72] and in benz-anthracenes [63] the correlation with the number of adjacent hydrogen atoms in each ring still holds, but as is to be expected with compounds of this complexity, additional bands can occur in the same regions. In these cases therefore the absence of a particular band is more diagnostic than its presence.

Marked deviations from these correlations can occur when the ring is heavily substituted with highly polar groups [54] such as CO, CF_3 or NO_2, and these special cases will be considered separately below.

5.5(a). Five Adjacent Ring Hydrogen Atoms. Mono-substituted Aromatics.

Whiffen and Thompson [31] originally proposed the range 760–740 cm.$^{-1}$ for the position of the out-of-plane CH bending absorption of mono-substituted aromatics, and this has been widened slightly by Colthup [20] to 770–730 cm.$^{-1}$. This wider range is in line with our own experience and with the larger volume of published data now available.[58, 61, 65] In a few instances in which the substituent interacts electrically with the ring it is not always possible to assign this frequency with certainty. For example, benzoic acid absorbs [68] very strongly at 714 cm.$^{-1}$ and weakly at 806 cm.$^{-1}$, and it is not clear which of these is associated with the particular mode which normally gives rise to the characteristic absorption. Normally, however, the band is easily recognised as being the strongest in this region of the spectrum, although the position of the band changes considerably within the range, with even small changes in molecular structure. There is, for example, a shift of 15 cm.$^{-1}$ on passing from phenylhydrazine to phenyl-hydrazine hydrochloride. The upper part of the range of this band overlaps the range of *ortho*-di-substituted materials, so that it cannot be used alone to differentiate mono-substitution from *ortho*-di-substitution. However, Whiffen [36,65] has pointed out that mono-substituted materials also absorb strongly near 690 cm.$^{-1}$, where *ortho*-substituted materials do not absorb to any appreciable extent, and the two can be differentiated in this way. This latter correlation has been confirmed by Colthup,[10] by Randall *et al.*,[19] by Josien and Lebas [61] and by Cannon and Sutherland.[42] The band in mono-substituted materials is almost always within ± 10 cm.$^{-1}$ of 700 cm.$^{-1}$, and is regarded by Randall *et al.* as being specific for the mono-substituted phenyl group. It should always be examined in conjunction with the 750 cm.$^{-1}$ band, as *meta*-substituted products and certain tri-substituted materials also absorb near 700 cm.$^{-1}$, although usually within a rather wider frequency range. The absence of a band within the range 700 cm.$^{-1}$ ± 10 cm.$^{-1}$ is strong evidence for the absence of a mono-substituted product, but the converse is not necessarily true, and confirmation must be sought from the 750 cm.$^{-1}$ region.

In certain very limited cases the 750 cm.$^{-1}$ band shows splitting into a group of weaker bands at the same frequency. This occurs in the *cis*-forms of phenyl propenyl carbinol and styryl methyl carbinol,[37] although the *trans* forms have only a single band of normal position and intensity. The reasons for this are not known, but it may be connected with steric interferences in the *cis*-compounds.

5.5(b). Four Adjacent Ring Hydrogen Atoms. *ortho*-Di-substituted Aromatics. As indicated above, *ortho*-di-substituted materials absorb in approximately the same range of frequencies as mono-substituted derivatives, and the appropriate strong band is found in the range 770–735 cm.$^{-1}$. The reduction in the number of adjacent free hydrogen atoms from five to four does not significantly affect the frequency. This correlation also holds for cyclic materials such as phthalic anhydride, as well as for naphthalenes, quinolines and larger rings. Colthup indicates, however, that a slightly wider range of frequencies is to be expected in such materials. In line with this correlation, Orr and Thompson [23] have traced a strong band near 750 cm.$^{-1}$ in a considerable number of carcinogenic hydrocarbons which contain 1 : 2-di-substituted poly-nuclear structures, although there were shifts of ± 10 cm.$^{-1}$ in many cases, and Cannon and Sutherland [42] identify bands at 750 cm.$^{-1}$ in 9 : 10-dihydroanthracene and at 725 cm.$^{-1}$ in anthracene itself as being due to this vibration. A large number of substituted naphth-alenes have been studied by Cencelj and Hadži [69] and by Werner *et al.*[60,70] In all cases in which one ring is unsubstituted a strong band corresponding to *ortho*-substitution is shown, whilst it is usually possible to trace the bands derived from the free hydrogen vibrations of the other ring, as corresponding to the appropriate type of tri- or tetra-substituted aromatic compound. When substituents are present in both rings, however, these bands are more difficult to identify, and the applications of these correlations would lead to errors in some cases. Bands in the 746–738 cm.$^{-1}$ range are shown by appropriately substituted benzanthracenes,[63] but as indicated above, the occurrence of additional bands lessens the general utility of this correlation for polycyclic compounds.

5.5(c). Three Adjacent Ring Hydrogen Atoms. 1 : 3- and 1 : 2 : 3-Substitution. Aromatic rings with three adjacent free hydrogen atoms show absorption in the 810–750 cm.$^{-1}$ range with a second band of medium intensity in the region 725–680 cm.$^{-1}$. Colthup [20] indicates a slightly narrower range in both cases for vicinal tri-substituted materials than for *meta*-di-substituted ones, but this may only reflect the more limited numbers of such tri-substituted products examined. Overlapping of these two bands with the ranges of mono-substituted materials may lead to complications in a few cases, but usually the frequency of the first band is above 770 cm.$^{-1}$, whilst the position of the second is much more variable than with mono-substitution, so that it only occasionally falls within the same narrow range.

The main 810–750 cm.$^{-1}$ band can also be traced without difficulty in the spectra of most substituted naphthalenes which contain three free adjacent hydrogen atoms.[69, 70] In the A.P.I. series, for example, 1 : 5-dimethylnaphthalene has a strong band at 790 cm.$^{-1}$, which is the strongest band in this region of the spectrum. Similarly, mono-substituted naphthalenes with the substituent at the 1 position also show this band, in addition to the 770–735 cm.$^{-1}$ band arising from the four free hydrogen atoms on the other ring. With further substitution, however, this region often becomes too complex for ready identification of the type of substitution.

5.5(d). Two Adjacent Ring Hydrogen Atoms. 1 : 4-, 1 : 2 : 4- and 1 : 2 : 3 : 4-Substitution. With a further reduction in the number of free adjacent hydrogen atoms on the ring, the absorption frequency of the out-of-plane CH vibrations shows a further shift to higher frequency, and a strong band occurs in the range 860–800 cm.$^{-1}$. Data on this band have recently been reviewed by Randle and Whiffen [65] and by Bomstein.[55] No strong band is shown in the 750–700 cm.$^{-1}$ range, although weak ones sometimes occur. Nevertheless, in cases in which the main band falls in the 810–800 cm.$^{-1}$ region, differentiation from *meta*-type substitution is usually possible by the absence or presence of a second 750–700 cm.$^{-1}$ band of medium or strong intensity. The same type of absorption is shown by mono-substituted naphthalenes,[70] which have this band in addition to that arising from the other ring. The best method of differentiation of the three possible types absorbing in the 860–800 cm.$^{-1}$ range is through a study of the 2000–1600 cm.$^{-1}$ region, but unsymmetrical tri-substitution can also be differentiated by the medium intensity band arising from the single free hydrogen atom situated between two substituents (see below). The number of 1 : 2 : 3 : 4-tetra-substituted materials reported in the literature or available for examination is small,[65] but the correlation holds good for the cases that are known. 1 : 2 : 3 : 4-Tetramethylbenzene, for example, absorbs at 804 cm.$^{-1}$. A band in this region is also shown by neosteroids, in which ring B is aromatic,[71] and by suitably substituted benzanthracenes.[68]

5.5(e). One Isolated Ring Hydrogen Atom. Situated between Two Substituents. 1 : 3-, 1 : 2 : 4-, 1 : 3 : 5-, 1 : 2 : 3 : 5-, 1 : 2 : 4 : 5-, and penta-Substituted Aromatics. As the number of adjacent free hydrogen atoms is reduced to one the expected high-frequency shift again occurs, and the CH absorption appears in the region 900–860 cm.$^{-1}$. The reduction in the number of vibrating groups also affects the intensity, so that this band is of medium strength, in contrast to the very strong bands in the cases cited above. In the case of 1 : 3 : 5-tri-substituted materials a strong band is shown in the range 865–810 cm.$^{-1}$ and another between 675 and 730 cm.$^{-1}$. 1 : 3 : 5-Trimethylbenzene, for example, absorbs at 881 cm.$^{-1}$ (w.), 835 cm.$^{-1}$ (s.) and 687 cm.$^{-1}$ (s.) (A.P.I. Spectrum 354). The last of these bands usually enables this particular type to be differentiated from *para*-substituted and similar products absorbing near 830 cm.$^{-1}$. McCaulay *et al.*[57] find this band between 874 and 835 cm.$^{-1}$ in *sym.*-trialkylbenzenes, and have discussed the effects of chain branching in the substituents upon the frequency. The number of tetra- and penta-substituted materials available for study, or having spectra reported in the literature, is small. We have records for about thirty such materials which comply with these correlations, but they must be treated with due caution until more spectra are available. The 900–800 cm.$^{-1}$ band can be traced with difficulty in the spectra of suitably substituted polynuclear hydrocarbons, but the pattern in this region is usually too complex to enable the recognition of these medium strength bands to be reliable.

5.5(f). The Influence of Substituent Groups. As has already been explained, the positions of these CH frequencies are determined almost wholly by the position of the substituents and are independent of their nature. This, however, is not strictly true, for the electron donating or accepting properties of the substituent play an important part in determining the precise position of the absorption

G

within the frequency range. In extreme cases, as in heavily nitrated compounds, the effects introduced in this way can be sufficient to shift the absorption out of the expected range altogether. In this connection we have examined twenty-six out of the twenty-nine possible mono-, di- and tri-substituted benzenes containing methyl and/or nitro-groups, in an attempt to assess the extent and direction of these frequency shifts. The results show that nitro-group substitution moves the band towards higher frequencies and that the extent of the shift follows the degree of substitution. With very heavy nitro-group substitution the bands reach positions from which they do not show any further movement with additional substitution of nitro-groups. The CH bending frequency of a single free hydrogen atom, for example, is very near 920 cm.$^{-1}$ for compounds containing three or more nitro-groups. Specialised studies of this kind can occasionally allow the recognition of the substitution pattern of such materials, provided some other fact, such as the number of nitro-groups, is known, but otherwise it is difficult to differentiate, for example, a *para*-substituted material with one nitro-group from a *meta*-substituted product with two. The interpretation of this spectral region therefore requires extreme caution when several nitro-groups are present, or when, for example, a strongly electron-attracting group is situated in the *para*-position to a strongly electron-donating one, as in *p*-aminobenzoic acid. In such cases multiple bands often appear, and interpretation is then difficult. Margoshes and Fassel [58] have illustrated a number of cases of this type. However, compounds containing high proportions of interfering substituents are rare, so that the picture of the substitution pattern obtained from this region is normally a relatively clear one and, coupled with a study of the 2000–1600 cm.$^{-1}$ region, it allows a positive identification of the type of substitution present. As indicated above, however, the certainty with which these correlations can be applied diminishes with the degree of substitution, so that identification of tetra- and penta-substitution is very much less precise than, for example, that of mono-substitution.

A number of workers have studied the possible relationships which these frequencies may have to the changes in the electron density around the ring following the introduction of substituents. For example, Bellamy [59] has discussed these absorptions in relation to the Hammett σ values of the substituents which measure their electron-donating or withdrawing properties. With the exception of halogen substituents, which appear to behave as though they had zero σ values, reasonably good relationships can be found connecting σ values and the frequencies of 3, 2 or 1 adjacent ring-hydrogen atoms, and this is occasionally useful in predicting the frequencies of unknown compounds. The anomaly of the halogens may be explained in terms of the recent findings of nuclear magnetic-resonance studies, which suggest that the electron densities of the ring carbon atoms are not appreciably altered by halogen substitution.[73]

The additivity of Hammett σ values is reflected in an approximate additivity in frequency shifts, and it has been noted, for example, that the frequency displacement from the mean, of a *para*-disubstituted compound, is approximately the sum of the displacements of the two separate mono-substituted materials.[58] Kross *et al.*[74] have also considered this question and put forward an explanation for the major shifts in nitro-compounds, etc., in terms of an orbital-following theory. No treatment is, however, yet entirely satisfactory, as in general both electron-withdrawing and electron-donating substituents lead to δCH frequencies which are higher than those of the methyl compounds.

5.6. CHARACTERISTIC ABSORPTIONS BETWEEN 1225 AND 950 CM.⁻¹

Aromatic compounds all show a series of relatively weak bands in this region, the positions of which vary with the type of substitution arrangement. Their low intensity renders them less generally useful for analytical purposes than the lower-frequency absorptions already described, but they afford a general confirmation of findings from other parts of the spectrum as to the presence of aromatic substituents and their substitution pattern. Randle and Whiffen [65, 67, 75] have studied these vibrations in some detail and shown them to be largely the C–H in plane-deformation modes, although in some instances frequencies sensitive to the mass of the substituent fall in this region.

Barnes *et al.*[18] noted the appearance of characteristic bands in this region in the spectra of aromatics and assigned them as follows. Mono-substitution 1075–1065 cm.⁻¹, *ortho*-substitution 1125–1085 cm.⁻¹, *meta*-substitution 1170–1140 cm.⁻¹ and *para*-substitution 1120–1090 cm.⁻¹. Thompson's [38] table follows this with some increases in the ranges and the observation of an additional *para*-substitution band in the range 1225–1175 cm.⁻¹. Colthup [20] has elaborated this considerably, extended it to a study of tri-substituted materials, and shown that up to six characteristic bands can occur in this region with certain types of substitution. There is also a considerable amount of overlapping, so that no one band can be used alone for the recognition of structure. Our own findings are in agreement with Colthup and Whiffen,[65] and we would classify the various absorptions in this region as indicated below.

5.6(a). 1 : 2-, 1 : 4- and 1 : 2 : 4-Substitution. Compounds

substituted thus show weak absorptions in the ranges 1225–1175 cm.$^{-1}$ and 1125–1090 cm.$^{-1}$, together with two additional weak bands in the range 1070–1000 cm.$^{-1}$. The bands are always very sharp, although weak, and are usually recognisable without great difficulty. The 1 : 2 : 4-compounds can be differentiated from the others by the presence of an additional band in the range 1175–1125 cm.$^{-1}$.

5.6(b). Mono-, 1 : 3-, 1 : 2 : 3- and 1 : 3 : 5-Substitution. Compounds thus substituted absorb weakly between 1175 cm.$^{-1}$ and 1125 cm.$^{-1}$, as do the 1 : 2 : 4-compounds mentioned above. In addition, the mono-, *meta*- and 1 : 2 : 3-substituted materials absorb between 1110 cm.$^{-1}$ and 1070 cm.$^{-1}$, and all four types show a further single band in the range 1070–1000 cm.$^{-1}$.

5.6(c). 1 : 2-, 1 : 2 : 3- and 1 : 2 : 4-Substitution. Compounds substituted thus usually absorb weakly between 1000 cm.$^{-1}$ and 960 cm.$^{-1}$.

It will be seen, therefore, that differentiation is possible between the main classes indicated above, on the basis of the numbers and positions of the bands in this region, but that identifications of single types within the main class will often depend on the recognition of a single weak band. As these bands occur in the general region of the spectrum associated with C–C and C–O stretchings, this is, of course, very unreliable, so that data from this portion of the spectrum cannot be used to supply anything more than a general confirmation of facts ascertained elsewhere.

As regards the positional stability of these bands in relation to the nature of the substituents, it is our experience that they are less affected by the presence of strongly directive groups than those in the low frequency region. The bands from dinitro-compounds, for example, all fall within the expected ranges, but further substitution of nitro-groups results in irregularities. However, Kross and Fassel [76] have shown that at least one band in this region is sensitive to the electronegative nature of the substituent group.

Pinchas and Samuel [56] have suggested that the triphenylmethyl group has a characteristic frequency near 1185 cm.$^{-1}$, but in view of the occurrence of a CH frequency at this point in many other aromatics, this is of limited value.

No attempt has been made to extend these correlations beyond tri-substituted aromatics and, in view of the complexity of this region with such materials, it is doubtful whether this would serve any useful purpose.

5.7. OTHER AROMATIC SYSTEMS

Tropolones and related materials containing three conjugated double bonds in a seven-membered ring have many of the characteristics of aromatic compounds. The infra-red spectra have been studied by several workers,[44-51] and the three regions 1624–1605 cm.$^{-1}$, 1570–1538 cm.$^{-1}$ and 1280–1250 cm.$^{-1}$ have been suggested as being characteristic; the first two of these are believed to originate in $C=C$ stretching vibrations. However, Nicholls and Tarbell[47] have recently shown the 1570–1538 cm.$^{-1}$ band to be absent from a number of benzotropolones, and that the 1275 cm.$^{-1}$ band is absent from the spectra of colchicines which have no hydroxyl group.[48] The usefulness of these correlations is therefore questionable, as the first cannot be readily differentiated from a normal phenyl absorption, whilst the last two are apparently not specific.

The aromatic compounds C_5H_5 and C_7H_7 have also been studied and shown to be basically similar to benzene.[77] The partial aromatic character of such compounds as thiophene[78] and similar materials is also reflected in their raised CH-stretching frequencies and general spectral character.

5.8. BIBLIOGRAPHY

1. Ingold, *Proc. Roy. Soc.*, 1938, **A169**, 149; Ingold *et al.*, *J. Chem. Soc.*, 1936, 912, 1210, and 1946, 222.
2. Wilson, *Phys. Review*, 1934, **45**, 706.
3. Langseth and Lord, *Danske Vidensk Selskab. Math. Fys.*, 1938, **16**, 6.
4. Angus, Bailey, Hale, Ingold, Leckie, Raisin, Thompson and Wilson, *J. Chem. Soc.*, 1936, 966, 971.
5. Bailey, Hale, Ingold and Thompson, *ibid.*, p. 931.
6. Herzberg, *Infra-red and Raman Spectra of Polyatomic Molecules* (Van Nostrand, 1945), p. 367.
7. Pitzer and Scott, *J. Amer. Chem. Soc.*, 1943, **65**, 803.
8. Plyler, *Discuss. Faraday Soc.*, 1950, **9**, 100.
9. Lecomte, *Compt. rend. Acad. Sci. Paris*, 1937, **204**, 1186; 1938, **206**, 1568; 1939, **208**, 1636.
10. Lecomte, *J. Phys. Radium*, 1937, **8**, 489; 1938, **9**, 13 and 512; 1939, **10**, 423.
11. Delay and Lecomte, *ibid.*, 1946, **7**, 33.
12. Fox and Martin, *J. Chem. Soc.*, 1939, 318.
13. *Idem, Proc. Roy. Soc.*, 1940, **A175**, 208.
14. *Idem, ibid.*, 1938, **A167**, 257.
15. Saier and Coggeshall, *Analyt. Chem.*, 1948, **20**, 812.
16. Rose, *J. Res. Nat. Bur. Stand.*, 1938, **20**, 129.
17. Young, Duvall and Wright, *Analyt. Chem.*, 1951, **23**, 709.
18. Barnes, Gore, Liddel and Van Zandt Williams, *Infra-red Spectroscopy* (Reinhold, 1944).
19. Randall, Fowler, Fuson and Dangl, *The Infra-red Determination of Organic Structures* (Van Nostrand, 1949).
20. Colthup, *J. Opt. Soc. Amer.*, 1950, **40**, 397.
21. Rasmussen, Tunnicliff and Brattain, *J. Amer. Chem. Soc.*, 1949, **71**, 1068.
22. Cf. Badger, *Quarterly Reviews*, 1951, **5**, 147.
23. Orr and Thompson, *J. Chem. Soc.*, 1950, 218.
24. Thompson, Vago, Corfield and Orr, *ibid.*, p. 214.
25. Marion, Ramsay and Jones, *J. Amer. Chem. Soc.*, 1951, **73**, 305.
26. Jones, Humphries, Packard and Dobriner, *ibid.*, 1950, **72**, 86.
27. Brownlie, *J. Chem. Soc.*, 1950, 3062.
28. Lippincott, Lord and McDonald, *J. Amer. Chem. Soc.*, 1951, **73**, 3370.
29. Richards and Thompson, *Proc. Roy. Soc.*, 1948, **A195**, 1.
30. Whiffen, Torkington and Thompson, *Trans. Faraday Soc.*, 1945, **41**, 200.

31. Whiffen and Thompson, *J. Chem. Soc.*, 1945, 268.
32. Richards and Thompson, *ibid.*, 1947, 1260.
33. Thompson, *ibid.*, 1948, 328.
34. Van Zandt Williams, *Rev. Sci. Instr.*, 1948, **19**, 135.
35. Cole and Thompson, *Trans. Faraday Soc.*, 1950, **46**, 103.
36. Whiffen, Thesis, Oxford, 1946.
37. Philpotts and Thain, *Nature*, 1950, **166**, 1028.
38. Friedel, Peirce and McGovern, *Analyt. Chem.*, 1950, **22**, 418.
39. Ferguson and Levant, *ibid.*, 1951, **23**, 1510.
40. Hales, *Analyst*, 1950, **75**, 146.
41. Perry, *Analyt. Chem.*, 1951, **23**, 495.
42. Cannon and Sutherland, *Spectrochimica Acta*, 1951, **4**, 373.
43. Laurer and McCaulay, *Analyt. Chem.*, 1951, **23**, 1875.
44. Koch, *J. Chem. Soc.*, 1951, 512.
45. Aulin-Erdtman and Theorell, *Acta Chem. Scand.*, 1950, **4**, 1490.
46. Bartels-Keith and Johnson, *Chem. and Ind.*, 1950, 677.
47. Nicholls and Tarbell, *J. Amer. Chem. Soc.*, 1952, **74** 4935.
48. Idem, *ibid.*, 1953, **75**, 1104.
49. Doering and Knox, *J. Amer. Chem. Soc.*, 1952, **74**, 5683.
50. Idem, *ibid.*, 1953, **75**, 297
51. Doering and Hiskey, *ibid.*, 1952, **74**, 5688.
52. Kamada, *Japan Analyst*, 1952, **1**, 141.
53. Tiers and Tiers, *J. Chem. Phys.*, 1952, **20**, 761.
54. Randle and Whiffen, *J. Chem. Soc.*, 1952, 4153.
55. Bomstein, *Analyt. Chem.*, 1953, **25**, 512.
56. Pinchas and Samuel, *J. Chem. Soc.*, 1954, 863.
57. McCaulay, Lien and Launer, *J. Amer. Chem. Soc.*, 1954, **76**, 2364.
58. Margoshes and Fassel, *Spectrochimica Acta*, 1955, **7**, 14.
59. Bellamy, *J. Chem. Soc.*, 1955, 2818.
60. Ferguson and Werner, *ibid.*, 1954, 3645.
61. Josien and Lebas, *Bull. Soc. Chim. Fr.*, 1956, 53, 57, 62.
62. Idem, *Compt. Rend. Acad. Sci. Paris*, 1955, **240**, 181.
63. Fuson and Josien, *J. Amer. Chem. Soc.*, 1956, **78**, 3049.
64. Whiffen, *Spectrochim. Acta*, 1955, **7**, 253.
65. Randle and Whiffen, *Molecular Spectroscopy* (Inst. of Petroleum, 1955) p. 111.
66. Depaigne-Delay and Lecomte, *J. Phys. Radium*, 1946, **7**, 38.
67. Whiffen, *J. Chem. Soc.*, 1956, 1350.
68. Bellamy, *ibid.*, 1955, 4221.
69. Cencelj and Hadži, *Spectrochim. Acta*, 1955, **7**, 274.
70. Werner, Kennard and Rayson, *Austral. J. Chem.*, 1955, **8**, 346.
71. Scheer, Nes and Smeetzer, *J. Amer. Chem. Soc.*, 1955, **77**, 3300.
72. Dannenberg, Schiedt and Steidle, *Z. Naturforsch.*, 1953, **8B**, 269.
73. Corio and Dailey, *J. Amer. Chem. Soc.*, 1956, **78**, 3043.
74. Kross, Fassel and Margoshes, *ibid.*, 1332.
75. Randle and Whiffen, *Trans. Faraday Soc.*, 1956, **52**, 9.
76. Kross and Fassel, *J. Amer. Chem. Soc.*, 1955, **77**, 5858.
77. Nelson, Fateley and Lippincott, *ibid.*, 1956, **78**, 4870.
78. Hildago, *Compt. Rend. Acad. Sci. Paris*, 1954, **239**, 253.

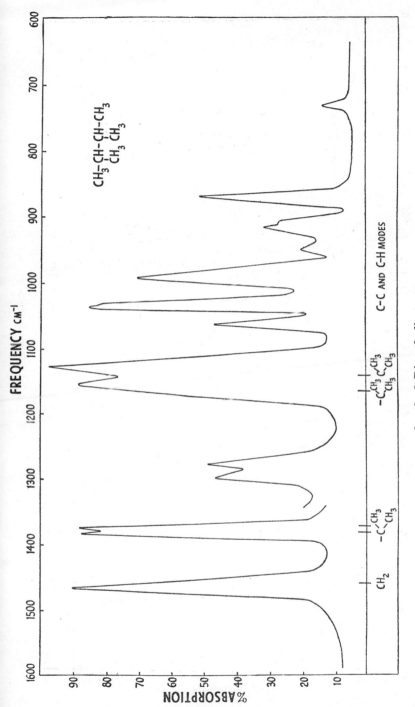

1. 2 : 3-Dimethylbutane

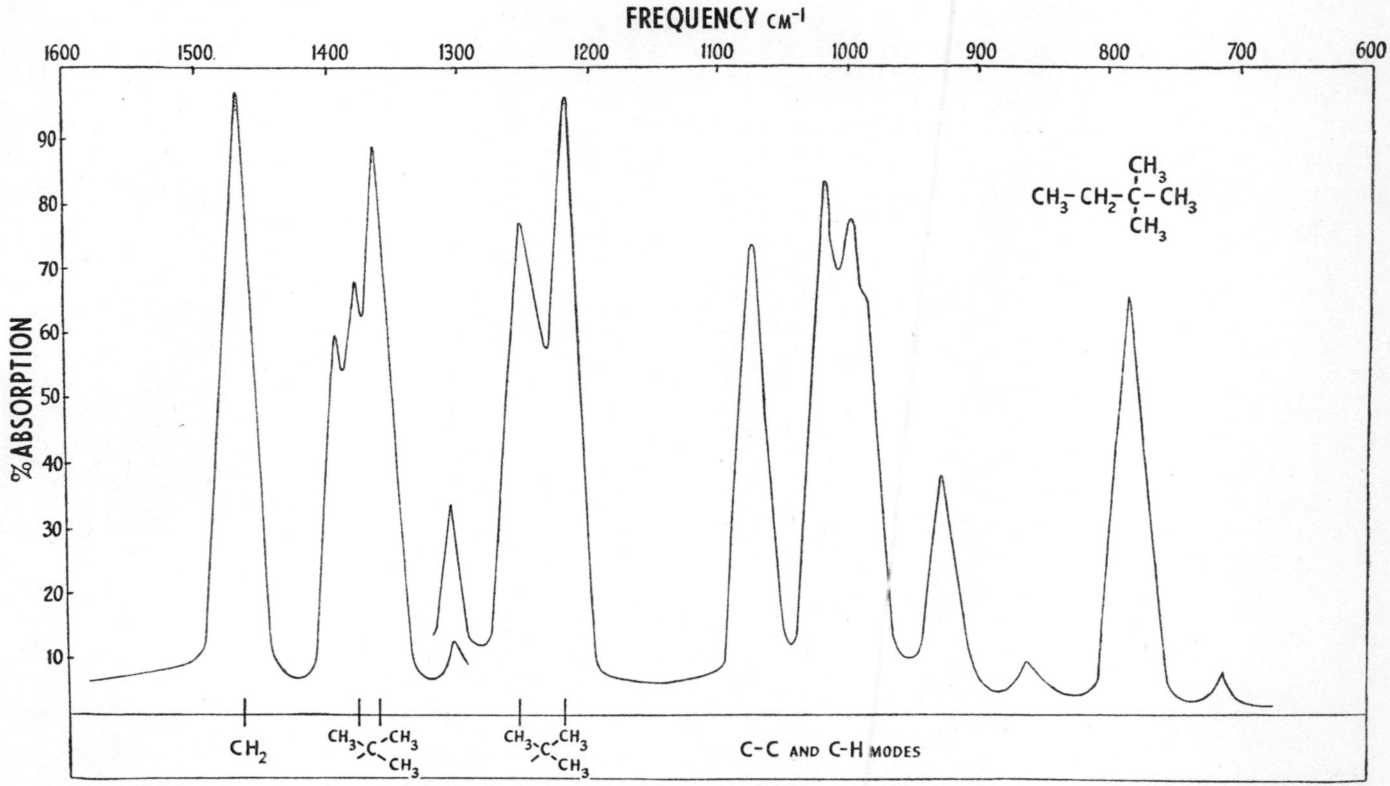

FREQUENCY cm⁻¹

%ABSORPTION

$$CH_3-CH_2-\overset{\overset{\displaystyle CH_3}{|}}{\underset{\underset{\displaystyle CH_3}{|}}{C}}-CH_3$$

C—C AND C—H MODES

$CH_3{>}C{<}^{CH_3}_{CH_3}$

$CH_3{>}C{<}^{CH_3}_{CH_3}$

CH_2

2. 2 : 2-Dimethylbutane

86

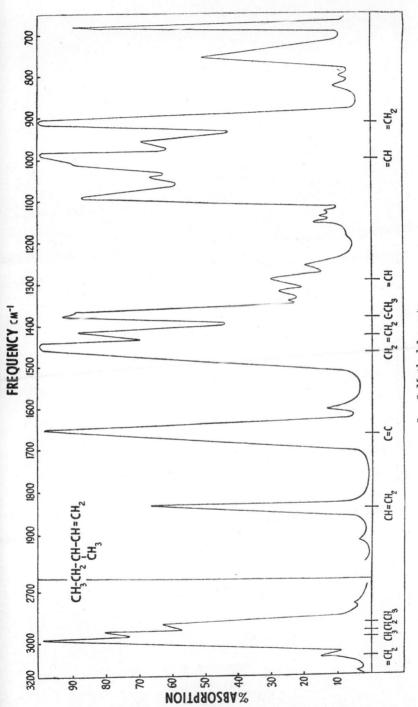

3. 3-Methyl-1-pentene

87

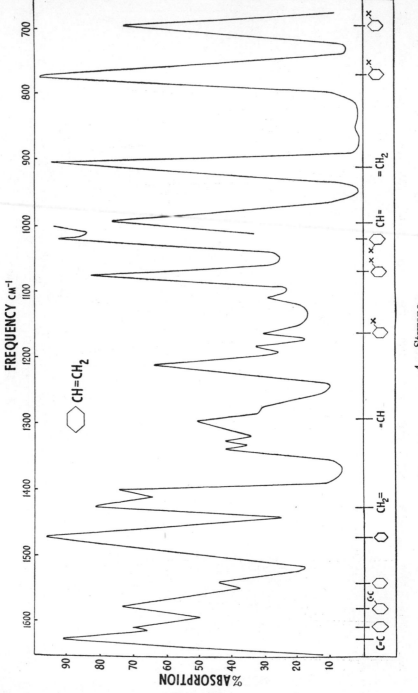

4. Styrene

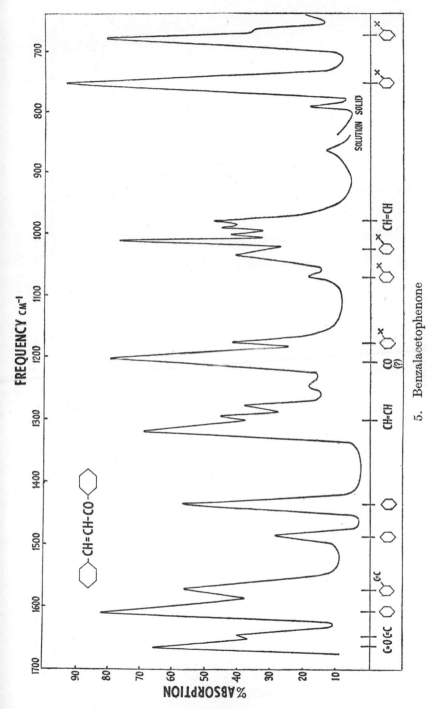

5. Benzalacetophenone

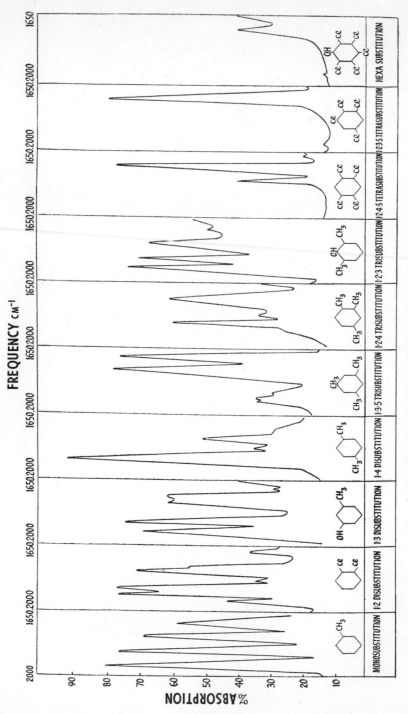

6. Aromatic substitution patterns. 2000–1600 cm⁻¹

90

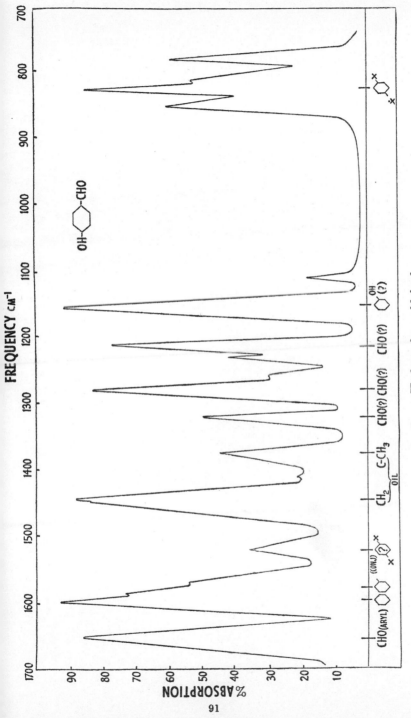

7. *p*-Hydroxybenzaldehyde

16

PART II

VIBRATIONS INVOLVING MAINLY CARBON–
OXYGEN AND OXYGEN–HYDROGEN LINKAGES

CHAPTER 6

Alcohols and Phenols

6.1. INTRODUCTION AND TABLE

THE infra-red absorption band arising from the O–H valence vibration is one of the earliest known and most studied of any. It was first noted by Aschkinass [1] and by Ransohoff [2] in 1895 that a band near 3300 cm.[-1] appeared to be associated with the hydroxyl group, and these observations were much extended by the work of Coblentz [3] and of Weniger. [4, 5] Many other early workers also interested themselves in this group absorption, and its study was intensified in 1933, following the observations of Wulf, Hendricks, Hilbert and Liddel [6-9] that infra-red spectrographic studies afforded a simple and convenient method of following the phenomenon of hydrogen bonding, since when this occurs, the OH bond-length is increased and the absorption band shifts to a lower frequency. These authors worked mostly in the overtone regions, but essentially similar results were obtained by Fox and Martin [10, 11] working on the OH fundamentals, whilst Badger and Bauer [12] were able to show that the magnitude of the shift of the OH fundamental, due to hydrogen bonding, could be used as a measure of the strength of the hydrogen bond formed, being about 35 cm.[-1] per kilo. calorie.

The spectroscopic study of the hydrogen bond has been very fully reviewed by a number of authors, [12-16, 94-96] and no attempt will be made here to do more than indicate the general effects of this phenomenon in relation to the interpretation of the infra-red spectra of alcohols. Similarly, the bibliography has been limited by the choice of a restricted number of examples in cases where much work has been done.

The hydroxyl group is very highly polar, and therefore associates with any other molecules having some degree of polar attraction, so that it is only in the vapour state and in dilute solution in non-polar solvents that the absorption of the free OH vibration is observed, although there are certain exceptions among compounds in which steric hindrance can prevent or reduce the amount of bonding. However, even in carbon disulphide in very dilute solution, alcohols show some change in the OH frequency due to solvent association, [78] whilst changes of state, such as, for example, the passage from liquids to solid crystals, also give rise to large frequency shifts owing to the increased possibilities for orientation in the crystal state. [17, 18] Similarly, temperature changes will markedly influence the position of OH absorption bands.[19,20] All these effects make it very difficult to indicate any specific frequency ranges for various types of bonding, but, as will be seen, it is nevertheless possible to differentiate between intermolecular, intramolecular and chelated bonds, and to decide, for example, whether or not intermolecular association is dimeric or polymeric in type. The approximate absorption ranges covering the various types of hydrogen bond are indicated in Table 6, but it should be appreciated that these are only indications, and that in assessing the type of bond involved account will have to be taken of the physical state of the sample, and in some cases even of the temperature at which the observations were made.

Absorption bands in the low-frequency regions of the spectrum are also to be expected from the C–O stretching mode and from the OH deformation mode. As will be seen, many alcohols exhibit two absorption bands, each covering a wide frequency range, which may be associated with these vibrations. Both, however, are susceptible to changes following hydrogen bonding, and are of limited value in interpretative work.

The correlations discussed are listed below (Table 6).

TABLE 6

OH *Stretching Frequencies*

Free OH . .	3650–3590 cm.$^{-1}$ (v.). Sharp	
Intermolecular hydrogen bonds	(1) Single-bridge compounds 3550–3450 cm.$^{-1}$ (v.). Sharp	Bridges broken on dilution
	(2) Polymeric association 3400–3200 (s.). Broad	
Intramolecular hydrogen bonds	(1) Single-bridge compounds 3570–3450 cm.$^{-1}$ (v.). Sharp	No change on dilution
Chelate compounds	Strong intramolecular bonds 3200–2500 cm.$^{-1}$ (w.). Very broad bands	

OH *Deformations*, C–O *Stretching Absorptions*

Primary alcohols .	Near 1050 cm.$^{-1}$ (s.), 1350–1260 cm.$^{-1}$ (s.)	Unbonding lowers. limited value in diagnosis
Secondary alcohols	Near 1100 cm.$^{-1}$ (s.), 1350–1260 cm.$^{-1}$ (s.)	
Tertiary alcohols .	Near 1150 cm.$^{-1}$ (s), 1410–1310 (s.)	
Phenols . .	Near 1200 cm.$^{-1}$ (s.), 1410–1310 (s.)	

6.2. THE FREE OH STRETCHING VIBRATION

The absorption range for the OH valence-stretching vibration of an unbonded hydroxyl group is usually quoted as being 3700–3500 cm.[-1].[22-25] The upper limit at which the absorption can occur is indicated by water, in which the band occurs at 3760 cm.[-1].[26, 27] However, this is rather a special case in which both hydrogens are attached to the same oxygen atom, and hydrogen peroxide is probably more typical in absorbing at 3590 cm.[-1].[28] Due to the difficulty in differentiating free hydroxyl absorptions from those arising from very weak hydrogen bonds with solvents, etc., the lower limit is difficult to define, but single-bridge dimers in which the OH bonding is weak absorb near 3500 cm.[-1],[29] and this point is often taken as being the lower end of the free OH absorption range.

However, this overall range 3700–3500 cm.[-1] is considerably greater than would be expected on theoretical grounds and by comparison with the similar C–H stretching absorptions. In the latter case the frequency is determined almost wholly by the degree of saturation of the carbon atom and by whether or not it is substituted in the α position with electron-attracting groups. In the case of –OH, therefore, even greater constancy in position is to be expected. The explanation of this probably lies in the low dispersive power of sodium chloride prisms, which were very largely used for the earlier work on this absorption, and which would not permit the observation of these frequencies with any greater accuracy. More recent papers utilising lithium fluoride prisms quote stretching frequencies for free OH groups within much narrower limits, which suggest that the overall range may not be greater than 3650–3590 cm.[-1], and, with some reservations, this is the range quoted in Table 6. Fox and Martin,[10] for example, find the free OH absorptions of a considerable series of aliphatic and aromatic alcohols between 3636 cm.[-1] and 3618 cm.[-1]. Kuhn[74] has also carried out accurate measurements of the free OH frequencies on a range of thirty-five alcohols and phenols. In all cases (except methanol) the absorption occurred between 3644 and 3605 cm.[-1]. Within any single class of compounds the overall range is smaller still and the free OH band of a large number of 1 : 2-diols[97,132] occurs at 3630 ± 5 cm.[-1]. Similarly, phenols are grouped together with αβ-unsaturated alcohols and absorb at the bottom of the overall range.[74, 98] The influence of the aromatic ring in lowering the free OH frequency slightly is confirmed by the work of Ingraham *et al.*,[75] who find this band at 3616–3588 cm.[-1] in twenty-five substituted phenols and at 3615–3592 cm.[-1] in fourteen substituted catechols. These workers have related the OH stretching frequencies of substituted phenols to the Hammett σ values of the aromatic substituents, and Goulden[98] has shown that they can also be related the Pk_a values. Hunsberger *et al.*[76] also have noted a systematic fall in the OH frequency throughout the series methanol (3645 cm.[-1]), phenol (3628 cm.[-1]), α- or β-naphthol (3618 cm.[-1]), and hydroxyphenanthrene (3605 cm.[-1]). The influence of an adjacent carbonyl group is considerably greater than that of an $\alpha\beta$-double bond, as monomeric acids absorb near 3520 cm.[-1], but α-fluorine substitution on the other hand has only a very small effect upon the free OH frequency, although it reduces the tendency towards hydrogen bonding.[79,80] In the Raman field Bateuv and Matveeva [30] claim to be able to differentiate primary, secondary and tertiary alcohols by characteristic absorptions at 3632 cm.[-1], 3622 cm.[-1] and 3615 cm.[-1]. In the infra-red similar distinctions are possible with simple alcohols. Cole and Jefferies [132] report unpublished data showing that primary alcohols absorb near 3642 cm.[-1] with extinction coefficients of 70, secondary alcohols near 3629 (ϵ 60–50) and tertiary alcohols near 3618 cm.[-1] (ϵ 45). This has been further studied by Anet and Bavin,[133] who find very similar results for a series of simple alcohols but report other instances in which the frequencies fall as low as 3545 cm.[-1]. These are tertiary alcohols which are near to the π clouds of double bonds, and they suggest steric effects may be involved. It is, however, possible that some form of weak hydrogen bonding to the π bond is involved here similar to the association effects shown by some proton donors in benzene. However, benzyl alcohol is also anomalous in absorbing at 3614 cm.[-1], and they conclude that it would be unwise to apply the original generalisation too far. However, in a known series, such as the steroid and triterpenes, these distinctions are probably valid, and Allsop *et al.*[134] have carried them a stage further by showing that axial and equatorial [30] hydroxy-groups can be differentiated in the triterpenes. In the former the absorption is at 3629–3630 cm.[-1], and in the latter at 3637–3639 cm.[-1].

These values all relate to free OH absorptions in non-polar solvents, and small changes occur with alterations in the polarity of the solvent and with changes of temperature and pressure. The former effects are probably due to changes in the dielectric constant of the medium, but in certain instances, such as phenol, molecular complexes may be involved.[99] Changes with temperature [100] and with pressure [101] are small, and arise from alterations in the distances separating the individual molecules.

The free OH stretching frequencies of N–OH groups in oximes are similar to alcohols and appear [136–138] between 3650 and 3500 cm.[-1]

6.3. HYDROGEN BONDED OH VIBRATIONS (GENERAL)

Freymann and Heilmann,[33] working in the overtone region, were able to differentiate three types of hydroxyl group bonding: intermolecular bonding between two or more molecules, intramolecular bonding, and chelation in which resonance structures are involved. Bonding systems of each of these types have been fully studied by many workers and, as a result, it is usually practicable to decide which of them is involved in any single case. The frequency of the bonded OH absorption is a direct measure of the strength of the hydrogen bond, and, for example, is very much the same in the structure C–OH . . . O–, as in C–OH . . . O=C–, unless resonance conditions are possible, in which case resonance stabilisation gives rise to a much stronger hydrogen bond, with a consequent big low-frequency shift. Diacetone alcohol, for example, absorbs at 3484 cm.$^{-1}$, which is very much the same as the normal OH vibration of dimeric alcohols, whereas acetyl acetone absorbs at 2700 cm.$^{-1}$.[34] Both these are instances of OH groups bonded to a carbonyl group, but the latter is stabilised by resonance, and the oxygen atoms are thereby brought closer together. In chelate compounds of this type it can be shown that the carbonyl frequency (which is an alternative measure of the strength of the hydrogen bond) is a linear function of the double-bond character of the $\alpha\beta$-double bond,[76,102] as this is the primary factor determining the O . . . O distances.

Several workers [77,84,103,104,135] have studied the connection between OH bonded frequencies and the distance apart of the two atoms linked by the hydrogen bond. Lord and Merrifield [84] showed that an approximately linear relationship existed between the OH frequency shift and the O . . . O distance in hydrogen-bonded acids and similar compounds. This treatment has been further elaborated by Nakamoto *et al.*[103] and by Pimentel.[104,135] Different relationships exist for any one type of X–H . . . Y bond, but each separate series obeys a simple linear relation, provided the three atoms involved are co-linear. This has led to the suggestion that deviations from linearity might be used as a measure of the angle of distortion of bent hydrogen bonds.

Measurements of the strengths of hydrogen (or deuterium) bonds can also be used to determine the relative proton-accepting powers of bases. Thus the OD stretching frequency of deuteromethanol in substituted pyridines is a direct function of their basic strength.[105]

6.4. INTERMOLECULAR HYDROGEN BONDS

Intermolecular hydrogen bonds in which no resonance structures are involved give rise to broad absorption bonds in the range 3450–3200 cm.$^{-1}$. The intensity of these bands is usually considerably greater than that of the free OH vibration, and their broad shape is usually attributed to the fact that the alcohol associates into various polymeric forms in which the molecules are involved in hydrogen bonding to different extents, so that the broad band observed is a composite of a number of sharper bands. The position of these bands within this range is only an indication of the strength of the bond and is a function of the physical state of the sample, the concentration and nature of the solvent, if in solution, and of the temperature,[106] as well as of the type of bond involved. However, a comparison of different types of alcohols under similar conditions indicates that only weak hydrogen bonds are involved in single-bridge dimers which, by virtue of steric hindrance, are unable to associate into polymeric forms,[29, 35, 36] so that these usually absorb near 3500 cm.$^{-1}$, whereas normal alcohols, in which very little dimeric association [19] occurs, absorb nearer the range 3400–3200 cm.$^{-1}$. In a limited series of compounds studied by Kuhn [74] the absorption of dimeric alcohols was in the range 3525–3472 cm.$^{-1}$ and that from polymeric materials in the range 3341–3338 cm.$^{-1}$. Marrinan and Mann [107, 108] quote 3347–3324 cm.$^{-1}$ for polymeric association in cellulose and 3404 cm.$^{-1}$ for single bridge dimeric bonds. They have also worked out a neat method for the determination of the crystalline/amorphous ratio in this material based on the different rates of deuterium exchange of the OH bonds. The nature of the R group of the R–OH compound also exerts a marked influence upon the intensity of the absorption band, and this can sometimes be used to obtain further data on the structure of a molecule. On the other hand, the quantitative analysis of mixtures based on the bonded OH absorption is rendered more difficult.

6.4(a). Single Hydrogen-bridge Complexes. In very dilute solutions in which dimerisation is precluded the strength of hydrogen bonds between alcohols and solvents can be studied. Work of this type has been done by many workers, such as Mecke,[38] who has examined the OH absorption in phenol in eighteen different solvents. The results are in agreement with those of earlier workers in that, on changing from indifferent solvents, such as *cyclo*-hexane and CCl$_4$, to solvents with polar properties, a broadening of the band accompanied by a diminution in intensity is observed. The relative influence of solvents in effecting this change is given by *cyclo*-hexane < carbon disulphide < chlorobenzene < benzene. It is interesting to note that at higher concentrations, where polymerisation of the alcohol is the predominating effect, this order changes, and is then conditioned also by such factors as dielectric constant and molecular size of the solvent. At such concentrations the association, as evidenced by the OH absorption frequency, increases in the order benzene < chloroform < carbon disulphide.[35] In single-bridge complexes of this type both the C–O–H . . . O– bridge and the C–O–H . . . O=C– bridge absorb at similar frequencies near 3510 cm.$^{-1}$. Coggeshall and Saier [31] have found a band at this point in dilute solutions of ethyl alcohol and acetone in carbon tetrachloride and also of ethyl alcohol and dioxan in the same solvent. Kuhn [74] gives values of 3492–3482 cm.$^{-1}$ for the OH band in the system ROH . . . OEt$_2$, where R is an alkyl group. Interactions with other solvents such as amines also occur in a similar way.[39]

In connection with solvent interaction, Mecke [38] has observed some interesting effects in solvents such as benzene, in which partial splitting of the absorption band is observed in the overtone region. He attributes this to the fact that the solvent molecules may be situated in two different positions relative to the OH bond.

Apart from interactions between dissimilar molecules, single-bridge complexes are formed only in special cases in which steric effects prevent full polymeric association. A common case of such steric effects is that of *ortho*-substituted phenols, which have been studied by many workers.[18, 31, 35, 36, 40, 41, 74, 139] It has long been known on chemical grounds that *ortho*-substituted phenols show differences from other types, whilst 2 : 6-substituted phenols with large substituents give no phenolic reactions and are insoluble in water. This is explicable on the basis of steric hindrance, and it can be shown that hydrogen bonding does not occur in 2 : 6-di-substituted phenols with large substituent groups, whilst it is much reduced in *ortho*-substituted phenols with groups larger than the methyl group. Sears and Kitchen [40] have published data on an extensive list of phenols of various types, which they have examined in the solid, liquid and solution states, and they have been able to show, for example, that the OH absorption in 2 : 6-di-*tert*.-butylphenol occurs in the normal position for free OH absorption, and that there is no significant shift on going from solutions to the liquid or solid states. With partly hindered phenols the wave-length shift from the free OH position is very much less than in the case of unhindered phenols, and Coggeshall [41] has shown that this is due to the fact that in such cases bonding proceeds by dimeric association rather than by polymeric association. However, Hunter [95] has pointed out that an alternative explanation of the limited degree of association would be that the inability of the OH group to achieve full co-planarity with the ring reduces its acidity and proton donating powers.

Another case of single-bridge dimerisation is that of branched-chain aliphatic alcohols in which the steric effects of the branched chains prevent polymeric association. Smith and Creitz [29] have observed this effect in a number of such alcohols, and they assign a requency of 3500 cm.$^{-1}$ to the hydrogen bridge so formed. They note also that in these cases the dimer contributes towards the free OH absorption as well as the monomer. A similar case is that of *tert*.-amyl alcohol, which, in the liquid state, has long been known to exhibit some free OH absorption due to steric effects, whilst the bonded OH absorption is also at a higher frequency than in the straight-chain alcohols. Other cases occur in carbohydrates, aluminium soaps and similar materials.[46, 47, 81]

6.4(b). Polymeric Association. This represents the commonest case of hydrogen bonding, in which long chains of molecules are linked by relatively strong hydrogen bonds. The usual absorption region in the absence of chelation effects is between 3400 cm.$^{-1}$ and 3200 cm.$^{-1}$, the actual position depending on the nature of any solvent, and on whether or not the material is examined in the solid or liquid state. In this connection it is interesting to note that the OH absorption bands arising from rapidly cooled melted films are generally much closer to the normal position for strong solutions than to the position in the crystalline state. This is in accordance with the view that the crystalline state represents that in which the molecules have oriented themselves in such a way as to give the maximum strength of hydrogen bonds.

The frequency range for this type of OH absorption is too much a matter of common experience to need detailed references, but a typical series of such absorptions is given by the spectra of the various simple alcohols included in the A.P.I. series of spectra. In the series methanol to decanol the bonded OH absorption in concentrated solution in non-polar solvents occurs in the range 3370–3344 cm.$^{-1}$. Kuhn [74] also gives a list of a considerable number of alcohols and diols, the OH frequencies of which, in concentrated solutions, all fall within the ranges given in Table 6.

Studies on the relative intensities of the free and bonded OH absorptions at different concentrations provide a convenient method for measuring the dissociation constants either of polymeric alcohols [140] or of alcohols associated with carbonyl groups.[141]

6.5. INTRAMOLECULAR HYDROGEN BONDS

The majority of cases of intramolecular hydrogen bonding are those in which the bond is resonance stabilised, and this gives rise to a particularly strong bond, with a consequent large OH frequency shift. These cases will be dealt with under chelate compounds in the following section. Intramolecular bonding without resonance stabilisation results in the formation of single-bridge hydrogen bonds similar to those of the dimeric associations discussed above. The hydrogen bond is accordingly weak, and a relatively weak absorption occurs in the range 3570–3450 cm.$^{-1}$. The essential difference between the two types lies in the fact that intermolecular hydrogen bonds are broken by dilution with non-polar solvents, whereas intramolecular bonds are independent of the concentration.

6.5(a). Single-bridge Complexes. Typical cases of single-bridge complexes are the internal bonds in ring compounds, as in 2-hydroxy*cyclo*hexanones,[109] phenols,[7, 42] nitro-alcohols,[110] 1 : 2-chlorhydrins [142] and cyclic 1 : 2-diols.[97, 132] In the last of these Kuhn [97] has shown that hydrogen-bonding studies can be used in the determination of the probable configurations of this series. The most stable bridged structures of this type are, as is to be expected, those

involving six-membered rings.[111]   With *ortho*-substituted phenols in
which hydrogen bonding of the OH on to the other substituent group
is possible an interesting case arises.   Pauling [43] has pointed out that
the C–O bond of phenols has some double-bond character which will
cause the hydrogen atom to lie in the plane of the ring.   Phenol can
therefore have the two equivalent configurations I and II.

I.   II.   III.   IV.   V.   VI.

With *ortho*-substitution of a halogen or other proton-accepting
group, the *cis*- and *trans*-configurations III and IV become possible,
which are not equivalent, whilst in 2 : 6-dichlorophenol equivalence
is again obtained with the structure V and VI.   Phenol and 2 : 6-
dichlorophenol are therefore to be expected to show one OH absorption, whereas *ortho*-chlorophenol should show two, as the *cis*-form
will be able to form a hydrogen bond, whilst the *trans* will not. This
is, in fact, the case. In the overtone region phenol absorbs at 7050
cm.$^{-1}$ and 2 : 6-dichlorophenol at 6890 cm.$^{-1}$; *ortho*-chlorophenol
shows absorptions at both points, with the second band much
stronger than the other.[44] This indicates that there is a considerably
higher proportion of the *cis*-form present, owing to its stabilisation
by the hydrogen bond. In liquid *ortho*-chlorophenol the *trans* absorption peak appears at 6620 cm.$^{-1}$ following intermolecular bonding
by dimerisation,[45] and comparable results are found in the fundamental region.[112,113]   Similar results are also obtained with *ortho*-
methoxy-, phenyl- and cyano-compounds,[20] whilst certain substituted
vinyl alcohols show a similar pair of bands corresponding to two configurations.[48] In catechols also,[75] a parallel effect is found, and in
this case the single-bridge intramolecular bond absorbs between
3575 cm.$^{-1}$ and 3535 cm.$^{-1}$.

An effect similar to the *ortho*-effect in intermolecular bonding of
phenols can also be observed in the intramolecular bonding of substituted bisphenol alkanes.[41, 82]   Intramolecular bonding between the
two phenolic hydroxyls occurs in one configuration, but a second
"*trans*" configuration is also stabilised because of the restriction of
free rotation by the presence of a large *ortho* substituent group. The
cis form therefore exhibits hydrogen bonding, whereas the *trans* form
absorbs at the free OH position unless the conditions are favourable
for intermolecular bonding.

   6.5(b). Chelate Compounds.   In the earlier studies of Hilbert,
Wulf, Hendricks and Liddel [6-9] and other workers, it was found that
ortho-phenols in which carbonyl or nitro-groups were substituted at

the *ortho* position exhibited very much stronger hydrogen bonds than the corresponding *meta* or *para* materials or differently substituted phenols. So much so that the free OH absorption near 7000 cm.$^{-1}$ in the overtone region disappeared altogether, and this disappearance was regarded as evidence for the presence of strong hydrogen bonds. As intramolecular bonds were involved, this effect persisted in solution. The same effect was observed for acetyl acetone, and this compound, together with other enolic β-diketones, was re-examined in the fundamental region by Rasmussen *et al.*[34] They found that the OH absorption in these compounds occurred near 2700 cm.$^{-1}$ and that the carbonyl frequency also shifted to a much greater extent than was usual in hydrogen bonding phenomena. These authors pointed out the similarity between the OH frequencies of these compounds and those of fatty acid dimers, which also exhibit unusual characteristics in this respect, Pauling [13] has accounted for the strong bonding in the fatty acid dimers on the basis of a large contribution of an ionic resonance structure along with the normal covalent structure; the OH bond is therefore subject to additional loosening owing to the charges, with the consequent formation of a stronger hydrogen bond.

Rasmussen *et al.*[34] suggest that a somewhat similar explanation can be applied to the enolic β-diketones which can have contributions from the resonance structures VIII and IX.

$$
\begin{array}{ccc}
\mathrm{O\!-\!H \ldots O} & & \mathrm{{}^{+}O\!-\!H \ldots O^{-}} \\
\quad\big|\qquad\; \| & \text{and} & \qquad\| \qquad\; \big| \\
\mathrm{R'C\!=\!CR''\!-\!CR'''} & & \mathrm{R'\!-\!C\!-\!CR''\!=\!CR'''} \\
\text{VIII.} & & \text{IX.}
\end{array}
$$

This also accounts for the disappearance of the 7000 cm.$^{-1}$ overtone band in the compounds studied by Wulf *et al.*, as all the compounds in which this effect was observed contained the structure

$$
\begin{array}{c}
\mathrm{OH \quad O} \\
\big| \qquad \| \\
\mathrm{R\!-\!C\!=\!C\!-\!C\!-}
\end{array}
$$

and a shift in the frequency corresponding to the 2700 cm.$^{-1}$ band observed in the fundamental would take the second harmonic completely out of the region examined, as it would then appear near 5000 cm.$^{-1}$. The term "conjugate chelation" has been suggested by Rasmussen *et al.* to describe this phenomenon. Similar findings in respect of the OH frequency have been reported by Martin,[49] who showed that salicaldehyde and *ortho*-hydroxyacetophenone exhibit broad weak OH absorption bands extending from 3500 cm.$^{-1}$ to beyond 2900 cm.$^{-1}$, comparable with, but much weaker than those of salicylic acid. *ortho*-Hydroxy benzyl alcohol, however, in which the possibility of an ionic structure is not present, showed a sharp band at 3600 cm.$^{-1}$ (free OH) and another at 3436 cm.$^{-1}$ (single-bridge intramolecular bond). Hunsberger [50] has demonstrated similar effects in hydroxynaphthaldehydes and similar materials, and many other examples of this effect have been described, as in acetyl acetones,[114, 115, 143] hydroxyanthraquinones,[51, 83, 93, 116, 144] hydroxy-flavones,[117] hydroxyindanones [118] and related compounds.[119, 120] An OH frequency of 2600 cm.[-1] has also been found in compounds involving a chelated hydroxyl group and a heterocyclic nitrogen atom.[121] In many cases of this type the absence of any OH absorption in the fundamental region has been reported, presumably owing to its being a weak band which has been superimposed upon the strong CH stretching absorption near 3000 cm.[-1]. One case in which this conjugate chelation can arise through intermolecular, rather than intramolecular, association is 5 : 5-dimethyl-1 : 3-*cyclo*hexanedione. This compound contains the β-keto-enol structure, and shows an OH stretching absorption at 2632 cm.[-1], but steric considerations will not allow of a direct intramolecular hydrogen bond, and Rasmussen *et al.*[34] suggest that it must therefore arise through dimerisation into a structure capable of a similar resonance stabilisation.

The lower frequency limits at which OH absorptions of this type occur are extremely difficult to define, as the absorption bands are relatively weak and extremely broad. However, Reid and Ruby [52] find a shallow OH absorption in 6-phenyl-4-hydroxy-5 : 6-dihydropyrone as low as 2500 cm.[-1], and they state that their unpublished work on tetronic acids has established that the OH frequency in these compounds also occurs near this frequency. Bellamy and Beecher [53] and Daasch and Smith [54] have also observed OH absorptions in organo-phosphorus acids at frequencies as low as this, although these are probably dimeric materials similar to the carboxylic acids. Absorption at 2440 cm.[-1] has also been observed in some hydroxy-compounds in solution,[55, 56] but it is not clear whether this might be due to the second harmonic of the CH deformation mode of chloroform,[57] although Gordy [56] assigns it to a weak OH vibration. In any case, however, the characteristic shape and appearance of absorption bands of strongly bonded OH groups are sufficiently distinctive to enable the recognition of structures of this type. However, difficulty is experienced in this identification when the OH absorption coincides with the strong CH absorptions near 3000 cm.[-1]. Thus Amstutz *et al.*[58] have reported the absence of any OH absorption in 1-nitroso-2-naphthol, whilst *ortho*-hydroxy-diphenylsulphoxide also shows no major band, but only rapidly increasing absorption between 3250 cm.[-1] and 2900 cm.[-1]. In cases such as these, additional data can sometimes be obtained by deuteration when the OD band appears at lower frequencies. However, this needs to be carefully carried out, as any exchange with the hydrogen atoms of CH groups will result in the appearance of CD absorptions in the same relative position as the OD. The strongest hydrogen bonds reported are those in which the hydrogen is close to a symmetrical position. In nickel dimethylglyoxime, for example, the OH frequency has been identified by deuteration studies [77] as an extremely weak band near 1775 cm.$^{-1}$.

6.6. THE INTENSITY AND SHAPE OF OH STRETCHING ABSORPTIONS

The shape of the OH absorption band and its relative intensity can sometimes be used to give an indication of the type of structure present. This aspect of the subject has not been very fully studied, but a good deal of work has been carried out on the reasons for the characteristic increase in intensity and broadness of the absorption bands of hydrogen-bonded hydroxyl groupings. The broad nature of these bands in the spectra of liquids has usually been ascribed to the molecules being involved in hydrogen bonding to different extents, so that the shape of the band is an indication of the distribution of various strengths of hydrogen bonding.[10, 57] However, as Kletz has pointed out,[59] this explanation cannot be applied to crystals, in which all hydrogen bonds would be expected to be equivalent. In the spectra of crystals of phenols the OH absorption band is sharper than in the spectrum of the liquid, but still much broader than in dilute solution. An alternative suggestion is that the width of these bands is due to combination with a number of low-frequency vibrations, including the deformation frequencies.[12, 60, 61] In agreement with this is the observation that the width of the band is generally greater with increased hydrogen bond strength, whilst with deuterium substitution the breadth of the band is much reduced. As regards crystals, the reasons for the breadth of the OH absorption have also been discussed by Mecke and by Ubbelohde,[62] and it seems to be generally accepted that crystal forces are one of the factors involved. Theories of the origins of intensity increases on bonding have also been discussed by Tsubomura,[122, 123] and intensity changes with temperature have been considered by Hughes *et al.*[100] and by Finch and Lippincott.[106]

The intensities of free OH stretching absorptions obey Beer's Law, and the extinction coefficient is essentially constant for any single class of related materials, such as, for example, phenols.[51] It varies considerably, however, from class to class. This observation has been used in the estimation of the *cis* and *trans* forms of hindered phenols. Similarly, in aliphatic materials the free OH content can be estimated by measurements in the 3610 cm.$^{-1}$ region.[29] With single-bridge bonding the shape of the OH absorption band remains essentially sharp,[38] and observations on limited groups of materials indicate that within any one class, at least, the extinction coefficients are reasonably constant and that Beer's Law is obeyed.[29, 35] In the case of single-bridge dimers the dimeric forms contribute to both the free and bonded OH absorption.

Barrow,[124] and Brown and Rogers [145] have studied the absolute intensities of OH absorptions in different types of alcohol. These can vary by as much as a factor of two, depending upon the nature of the substituents. Phenol, for example, absorbs much more strongly than *tert.*-butanol. Brown and Rogers [145] associate this with the inductive effects of the substituents, and have shown that the intensity in carbon tetrachloride rises as the electro-negativity of the substituents is increased. In solvents in which association effects occur the intensity is greatly increased,[124] so that in ether the intensity of the methanol hydroxyl group is approximately eight times as large as in carbon tetrachloride, and in triethylamine this ratio increases to twelve times.

With stronger intermolecular bonding, broad and very intense bands are observed. The intensity varies with different types of material, but is again reasonably constant within any single class. Friedel [35] found the average absorption intensity of ten phenols, variously substituted in the *meta-* and *para*-positions, to be constant within ± 2.1 per cent. However, with chelated materials the intensity is considerably diminished, and the band becomes extremely broad and weak. The intensities are very much less than those, for example, from the bonded OH absorptions of dimeric acids, and they are so broad that the measurement of extinction coefficients would serve very little purpose.

These variations in both the frequency and intensity of hydroxyl absorption are of the first importance from the point of view of quantitative analysis, and it is obvious that any work of this type based on OH bands must be undertaken under very carefully standardised conditions. However, the fact that these shifts occur can sometimes be turned to advantage. Coggeshall and Saier [31] have used intensity measurements in studies on the degree of poly-merisation, although Francis,[63] in a discussion on the intensities of bonded OH bands, has questioned their methods of assessment of intensity.

The intramolecular hydrogen bonding occurring with *ortho*-brominated phenols has been neatly turned to advantage by Simard *et al.*[64] in the estimation of mixed phenols, cresols and xylenols, as measurement of the free OH absorption in dilute solutions, before and after bromination, allows the determination of phenols with *ortho*-substituents. The OH frequency of the latter is, of course, unaffected, whereas all others undergo intramolecular hydrogen bonding, with the consequent appearance of a second OH band.

In general, quantitative studies on alcohols and phenols are best carried out in dilute solutions in which the complications of hydrogen bonding are at least reduced to the intramolecular bonds, but by standardisation of conditions and solvents it is sometimes possible to carry out reasonably reliable analyses based on bonded OH absorptions. The extinction coefficients used, however, must always relate to the same or very closely similar molecules examined under the same conditions, and should be based on measurements made on the area under the absorption bands.

The examination of the appearance or otherwise of OH absorption bands from single crystals examined in polarised radiation has also been employed in the determination of structures—as, for example, in the study of the bonded OH groups in polyvinyl alcohol [65] and in carbohydrates.[46] As in the case of free OH groups, deuteration is often of considerable assistance in identifying OH groups and in studying bonding effects, and it has been employed for this purpose by Rowen and Plyler,[66] Sheppard,[116] Sutherland [125] and many others.

6.7. C–O STRETCHING AND O–H DEFORMATION VIBRATIONS

Both the above vibrations might reasonably be expected to give rise to strong absorption bands by which alcohols could be characterised. As will be seen, most alcohols do give rise to two bands in the lower frequency region which are sensitive to hydrogen bonding changes and which move to lower frequencies following dilution. Unfortunately, however, due to coupling effects there has been a good deal of confusion as to which of them is which. Recent studies have gone some way to resolve these difficulties, but the position is not wholly clear.

The first of these bands, and usually the strongest, was first noted by Weniger [4] in 1910, who found a strong band in the spectra of liquid primary alcohols near 1050 cm.$^{-1}$, in secondary alcohols near 1100 cm.$^{-1}$ and in tertiary alcohols near 1150 cm.$^{-1}$. This was confirmed by Lecomte,[67, 85] who was able to show that they were associated with the hydroxyl group, as, over a long series of aliphatic alcohols, the intensity was observed to diminish systematically as the chain length was increased and the proportion of OH groups reduced. He also noted the sensitivity of these absorptions to structural changes, and observed a marked reduction in the intensity of absorption at 1100 cm.$^{-1}$ in some vinyl carbinols as compared with saturated secondary alcohols. The spectrum of phenol was considered too complex for any useful assignments to be made.

More recently a systematic study of the position of this absorption in relation to the surrounding structure has been made by Zeiss and Tsutsui.[86] In saturated straight-chain alcohols they find that this band occurs within the relatively narrow frequency ranges of 1075–1010 cm.$^{-1}$ for primary alcohols, 1119–1105 cm.$^{-1}$ for secondary alcohols and near 1140 cm.$^{-1}$ for tertiary alcohols. These findings have been substantially confirmed by Stuart and Sutherland,[125] working on liquid alcohols. However, α-branched, αβ-unsaturated and alicyclic alcohols all show frequency shift away from these ranges, and the extent and directions of these show a number of curious anomalies. Chain branching at the α-carbon atom reduces the frequency in all three cases by 10–15 cm.$^{-1}$, but the effect is reversed when the chain is doubly branched at this point so that di-*tert.*-butyl alcohol absorbs at 1163 cm.$^{-1}$ within the normal range. αβ-Unsaturation lowers the frequency considerably, and in secondary alcohols the band falls between 1074 and 1012 cm.$^{-1}$, but the shift is found to be greater for aryl than for alkenyl unsaturation despite the weaker nature of the double bonds involved. Although fewer examples are available a similar shift to low frequencies appears to occur in the corresponding primary and tertiary alcohols, and here again allyl alcohol has been found to absorb at a higher frequency (1030 cm.$^{-1}$) than benzyl alcohol (1010 cm.$^{-1}$). In alicyclic secondary alcohols the frequency gradually falls with increasing ring size from *cyclo*butanol (1090 cm.$^{-1}$) to *cyclo*heptano (1025 cm.$^{-1}$), so that those showing the greatest frequency shift are those with the lowest ring strain. In sterols the band falls between 1075 and 1000 cm.$^{-1}$ in solution, but as a result of a good deal of detailed work, its position within this range has been correlated with the stereochemical arrangement of the C_3 hydroxyl group,[87-90] so that valuable structural information can now be obtained in this way. Similarly in the triterpenes, differentiation between axial and equatorial 3-hydroxy groups is possible.[134] A somewhat similar effect has been observed in the decanols,[91] although the differences are less clearly defined.

The considerable degree of overlapping of the frequency ranges for different types of alcohols with various functional groups makes it very difficult to identify the type of structure present from observations on this region alone, but when additional evidence is available it can often afford some extremely valuable information.

The second band of alcohols usually arises in the region of 1300 cm.$^{-1}$,[69] but its position varies considerably with structural effects and it has not been made the subject of any systematic study. Both these absorptions are sensitive to changes of state, indicating that they are associated with hydrogen-bonding effects, and there is a good deal of disagreement in the literature as to which of them is to be assigned to the OH deformation vibration. In the case of methyl alcohol, some workers assign the OH deformation to a band at 1109 cm.$^{-1}$,[70] whilst others prefer the band at 1340 cm.$^{-1}$.[71,26] In addition, methanol has a strong 1034 cm.$^{-1}$ band which is associated with the C–O vibration.[72,73] Similarly, in phenol, despite studies in a series of different states, and on deuteration,[32, 68] there is still doubt as to whether the OH deformation mode occurs near 1200 cm.[-1] or near 1350 cm.[-1], as both these absorptions are sensitive to changes in the hydrogen bonding pattern. In this last case the two bands are closer together, and some coupling is to be expected in analogy with carboxylic acids.[37] Kuratani[92] in deuteration studies on pentachlorphenol assigns two bands (at 1280 cm.[-1] and 1195 cm.[-1]) to the OH deformation on account of coupling effects. The identification of these bands in substituted phenol has also been discussed by Mecke and Rossmy[126] and by Davies and Jones.[127] In the sterol series most workers regard the 1075–1000 cm.[-1] absorption as deriving from the C–O stretching mode,[87–89] but others relate it to the OH deformation.[90] The position is even further complicated by the appearance in certain alcohols of additional bands which are sensitive to deuteration, which may arise from rotational isomerism.[146]

Recently a good deal of work has been carried out on deuterated alcohols in an attempt to resolve this difficulty, notably by Sutherland and his co-workers[21, 125, 128, 129] and also by Quinan and Wiberley.[130, 131] The results are not wholly conclusive, and indeed, these two groups differ in their final assignments, but it does appear to be more probable that the band near 1100 cm.[-1] in aliphatic alcohols is associated primarily with the C–O stretching mode, whereas the single or double peak in the 1400–1300 cm.[-1] region is connected with the in-plane OH deformation frequency. It has been pointed out that the latter would be expected to couple with adjacent CH_2 deformations leading to mixed vibrations which would not follow the expected pattern of change on deuteration. Bratoz *et al.*[114] have made a somewhat similar set of assignments for acetyl acetone derivatives, in which the OH deformation is placed at 1435 cm.[-1], and the C–O stretching mode, the frequency of which is raised by resonance, at 1284 cm.[-1].

In phenols and similar compounds the situation is rather different, as the C–O stretching mode now absorbs at higher frequencies under the influence of the aromatic ring. There are, therefore, possibilities of coupling between the OH and C–O frequencies or between the latter and aromatic ring vibrations. Sheppard[116] has accordingly assigned the higher of the two main deuterium sensitive frequencies of hydroxyquinones to the C–O stretching mode. Mecke and Rossmy[126] have also made a similar assignment in the case of phenol, in which they regard the 1180 cm.[-1] band as being that which possesses the strongest OH character. The main coupling partner in this case is probably the aromatic ring absorption at 1310 cm.[-1], although other aromatic absorptions could also be involved.

It is clear from this that most alcohols show two bands which, whatever their origin, might be sufficiently characteristic to enable structural data to be obtained, provided a sufficiently large volume of data were available relating their frequencies to various structural changes. However, at present such data are available only in special cases, and this together with the complications arising from the many changes in the spectra between 1450 cm.$^{-1}$ and 600 cm.$^{-1}$ following changes of state, limits the value of these regions for structural analysis.

In addition, all alcohols show very broad bands in the liquid state in the range 750–650 cm.$^{-1}$. These arise from out of plane bonded OH deformation frequencies, but they have no useful applications in correlation work.

6.8. BIBLIOGRAPHY.

1. Aschkinass, *Wied. Ann.*, 1895, **55**, 401.
2. Ransohoff, Dissert Berlin, 1896.
3. Coblentz, *Investigations of Infra-red Spectra*, Part I (Carnegie Institute, 1905), p. 35.
4. Weniger, *Phys. Review*, 1910, **31**, 388.
5. *Idem, J. Opt. Soc. Amer.*, 1923, **7**, 517.
6. Liddel and Wulf, *J. Amer. Chem. Soc.*, 1933, **55**, 3574.
7. Wulf and Liddel, *ibid.*, 1935, **57**, 1464.
8. Hilbert, Wulf, Hendricks and Liddel, *Nature*, 1935, **135**, 147.
9. *Idem, J. Amer. Chem. Soc.*, 1936, **58**, 548 and 1991.
10. Fox and Martin, *Proc. Roy. Soc.*, 1937, **A162**, 419; 1941, **A175**, 208.
11. *Idem, Trans. Faraday Soc.*, 1940, **36**, 897.
12. Badger and Bauer, *J. Chem. Phys.*, 1937, **5**, 839.
13. Pauling, *The Nature of the Chemical Bond* (Oxford University Press, 1950), pp. 316 *et seq.*
14. Wright, *Ind. Eng. Chem.* (*Anal. Ed.*), 1941, **13**, 1.
15. Hunter, Price and Martin, *Report of a Symposium on the Hydrogen Bond* (Institute of Chemistry Monograph, 1950).
16. Huggins, *J. Org. Chem.*, 1936, **1**, 407.
17. Kletz and Price, *J. Chem. Soc.*, 1947, 644.
18. Richards and Thompson, *ibid.*, 1947, 1260.
19. Hoffmann, *Z. physikal. Chem.*, 1943, **B53**, 179.
20. Lüttke and Mecke, *Z. Elektrochem.*, 1949, **53**, 241.
21. Cf. Ramsay and Sutherland, *Discuss. Faraday Soc.*, 1950, **9**, 274.
22. Thompson, *J. Chem. Soc.*, 1948, 328.
23. Colthup, *J. Opt. Soc. Amer.*, 1950, **40**, 397.
24. Barnes, Gore, Liddel and Van Zandt Williams, *Infra-red Spectroscopy* (Reinhold, 1944).
25. Randall, Fowler, Fuson and Dangl, *Infra-red Determination of Organic Structure* (Van Nostrand, 1949).
26. Herzberg, *The Infra-red and Raman Spectra of Polyatomic Molecules* (Van Nostrand, 1945), p. 280.
27. Cross, Burnham and Leighton, *J. Amer. Chem. Soc.*, 1937, **59**, 1134.
28. Giguere, *J. Chem. Phys.*, 1950, **18**, 88.
29. Smith and Creitz, *J. Res. Nat. Bur. Stand.*, 1951, **46**, 145.
30. Bateuv and Matveeva, *Izvest. Akad. Nauk. S.S.S.R. Otdel Khim Nauk.*, 1951, 448.
31. Coggeshall and Saier, *J. Amer. Chem. Soc.*, 1951, **73**, 5414.
32. Williams, Hofstadter and Herman., *J. Chem. Phys.*, 1939, **7**, 802.
33. Freymann and Heilmann, *Compt rend. Acad. Sci. Paris*, 1944, **219**, 415.
34. Rasmussen, Tunnicliff and Brattain, *J. Amer. Chem. Soc.*, 1949, **71**, 1068.

I

35. Friedel, *ibid.*, 1951, **73**, 2881.
36. Coggeshall, *ibid.*, 1947, **69**, 1620.
37. Hadži and Sheppard, *Proc. Roy. Soc.*, 1953, **A216**, 247.
38. Mecke, *Discuss. Faraday Soc.*, 1950, **9**, 161.
39. Baker, Davies and Gaunt, *J. Chem. Soc.*, 1949, 24.
40. Sears and Kitchen, *J. Amer. Chem. Soc.*, 1949, **71**, 4110.
41. Coggeshall, *ibid.*, 1950, **72**, 2836.
42. Lüttke and Mecke, *Z. physikal. Chem.*, 1950, **56**, 196.
43. Pauling, *J. Amer. Chem. Soc.*, 1936, **58**, 94.
44. Wulf, Liddel and Hendricks, *ibid.*, p. 2287.
45. Errera and Mollet, *J. Phys. Radium*, 1935, **6**, 281.
46. Thompson, Nicholson and Short, *Discuss. Faraday Soc.*, 1950, **9**, 222.
47. Brown, Holliday and Trotter, *J. Chem. Soc.*, 1951, 1532.
48. Buswell, Rodebush and Whitney, *J. Amer. Chem. Soc.*, 1947, **89**, 770.
49. Martin, *Nature*, 1950, **166**, 474.
50. Hunsberger, *J. Amer. Chem. Soc.*, 1950, **72**, 5626.
51. Flett, *J. Chem. Soc.*, 1948, 1441.
52. Reid and Ruby, *J. Amer. Chem. Soc.*, 1951, **73**, 1054.
53. Bellamy and Beecher, *J. Chem. Soc.*, 1952, 1701.
54. Daasch and Smith, *Analyt. Chem.*, 1951, **23**, 853.
55. Buswell, Rodebush and Roy, *J. Amer. Chem. Soc.*, 1938, **60**, 2528.
56. Gordy, *J. Chem. Phys.*, 1939, **7**, 163.
57. Sutherland, *Trans. Faraday Soc.*, 1940, **36**, 889.
58. Amstutz, Hunsberger and Chessick, *J. Amer. Chem. Soc.*, 1951, **73**, 1220.
59. Kletz, *Discuss. Faraday Soc.*, 1950, **9**, 211.
60. Davies and Sutherland, *J. Chem. Phys.*, 1938, **6**, 755, 762.
61. Davies, *J. Chem. Phys.*, 1940, **8**, 577; *Discuss. Faraday Soc.*, 1950, **9**, 212.
62. *Ibid.*, p. 213.
63. Francis, *J. Chem. Phys.*, 1951, **19**, 505.
64. Simard, Hasegawa, Bandaruk and Headington, *Analyt. Chem.*, 1951, **23**, 1384.
65. Glatt, Webber, Seaman and Ellis, *J. Chem. Phys.*, 1950, **18**, 413.
66. Rowen and Plyler, *J. Res. Nat. Bur. Stand.*, 1950, **44**, 313.
67. Lecomte, *Traité de Chimie Organique* (Masson et Cie, Paris, 1936), **2**, 143.
68. Brattain, *J. Chem. Phys.*, 1938, **6**, 298.
69. Lecomte, *Compt. rend. Acad. Sci. Paris*, 1925, **180**, 825.
70. Davies, *J. Chem. Phys.*, 1948, **16**, 267.
71. Noether, *ibid.*, 1942, **10**, 693.
72. Borden and Barker, *ibid.*, 1938, **6**, 553.
73. Barker and Bosschieter, *ibid.*, p. 563.
74. Kuhn, *J. Amer. Chem. Soc.*, 1952, **74**, 2492.
75. Ingraham, Corse, Bailey and Stitt, *ibid.*, p. 2297.
76. Hunsberger, Ketcham and Gutowsky, *ibid.*, p. 4839.
77. Rundle and Parasol, *J. Chem. Phys.*, 1952, **20**, 1487.
78. Stuart, *ibid.*, 1953, **21**, 1115.
79. Henne and Francis, *J. Amer. Chem. Soc.*, 1953, **75**, 991.
80. Haszeldine, *J. Chem. Soc.*, 1953, 1757.
81. Harple, Wiberley and Bauer, *Analyt. Chem.*, 1952, **24**, 635.
82. Amberlang and Binder, *J. Amer. Chem. Soc.*, 1953, **75**, 947.
83. Josien, Fuson, Lebas and Gregory, *J. Chem. Phys.*, 1953, **10**, 331.
84. Lord and Merrifield, *ibid.*, 166.
85. Tuot and Lecomte, *Bull. Soc. Chim. France*, 1943, **10**, 542.
86. Zeiss and Tsutsui, *J. Amer. Chem. Soc.*, 1953, **75**, 897.
87. Rosenkrantz, Milhorat and Farber, *J. Biol. Chem.*, 1952, **195**, 509.
88. Cole, Jones and Dobriner, *J. Amer. Chem. Soc.*, 1952, **74**, 5571.
89. Rosenkrantz and Zablow, *ibid.*, 1953, **75**, 903.
90. Furst, Kuhn, Scotoni and Gunthard, *Helv. Chim. Acta*, 1952, **35**, 951.
91. Dauben, Hoerger and Freeman, *J. Amer. Chem. Soc.*, 1952, **74**, 5206.
92. Kuratani, *J. Chem. Soc. Japan*, 1952, **73**, 758.
93. Hergert and Kurth, *J. Amer. Chem. Soc.*, 1953, **75**, 1622.
94. Wheland, *Resonance in Organic Chemistry* (Wiley, New York, 1955), pp. 47 *et seq.*

95. Hunter, *Progress in Stereochemistry*, Vol. 1 (Butterworth, London, 1954), pp. 224, *et seq.*
96. Ferguson, *Electronic Theories of Organic Chemistry* (Prentice Hall, New York, 1952).
97. Kuhn, J. *Amer. Chem. Soc.*, 1954, **76**, 4323.
98. Goulden, *Spectrochim. Acta*, 1954, **6**, 129.
99. Josien and Dizabo, *Compt. Rend. Acad. Sci. Paris*, 1956, **243**, 44.
100. Hughes, Martin and Coggeshall, *J. Chem. Phys.*, 1956, **24**, 489.
101. Fishman and Drickamer, *ibid.*, 548.
102. Bellamy and Beecher, *J. Chem. Soc.*, 1954, 4487.
103. Nakamoto, Margoshes and Rundle, *J. Amer. Chem. Soc.*, 1955, **77**, 6480.
104. Pimentel and Sederholm, *J. Chem. Phys.*, 1956, **24**, 639.
105. Tamres, Searles, Leighly and Mohrman, *J. Amer. Chem. Soc.*, 1954, **76**, 3983.
106. Finch and Lippincott, *J. Chem. Phys.*, 1956, **24**, 908.
107. Marrinan and Mann, *J. App. Chem.*, 1954, **4**, 204.
108. *Idem, Trans. Faraday Soc.*, 1956, **52**, 481, 487, 492.
109. Huitric and Kumler, *J. Amer. Chem. Soc.*, 1956, **78**, 1147.
110. Urbanski, *Bull. Acad. Polon. Sci. Cl. III*, 1956, **4**, 87.
111. Hoyer, *Chem. Ber.*, 1956, **89**, 146.
112. Rossmy, Lüttke and Mecke, *J. Chem. Phys.*, 1953, **21**, 1606.
113. Keussler and Rossmy, *Z. Electrochem.*, 1956, **60**, 136.
114. Bratoz, Hadži and Rossmy, *Trans. Faraday Soc.*, 1956, **52**, 464.
115. Eistert and Reiss, *Chem. Ber.*, 1955, **88**, 92.
116. Hadži and Sheppard, *Trans. Faraday Soc.*, 1954, **50**, 911.
117. Shaw and Simpson, *J. Chem. Soc.*, 1955, 655.
118. Farmer, Hayes and Thomson, *ibid.*, 1956, 3600.
119. Musso, *Chem. Ber.*, 1955, **88**, 1915.
120. Duncanson, *J. Chem. Soc.*, 1953, 1207.
121. Branch, *Nature*, 1956, **177**, 671.
122. Tsubomura, *J. Chem. Phys.*, 1956, **24**, 927.
123. *Idem, ibid.*, 1955, **23**, 2130.
124. Barrow, *J. Phys. Chem.*, 1955, **59**, 1129.
125. Stuart and Sutherland, *J. Chem. Phys.*, 1956, **24**, 559.
126. Mecke and Rossmy, *Z. Electrochem.*, 1955, **59**, 866.
127. Davies and Jones, *J. Chem. Soc.*, 1954, 120.
128. Stuart and Sutherland, *J. Phys. Radium*, 1954, **15**, 321.
129. Krimm, Liang and Sutherland, *J. Chem. Phys.*, 1956, **24**, 778.
130. Quinan and Wiberley, *ibid.*, 1953, **21**, 1896.
131. *Idem, Analyt. Chem.*, 1954, **26**, 1762.
132. Cole and Jefferies, *J. Chem. Soc.*, 1956, 4391.
133. Anet and Bavin, *Can. J. Chem.*, 1956, **34**, 1756.
134. Allsop, Cole, White and Willix, *J. Chem. Soc.*, 1956, 4868.
135. Huggins and Pimentel, *J. Phys. Chem.*, 1956, **60**, 1615.
136. Palm and Werbin, *Can. J. Chem.*, 1953, **31**, 1004.
137. Califano and Lüttke, *Z. Phys. Chem.*, 1955, **5**, 240.
138. *Idem, ibid.*, 1956, **6**, 83.
139. Bowman, Stevens and Baldwin, *J. Amer. Chem. Soc.*, 1957, **79**, 87.
140. Ens and Murray, *Can. J. Chem.*, 1957, **35**, 170.
141. Widom, Philippe and Hobbs, *J. Amer. Chem. Soc.*, 1957, **79**, 1383.
142. Nickson, *ibid.*, 243.
143. Mecke and Funck, *Z. Electrochem.*, 1956, **60**, 1124.
144. Shigorin and Dokunichiv, *Doklady Akad. Nauk. S.S.S.R.*, 1955, **100**, 323.
145. Brown and Rogers, *J. Amer. Chem. Soc.*, 1957, **79**, 577.
146. Maclou and Henry, *Compt. Rend. Acad. Sci. Paris*, 1957, **244**, 1494.

CHAPTER 7

Ethers, Peroxides and Ozonides

7.1. INTRODUCTION AND TABLE

THE only characteristic feature of ethers by which they can be identified from their infra-red spectra is the very intense absorption arising from the single bond C–O– stretching vibration. It has been seen that in alcohols this occurs near 1050 cm.$^{-1}$ in structures containing the CH_2OH group, but that this frequency is very sensitive to environmental changes, so that even chain branching, as in secondary alcohols, causes a shift towards 1100 cm.$^{-1}$. In the case of ethers, therefore, it is not to be expected that this band position will be constant, particularly as in this case interactions will occur between the C–O– and O–R vibrations, so that the nature of the substituents on either side of the link will be liable to alter the frequency. However, correlations are possible for limited types of structure, as in the case of the alcohols, and the group CH_2–O–CH_2, for example, can be expected to absorb within a considerably narrower range than the 1150–1000 cm.$^{-1}$ which was originally given by Lecomte [1] for saturated ethers as a whole. However, although the band arising from this structure can usually be recognised from its very high intensity, this correlation cannot be used to give more than a possible indication of the presence of this group. This is due partly to the fact that branched-chains and similar type ethers have not so far been adequately examined and to the influence of structural changes on the frequency studied, and partly because of the overlapping between this correlation and, for example, the strong bands from secondary and tertiary alcohols and peroxides and from the structures P–O–C and Si–O–C.

One instance in which structural changes result in a very considerable frequency shift of the C–O vibration is in compounds containing the group =C–O–. In the case of alcohols, such as phenol, a high-frequency shift towards 1250 cm.$^{-1}$ is found as a result of this, and esters and acids show the same effect. It is therefore not surprising that aryl ethers and similarly unsaturated ethers also show their strong C–O absorption near 1250 cm.$^{-1}$. The fact that so many related materials also show this band is another illustration of the difficulty in using this region for structural identifications. A strong band near 1250 cm.$^{-1}$ is, at best, only a reasonably good indication of the presence of a C–O link, the carbon atom of which is unsaturated, and a study of the rest of the spectrum must be made

114

to ascertain whether or not this is likely to arise from esters, alcohols or any of the other alternative structures.

A second complication can arise from the fact that the position and nature of substituents on the aromatic ring also have an effect upon the C–O– bond-length. Colthup [2] finds that the C–O stretching frequency of *meta*-substituted aromatic ethers is higher than normal, and his chart shows values up to 1300 cm.$^{-1}$ for this vibration. He also indicates the presence of a medium intensity band between 1070 cm.$^{-1}$ and 1000 cm.$^{-1}$ in mono-aryl ethers, CH_2–O–Ph. We have observed such a band in a number of cases, as have others,[30] and it may possibly be connected with the vibration of the CH_2–O– residue of the molecule. However, so many carbon–carbon and similar skeletal vibrations give bands of medium intensity in this region that this observation cannot usefully be employed in analysis.

Cyclic ethers are in rather a different position from the open-chain products, in that the ring itself may have certain modes of its own which, although not C–O vibrations as such, are nevertheless sufficiently characteristic to enable the ring to be identified. Work along these lines is being done on the epoxy group, for example, and some very useful specific correlations for various types of cyclic structures in the sugars have also been developed along these lines. It is, for example, possible in this way to differentiate α and β anomers, and furanose derivatives from characteristic frequencies related to tetrahydropyrane and tetrahydrofuran rings.[32-35]

A correlation for the –O–O– peroxide linkage has been suggested which associates this group with absorption at 890–830 cm.$^{-1}$, but some doubt has been cast on the validity of certain of the results employed in arriving at this, as other structures such as the skeleton

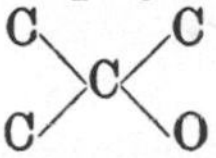

$$\begin{matrix} C & & C \\ & C & \\ C & & O \end{matrix}$$

have been found to absorb in the same region. Peroxides containing the –CO–O–O– group may also be identified by the characteristic carbonyl vibration (Chapter 9). No satisfactory correlations for ozonides have yet been developed.

The correlations discussed are listed in Table 7.

TABLE 7

Alkyl ethers –CH_2–O–CH_2– . . .	1150–1060 cm.$^{-1}$ (v.s.)
Aryl ethers and others with the group =C–O–	1270–1230 cm.$^{-1}$ (v.s.)
Cyclic ethers (1) Epoxy compounds .	Near 1250 cm.$^{-1}$ (s.)
	Near 890 cm.$^{-1}$ (*trans*)
	Near 830 cm.$^{-1}$ (*cis*) (m.)
(2) Larger ring compounds	1140–1070 cm.$^{-1}$ (v.s.)
Alkyl peroxides	890–820 cm.$^{-1}$ (v.-w.)

7.2. ALIPHATIC ETHERS

The spectra of a number of simple aliphatic ethers have been given by Barnes *et al.*[3] The exact positions of the C–O–C bands are not given, but from the spectra it can be seen that they all absorb in the approximate range 1150–1060 cm.[-1]. They have also given the spectra of allyl ethyl ether and of diallyl ether, in both of which the C–O–C band is in approximately the same position as in the saturated materials. This last observation would appear to indicate that the structure C=C–C–O–C does not have any marked effect on the C–O frequency, and this agrees with Lecomte's [1] observation that the C–O stretching frequencies of vinyl alcohols are essentially normal.

Again, by analogy with alcohols, it is likely that chain branching at the carbon atom carrying the ether link will seriously modify the C–O frequency. Little or no information is available on this, but it is worth noting that the spectrum of di*iso*propyl ether given by Barnes *et al.*[3] shows a triplet structure in the 1100–1070 region, whereas di*iso*amyl ether [4] in which the chain branching is removed farther from the C–O band has only a single strong band at 1111 cm.[-1]. Tschamler and Leutner [30,36] quote 1150–1080 cm.[-1] for saturated ethers and have noted that ethers containing the group C–O–C–O–C a strong doublet is shown in this range. This observation has been extended by Bergmann and Pinchas,[37] who have studied eighteen ketals and acetals, many of which are cyclic dioxolanes, and identified a series of four bands in the 1200–1000 cm.[-1] region which they regard as specific for the C–O–C–O–C grouping and which they assign to various coupled C–O vibrations. However, Lagrange and Mastagli [38] have discussed this correlation and pointed out that many of these bands appear in dioxane derivatives also and that they are not always all present in dioxolanes.

Apart from these compounds, there is very little information available in the literature on the infra-red spectra of ethers. The only others commonly encountered in industry are the various poly-glycols, mono- and di-ethers of ethylene glycol and diethylene glycol and substituted phenoxyacetic esters. We have examined di-, tri- and various higher poly-ethylene glycols and also the methyl, ethyl and butyl cellosolves and carbitols, and all of these show very broad strong bands within the approximate range quoted. The C–O band in the phenoxy-acetic esters is also normal, although the ester C–O at 1250 cm.[-1] is also shown. Similarly β-chloro-ethyl ether is normal in respect of the C–O vibration. The influence of halogen substitution at the α-carbon atom has not, however, been examined. Davison [39] has studied the spectral changes which occur on crystal-lisation of polyethylene glycol and suggested that, as in the case of dimethyl ether, two C–O–C frequencies, corresponding to anti-symmetric and symmetric stretching modes, occur at 1120 and 1061 cm.$^{-1}$. Ethers of polyethylene glycols have also been studied by Chakhovskoy et al.,[40] and work has also been done on polyoxymethylene [41] and polypropylene oxide.[42]

On the basis of the above, the tentative range 1150–1060 cm.$^{-1}$ has been suggested. It should be remembered, however, that this is based on a limited number of types of compound and that this range may well need extending to cover special types of aliphatic ethers, such as those containing the group –CH–O–CH$_2$–, etc. The characteristic intensity of the C–O–C group will also be reduced in higher molecular weight materials in which the number of ether links is low. In alkyl acetals the CH$_2$ group adjacent to the oxygen atom appears to have a characteristic frequency [57] near 2825 cm.$^{-1}$.

7.3. ARYL AND ARALKYL ETHERS

As in the case of aliphatic ethers, the data available on aryl ethers are largely contained in the fairly extensive series of spectra of simple ethers of this type given by Barnes et al.[3] In all of these a strong band is shown in the approximate region 1270–1230 cm.$^{-1}$ and the comparison of *ortho-*, *meta-* and *para-*isomerides indicates that, in agreement with Colthup,[2] the *meta-*substituted materials show this band at slightly higher frequencies than the others.

The work of Lecomte [1] also supports this assignment. In addition to a number of normal aryl ethers he has examined compounds of the series C$_6$H$_5$O(CH$_2$)$_n$OC$_6$H$_5$, in which n is varied from 1 to 10. In all of these the strong bands near 1250 cm.$^{-1}$ remained stationary. In these spectra a second band occurs in the 1150–1060 cm.$^{-1}$ region which is probably due to the CH$_2$–O– vibration. Tschamler and Leutner [30] have also found bands in both regions in aralkyl ethers, and diphenyl ethers have been studied by Kimoto.[43] Our own observations on a number of aryl ethers agree with these assignments, but, as before, the overall number examined is still relatively small, and variations outside the ranges given are not unlikely, especially in materials such as nitro-aryl ethers, etc. Much of the limited information available concerns aryl ethers, and the application of this correlation to vinyl ethers is even less certain. For example, the *cis-* and *trans-*butylenyl butyl ethers show considerable differences in this region, and the strongest bands occur in the 1200–1100 cm.$^{-1}$ range.[11] From the limited number of such materials examined [30, 44] it would appear that the C–O vibration occurs somewhere between 1240 cm.$^{-1}$ and 1150 cm.$^{-1}$. There is also some evidence that conjugation of the double bonds does not affect this frequency.

In making use of these assignments the fact that phenols, esters, acids and other compounds containing the structure $=$C–O– may also absorb near 1250 cm.$^{-1}$ should not be overlooked.

7.4. CYCLIC ETHERS

7.4(a). Epoxy Compounds. Ethylene oxide has been studied by a number of workers,[5, 6, 7, 45] who have associated bands at 865 cm.$^{-1}$, 1165 cm.$^{-1}$ and 1265 cm.$^{-1}$ with the epoxy group. This group is of considerable interest in connection with the oxidation of vegetable oils and hydrocarbons, and a number of workers have therefore interested themselves in the possibility of finding a characteristic absorption frequency for it. Field, Cole and Woodford [8] studied eight epoxy compounds of some complexity, such as *iso*butylene oxide, styrene oxide, etc., and examined the spectra for characteristic bands in the regions given above. Although they identified bands in each of these regions in all these compounds, they consider that only the 1250 cm.$^{-1}$ band could be identified with any reasonable certainty as being due to the epoxy group, and in the compounds examined it fell constantly in the range 1260–1240 cm.$^{-1}$. The identification of the remainder they regarded as being much less certain on account of the increased number of C–C and C–H rocking frequencies in these molecules.

Shreve *et al.*[9] have also studied this problem, and have given the spectra of a few simple epoxy compounds, and also of the epoxy derivatives of some 1 : 2-olefines of long-chain length. Their results agree with those of Field *et al.*[8] in so far as they find a band close to 1260–1250 cm.$^{-1}$ in all cases, and it is noticeable that, although this band is relatively strong in the simple compounds, it is of only medium to weak intensity in, for example, 1 : 2 epoxytetradecane, in which the molar concentration of epoxy group is much lower. In α-methyl styrene oxide this band is absent, although Patterson [46] has detected it in twenty-five other epoxy compounds. Günthard *et al.* have also noted the absence of this band in steroid epoxides.[47] However, Shreve *et al.*[9] do not consider this band, which, with others at 1430 cm.$^{-1}$ and 1136 cm.$^{-1}$, they believe to be associated with C–O stretching modes, to be the most characteristic for epoxy structures in all cases. In all the compounds referred to they found bands close to 910 cm.$^{-1}$ and 830 cm.$^{-1}$, although the second of these was shifted to 818 cm.$^{-1}$ in 3 : 4-epoxy-1-butene, possibly under the influence of the conjugated double bond. Extension of this work to the epoxy derivatives of mono-unsaturated fatty acids, esters and alcohols showed that spectra of the *trans*-epoxy materials were qualitatively similar to the saturated compounds, except for a new band near 890 cm.$^{-1}$, whilst the *cis*-epoxy materials all showed a band near 830 cm.$^{-1}$. They have therefore tentatively ascribed these bands to ring vibrations of the epoxy ring in *cis*- and *trans*-

compounds. These lower-frequency absorptions have also been studied by Patterson [46] and by Günthard *et al.*[47] In the compounds studied by the former, two bands were found in the overall range 950–863 cm.$^{-1}$ and 864–786 cm.$^{-1}$, with the majority falling near 910 and 830 cm.$^{-1}$ in good agreement with the earlier workers. On the other hand, in steroid epoxides Günthard *et al.* find bands corresponding to the epoxy group between 900 and 800 cm.$^{-1}$ in some compounds and between 1050 and 1035 cm.$^{-1}$ in others.

The application of these findings will need considerable caution until further spectra are available and, in view of the many different groups which can cause absorption near 830 cm.$^{-1}$ and 890 cm.$^{-1}$, it would be unwise to apply these correlations, other than very tentatively, to compounds not closely similar to those described.

In addition, Tuot and Barchewitz [12] have suggested that in the overtone region, absorption at 7042 cm.$^{-1}$ may be characteristic of epoxides, but the number of materials examined is small, and this possibility requires further study.

7.4(b). Four-, Five- and Six-Membered Ring Compounds.

With larger rings in which the strain is reduced, the C–O–C stretching frequency should approach nearer to the normal value. Shreve *et al.*[9] give the spectra of tetrahydropyran and dioxan, in both of which a series of bands in the range 1124–1030 cm.$^{-1}$ are shown. The band at 1100 cm.$^{-1}$ in tetrahydropyrane has been ascribed to the C–O vibration.[31] Tschamler *et al.*[30,48] quote a few similar cases, and again find that the group C–O–C–O–C gives rise to a doublet in the same frequency range. Studies on dioxanes and dioxolanes have confirmed that multiple-band structures are shown, but the precise number of characteristic frequencies produced in the two cases are not clearly defined.[37,38] In unsaturated cyclic compounds with the structure =C–O–C= the band moves to higher frequencies. Tetrahydrofuran, with a five-membered ring, absorbs at 1076 cm.$^{-1}$, and Barrow and Searles [31] have found five other related compounds absorbing between 1100 and 1075 cm.$^{-1}$. With other heterocyclic systems, such as azoximes and oxadiazoles, a strong 1030 cm.$^{-1}$ band is found which is absent from the furazans [10] and is probably associated with the C–O bond. The influence of ring-strain becomes more pronounced with four-membered rings and the C–O absorption of trimethylene oxides occurs in the 980–970 cm.$^{-1}$ region.[31] This supports indirectly the 890–830 cm.$^{-1}$ range suggested for epoxy compounds which would be expected to absorb at lower frequencies.

However, too little information is yet available for any detailed correlations to be made, beyond the generalisation that the ether link in large ring compounds of this type probably absorbs at something like the same frequency as it does in open-chain products. Jones and Sandorfy have compiled a useful bibliographical table of a number of cyclic ethers.[49]

7.5. PEROXIDES

The possibility of detecting peroxide and hydroperoxide structures by infra-red methods is also of practical interest in connection with the mechanism of oxidative processes in hydrocarbons. The theoretical aspects of such a correlation have been discussed by Sheppard,[13] who points out that it is unlikely that peroxides of the type R–O–O–R′ will have any very characteristic bands for the O–O vibration, as this mode would be relatively symmetrical, and not associated with any great change in dipole moment, so that the corresponding frequency would be expected to be weak in the infra-red. Furthermore, the masses and force constants of the O–O group are so similar to those of C–O and C–C groups that it is unlikely that any very characteristic frequency will result. With hydroperoxides, where the O–O group is at the end of a chain, the possibilities are a little greater but, even so, the O–O vibration will contribute to the skeletal modes of the molecule as a whole, and the frequency will therefore be subject to changes with the nature of the substituent groups. Sheppard suggested, however, that some correlations might be found, covering limited groups of substituents in the same way as correlations have been found, for example, for primary, secondary and tertiary alcohols, although this will involve a study of a considerable number of compounds of a variety of different types.

The region in which any O–O skeletal vibration is to be expected is readily obtainable from the spectrum of hydrogen peroxide which has been studied by several workers.[14, 15] Giguère [14] has shown that the 877 cm.$^{-1}$ band of H_2O_2 is essentially unchanged in position in D_2O_2, so that it is reasonable to assign it to the O–O stretching mode. Furthermore, this assignment corresponds to a bond length nearly equal to that derived from electron diffraction measurements.

This observation has been followed up by Leadbeater,[16] who obtained the infra-red and Raman spectrum of the peroxide of ethyl ether, and the Raman spectrum of the corresponding α-mono- and α-di-hydroxyperoxides, and of benzoyl peroxide. In all cases he found a fairly strong band in the range 883–881 cm.$^{-1}$, and, in contrast to Sheppard's comments, he notes that on passing from the O–O vibration of H_2O_2 to higher molecules there are no frequency changes such as occur with the C–C links of hydrocarbons. The range of materials studied is, however, very limited, and one of them, at least, must be considered as being suspect in regard to its purity, as Shreve *et al.*[17] have found no band at 883 cm.$^{-1}$ in the infra-red spectrum of benzoyl peroxide, and we have confirmed this observation.

Nevertheless, it is fairly clear from the work of others that aliphatic materials of this type do absorb in the 870 cm.$^{-1}$ region, although, as is to be expected, the frequency range is relatively wide. Minkoff [18,50] has studied some thirty pure peroxides, hydroperoxides and peracids, and in all cases has found a band in the range 890–830 cm.$^{-1}$. Whilst assigning this provisionally to the O–O vibration, he points out that the intensity of the band is not high and that it may be hidden by, or confused with, several skeletal frequencies of comparable intensities in large molecules. All the compounds examined were aliphatic, and the majority were simple methyl, ethyl and butyl derivatives. However, despite the low intensity of this band, absorption at 813 cm.$^{-1}$ has been used by Raley *et al.*[20] for estimating di-*tert.*-butyl peroxide in *tert.*-butyl alcohol.

Confirmation of this assignment is forthcoming from other studies on groups of compounds containing the O–O link,[17, 19, 51–53] and from a number of scattered observations on isolated molecules.[54–56] However, as before, the band is weak and difficult to identify. This is particularly apparent, for example, in the work of Williams and Mosher,[51] who compared the spectra of a number of alkylhydroperoxides with those of the corresponding alcohols. Although marked differences were found in this region, many of the alcohols themselves absorbed in the same spectral region. As mentioned above, benzoyl peroxide does not follow this correlation, but shows a strong absorption near 1000 cm.$^{-1}$. Shreve *et al.*[17] point out that phthaloyl peroxide, *p*-chlorobenzoyl peroxide and benzaldehyde peroxide also absorb near this point, and suggest tentatively that this may represent the characteristic frequency for the O–O absorption in aryl peroxides. We have examined perbenzoic acid and find absorption near 1030 cm.$^{-1}$ and 880 cm.$^{-1}$.

It is clear therefore that the absorption band arising from the O–O vibration is likely to occur somewhere in the range 890–820 cm.$^{-1}$ in aliphatic compounds and possibly near 1000 cm.$^{-1}$ in aryl peroxides. The band positions for corresponding peroxides and hydroperoxides will occur at different points within this range. It is doubtful, however, whether it is worthwhile attempting to subdivide this range into narrower classes in view of the difficulties already mentioned. It would, for example, be extremely dangerous to assign a band near the 870 cm.$^{-1}$ in an unknown compound to the peroxide link unless there was also very strong supplementary evidence available. This is especially the case, since it has been shown by Philpotts and Thain [21] that the structure $\begin{matrix} C & & C \\ & \diagdown C \diagup & \\ C & & O \end{matrix}$ also gives rise to a strong absorption band in the 920–800 cm.$^{-1}$ region. This observation is based on the comparison of the spectra of several series of tertiary

peroxides, hydroperoxides and alcohols in which the band previously assigned to the O–O group was found to persist in the
alcohols. In support of this we have, ourselves, noted a strong
absorption at 901 cm.$^{-1}$ in aluminium *tert.*-butoxide which is absent
from aluminium *iso*propoxide. This does not seriously weaken the
O–O assignment in view of the considerable body of evidence available, but it emphasises the need for caution in the use of this
correlation.

A number of other possibilities also exist for the recognition of
peroxide and similar structures. The peroxidic carbonyl, for
example, is highly characteristic (Chapter 9), whilst one might also
expect that the typical frequencies of the OH group when attached
to an oxygen atom in peracids and hydroperoxides might be
sufficiently different from those of carboxylic acids and alcohols to
permit identification. A number of tentative approaches have been
made along these lines, but further detailed work is required to
clarify the position. Possibly the most promising of these frequencies
is the OH stretching mode in hydroperoxides. This would be expected from electronegativity considerations to fall at a distinctly
lower frequency than in alcohols, and Karyakin *et al.*[52] have assigned
it at 3450 cm.$^{-1}$ in solution on the basis of a very limited number of
materials. Some indirect support for this is available from the
observation that, in the condensed phase, the OH stretching frequency is consistently lower than that of the corresponding alcohols.[51]
This approach is not, however, applicable to peracids which exist as
intramolecularly bonded systems,[53, 56] with OH frequencies near
3280 cm.$^{-1}$.

A number of other attempts have been made to assign OH deformation and C–O stretching frequencies,[19, 52, 53] but the direct
comparisons with alcohols [51] indicates that these are less likely
to be valuable. In the case of peracids the OH deformation frequency occurs near 950 cm.$^{-1}$, as in carboxylic acids, but is noticeably
weaker.[53] A few other tentative correlations for hydroperoxides [51]
and for narrow classes, such as percarbonates and peresters,[50] have
been suggested, but require more detailed study before they can be
fully substantiated.

7.6. OZONIDES

The possibility of using infra-red methods for the study of the
formation, stability and decomposition of ozonides was first explored by Briner and his co-workers.[22–24] In preliminary studies
they have passed ozone into carbon tetrachloride solutions of unsaturated compounds and observed the spectral changes following
varying degrees of ozonolysis. This at first led them to believe
that ozonides absorbed in the carbonyl region, but subsequent

work by their own group [25], [26] and by Criege *et al.*[27] has shown that these bands arise from decomposition products. The latter workers studied some eighteen ozonides of various types and noted that in the greater proportion of them a new medium strong absorption band appeared after ozonolysis in the range 1064–1042 cm.$^{-1}$. These probably correspond to C–O stretching frequencies of the ozonide system. Briner and Dallwigk [25], [26] have confirmed this finding, and Garvin and Schubert [28] have also found ozonide absorptions in this region. The correlation is, however, of very limited value in view of the many other types of C–O stretching absorptions found hereabouts.

Some studies have also been made on the action of ozone on elastomers such as natural rubber, neoprene, etc.[8] In these cases, however, there is no suggestion of the detection of any ozonides, but only of decomposition products characterised by OH and carbonyl absorptions.

7.7. BIBLIOGRAPHY

1. Lecomte, *Traité de Chimie Organique* (ed. Grignard et Baud, Masson et Cie, Paris, 1936), **2**, 143.
2. Colthup, *J. Opt. Soc. Amer.*, 1950, **40**, 397.
3. Barnes, Gore, Liddel and Van Zandt Williams, *Infra-red Spectroscopy* (Reinhold, 1944).
4. Randall, Fowler, Fuson and Dangl, *Infra-red Determination of Organic Structures* (Van Nostrand, 1949).
5. Herzberg, *Infra-red and Raman Spectra of Polyatomic Molecules* (Van Nostrand, 1945), p. 340.
6. Bonner, *J. Chem. Phys.*, 1937, **5**, 704.
7. Thompson and Cave, *Trans. Faraday Soc.*, 1951, **47**, 946.
8. Field, Cole and Woodford, *J. Chem. Phys.*, 1950, **18**, 1298.
9. Shreve, Heether, Knight and Swern, *Analyt. Chem.*, 1951, **23**, 277.
10. Milone and Borello, *Gazz. Chim. Italia*, 1951, **81**, 368.
11. Hall, Philpotts, Stern and Thain, *J. Chem. Soc.*, 1951, 3341.
12. Tuot and Barchewitz, *Bull. Soc. chim.* (*France*), 1950, 851.
13. Sheppard, *Discuss. Faraday Soc.*, 1950, **9**, 322.
14. Giguère, *J. Chem. Phys.*, 1950, **18**, 88.
15. Taylor, *ibid.*, 898.
16. Leadbeater, *Compt. rend. Acad. Sci. Paris*, 1950, **230**, 829.
17. Shreve, Heether, Knight and Swern, *Analyt. Chem.*, 1951, **23**, 282.
18. Minkoff, *Discuss. Faraday Soc.*, 1950, **9**, 320.
19. Whitcomb, Moorhead and Sharp, *Symposium on Molecular Structure and Spectrography* (Ohio, 1950).
20. Raley, Rust and Vaughan, *J. Amer. Chem. Soc.*, 1948, **70**, 1336.
21. Philpotts and Thain, *Analyt. Chem.*, 1952, **24**, 638.
22. Briner, Susz and Dallwigk, *Arch. Sci. Phys. Nat.*, 1951, **4**, 199.
23. Susz, Dallwigk and Briner, *ibid.*, 202.
24. Briner, Susz and Dallwigk, *Compt. rend. Acad. Sci. Paris*, 1952, **234**, 1932.
25. Briner and Dallwigk, *Helv. Chim. Acta*, 1956, **39**, 1446, 1826.
26. *Idem, Compt. Rend. Acad. Sci. Paris*, 1956, **243**, 630.
27. Criegee, Kerckow and Zinke, *Chem. Ber.*, 1955, **88**, 1878.
28. Garvin and Schubert, *J. Phys. Chem.*, 1956, **60**, 807.
29. Allison and Stanley, *Analyt. Chem.*, 1952, **29**, 630.
30. Tschamler and Leutner, *Monatsh.*, 1952, **83**, 1502.
31. Barrow and Searles, *J. Amer. Chem. Soc.*, 1953, **75**, 1175.
32. Barker, Bourne, Stacey and Whiffen, *J. Chem. Soc.*, 1954, 171.

33. Barker, Bourne, Stephens and Whiffen, *ibid.*, 1954, 3468, 4211.
34. Barker and Stephens, *ibid.*, 1954, 4550.
35. Whistler and House, *Analyt. Chem.*, 1953, **25**, 1463.
36. Tschamler, *Spectrochim. Acta.*, 1953, **6**, 95.
37. Bergmann and Pinchas, *Rec. trav. chim.*, 1952, **71**, 161.
38. Lagrange and Mastagli, *Compt. Rend. Acad. Sci. Paris*, 1955, **241**, 1947.
39. Davison, *J. Chem. Soc.*, 1955, 3270.
40. Chakhovskoy, Martin and Van Nechel, *Bull. Soc. Chim. Belges*, 1956, **65**, 453.
41. Philpotts, Evans and Sheppard, *Trans. Faraday Soc.*, 1955, **51**, 1051.
42. Price and Osgan, *J. Amer. Chem. Soc.*, 1956, **78**, 4787.
43. Kimoto, *J. Pharm. Soc. Japan*, 1955, **75**, 763.
44. Meakins, *J. Chem. Soc.*, 1953, 4170.
45. Lord and Nolin, *J. Chem. Phys.*, 1956, **24**, 656.
46. Patterson, *Analyt. Chem.*, 1954, **26**, 823.
47. Günthard, Heusser and Fürst, *Helv. Chim. Acta*, 1953, **36**, 1900.
48. Tschamler and Voetter, *Monatsh.*, 1952, **83**, 303, 1228.
49. Jones and Sandorfy, *Chemical Applications of Spectroscopy* (Interscience, New York, 1956), p. 438.
50. Minkoff, *Proc. Roy. Soc.*, 1954, **A.224**, 176.
51. Williams and Mosher, *Analyt. Chem.*, 1955, **27**, 517.
52. Karyakin, Nikitin and Ivanov, *Zhur. Fiz. Khim.*, 1953, **27**, 1856.
53. Swern, Witnauer, Eddy and Parker, *J. Amer. Chem. Soc.*, 1955, **77**, 5537.
54. Criegee and Paulig, *Chem. Ber.*, 1955, **88**, 712.
55. Milos and Mageli, *J. Amer. Chem. Soc.*, 1953, **75**, 5970.
56. Giguere and Olmos, *Can. J. Chem.*, 1952, **30**, 821.
57. Brugel and Oster, *Angew. Chem.*, 1956, **68**, 441.

CHAPTER 8

Acid Halides, Carbonates, Anhydrides and Metallic Carbonyls

8.1. INTRODUCTION AND TABLE

NONE of these classes of compounds has received much systematic study, but a number of workers have examined small groups of compounds, and the results are sufficiently consistent and in accordance with expectation to form a reasonable basis for correlations to be drawn up.

The correlations discussed are shown in Table 8.

TABLE 8

C=O *Vibrations* (all strong bands)

Acid halides . . .	1815–1770 cm.$^{-1}$. (Conjugated materials in lower part of the range.)	
Carbonates . . .	1780–1740 cm.$^{-1}$	
Anhydrides (open-chain).	1850–1800 cm.$^{-1}$ and 1790–1740 cm.$^{-1}$	Conjugation lowers by 20 cm.$^{-1}$ in each case
„ Cyclic (5-ring)	1870–1820 cm.$^{-1}$ and 1800–1750 cm.$^{-1}$	
Peroxides (alkyl) . .	1820–1810 cm.$^{-1}$ and 1800–1780 cm.$^{-1}$	
„ (aryl) . .	1805–1780 cm.$^{-1}$ and 1785–1755 cm.$^{-1}$	

C–O *Vibrations*

Anhydrides (open-chain).	1170–1050 cm.$^{-1}$ (s.)
„ (cyclic) .	1300–1200 cm.$^{-1}$ (s.)

C≡O *Vibrations* . . Near 2050 and 2040 cm.$^{-1}$ (m.)

All the ranges quoted for carbonyl absorptions are rather wide, but this is due to the limited amount of data available, and more precise correlations would probably be possible if a sufficiently wide range of materials were to be studied.

8.2. ACID HALIDES

In esters, acids and ketones the substitution of a chlorine or bromine atom on an α-carbon atom to the carbonyl group results in a shift in the C=O frequency to a higher value. With a direct attachment of the halogen to the carbonyl group, a considerably bigger shift in this direction is to be expected, and this is what is found in practice. Phosgene gas absorbs at 1828 cm.[-1], and acetyl chloride [1, 2] and acetyl bromide at 1802 cm.[-1] and 1812 cm.[-1] respectively. An increase in the size of the remainder of the molecule does not appear to affect this frequency significantly, and phenylacetyl chloride absorbs at 1802 cm.[-1,1, 2] whilst we have found a value of 1790 cm.[-1] for n-octoyl chloride. Similar results are given in Raman spectra for oxalyl chloride (1776 cm.[-1]) and propionyl chloride (1786 cm.[-1]).

Conjugation of the acid halide with an $\alpha\beta$ double bond or an aryl group would be expected to lower the CO frequency again, and this is found in benzoyl chloride, which absorbs at 1773 cm.[-1,1, 2] This compound, however, shows a second CO band at 1736 cm.[-1], the origin of which is not known. Very few acid fluorides have been reported in the infra-red literature, and owing to the very high electronegativity of fluorine, these absorb at considerably higher frequencies. The compound COF_2, for example,[18] absorbs at 1928 cm.[-1], which is one of the highest carbonyl frequencies known whilst acetyl fluoride absorbs at 1872 cm.[-1] in the vapour state. α-Halogen substitution also raises the carbonyl frequency, and trifluoroacetyl fluoride absorbs at 1901 cm.[-1]. With less halogen substitution the possibility of rotational isomerism leads to two carbonyl frequencies, in chloroacetyl chloride and similar compounds studied by Mizushima *et al.*[19] In general, this leads to a pair of carbonyl frequencies, one of which is higher than acetyl chloride and the other lower.[20] The higher frequency is associated with the isomer in which the chlorine atom is near in space to the oxygen atom, whilst the lower corresponds to the form in which the two halogen atoms approach each other. In the latter case the internal field effects probably operate to lower the effective electronegativity of the directly attached halogen atom, with a consequent fall in the frequency. The frequencies of a number of alkyl acid halides and their halogen-substituted derivatives have been discussed by Bellamy and Williams,[20] and fluorinated halides have also been studied by Haszeldine,[17] Husted and Ahlbrecht[16] and Wieblen.[21]

Except where stated, the above values refer to determinations made in solution or in the liquid state. In the vapour state a further frequency rise of about 20 cm.[-1] is observed,[3] indicating that some form of association occurs in the liquid or in solution.

8.3. CARBONATES AND CHLOROFORMATES

The data available on organic carbonates and chloroformates is limited to that included in a single paper by Hales, Jones and Kynaston[41] and to a detailed assignment of ethylene carbonate.[42] It is to be expected that the influence of two oxygen atoms in carbonates will raise the frequency of the carbonyl absorption above that of esters, and this will be true also in chloroformates. This is realised in practice. Diacyl carbonates ROCOOR absorb [41] in the range 1760–1740 cm.$^{-1}$, the precise value depending in part upon the stereoisomeric form. Diphenyl carbonate shows a typical vinyl ester effect and absorbs higher at 1775 cm.$^{-1}$. Halogen substitution on the R substituents raises the carbonyl frequencies further, and $CCl_3OCOOCCl_3$, for example, absorbs at 1832 cm.$^{-1}$. In cyclic carbonates the influence of ring strain is superimposed on other effects, and in the five-membered ring systems studied [41,42] the carbonyl frequencies fall in the 1830–1800 cm.$^{-1}$ range. There is some variation in these values with changes of state which is illustrated by ethylene carbonate,[42] which absorbs at 1870 cm.$^{-1}$ in the vapour, 1830–1820 cm.$^{-1}$ in non-polar solvents and 1805 cm.$^{-1}$ in the liquid. In some cases a second absorption is shown near 1780 cm.$^{-1}$, which has been attributed to an overtone frequency.

Both cyclic and open-chain carbonates also show strong bands due to the C–O stretching frequencies.[41] In open-chain compounds these appear to be somewhat similar to the corresponding bands in esters, but in five-membered ring systems some shifts occur under the influence of ring strain.

Chloroformates absorb at somewhat higher frequencies than carbonates, and the C=O band is usually found between 1780 and 1770 cm.$^{-1}$. This is again raised by α-halogen substitution, the CCl_3 derivative absorbing at 1806 cm.$^{-1}$.

8.4. ANHYDRIDES

No systematic study of anhydride absorptions has been carried out, and the whole of the available data consists of scattered observations, usually on one or two isolated materials. These are difficult to compare amongst themselves because the measurements have often been made in different physical states. However, anhydrides all show two carbonyl absorption bands. The position, separation and intensity of these depend on whether or not the carbonyls are conjugated, and whether they are part of a strained five-membered ring, as in cyclic anhydrides. Randall *et al.*[1] directed attention to the fact that the two bands are always approximately the same distance apart (*c.* 60 cm.$^{-1}$), and, although a number of exceptions are known, this is a very useful pointer in their identification. Typical values for unstrained materials are as follows:

Acetic anhydride [1]	. .	1824 cm.$^{-1}$ and 1748 cm.$^{-1}$
Phenyl acetic anhydride	.	1808 cm.$^{-1}$ and 1745 cm.$^{-1}$
Caproic anhydride [4]	. .	1825 cm.$^{-1}$ and 1760 cm.$^{-1}$
Glutaric anhydride [6]	.	1802 cm.$^{-1}$ and 1761 cm.$^{-1}$

K

$\alpha\beta$-conjugation results in a lowering of these values by 20–40 cm.$^{-1}$. Crotonic anhydride [4] absorbs near 1780 cm.$^{-1}$ and 1725 cm.$^{-1}$, and we have found these bands in benzoylbenzoate to occur at 1789 cm.$^{-1}$ and 1727 cm.$^{-1}$. It will be seen from these values that the distance apart of the two bands is reasonably consistent, despite the variations in individual frequencies. The factors which determine the separation of these bands have been discussed by Cooke.[25]

With cyclic materials in which the CO groups form part of a five-membered ring, the influence of ring strain induces a shift to higher frequencies, similar to that found in cyclic ketones and lactones with five-membered rings. Succinic anhydride,[1] for example, absorbs at 1865 cm.$^{-1}$ and 1782 cm.$^{-1}$. In cyclic materials also, conjugation lowers these values to some extent, so that differentiation between an $\alpha\beta$-unsaturated cyclic anhydride and a saturated open-chain anhydride is not always possible on the basis of the carbonyl absorptions alone. Typical values for unsaturated cyclic products are 1845 cm.$^{-1}$ and 1775 cm.$^{-1}$ for phthalic anhydride,[4] and 1848 cm.$^{-1}$ and 1790 cm.$^{-1}$ for maleic anhydride.[4] Naphthalene-1 : 2-dicarboxylic anhydride and some substituted derivatives [7] absorb at 1848–1845 cm.$^{-1}$ and 1783–1779 cm.$^{-1}$. In the case of cyclic six-membered ring anhydrides condensed to aromatic systems a much smaller separation of the two frequencies (34 cm.$^{-1}$) has been recorded [22] with rather lower frequencies (1770 cm.$^{-1}$, 1736 cm.$^{-1}$) than is usual. Other isolated observations on anhydrides are included in papers by Walker,[24] Koo,[25] Stork and Breslow,[26] and Hochstein *et al.*,[27] the last including 3-methoxy-6-methyl pyromellitic acid anhydride with two anhydride systems attached to the same aromatic ring, which leads to four carbonyl frequencies. α-Fluorine substitution, as is usual with carbonyl frequencies, results in an upward shift of both bands, and perfluoroacetic anhydride absorbs [28] at 1884 cm.$^{-1}$ and 1818 cm.$^{-1}$.

The doubling of the carbonyl frequency in anhydrides and peroxides (see below) presents an interesting puzzle which has not yet been adequately solved. The usual explanation, and perhaps the most likely one, is that the two carbonyl frequencies are coupled together, leading to resonance splitting. However, there are certain difficulties in this explanation, as the lower of the two carbonyl frequencies is, in many cases, at approximately the same frequency as the corresponding ester or lactone and is not appreciably displaced, whilst in the special cases of long-chain alkyl anhydrides dissolved in polyethylene only the low-frequency absorption appears (1757 cm.$^{-1}$), accompanied by weak shoulders at still lower frequencies.[29]

The intensity pattern also varies in an unpredictable way. In most anhydrides the higher-frequency band is the more intense, in contrast to the usual behaviour of peroxides.[15] However, in some

instances, such as phthalic anhydride [4] and some substituted
1 : 2-dicarboxynaphthalene anhydrides,[7] the lower-frequency band
is the stronger. There is accordingly a clear need for further work
on this problem.

In addition to the carbonyl absorptions, anhydrides also show
strong bands due to the C–O–C stretching vibration. These can
usually be identified by their high intensity but, as in the case of
ethers, the frequency range in which they occur is large. Colthup [5]
quotes a range of 1175–1045 cm.$^{-1}$ for this vibration in open-chain
materials, and 1310–1210 cm.$^{-1}$ in cyclic materials in which ring
strain is involved. These bands are useful in giving negative
evidence, and the absence of an anhydride can reasonably be de-
duced if there are no very strong bands in either of these regions.
On the other hand, the occurrence of a band here is not evidence for
the presence of an anhydride, as many other types of compound can
give rise to strong bands in this region.

8.5. PEROXIDES

The CO absorptions of peroxides containing the structures
CO–O–O–CO are very closely similar to those of anhydrides. The
actual bands occur at comparable frequencies in each case, but in the
case of the peroxides the splitting of these two in peroxides is
rarely more than 30 cm.$^{-1}$, whereas the corresponding value for
anhydrides is usually about 60 cm.$^{-1}$.

Most of the data in this field are due to Davison,[15] who examined
a series of acyl, aryl and unsymmetrical peroxides and compared the
frequencies obtained. Seven dialkyl peroxides absorbed between
1820 cm.$^{-1}$ and 1811 cm.$^{-1}$ and between 1796 cm.$^{-1}$ and 1785 cm.$^{-1}$,
with an average distance apart of 25 cm.$^{-1}$. The introduction of
two aryl groups lowers both frequencies, as is to be expected, although
the distance apart remains about the same.

Eleven diaryl peroxides absorbed in the ranges 1805–1780 cm.$^{-1}$
and 1783–1758 cm.$^{-1}$. With unsymmetrical products in which one
aryl and one alkyl group are involved, the mean splitting of the CO
frequencies is greater than normal, due to the effect of the aryl
conjugation on the nearest carbonyl group. However, the effect is
not sufficient to raise the band separation to anything like the level
of anhydrides.

Peracids and esters have also been examined in small numbers,
by Davison [15] and by Swern *et al.*[30], whilst Minkoff [31] reproduces
a few additional spectra without comment on the carbonyl frequencies. These compounds show only a single carbonyl absorption
in the overall range 1790–1740 cm.$^{-1}$. Davison finds a rather wider
frequency spread than do Swern *et al.*, who found a considerable
number of peracids absorbing at 1747–1748 cm.$^{-1}$. This frequency did

not change appreciably on passing from the solid phase into solution, confirming that these acids exist in intramolecularly bonded forms.[32]

8.6. METALLIC CARBONYLS

The spectra of the metallic carbonyls are primarily of interest for the light they throw on the nature of the carbon–oxygen and carbon–metal linkages, and have little practical application. However, the results of the limited amount of work done in this field are given briefly below.

Carbon monoxide absorbs at 2143 cm.$^{-1}$ in the region normally associated with triple-bond vibrations,[8] and the fact that this compound exists at least in part with a triple-bond structure is now fairly generally accepted. However, in the case of metallic carbonyls there is still a considerable measure of disagreement as to whether the X—C≡O or X=C=O structures occur. Nickel carbonyl has been examined by Crawford [9, 10] and shown to absorb at 2039 cm.$^{-1}$ and 2050 cm.$^{-1}$, whilst a series of other carbonyls, including $Fe(CO)_5$, $Fe_3(CO)_{12}$ and $Fe_2(CO)_9$, have been examined by Sheline [11, 12] and by Sheline and Pitzer.[13] Each of these compounds shows a similar pair of bands, while $Fe_3(CO)_{12}$ and $Fe_2(CO)_9$ both show an additional band near 1830 cm.$^{-1}$. The carbonyls of manganese, rhenium [33,34] and chromium [35] show absorption only in the 2000 cm.$^{-1}$ region, but additional absorptions near 1850 cm.$^{-1}$ are shown by dicobalt octacarbonyl and $CO_4(CO)_{12}$.[36,37]

The occurrence of the absorption bands in the triple-bond region is taken by Sheline as strong evidence for the existence in metallic carbonyls of the –C≡O structure, although this is not unequivocal evidence, as many structures of the type X=C=X give characteristic absorption frequencies nearer to the normal triple-bond region than to the double-bond region. However, there is additional evidence available for the –C≡O structure in these materials, as the force constants derived from the frequencies for the metal–carbon linkages [38] correspond to those of metallic alkyls in which the single bond structure is known to exist. The metal–carbon stretching frequencies in iron and nickel carbonyls have been assigned by King and Lippincott [38] at 410 cm.$^{-1}$ and 382 cm.$^{-1}$ respectively.

The occurrence of absorptions near 1830 cm.$^{-1}$ in certain iron and cobalt carbonyls is particularly interesting, as X-ray diffraction data indicate that these exist as bridged ring systems in which some of the carbonyl groups are essentially ketonic, whilst others are attached at the perimeter as –C≡O groupings. From X-ray diffraction data [14] the >C=O angle of $Fe_2(CO)_9$ is given as 87°. This represents a degree of strain even greater than that in a four-membered lactone or lactam structure, and the absorption band at 1828 cm.$^{-1}$ is therefore in about the expected position for so high a degree of strain.

$Fe_3(CO)_{12}$ also absorbs at 1833 cm.$^{-1}$, and has therefore a similar bond angle. In the case of the bridged cobalt carbonyl systems independent evidence for the bridged structure can be obtained from the replacement of the bridging carbonyl groups with acetylene links.[39] Cobalt also forms an interesting hydrocarbonyl derivative $HCo(CO)_4$. This contains no hydroxyl group, and the hydrogen atom is itself bound in a type of bridge system.[37,40]

8.7. BIBLIOGRAPHY

1. Randall, Fowler, Fuson and Dangl, *Infra-red Determination of Organic Structures* (Van Nostrand, 1949).
2. Rasmussen and Brattain, *J. Amer. Chem. Soc.*, 1949, **71**, 1073.
3. Hartwell, Richards and Thompson, *J. Chem. Soc.*, 1948, 1436.
4. Barnes, Gore, Liddel and Van Zandt Williams, *Infra-red Spectroscopy* (Reinhold, 1944).
5. Colthup, *J. Opt. Soc. Amer.*, 1950, **40**, 397.
6. Wasserman and Zimmerman, *J. Amer. Chem. Soc.*, 1950, **72**, 5787.
7. Modest and Szmuszkovicz, *ibid.*, p. 577.
8. Herzberg, *Molecular Spectra and Molecular Structure*, Vol. I. *Diatomic Molecules* (Van Nostrand, 1950), p. 123.
9. Crawford and Cross, *J. Chem. Phys.*, 1938, **6**, 525.
10. Crawford and Horwitz, *ibid.*, 1948, **16**, 147.
11. Sheline, *J. Amer. Chem. Soc.*, 1950, **72**, 5761.
12. Idem, *ibid.*, 1951, **73**, 1615.
13. Sheline and Pitzer, *ibid.*, 1950, **72**, 1107.
14. Powell and Ewens, *J. Chem. Soc.*, 1939, 286.
15. Davison, *ibid.*, 1951, 2456.
16. Husted and Ahlbrecht, *J. Amer. Chem. Soc.*, 1953, **75**, 1605.
17. Haszeldine, *Nature*, 1951, **168**, 1028.
18. Nielsen, Burke, Woltz and Jones, *J. Chem. Phys.*, 1952, **20**, 596.
19. Nakagawa, Ichishima, Kurtani, Miyazawa, Shimanouchi and Mizushima, *ibid.*, 1952, **20**, 1720.
20. Bellamy and Williams, *J. Chem. Soc.*, to be published.
21. Wieblen, *Fluorine Chemistry*, Ed. Simons. Vol. 2 (Academic Press, New York, 1954), p. 449.
22. Brown and Todd, *J. Chem. Soc.*, 1954, 1280.
23. Cooke, *Chem. and Ind.*, 1955, 142.
24. Walker, *J. Amer. Chem. Soc.*, 1953, **75**, 3387, 3390.
25. Koo, *ibid.*, 1953, **75**, 720.
26. Stork and Breslow, *ibid.*, 1953, **75**, 3291.
27. Hochstein, Conover, Regna, Pasternack, Gordon and Woodward, *ibid.*, 1953, **75**, 5455.
28. Fuson, Josien, Jones and Lawson, *J. Chem. Phys.*, 1952, **20**, 1627.
29. Rugg, Smith and Bacon, *J. Polymer. Sci.*, 1954, **13**, 535.
30. Swern, Witnauer, Eddy and Parker, *J. Amer. Chem. Soc.*, 1955, **77**, 5537.
31. Minkoff, *Proc. Roy. Soc.*, 1954, A**224**, 176.
32. Giguere and Olmos, *Can. J. Chem.*, 1952, **30**, 821.
33. Brimm, Lynch and Sensy, *J. Amer. Chem. Soc.*, 1954, **76**, 3831.
34. Cotton, Liehr and Wilkinson, *J. Inorg. Nuclear Chem.*, 1956, **2**, 141.
35. Shufler, Sternberg and Friedel, *J. Amer. Chem. Soc.*, 1956, **78**, 2867.
36. Cable, Nyholm and Sheline, *ibid.*, 1954, **76**, 3373.
37. Friedel, Wender, Shufler and Sternberg, *ibid.*, 1955, **77**, 3951.
38. King and Lippincott, *ibid.*, 1956, **79**, 4192.
39. Greenfield, Sternberg, Friedel, Wotiz, Markby and Wender, *ibid.*, 1956, **78**, 120.
40. Edgell, Magee and Gallup, *ibid.*, 1956, **78**, 4185.
41. Hales, Jones and Kynaston, *J. Chem. Soc.*, 1957, 618.
42. Angell, *Trans. Faraday Soc.*, 1956, **52**, 1178.

CHAPTER 9

Aldehydes and Ketones

9.1. INTRODUCTION AND TABLES

THE infra-red absorption band arising from the C=O stretching vibration has probably been more extensively studied than any other, and a good deal is now known of the factors which influence its frequency and its intensity. In both cases the frequency of the carbonyl absorption is determined almost wholly by the nature of its immediate environment, and the structure of the rest of the molecule

TABLE 9

*† *CHARACTERISTIC FREQUENCIES OF KETONIC CARBONYL VIBRATIONS*

Saturated open-chain ketones . .	$-CH_2-CO-CH_2$	1725–1705 cm.$^{-1}$
$\alpha\beta$ - Unsaturated ketones . .	$-CH=CH-CO-$	1685–1665 cm.$^{-1}$
$\alpha\beta$ - $\alpha'\beta'$ - Unsaturated ketones . .	$-CH=CH-CO-CH=CH-$	1670–1663 cm.$^{-1}$
‡ Aryl ketones . .	Ph–CO–	1700–1680 cm.$^{-1}$
‡ Diaryl ketones .	Ph–CO–Ph	1670–1660 cm.$^{-1}$
α - Halogen - substi - tuted ketones .	$-CBr-CO$ etc.	1745–1725 cm.$^{-1}$
$\alpha\alpha'$-Dihalogen-substi- tuted ketones .	$-CBr-CO-CBr$ etc.	1765–1745 cm.$^{-1}$
α-Diketones . .	$-CO-CO-$	1730–1710 cm.$^{-1}$
β-Diketones (enolic) .	$-CO-CH_2-CO-$	1640–1540 cm.$^{-1}$
$\alpha\beta$ - Unsaturated - β - hydroxy- or amino- ketones . .	$-CO-C=C-$ OH or NH_2	1640–1540 cm.$^{-1}$
1-Keto-2-hydroxy- or amino-, aryl ketones . .	(benzene ring)–CO– OH or NH_2	1655–1635 cm.$^{-1}$ ‡
γ-Diketones . .	$-CO-CH_2-CH_2-CO-$ $-CO-CH_2-O-CO-$	1725–1705 cm.$^{-1}$ 1745–1725 cm.$^{-1}$
Six- and seven-mem- bered-ring ketones	—	1725–1705 cm.$^{-1}$
Five - membered - ring ketones . .	—	1750–1740 cm.$^{-1}$
Four-membered-ring ketones . .	—	Near 1775 cm.$^{-1}$
Quinones . . .	2 CO's in 1 ring 2 CO's in 2 rings	1690–1660 cm.$^{-1}$ 1655–1635 cm.$^{-1}$
Tropolones . .	—	Near 1600 cm.$^{-1}$
Other vibrations .	Alkyl ketones Aryl ketones	1325–1215 cm.$^{-1}$ (s.) 1225–1075 cm.$^{-1}$ (s.)

TABLE 9a

---

*† ALDEHYDES

CO *Vibrations*

Saturated aliphatic aldehydes . .	1740–1720 cm.$^{-1}$
αβ-Unsaturated aldehydes . .	1705–1680 cm.$^{-1}$
αβ-γδ-Unsaturated aldehydes . .	1680–1660 cm.$^{-1}$
‡ Aryl aldehydes	1715–1695 cm.$^{-1}$
αβ-Unsaturated β-hydroxyaldehydes	1670–1645 cm.$^{-1}$

C–H *Stretching Vibration*

All types . . .	2900–2700 cm.$^{-1}$ (w.). Usually two bands with one near 2720 cm.$^{-1}$

C–H *Deformation Vibrations*

All types	975–780 cm.$^{-1}$ (m.)

Other Vibrations

Aliphatic aldehydes . . .	1440–1325 cm.$^{-1}$ (s.)
Aromatic aldehydes . . .	1415–1350 cm.$^{-1}$ (s.), 1320–1260 cm.$^{-1}$ (s.), 1230–1160 cm.$^{-1}$ (s.)

---

* The characteristic shifts indicated are usually additive, so that for example the CO-frequency of an α-bromo-αβ-unsaturated aliphatic ketone will be shifted from the normal by the resultant of the raising of the frequency by the bromine and its lowering by the conjugation.

† All the values quoted refer to dilute solutions. Considerable frequency shifts occur in the condensed phase, in solvents of differing polarity. All carbonyl absorptions are strong.

‡ Modified also by the nature and position of ring substituents.

is of little importance unless it is such as to give rise to chelation or some similar effect. Thus the carbonyl frequency shifts away from the normal position in αβ-unsaturated materials and in carbonyl compounds with strongly electronegative substituents on the α-carbon atom, whilst in cyclic ketones the frequency shift and its direction are related to the degree of strain of the ring. Frequency shifts due to chelation and to mutual interference effects can also be considerable in some cases. However, in each of these cases the extent of the frequency shift to be expected is known, and the new range of frequencies falls within comparatively narrow limits. It is therefore often possible to identify the presence of a carbonyl group, and at the same time obtain a considerable amount of data as to the nature of its environment, by the study of the position and intensity of this one band.

This subject has recently been reviewed by Lecomte,[82] and some very useful tables of typical carbonyl frequencies have been compiled by Jones and Sandorfy [83] and by Jones and Herling.[84] The factors responsible for group frequency shifts have been considered by a number of workers,[83, 85-87] and these are discussed more fully in Chapter 23. In this connection, however, a number of useful relationships have been suggested connecting carbonyl frequency shifts with changes in such physical properties as bond lengths,[89] half-wave potentials,[90] electron densities,[91] the electro-negativities [88] and mesomeric effects of the substituents,[87] and, in selected cases, with reactivities [90, 92] and with the C–O bond dipole.[93]

There is, of course, a certain amount of overlapping between some of these frequency ranges and those arising from other types of carbonyl absorption, but in some cases this difficulty can be resolved by intensity studies. In addition to the major factors causing a frequency shift which have been mentioned above, small shifts also arise from changes of state and from hydrogen bonding effects. These will be discussed in the section on normal simple ketones, but the findings are, of course, equally applicable to other types of ketones.

Aldehydes have been less extensively studied, but there is a considerable body of evidence to show that the frequency shifts caused by environmental changes are closely parallel to those of ketones. The identification of aldehydes can usually be confirmed by a study of the C–H stretching frequency of the aldehydic group. By virtue of the strong influence of the carbonyl oxygen, this C–H frequency is virtually independent of the rest of the molecule, and is therefore highly characteristic.

The ranges of characteristic frequencies of various types of aldehydes and ketones are shown in Tables 9 and 9a.

9.2. C=O STRETCHING VIBRATIONS IN OPEN-CHAIN KETONES

9.2(a). Position. A carbonyl group situated between two methylene groups represents the simplest case of an undisturbed C=O stretching vibration. Weniger [1] was the first to point out in 1910 that aldehydes and ketones always exhibit a strong band near 1680 cm.$^{-1}$ which could be associated with the carbonyl grouping, and Barnes *et al.*[2] in 1944 listed a series of ten ketones for which the carbonyl absorptions fell within the range 1725–1690 cm.$^{-1}$, and noted that conjugation induced a low-frequency shift. Since then studies by many workers have shown that in solution the frequency of the carbonyl absorption of simple ketones of this type always lies within the narrow range 1725–1706 cm.$^{-1}$, provided that no hydrogen bonding or other interference effects occur.

Thus, Thompson and Torkington [3] have found a series of eight such materials to absorb uniformly close to 1710 cm.$^{-1}$, and further data in support of this proposed range have been given by Rasmussen, Tunnicliff and Brattain [4]; Bonino and Scrocco,[5] Cromwell *et al.*,[6] and Josien *et al.*,[90, 94] Jones and his co-workers [7-11, 62, 84] have published an extensive series of papers on the frequencies of carbonyl absorptions in sterols and have been able to show that within this specialised class of compounds further refinements are possible. For example, they have been able to differentiate sterols with a carbonyl group in the side-chain on the C_{20} carbon atom, from others in which the carbonyl group is situated in a six-membered ring. As will be seen later, carbonyl groups in unstrained saturated rings absorb within the same overall frequency range 1720–1706 cm.[-1], but in the case of the sterols all the C_{20} carbonyl materials (over thirty examples) were found to fall within the much narrower range 1710–1706 cm.[-1], whereas the ring carbonyls absorbed at slightly higher frequencies. This group of workers have examined many hundred sterols containing carbonyl groups of one kind or another, and have done much to clarify the types of structures giving rise to frequency shifts. Comparisons of this type, in which only small differences are involved, must be made under conditions identical with the original observation. Changes of solvent, for example, can have a significant effect. Thus certain 3-keto-compounds have been found to absorb at 1719–1715 cm.[-1] in carbon disulphide solution, but at 1702–1705 cm.[-1] in chloroform.[62] This is almost precisely the difference between a C_{20} and C_3 carbonyl absorption. Related studies on carbonyl groups in different situations in the triterpene skeleton have been made by Cole and Thornton.[95]

The above correlations therefore relate only to spectra obtained in non-polar solvents, and departures from them are common when samples are examined in the solid or liquid state. Hartwell, Richards and Thompson [12] carried out a general study of the influence of physical state on a series of carbonyl compounds and found seven normal single ketones to absorb in the range 1747–1714 cm.[-1] in the liquid state. Similarly, in the vapour phase the carbonyl frequencies were found to be appreciably different from those obtained in solution. Acetone, for example, absorbed at 1742 cm.[-1] in the vapour phase, whereas in solution the frequency lay between 1728 cm.[-1] and 1718 cm.[-1], depending on the solvent. Similarly, didecyl ketone absorbed at 1740 cm.[-1] in the vapour state, and between 1724 cm.[-1] and 1717 cm.[-1] in solution. It is probable that some form of dipolar association is occurring in the condensed phase,[100, 101] resulting in a low-frequency shift of the order of 20 cm.[-1]. As far as possible, therefore, frequency measurements on ketones should be carried out in solution.

The minor variations shown by carbonyl frequencies in different solvents have been studied in some detail by several workers.[96-99] The reasons for these effects are not fully understood, but it is probable that some form of dipolar interaction between solvent and solute is involved. In cases in which the solvent is capable of hydrogen bonding to the carbonyl group a small shift results, but the effect is trivial in comparison with that produced by resonance-stabilised interactions. Rasmussen *et al.*,[4] for example, find that the carbonyl absorption of diacetone alcohol occurs at 1712 cm.$^{-1}$ despite the fact that the OH frequencies indicate strong hydrogen bonding, whilst Grove and Willis [13] estimate the influence of hydrogen bonds on certain carbonyl groups as being not greater than 10 cm.$^{-1}$.

9.2(b). The Influence of Olefinic Conjugation. Conjugation of a carbonyl group with a C=C linkage results in a lowering of the frequency by an amount depending on the nature of the double bond. This general finding was known earlier from Raman spectra,[14] and has been fully confirmed in the infra-red.

An aliphatic C=C bond in conjugation with a carbonyl group reduces its frequency by about 40 cm.$^{-1}$ to 1685–1665 cm.$^{-1}$. Thus isophorone absorbs at 1672 cm.$^{-1}$.[4] Turner and Voitle [15] have recently measured the CO frequency of 1-acetyl-2-methyl-Δ^1-*cyclo*-hexene in comparison with the Δ^2 material in which the carbonyl is not conjugated and they obtained values of 1686 cm.$^{-1}$ and 1709 cm.$^{-1}$, respectively. Mecke and Noack [102] have demonstrated corresponding shifts in comparisons between ketones with either $\alpha\beta$ or $\beta\gamma$ double bonds, and further supporting evidence has been given by Fuson *et al.*[90] Heilmann *et al.*[103] have shown that the degree of frequency shift is unaffected by the type of olefinic substitution. In the case of *cis*- and *trans*-isomers, however, the carbonyl frequency of the former is usually 10–20 cm.$^{-1}$ higher. In the sterol series $\alpha\beta$-unsaturated carbonyl groups in both the side chain [7] and in six-membered rings [9] absorb in the same overall range.[84]

Further conjugation by a $\gamma\delta$ double bond has only a small influence in shifting this absorption towards the bottom of the frequency range, and a further three sterols examined by Jones *et al.*[9] which were of this type all absorbed in between 1669 and 1663 cm.$^{-1}$. This is confirmed by Cromwell *et al.*,[6] who note that any additional frequency shift produced in this way is not appreciable. This is not unexpected, as Blout, Fields and Karplus [16] have shown that the frequency of an $\alpha\beta$-unsaturated aldehydic carbonyl group is not lowered by more than a few wave numbers even by long conjugated chains of up to seven double bonds.

Similarly, $\alpha\beta$-$\alpha'\beta'$ conjugation does not have any marked additional effect other than in driving the frequency towards the bottom end of the range quoted. Jones *et al.*[7] report five cases of this type, in which the frequency of $\alpha\beta$-$\alpha'\beta'$-unsaturated carbonyl group occurs in the range 1666–1663 cm.$^{-1}$.

In contrast to this, diaryl ketones give a further frequency shift beyond that given by a single aryl group and absorb in the same overall range as the corresponding olefinic compounds. Conjugation by acetylenic links has been studied in a number of cases,[104-106] and appears to result in frequency shifts of about the same order and direction as with olefines.

These frequency shifts continue to occur to about the same extent in ketones which have already undergone a shift from some other cause. Thus 2-bromo-3-keto-steroids absorb near 1735 cm.$^{-1}$ due to the influence of the halogen, and Δ^1-2-bromo-3-keto-steroids [7] at 1697 cm.$^{-1}$, a fall of 40 cm.$^{-1}$, which is of the same order as in normal $\alpha\beta$-conjugation. Similar effects are also found with carbonyl absorptions the frequency of which has been raised by inclusion in a five-membered ring. It will therefore be appreciated that the correlation given for this type of structure is applicable only when no other factors are present which are also capable of affecting the frequency. However, in general, the individual frequency shifts produced by each factor seems to be additive, so that it is still possible to make a reasonable assessment of the likely position of a carbonyl absorption.

This correlation is not applicable to $\alpha\beta$-unsaturated ketones, aryl or alkyl, which have also a hydroxyl group or an amino-group at the β-carbon atom. In these compounds chelation occurs which has a very big effect on the carbonyl frequencies. These, therefore, represent a special case, and they will be considered separately in the section following that on β-diketones, to which they are closely related.

9.2(c). The Influence of Aryl Conjugation. When an aryl group is directly attached to the carbon atom of a carbonyl group, the frequency shift of the carbonyl is less than that occurring with a full double bond in conjugation, and the absorption band occurs in the range 1700–1680 cm.$^{-1}$. Thompson and Torkington [3] give examples of three such cases, and acetophenone, for example, absorbs at 1686 cm.$^{-1}$, in contrast to isophorone at 1672 cm.$^{-1}$. With two aryl groups directly attached, however, there is a further fall in the frequency to 1670–1660 cm.$^{-1}$. Hunsberger [17] has suggested that the smaller effect of the aromatic ring may be associated with the greater double-bond character of the aliphatic C=C linkages. Benzal acetophenone, which has an aliphatic double bond and an aryl ring in conjugation with the CO group, absorbs at 1667 cm.$^{-1}$. As with other types of ketones, changes of state can influence this frequency considerably, and all the above values relate to dilute solutions. Thus Hartwell, Richards and Thompson [12] record a value of 1707 cm.$^{-1}$ for phenyl methyl ketone in the condensed phase.

It has been noted above that substitution of OH or NH_2 groups on the ring *ortho* to the carbonyl group present a special case of chelation which will be dealt with later. However, other substituents on the ring are also able to affect the frequency to some extent. The substitution of alkyl groups in the *ortho* positions, for example, results in an upward frequency shift due to the reduction in the degree of coplanarity which the carbonyl group can achieve with the ring.[107] Acetomesitylene absorbs at 1701 cm.$^{-1}$ in the liquid state, which is 9 cm.$^{-1}$ higher than the corresponding value for acetophenone. Similar results have been found in some benzocyclanones. In addition, the carbonyl frequencies of substituted acetophenones vary over a considerable range, depending upon the electron attracting or repelling properties of the substituent groups. Soloway and Freiss [18] showed that there was a considerable variation in the solid state, and more detailed solution studies on acetophenones and benzophenones [90,169] have shown that the observed carbonyl frequencies can be correlated directly with the Hammett σ values of the substituents. These σ values are derived from kinetic studies, and are a direct measure of the electron donation or withdrawal produced by the substituent group. In the case of benzophenones these frequency shifts have also been related to the polarographic half-wave potentials,[90] whilst in acetophenones they are also a direct function of the calculated carbonyl bond order.[108]

As in the earlier cases, the influence of an α aryl group will be additive with that of any other structure which is capable of influencing the C=O frequency. Thus Gutsche [19] has given data on a number of tricyclic ketones containing one aromatic ring. With a six-membered ring C=O with an α-aryl group, the frequency was found to be 1695–1686 cm.$^{-1}$, which is the same as with similar open-chain materials. With a five-membered ring C=O, however, the frequency rose to 1715–1706 cm.$^{-1}$, the strain of the five-membered ring being offset to some extent by the aromatic conjugation.

9.2(d). The Influence of *cyclo*Propane Conjugation. It is well known that the high electron density at the centre of the *cyclo*propane ring results in its behaving in a manner similar to a olefinic double bond. Not very many data are available on the effects of *cyclo*propane rings when attached to carbonyl groups, but a small number of alkyl *cyclo*propyl ketones examined by Wiberley and Bunce [109] and by Cromwell,[170] showed lowered carbonyl frequencies in the liquid state (1704–1686 cm.$^{-1}$). Other examples of this effect have been described by Fuson *et al.*,[90,110,111] and these include some interesting examples of *i*-sterols, such as *i*-cholestane-6-one.

The influence of other types of strained ring systems is less certain. " Conjugation " with an epoxy ring in a small number of cases produces no change in the carbonyl frequency, but Cromwell and Hudson [112] have observed a lowering in certain ethyleneimine compounds with an α-carbonyl group. They have discussed the steric requirements for conjugation effects to occur in such systems, but it has been pointed out [90] that the comparison of frequencies obtained in the solid state can be misleading, and further confirmation of their findings is desirable.

9.2(e). The Influence of α-Halogen Groups. It has been known for many years that halogen substitution in the immediate vicinity of a carbonyl group results in a high-frequency shift of the carbonyl absorption. This is particularly marked in the acid chlorides, where a chlorine is directly attached to the carbonyl group, but there is still an appreciable effect when the halogen is situated on the α-carbon atom.

This well-known effect has been extensively investigated in the Raman field.[20] It is applicable to all types of carbonyl absorption, and Hampton[21] and Hartwell, Richards and Thompson[12] have observed a similar effect for esters, which the latter authors attribute to an increase in the double-bond character of the carbonyl group. With ketonic carbonyls this effect has been most extensively studied in steroids by Woodward,[22] Djerassi and Scholz,[23] Dickson and Page,[113] and especially by Jones et al.[9,10,63,83,119] In cyclic systems of this series the individual rings are rigidly locked in chair or boat forms, so they are particularly well suited to the study of the stereochemical effects of different halogen configurations.

In general, they find that substitution of an α-bromo-group results in a rise in the C=O frequency of about 20 cm.$^{-1}$. Thus non-conjugated 3-keto-steroids absorb at 1719–1715 cm.$^{-1}$, whereas 2- or -4-bromo-3-keto-steroids absorb near 1735 cm.$^{-1}$. Similarly, Δ^1-3-keto-steroids absorb at 1684–1680 cm.$^{-1}$ due to the conjugation, and this is raised to 1697 cm.$^{-1}$ in Δ^1-2- or -4-bromo-3-keto-steroids.

This displacement of the CO band is increased by halogen substitution on both sides of the carbonyl group, so that 2 : 4-dibromo-3-ketones absorb near 1760 cm.$^{-1}$, the second frequency increment being the same as the first. However, the substitution of two bromines on the same α-carbon atom has very little more effect than one, and 2-bromocholestanone-3, and 2 : 2-dibromocholestanone-3 both absorb at 1739–1735 cm.$^{-1}$. This is due to the fact that this effect is exerted only if the C–Br link is coplanar with the ketonic group so that the proportion of the polar structure II is increased.[63]

Thus bromine substituted at an α-equatorial position in a ring with a chair configuration will raise the frequency of an adjacent CO group by 20 cm.$^{-1}$. On the other hand, substitution in a polar position does not result in any alteration in the frequency.[63] Similarly a C_{20} carbonyl group has its frequency increased by 20 cm.$^{-1}$ by bromine substitution at C_{21}, but the frequency remains unchanged when bromine is substituted at $C_{17}\alpha$.

Very extensive studies have been carried out by Corey and his co-workers,[115-118] by Sandris and Ourisson [119] and by Inayama [120] on the simpler systems of α-halogenated *cyclo*hexanones and pentanones. Their results are closely parallel to those found in the sterol series and provide a measure of additional support for them, but the relative ease of interconversion of the chair and boat forms in such cases must make their findings less decisive, and indeed they have recently been questioned on the basis of dipole moment studies.[121] In *cyclo*pentanones the principle that carbonyl halogen interaction occurs in equatorial and not in polar configurations has also been used in an attempt to assess the degree of puckering of the *cyclo*pentanone ring.[122] Parallel effects have also been noted in the *cyclo*heptanone series.[25, 70]

The steric specificity of this effect led Jones and Sandorfy [83] and Bellamy and Williams [93, 123] to suggest independently that the mechanism was primarily one of field effects operating across space rather than inductive effects operating along the bonds. In such a case the possibility of rotation about C–C bonds of α-halogen alkyl ketones should lead to the existence of rotational isomers showing two carbonyl frequencies. In the cases of chloroacetone [124] and 1 : 3-dichloroacetone [125] rotational isomerism had already been established, and further work on these, and related materials, and on ω-chloroacetophenones has shown clearly that two carbonyl frequencies are found in mono- and di-halogenated alkyl ketones in the liquid or solution state and that the higher of these is associated with the more polar configuration (I), in which the halogen atom is near in space to the carbonyl oxygen. The lower frequency, which is usually very little different from that of the original ketone, corresponds to form (II) below. As is usual with rotational isomers, the relative intensities of these bands change very considerably with the polarity of the solvent, so that in highly polar solvents or in the liquid itself the lower-frequency band is much reduced

in intensity. On the other hand, only one state exists in the solid, and so only one frequency is observed. In some instances also only one form is stable in the vapour. The steric dependence of this effect affords a ready explanation of the observation that the substitution of a second halogen atom at the same α-carbon does not significantly raise the carbonyl frequency, as only one of these can be close to the oxygen atom. The nature of these effects is discussed further in Chapter 23. The extent of carbonyl-frequency shift produced by either chlorine or bromine is roughly the same, but fluorine has, as would be expected, an increased effect. Thus 1:1:1-trifluoroacetone [176] absorbs at 1780 cm.$^{-1}$, 40 cm.$^{-1}$ higher than acetone in the vapour phase, and Haszeldine reports similar values for α-fluoroketones.[68] Similar stereospecific effects are found also in α-halogenated esters, acid halides, aldehydes and probably in amides.[93]

Very little is known of the influence of other α-substituted polar groups, but α-hydroxyl groups usually lead to a lowering of the carbonyl frequency, presumably as a result of hydrogen bonding.[13,127]

9.3. C=O STRETCHING VIBRATION IN DIKETONES

9.3(a). α-Diketones. Raman studies on α-diketones indicate that there is very little interaction between adjacent carbonyl groups and that any increase in the frequencies produced in this way is not greater than 5–15 cm.$^{-1}$. Kohlrausch and Pongratz [27] found a high-frequency Raman shift of only 5 cm.$^{-1}$ for benzil above acetophenone, whilst Thompson [28] quotes glyoxal as absorbing at 1730 cm.$^{-1}$, as against formaldehyde at 1745 cm.$^{-1}$, and this is a shift in the opposite direction. The single infra-red bands given by benzil and by diacetyl in the carbonyl region are explained by Rasmussen *et al.*[4] by the suggestion that these compounds exist in the *trans* form, so that only one band is active in the infra-red region in each case. The Raman frequencies are only very slightly different, and this affords further evidence that any interaction is slight.

In the steroid field Jones *et al.*[9] have examined a number of 11 : 12-diketones in solution, and find the carbonyl frequencies at 1726 cm.$^{-1}$. This represents only a small frequency rise above the range 1716–1706 cm.$^{-1}$ in which the individual 11- and 12-ketones absorb. Barnes and Pinkney,[69] and Leonard *et al.* [70 127] have also examined numbers of α-diketones in which only very slight interaction effects are observed.

In general, therefore, only a small frequency rise is to be expected for α-diketones, but an exception has been noted for the α-keto ester methyl pyruvate,[29] in which both the ester and ketonic carbonyl absorb at 1748 cm.$^{-1}$, and for pyruvic acid, in which they both absorb at 1745 cm.$^{-1}$. Exceptions may also be expected in some cyclic systems in which it is not possible for the carbonyl groups to take up a *trans* configuration. Interactions, which may be dipolar and similar to those of α-halogenated ketones, can then occur. Alder *et al.*[128] have observed elevated carbonyl frequencies in some such cases.

9.3(b). β-Diketones.

Rasmussen *et al.*[4] have described a chelation effect in certain β-diketones which gives rise to a very considerable shift of the carbonyl frequency. Both acetyl acetone and dibenzoylmethane are known from chemical and Raman evidence to exist largely in the mono-enol form, but neither show any CO absorption band corresponding to a normal conjugated ketone. Instead, a very broad band, estimated to be more than a hundred times as strong as the normal carbonyl vibration, is observed in the range 1639–1538 cm.$^{-1}$. These workers believe this absorption to arise from a carbonyl group which has had its double-bond character reduced by resonance between the forms

$$\begin{array}{ccc} \underset{|}{\text{OH}}\ldots\overset{\|}{\text{O}} & & \underset{\|}{\text{OH}}\ldots\underset{|}{\text{O}^-} \\ \text{R–C=CR'–C–R''} & \text{and} & \text{R–C–CR'=C–R''} \end{array}$$

This resonance effect is described as "conjugate chelation", to differentiate it from a normal hydrogen bonding effect such as that given by diacetone alcohol, and it can arise from any structure

$$\underset{\text{C=C–C}}{\overset{\text{X–H   Y}}{|\qquad\|}}$$

, in which X and Y can act as electron donors or acceptors, and a number of examples have been studied. In all these cases very large changes in the OH region of the spectrum lend support to the view that the bonds produced are very much stronger than normal hydrogen bridges. Similar chelation effects in esters have also been described by Rasmussen and Brattain.[30] The extent of the carbonyl frequency shift has been shown to be a direct function of the double-bond character of the αβ link.[64, 129] In enolic diketones this is normally a full olefinic bond, and frequencies close to 1600 cm.$^{-1}$ are found, but in cases in which the αβ unsaturation is provided by an aromatic system the shifts are somewhat reduced. Other instances of enolic β-diketones showing chelation have been discussed by Shigorin,[130] and Park, Brown and Lacher,[131] who were able to show that disubstitution of the central methylene group prevented enolisation and gave rise to normal carbonyl frequencies. This phenomenon has also been observed in chalkones,[67, 71] in substituted aromatics containing the group –CO–CH$_2$–CO–[69] and even in tetronic acids[143] and in β-triketones in which a single hydrogen atom is retained at the central carbon atom.[72]

Resonance systems of this type can also be produced by dimerisation. 5 : 5-Dimethyl*cyclo*hexane-1 : 3-dione, for example,[4] absorbs at 1700 cm.$^{-1}$ and at 1605 cm.$^{-1}$. The first band is attributed to the normal carbonyl and the second to a conjugated chelated type produced by dimerisation. In this case, however, the intermolecular bonds are broken on dilution in non-polar solvents, and reversion to unchelated frequencies is observed.[129,132] Corresponding changes in the OH stretching region are also found.

9.3(c). αβ-Unsaturated β-Hydroxy Ketones. With aromatic compounds it is possible for one of the ring double bonds to function as the αβ-unsaturated unit, so that 1-keto-2-hydroxy-compounds also show abnormal carbonyl frequencies. Gordy[31] has reported the carbonyl absorption of *ortho*-hydroxyacetophenone at 1639–1613 cm.$^{-1}$, and Hunsberger[17] has examined a number of naphthalene derivatives in which he has found frequency shifts of 50–60 cm.$^{-1}$ due to this effect. α- and β-Acetonaphthone, for example, absorb at 1685 cm.$^{-1}$, corresponding to a normal αβ-α'β'-unsaturated aromatic ketone. However, both 1-hydroxy-2-acetonaphthone and 2-hydroxy-1-acetonaphthone absorb at 1625 cm.$^{-1}$ due to chelation. In this connection it is particularly interesting to note that 3-hydroxy-2-acetonaphthone absorbs at 1657 cm.$^{-1}$. This represents a considerably smaller shift, and it is attributed to the weaker double-bond character of the 2 : 3-double bond due to bond fixation. Cases of aldehydes showing parallel behaviour are also given. In general, the shift produced in this way is not as great as with true β-diketones, but it is nevertheless very well marked. Similar results have been obtained from phenanthrene derivatives which contain an hydroxyl group at C_{10} and a $COOCH_3$ group at C_9.[64] In this case the shift is of the order 75 cm.$^{-1}$ compared with the methylated phenanthryl ester or ketone, which indicates that the 9 : 10-double bond of phenanthrene has rather more olefinic character than the 1 : 2 double bond of naphthalene. The fact that the lowering is not simply due to the increased aryl conjugation is clearly shown by the fact that the CO frequencies of CHO, $COCH_3$ and $COOCH_3$ groups substituted at C_9 in phenanthrene are only 2 cm.$^{-1}$ lower than the corresponding naphthalene derivatives, when no OH groups are present. The study of the frequency shifts of carbonyl groups with an *ortho*-hydroxy substituent has been used by Hunsberger *et al.*[133] to assess the relative double-bond characters of the various cyclic bonds of indane.

One further way in which this phenomenon can arise, is when the carbonyl group is part of a ring system but maintains the αβ-unsaturation and the OH substitution on the β carbon atom. Such cases are 1-hydroxyanthraquinones, anthrones and oxanthrones, which have been extensively studied by Flett[32] and by Hadži and Sheppard,[134] and the hydroxy quinones studied by Josien *et al.*[73]

Both anthraquinone and 2-hydroxyanthraquinone absorb between 1673 cm.$^{-1}$ and 1676 cm.$^{-1}$, whereas 1-hydroxyanthraquinone shows two CO bands at 1680–1675 and 1630–1622, corresponding to free and bonded carbonyl groups. With two hydroxyl groups in each of the β positions only one band is shown at 1639–1623 cm.$^{-1}$, whilst in the extreme case of 1 : 4 : 5 : 8-tetrahydroxyanthraquinone the carbonyl frequency has fallen to 1595 cm.$^{-1}$.

Similarly, 1-hydroxyanthrone shows a fall of 20 cm.$^{-1}$ in the carbonyl frequency and 4-hydroxyanthrone a fall of 10 cm.$^{-1}$. The reason for this second case is not clear, but, as will be seen below, numerous other cases are known in which 4-amino-substitution has a similar effect.

Although conjugate chelation would appear to be a generally satisfactory explanation of these effects, there are still a number of factors which are not fully understood and which require further study. Apart from the anomaly of the influence of 4-substitution in the anthraquinones, Woodward et al.[33] have found marked carbonyl shifts in β diketo-enol ethers in which substitution precludes either normal hydrogen bonding or chelation. They quote work on dimedone methyl ether, on 3- and 4-methoxytoluoquinones and on adducts of these with certain diones, as showing that strong absorption at 1660 cm.$^{-1}$ and 1625 cm.$^{-1}$ is characteristic of such systems. Some interesting anomalies also occur in flavones and flavanones.[71, 115] 5-Hydroxy-flavanone is essentially normal in showing a reduction of the carbonyl frequency of 40 cm.$^{-1}$ due to the formation of a six-membered chelate ring (I). In 5-hydroxyflavone,

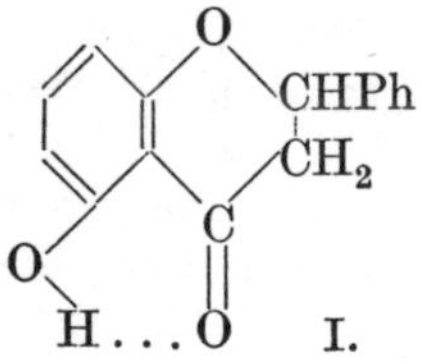

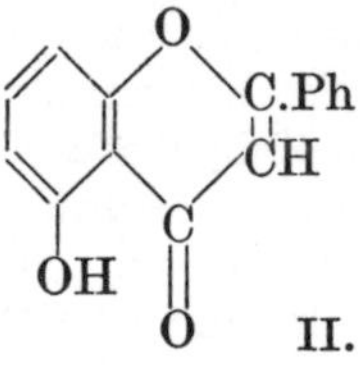

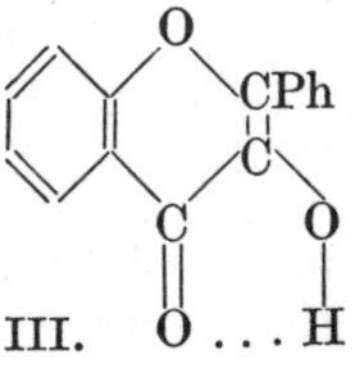

however, no frequency shift occurs despite the similarity of structure (II). On the other hand, substitution of a hydroxy group in the 3 position of flavones does result in a frequency fall of some 30 cm.$^{-1}$ (III), even though the five-ring chelate produced might be expected to be less stable than a six-membered system. In 3 : 5-dihydroxyflavones there is again no frequency shift, which is even more remarkable, but no satisfactory explanation for this is yet available.

9.3(d). αβ-Unsaturated β-Amino Ketones. Compounds of this type would be expected to chelate in the same way as the hydroxy-materials dealt with above. However, it is not clear how far this analogy can be taken with safety, as they can also be regarded as being vinylogs of amides, which in some ways they resemble, so that the nitrogen atom may be exerting an influence on the carbonyl frequencies independently of any chelation effects. This is certainly the case, for example, in the γ-quinolones.

In confirmation of this expectation, Cromwell *et al.*[6, 35] have found carbonyl shifts of the order of 20–80 cm.$^{-1}$ in β-amino-unsaturated ketones, although α-amino $\alpha\beta$-unsaturated ketones are normal. They find, however, that there is still a considerable frequency shift in fully substituted amines, although it is not so great as that occurring with materials which can form hydrogen bonds. They conclude that in these substituted amines a resonance is occurring between the structures

$$\text{R–CO–}\overset{-N-}{\underset{|}{C}}\text{=}\overset{|}{C}\text{–} \rightleftharpoons \text{R–}\overset{O^-}{\underset{|}{C}}\text{=}\overset{-N^+-}{\underset{||}{C}}\text{–C–} \ .$$

Flett[32] has found similar effects with amino-anthraquinones and he has shown that in these structures hydrogen bonding can play only a small part, even with unsubstituted amines. Thus the NH stretching frequency of 1-amino-anthraquinone is not very different from that of 2-naphthylamine, and the NH frequency of 1-methyl-amino-anthraquinone is only 100 cm.$^{-1}$ lower than is usual for secondary amines. This contrasts sharply with the behaviour of the corresponding hydroxy-compounds, in which no OH stretching frequencies are shown in the normal frequency range. Furthermore, Flett finds that 2-amino-anthraquinones show nearly as much movement of the carbonyl absorption as the 1-amino-materials, and he concludes that resonant structures of the types I and II may be involved.

I.   II.

Similar changes occur with 4-amino-substituted materials which could not chelate in the same way as the 1-amino-compounds.

It is evident, therefore, that whilst this system shows many analogies to that of $\alpha\beta$-unsaturated ketones with β-hydroxyl groups, it also has characteristic features of its own, so that considerable caution is required in the interpretation of ketonic carbonyl frequencies of $\alpha\beta$-unsaturated materials with β- or even γ-amino-substitution.

9.3(e). Metallic Chelates of β-Diketones.

β-Diketones chelate readily with a number of metallic atoms in the production of compounds such as the metallic acetylacetonates. These have been studied by Lecomte[36, 66] and by Morgan.[37] Lecomte finds a strong band between 1562 cm.$^{-1}$ and 1550 cm.$^{-1}$ in a series of eleven acetyl acetonates which he attributes to the carbonyl group weakened by resonance between the C–O–M and C=O . . . M links. This is a shift parallel to that given by ionised fatty acids in which a rather similar state of affairs exists.[38, 39] In all these substances there is a second band near 1515 cm.$^{-1}$, which is attributed to the C=C link. These findings have been confirmed by Bellamy and Branch,[136] who have examined a series of copper chelates with different β-diketones and also chelates with the same ligands and different metals. In general, the observed frequencies fall in the ranges 1608–1524 cm.$^{-1}$ and 1390–1309 cm.$^{-1}$, but salicaldehyde shows considerably smaller shifts due to the reduced double-bond character, and in this series the carbonyl frequency is a direct function of the stability of the chelate. Bender and Figueras [137] have also noted a frequency shift attributed to the enolate ion in acetylacetone to which sodium ethoxide is added. The carbonyl frequency then occurs at 1604 cm.$^{-1}$. A very similar value is given by zinc glycinate.[138] The carbonyl frequencies of complexes of ketones with aluminium trichloride or antimony trichloride were also originally assigned [139, 140] near 1550 cm.$^{-1}$ There is indeed a band at this point which has been studied in benzoyl compound by Jewell and Spur.[141] However, its origin is no longer clear as recent studies by Susz *et al.*[177] have suggested that the true carbonyl absorption in such compounds actually rises and that it falls near 2390 cm^{-1}, due to contributions from forms such as $[Ch_3 Co]^+ AlCl_4^-$.

9.3(f). γ- and δ-Diketones and Related Materials. The carbonyl groups of γ- and δ-diketones are too far removed from each other for any direct interaction. However, it should be remembered that lactonisation can occur when one of the carbonyl groups is part of an acid or ester group. The ketonic carbonyl frequency is then lost, and the acid or ester carbonyl frequency is replaced by that of the lactone. In many instances these two forms co-exist, so that all three frequencies can be found. In other cases either form can be produced at will by slight variations in the external conditions. Munday, for example, has suggested that the keto-form of penicillic acid can be wholly converted into the lactone form by grinding in nujol.[40] A number of other cases of lactonisation have been examined by Grove and Willis.[13]

One other case of γ-diketone interaction has been found. This concerns the structure CO–C–O–CO–, in which there appears to be some true interaction between the carbonyl groups, as distinct from the chemical re-arrangements of lactonisation. Jones *et al.*[9, 62] have listed a considerable number of 21-acetoxy-20-keto-steroids in which the C=O frequencies of both the keto and ester carbonyl absorptions are raised by about 20 cm.$^{-1}$ and 10 cm.$^{-1}$, respectively, due to an interaction effect. The origin of this effect is not understood, but it has been observed for both polar and equatorial configurations of the acetoxy group of 12-acetoxy-11-keto steroids.[113] On the other hand, it does not seem to occur in 17-acetoxy-16-keto compounds in which the keto group is part of a five-membered ring system. This has led Bellamy and Williams [142] to suggest that a dipolar mechanism is involved and that the frequency shift is due to the near approach of the two carbonyl oxygen atoms.

9.4. C=O STRETCHING VIBRATIONS IN ALIPHATIC CYCLIC SYSTEMS

9.4(a). Seven-membered Rings. Carbonyl groups included in aliphatic seven-membered rings show normal frequencies very close to those of open-chain materials. This was indicated by the Shell group as a result of their studies on cyclic ketones in connection with the chemistry of penicillin,[41] and has since been confirmed by other workers. Scott and Tarbell [25] quote a value of 1699 cm.$^{-1}$ for *cyclo*heptanone, whilst 2-chloro*cyclo*heptanone absorbs at 1715 cm.$^{-1}$, due to the influence of the halogen atom. Tetrahydrocolchicine, which is believed to be a seven-ring ketone with α-electron-attracting substituents, also absorbs at 1710 cm.$^{-1}$.

The behaviour of this carbonyl absorption under the influence of conjugation etc. is also closely parallel to that of open-chain materials. Gutsche [43] has shown that 2- and 3-phenyl*cyclo*heptanones absorb at 1690 cm.$^{-1}$ in the liquid state, whilst Scott and Tarbell [25] quote 1683 cm.$^{-1}$ for 2 : 3-benzo*cyclo*heptanone and 1661 cm.$^{-1}$ for the doubly conjugated 2 : 6 : 6-trimethyl*cyclo*heptadiene-2 : 4-one.

There is also considerable Raman data on *cyclo*heptanones [44, 45] which confirms that their carbonyl frequencies are essentially the same as those of open-chain ketones.

9.4(b). Six-membered Rings. It is to be expected that the carbonyl frequencies of unstrained six-membered rings will be the same as for open chains, and this is so. Whiffen and Thompson [46] have found a value of 1710 cm.$^{-1}$ for the carbonyl absorption of *cyclo*hexanone, and the general frequency range has been confirmed by the Shell group.[41]

In the steroid field Jones *et al.*[7-11] have examined a very large number of steroids containing carbonyl groups in six-membered and five-membered rings, and they have found all the former to behave exactly like open-chain materials. There are very small but real differences between the carbonyl frequencies of C=O groups situated in the different six-membered sterol rings, but in no case does the frequency fall outside the overall range 1720–1706 cm.$^{-1}$ unless conjugation or other interference effects occur.

All the factors, such as α-halogenation, αβ-conjugation, etc., which influence the frequency of normal carbonyl groups influence the frequencies of six-membered ring carbonyl groups to precisely the same extent. For example, twenty-nine $\alpha\beta$-unsaturated six-membered ring ketones were all found by Jones *et al.*[9] to absorb in the range 1684–1674 cm.$^{-1}$, whilst five materials with $\alpha\beta$-$\alpha'\beta'$-conjugation absorbed in the range 1663–1660 cm.$^{-1}$. References have already been given to the considerable volume of work on α-halogenated *cyclo*hexanones.[115-121]

The introduction of a hetero atom into the ring can, however, give a marked effect. The normal cases of lactones and lactams are considered later in the appropriate chapters, but pyrones and thiapyrones also give abnormal carbonyl frequencies, and their reactivities are widely different from those of normal ketones. Tarbell and Hoffmann [144] have found the carbonyl frequency of 1 : 4-thiapyrone as a very strong band near 1609 cm.$^{-1}$, with a second strong band at 1574 cm.$^{-1}$. That this is due to the greatly increased resonance arising from the lone pair of electrons of the sulphur atom is neatly demonstrated by conversion to the sulphone. This shows a normal carbonyl frequency for an $\alpha\beta$-$\alpha'\beta'$-unsaturated compound (1657 cm.$^{-1}$).

Fusion of additional rings as in bridged cyclic structures usually leads to an increase in ring strain, so that higher carbonyl frequencies than usual result.[171, 172] However, when *cyclo*pentadienones are fused on to aromatic systems Josien and Fuson [145] have noted a systematic fall in the CO frequency as the number of fused rings is increased. This is presumably due to increased resonance in this case.

9.4(c). Five-membered Rings. Hartwell, Richards and Thompson [12] found that *cyclo*pentanone absorbed at 1772 cm.$^{-1}$ in the vapour state, and Whiffen and Thompson [46] found a value of 1740 cm.$^{-1}$ in solution. Since then Jones's work on sterols [9] has fully confirmed this indication that the carbonyl frequencies are raised in five-membered ring systems, as he has, for example, listed twenty-two materials containing this type of carbonyl group, all of which absorb in the range 1749–1745 cm.$^{-1}$ in solution. On this basis he has been able to differentiate carbonyl groups in five- and six-membered rings. Similar frequency increases are shown by five-membered ring lactones, above the values for the corresponding esters.

This strengthening of the C=O bond with increased ring strain appears to be part of a general phenomenon which has been fully discussed from a theoretical point of view [47]; it appears to have its basis in the *sp* hybridisation ratio changes of the carbon σ valency orbitals, with the result that all bonds directly attached to a strained ring become stronger, whereas the bonds of the ring itself become weaker.

Five-membered ring ketones show frequency shifts on conjugation which are of the same order as those of unstrained rings. Thus αβ-unsaturated CO groups in five-membered rings absorb [9,90] at 1716 cm.$^{-1}$, a fall of 38 cm.$^{-1}$, which is the same as for normal αβ-unsaturated ketones. Further conjugation does not, however, have an appreciable effect and tetracyclone [146] absorbs at 1713 cm.$^{-1}$ There are, however, some differences between endo and exo conjugation,[90] and the compounds of the latter type absorb at rather lower frequencies (1690 cm.$^{-1}$). Jones [9] has shown that βγ-unsaturation has no effect on the carbonyl frequency, and two Δ^{14}-17-keto-steroids absorb at 1754 cm.$^{-1}$. α-Halogen substitution raises the carbonyl frequency to a smaller extent than in *cyclo*hexanone, and the degree of shift depends in part on the extent of puckering of the *cyclo*pentanone ring.[119, 122]

9.4(d). Four-membered Rings. Four-membered carbonyl rings have not been extensively investigated except in the special case of β-lactams, but the theoretical background discussed above would indicate a frequency even higher than for five-membered rings. This is supported by the limited data available, as *cyclo*butanone in solution [46] absorbs at 1775 cm.$^{-1}$.

9.4(e). Large Ring Systems. The dependence of the carbonyl frequency upon the ring size has been studied by a number of workers, and recently these have been supplemented by intensity studies. Freiss and Frankenberg [147] showed that very small changes took place in six-, seven- and eight-membered ring systems and that the frequencies did not parallel the carbonyl reactivities. Prelog [148] and Günthard [149, 173] have confirmed this over the series $(CH_2)_n C = O$, $n = 3$ to $n = 14$, and have discussed the variations in frequency, dipole moment and intensity with ring sizes. The frequency levels off at $n = 5$ and shows only minor variations thereafter. The absorption coefficient, however, falls steadily up to about $n = 9$ before reaching a stable value, whilst the half-band width shows an alternative rise and fall as the ring size increases.

Parallel results, in so far as the frequency is concerned, have been obtained in very large ring systems derived from benzoyl *cyclo*anones.[107, 150]

9.4(f). *Trans*-Annular Effects in Large Ring Systems. Abnormal carbonyl frequencies have been found in certain large ring systems which contain a nitrogen atom even though this is well separated from the carbonyl group by (CH_2) groups. This effect is operative only in rings of a certain size and configuration. It was first observed in some alkaloid derivatives which gave rather lower carbonyl frequencies than were expected [151] and has been fully confirmed by extensive studies by Leonard *et al.*[152-158] In a system such as (I) below it is found that the C=O frequency (R=CH$_3$ or C$_2$H$_5$) is near 1665 cm.$^{-1}$ for $n = 3$ or $n = 2$ and 3, but near 1700 cm.$^{-1}$ for values of $n = 2$ or 4 or for ring sizes of 11, 13, 15, 17,

19 or 23.   The origin of this effect becomes clear when the formula of the nine-membered ring system is written as in (II), and it is now reasonably certain that the close proximity of the nitrogen atom

$$R-N\begin{cases}(CH_2)_n-C{\equiv}O\\(CH_2)_n-CHOH\end{cases}$$

I.

II.

with a lone pair of electrons is resulting in a direct effect upon the carbonyl group across intramolecular space.   The proximity of the nitrogen and carbonyl groups in this system is supported by the production of a bridged-ring derivative with perchloric acid, and the fact that the carbonyl frequency rises with increased size of the R group which exerts a steric effect.   These findings are of particular interest from the point of view of the origins of frequency shifts. Further examples of this effect have also been noted by Marion *et al.*[158, 159]

9.5.   C=O STRETCHING VIBRATIONS IN AROMATIC CYCLIC SYSTEMS

9.5(a).   Quinones.   The infra-red spectra of quinones present a number of interesting features.   *p*-Benzoquinone shows two carbonyl frequencies in solution (1669 cm.$^{-1}$ and 1656 cm.$^{-1}$), although the lower-frequency band is appreciably weaker.[91]   Many other quinones in which the quinonoid ring is fused to only one other ring behave similarly, but only one band is shown in compounds such as 9 : 10-anthraquinone, in which the quinonoid ring is central. Similarly, some substituted *p*-benzoquinones show two frequencies and others do not.[160,161]   This behaviour has led to much discussion, which is not yet finally resolved, as to whether the second band represents a C=C mode, is due to interaction or to a carbonyl absorption appearing independently for each of the two C=O groups. However, the main peak in most cases occurs in the expected position for an αβ, α'β'-unsaturated ketone, although its position is modified by the nature and number of attached rings and by the electrical character of any substituents.[174]   The carbonyl frequencies in polycyclic quinones can be related to the calculated electron densities at the carbonyl carbon atoms.[91]

Flett [32] has examined a series of anthraquinones with various substituents on the ring.   Anthraquinone itself absorbs at 1681 cm.$^{-1}$, which is a little above the normal for an αβ-α'β'-diaryl ketone.   Substitution by various groups (apart from hydroxyl and amino-groups which could form chelates) resulted in an overall variation of 1692 cm.$^{-1}$ (1 : 8-dichloroanthraquinone) to 1675 cm.$^{-1}$ (1-methoxy-anthraquinone). Similar small changes were found with anthrones and oxanthrones. Substitution other than of conjugated chains or rings therefore does not appear to affect the carbonyl frequency of multiple-ring quinones appreciably so long as no chelating groups are present, although the nature and number of such rings have an influence on the carbonyl frequency. The extent to which this occurs is not fully predictable. Thus, in solution, benzoquinone absorbs at 1664 cm.$^{-1}$, anthraquinone at 1681 cm.$^{-1}$, anthrone at 1653 cm.$^{-1}$ and oxanthrone at 1676 cm.$^{-1}$. Josien and Fuson [48] find the carbonyl absorption of pyrenequinone at 1639 cm.$^{-1}$, and they suggest that this large shift may be related to the size of the highly conjugated molecule. Chrysenequinone is more normal in absorbing at 1658 cm.$^{-1}$, and in general there is an increase in the carbonyl frequency as the number of rings is increased, provided that the additional rings do not make an angle with that containing the carbonyl group.[73] Polycyclic quinones have also been examined by Hadži and Sheppard.[49] In general, they find that the carbonyl frequencies are lower when two quinonoid carbonyls are in different rings than they are when they are in the same ring. Compounds of the first type [49] absorb in the range 1655–1635 cm.$^{-1}$, and the second type [49, 65] in the range 1680–1660 cm.$^{-1}$. Josien and Fuson [65, 73, 74, 90] have confirmed the latter range. Bergmann and Pinchas [75, 81] have also discussed the spectra of polycyclic quinones.

ortho-Quinones have received less attention, although a number of these have been studied by Josien and Fuson,[90] and by Otting and Staiger.[162] The frequencies do not appear to differ very widely from the *para* compounds, although the latter workers report rather low values in some instances in the solid state. In diphenoquinones the increased resonance leads to lower carbonyl frequencies,[90] and compounds of this type absorb near 1640 cm.$^{-1}$.

9.5(b). Tropolones. In addition to aromatic six-membered rings, a good deal of work has been carried out on the carbonyl frequencies of seven-membered rings, which have three double bonds in a state of resonance.[25, 34, 42, 50, 57, 76–78, 163] A typical compound of this type is tropolone, which absorbs at 1615 cm.$^{-1}$. This could be due in part to hydrogen bonding to the hydroxyl group which is also present in the molecule, but the degree of hydrogen bonding is less than in β-diketones, and the OH stretching vibration occurs at 3100 cm.$^{-1}$. The lowering of the carbonyl frequency must therefore arise from some other cause, and Koch [50] attributes it to the ring size. Just as a five-membered ring results in a strengthening of the C=O bond and a weakening of the C–C bonds of the ring, he believes that a seven-membered aromatic type of ring will show the reverse effect with a weakening of the C=O bond and a strengthening of the ring. Tropolones can also form chelates with copper compounds, and in these the carbonyl frequency shows a further fall to 1590 cm.$^{-1}$ and 1595 cm.$^{-1}$. Somewhat surprisingly the carbonyl frequency is reduced even further than this [114] by the presence of *ortho*-carboxylic acid groups, when the ring carbonyl absorbs at 1580–1570 cm.$^{-1}$.

A number of analogous cases are known in the colchicine series, in which a similar type of structure is believed to exist. Scott and Tarbell [25] have found a strong 1620–1612 cm.$^{-1}$ band in six colchicine derivatives which they attribute to the carbonyl group, and this is confirmed to some extent by the fact that this band vanishes in tetrahydrocolchicine and is replaced by a 1710 cm.$^{-1}$ band which corresponds to the normal carbonyl frequency of a seven-membered saturated ring. A similar band near 1610 cm.$^{-1}$ has been found by Nicholls and Tarbell [42] and by Fabian, Delaroff, Poirier and Legrand [165] in a series of benzotropolones and in colchicines.[79]

9.6. THE INTENSITIES OF CARBONYL ABSORPTIONS

The intensity of the carbonyl absorption renders it particularly suitable for quantitative work, so that there has been a good deal of work carried out on the molecular extinction coefficients of various carbonyl compounds. Hampton and Newell [21] showed that there was considerable variation in the extinction coefficients of ester carbonyl bands which paralleled to some extent the frequency shifts introduced by conjugation etc. Esters of very similar types absorbing at about the same frequencies also showed comparable molecular extinction coefficients. Even so, the overall intensity range of ester carbonyls is very different from that of ketonic carbonyls, so that some sort of rough differentiation is possible on this basis. For example, steroid ketonic carbonyl groups show an intensity range of 350–1350 in terms of the molecular extinction coefficient, whereas esters have the range 350–770. On this basis Marion, Ramsay and Jones [55] have been able to differentiate ester and ketonic carbonyl absorptions in a series of twenty-two alkaloids by making use of the characteristic intensities as well as the characteristic frequencies.

More recently Cross and Rolfe [56] have measured the molecular extinction coefficients of a wide range of carbonyl compounds. Their results confirm that the same factors which influence the frequency of a carbonyl absorption influence also its characteristic intensity, but that within a given class the intensities show the same order of stability as the frequencies. Thus the molecular extinction coefficients for seven dialkyl ketones absorbing between 1724 cm.$^{-1}$ and 1715 cm.$^{-1}$ ranged from 174 to 199. Those of four cyclic six-membered ring ketones absorbing between 1721 cm.$^{-1}$ and 1716 cm.$^{-1}$ ranged from 301 to 334, and those of two diaryl ketones absorbing between 1665 cm.$^{-1}$ and 1664 cm.$^{-1}$ ranged from 404 to 412. At the other end of the scale two saturated aliphatic aldehydes absorbing between 1736 cm.$^{-1}$ and 1735 cm.$^{-1}$ had molecular extinction coefficients of only 130 and 148.

The study of the intensity of carbonyl absorption bands therefore offers an alternative way of characterising carbonyl groups, and when combined with the band position it should allow of ready differentiation between the various types of carbonyl which could give rise to absorption at any given frequency. Indeed, in respect of the differentiation between six-membered rings and open chains the intensity method is more selective and will indicate which type is present, even although the carbonyl frequencies are the same. This has been used with success by Jones *et al.*[10, 83] for the identification of ring and side-chain carbonyl groups in sterols.

This approach to carbonyl characterisation by way of band intensities is a relatively new development, and although it is becoming clear that it will be extremely valuable, it has only been extensively explored in relation to steroid ketones, which have been investigated by Jones, Ramsay, Keir and Dobriner.[10] These workers have used integrated absorption areas rather than molecular extinction coefficients, and in this way they have obtained a more satisfactory unit of intensity. They have examined fifty-five different keto-steroids for carbonyl absorption intensity, and have found an overall variation from 1·2 to 4·1 integrated intensity units. Different types of ketonic carbonyl groups can therefore differ in intensity by as much as a factor of four, and this is in agreement with the earlier studies of Richards and Burton.[58] However, within this range the intensity is constant for any single specific type of carbonyl compound. Thus, the intensity of the carbonyl absorption does not change appreciably with different positions of nuclear substitution in the sterols, but is markedly different from the intensity shown by compounds with the carbonyl group in the side-chain. Similarly, systematic changes in the carbonyl intensities are shown when the carbonyl is conjugated or has a halogen atom on an adjacent methylene group. The variations of molecular extinction coefficient with the type of carbonyl group in steroids have been reviewed by Jones and Sandorfy.[83] Typical values for some of these classes, in terms of their intensity units, are given below to illustrate this point.

α-Bromo-ketones	1·2–1·99
20-Keto-steroids (side-chain CO) . . .	1·79
Saturated ring keto-steroids. . . .	2·16–2·74
αβ-Conjugated keto-steroids (ring) . .	3·4–4·1

These workers have also found that in di- and poly-carbonyl steroids the C=O intensities are additive, so that it becomes possible to determine the number of carbonyl groups present in an unknown, even when the bands overlap, provided the types likely to be present are known.

This approach is therefore clearly an essential adjunct to characterisation by frequency alone, and characterisation by frequency and intensity together should usually lead to an unequivocal identification of a particular type of carbonyl structure. The accurate determination of intensities in solution is an extremely difficult task, and has given rise to much discussion. Nevertheless, for diagnostic purposes the differences are sufficiently gross to permit of considerable errors in measurement without invalidating the conclusions. However, before much extension of this work is possible more basic data must be accumulated on intensity variations with environment. There is, however, every reason to believe that useful diagnostic information will be obtainable in this way, and this is supported by recent studies by Francis,[80] Bürer and Günthard,[149] and Barrow.[24] Barrow's work is particularly interesting in that, over a wide range of carbonyl types, he has been able to establish a relationship between carbonyl intensities and the resonance energy of the system.

9.7. CHARACTERISTIC KETONIC FREQUENCIES OTHER THAN THE C=O STRETCHING ABSORPTION

The presence of the carbonyl group in a molecule often gives rise to the appearance of a medium intensity band in the single bond stretching region, in addition to the carbonyl absorption itself. Hadži and Sheppard [49] have observed a strong band between 1350 cm.$^{-1}$ and 1200 cm.$^{-1}$, for example, in polycyclic quinones which is absent from the corresponding hydrocarbons, and have suggested that it may arise from some motion of the carbonyl group coupled with the rest of the molecule. Certainly most ketones give a band in this region, and Colthup [59] has made the broad classification of aliphatic ketones 1325–1215 cm.$^{-1}$ and aromatic ketones 1225–1075 cm.$^{-1}$. However, this is such a broad range, and so many other vibrations absorb at comparable frequencies that it is of no use for the recognition of ketones as such, although a study of this region for a limited group of very closely related compounds might give useful information in certain cases. These and other possible carbonyl absorptions at low frequencies have been discussed by Jones *et al.*[52, 53]

One other possibility for the identification of ketones is the deformation vibration of the C=O group. The group –CO–CH$_3$ gives rise to three bands associated with this mode,[51] near 600, 500 and 400 cm.$^{-1}$, but considerable alterations follow chain branching if this occurs near to the carbonyl group, so that the bands cannot be identified in methyl *iso*propyl ketone. This correlation is therefore mainly of academic interest.

9.8. THE C=O STRETCHING ABSORPTION IN ALDEHYDES

Very much less information is available for aldehydes than for ketones, but such evidence as there is indicates that the factors influencing frequency shifts are very much the same in both cases. Normal unconjugated alkyl aldehydes show their carbonyl band at a slightly higher frequency than the corresponding ketones, and absorb in the approximate range 1740–1720 cm.$^{-1}$. As with ketones, values for this frequency obtained from vapour-phase studies are notably higher, and Hartwell *et al.*[12], for example, quote 1752 cm.$^{-1}$ for acetaldehyde and 1757 cm.$^{-1}$ for propionaldehyde. Similarly there is little interaction between two adjacent aldehyde groups, and glyoxal absorbs at very much the same frequency as formaldehyde.[28]

Unsaturated aldehydes with the double bond in the αβ-position show a fall in the carbonyl frequency of the same order as occurs with ketones, and absorb in the range 1705–1685 cm.$^{-1}$. The effect of lengthening the conjugated chain has been fully studied by Blout *et al.*[16] In a series of polyene aldehydes they find that the first member, crotonaldehyde, absorbs at 1685 cm.$^{-1}$ in solution, whilst the remainder of the series, which contain from two to seven double bonds in conjugation, absorb between 1677 cm.$^{-1}$ and 1664 cm.$^{-1}$. They conclude, therefore, that the influence of the second γδ conjugated bond is small and that the effect of any additional conjugation is insignificant. Similarly, a series of α-furyl aldehydes containing long polyene chains and a furyl residue did not show any marked frequency shift in the carbonyl absorption after the first member of the series. Similar results have been obtained by Scrocco and Salvetti,[54] who have discussed them from a theoretical point of view.

Aromatic rings in conjugation with the aldehyde groups have a less marked effect on the frequency, and aryl aldehydes absorb in the range 1710–1695 cm.$^{-1}$ in solution. Benzaldehyde absorbs at 1704 cm.$^{-1}$ and α- and β-naphthaldehydes absorb [17] at 1700 cm.$^{-1}$ and 1702 cm.$^{-1}$, respectively. Here also, the substitution of strongly electron attracting or donating groups in the ring has a marked effect on the carbonyl frequency.

α-Halogen substituents have not been widely studied, but there is every reason to expect that field effects will operate, as in the corresponding ketones, to raise the carbonyl frequency. In chloral, for example, the carbonyl absorption is at 1762 cm.$^{-1}$ in solution. In the same way rotational isomerism in mono- and di-α-halogen aldehydes is likely to give rise to two carbonyl frequencies.

Chelation effects in β-hydroxy-αβ-unsaturated aldehydes are also common. Hunsberger [17] has found such effects with 1-hydroxy-2-naphthaldehyde and with 2-hydroxyl-1-naphthaldehyde. The effect is smaller with 3-hydroxy-2-naphthaldehyde, which he attributes to some degree of bond fixation in naphthalene. The methyl ethers of this series show normal carbonyl frequencies and are not chelated. Parallel effects are found in aldehydes of the indane series,[133] and in aldehydes related to camphor.[26] On the other hand, as in α-diketones, no interaction occurs between neighbouring carbonyl groups. Cosgrove *et al*.[166] have studied a number of compounds, such as phenylglyoxal and similar ketoaldehydes, in which both carbonyl frequencies are essentially normal.

The intensities of aldehydic carbonyl absorptions have not been systematically studied, but Cross and Rolfe [56] have given a few values for the extinction coefficients of aldehydes which can be compared with those of the corresponding ketones. Propional and heptanal (1735 cm.[-1] and 1736 cm.[-1]) have a molecular extinction coefficient of 130 and 148 as compared with about 180 for dialkyl ketones. Crotonaldehyde has a value of 234 and benzaldehyde of 324. This latter value is comparable with the value of 310 given by acetophenone. From the limited data available, therefore, it would appear that the intensities of the carbonyl bands of aldehydes will vary with structural features in much the same way as do those of ketones.

In alcoholic solution there is a distinct fall in the intensity of aldehyde carbonyl absorptions, due to the reaction RCHO + ROH $\longrightarrow$ R·CH(OH)OR.

Ashdown and Kletz [60] have reported a number of such cases, and have shown that a corresponding reduction in the intensities of the aldehydic C–H stretching and deformation modes also occurs, whilst a new band appears near 1020–1110 cm.[-1] which may be associated with the C–O– linkage.

9.9. THE C–H STRETCHING ABSORPTION IN ALDEHYDES

The highly characteristic nature of C–H stretching vibrations has already been discussed in an earlier section, and it is to be expected that aldehydes will show a characteristic absorption in this region arising from the valence vibration of the hydrogen atom attached to the carbonyl group. This would be expected to be at a frequency different from that of a CH vibration attached to a methylene group. Although the number of compounds studied is very limited, it is clear that this is the case. Colthup [59] quotes the range 2900–2700 cm.[-1] for this vibration, but Pozefsky and Coggeshall [61] have recently found two bands in this region from a number of aldehydes. These are near 2720 cm.[-1] and 2820 cm.[-1]. The origin of two bands is presumed to be due to the appearance of an overtone or combination band in addition to the fundamental. Which of these is which is, however, not clear. Nevertheless, the appearance of a band near 2720 cm.$^{-1}$ coupled with the appearance of the C=O absorption is good evidence for the presence of the CHO group, and Pinchas [167, 175] has also observed this band in a number of aldehydes. He notes, however, that it is sometimes shifted towards higher frequencies, particularly in *ortho*-substituted benzaldehydes, and suggests that this may be due to hydrogen bonding effects. This would seem to be improbable, as the frequency shift would be expected to occur in the reverse direction. Nevertheless, these papers include a good deal of useful data on the location of the two C–H absorptions in aldehydes.

9.10. OTHER CHARACTERISTIC ALDEHYDE VIBRATIONS

The hydrogen deformation of the CHO group is much more difficult to identify with certainty, but it probably falls near 900 cm.$^{-1}$. As it is not a strong band, it is difficult to identify amongst the many others present in the same region, and it is not therefore especially useful for analysis. Colthup [59] gives the range 975–825 cm.$^{-1}$ for this vibration, which reflects the variability in position, whilst Ashdown and Kletz [60] quote values of 780 cm.$^{-1}$ for *n*-butaldehyde and 795 cm.$^{-1}$ and 905 cm.$^{-1}$ for *iso*butaldehyde.

As in the case of ketones the presence of the carbonyl grouping appears also to activate certain adjacent C–C vibrations, so that additional bands appear in the carbon–carbon stretching region. They are of only moderate intensity, and can never be used to supply more than rather weak confirmatory evidence for the presence of the aldehyde group. Colthup [59] quotes the ranges as follows: Aliphatic aldehydes, 1440–1325 cm.$^{-1}$; aromatic aldehydes, 1415–1350 cm.$^{-1}$, 1320–1260 cm.$^{-1}$ and 1230–1160 cm.$^{-1}$. The limited numbers of aldehydes which we have ourselves examined all show bands in these regions, but we have noted marked shifts within the given ranges for aromatic compounds which differ only in the relative positions of another ring substituent. There are clearly a number of different factors involved in determining these frequencies, and until they are better understood it would be unwise to employ this region to any extent in the identification of aldehydes.

9.11. BIBLIOGRAPHY

1. Weniger, *Phys. Rev.*, 1910, **31**, 388.
2. Barnes, Gore, Liddel and Van Zandt Williams, *Infra-red Spectroscopy* (Reinhold, 1944).
3. Thompson and Torkington, *J. Chem. Soc.*, 1945, 640.
4. Rasmussen, Tunnicliff and Brattain, *J. Amer. Chem. Soc.*, 1949, **71**, 1068.
5. Bonino and Scrocco, *Atti accad. Naz. Lincei*, 1949, **6**, 421.
6. Cromwell, Miller, Johnson, Frank and Wallace, *J. Amer. Chem. Soc.*, 1949, **71**, 3337.

7. Jones, Van Zandt Williams, Whalen and Dobriner, *ibid.*, 1948, **70**, 2024.
8. Jones, Humphries and Dobriner, *ibid.*, 1949, **71**, 241.
9. *Idem, ibid.*, 1950, **72**, 956.
10. Jones, Ramsay, Keir and Dobriner, *ibid.*, 1952, **74**, 80.
11. Jones and Dobriner, *Vitamins and Hormones*, Vol. 7 (N.Y. Academic Press, 1949), p. 294.
12. Hartwell, Richards and Thompson, *J. Chem. Soc.*, 1948, 1436.
13. Grove and Willis, *ibid.*, 1951, 877.
14. Kohlrausch and Pongratz, *Z. Physik. Chem.*, 1934, **B27**, 176.
15. Turner and Voitle, *J. Amer. Chem. Soc.*, 1951, **73**, 1403.
16. Blout, Fields and Karplus, *ibid.*, 1948, **70**, 194.
17. Hunsberger, *ibid.*, 1950, **72**, 5626.
18. Soloway and Friess, *ibid.*, 1951, **73**, 5000.
19. Gutsche, *ibid.*, 1951, **73**, 786.
20. Cheng, *Z. physikal Chem.*, 1934, **B24**, 293.
21. Hampton and Newell, *Analyt. Chem.*, 1949, **21**, 914.
22. Woodward, *J. Amer. Chem. Soc.*, 1941, **63**, 1123.
23. Djerassi and Scholz, *ibid.*, 1948, **70**, 1911.
24. Barrow, *J. Chem. Phys.*, 1953, **21**, 2008.
25. Scott and Tarbell, *J. Amer. Chem. Soc.*, 1950, **72**, 240.
26. Bonino and Mirone, *Gazz.*, 1954, **89**, 1058.
27. Kohlrausch and Pongratz, *Ber.*, 1934, **67**, 976.
28. Thompson, *Trans. Faraday Soc.*, 1940, **36**, 988.
29. Randall, Fowler, Fuson and Dangl, *Infra-red Determination of Organic Structures* (Van Nostrand, 1949).
30. Rasmussen and Brattain, *J. Amer. Chem. Soc.*, 1949, **71**, 1073.
31. Gordy, *J. Chem. Phys.*, 1940, **8**, 516.
32. Flett, *J. Chem. Soc.*, 1948, 1441.
33. Woodward, Stork, Wineman, Nelson and Bothner-By.   To be published. Woodward and Kovach, *J. Amer. Chem. Soc.*, 1950, **72**, 1009.
34. Aulin-Erdtman and Theorell, *Acta Chem. Scand.*, 1950, **4**, 1490.
35. Cromwell, Barker, Wankel, Vanderhorst, Olson and Anglin, *J. Amer. Chem. Soc.*, 1951, **73**, 1044.
36. Lecomte, *Discuss. Faraday Soc.*, 1950, **9**, 125.
37. Morgan, U.S. Atomic Commission, 1949, AECD 12659, 16.
38. Lecomte, *Rev. Optique*, 1949, **28**, 353.
39. Duval, Lecomte and Douville, *Ann. Physique*, 1942, **17**, 5.
40. Munday, *Nature*, 1949, **163**, 443.
41. *The Chemistry of Penicillin* (Princeton University Press, 1949), p. 404.
42. Nicholls and Tarbell, *J. Amer. Chem. Soc.*, 1952, **74**, 4935.
43. Gutsche, *ibid.*, 1949, **71**, 3513.
44. Biguard, *Bull. Soc. Chem.*, 1940, (5), **7**, 894.
45. Godchot and Canquil, *Compt. rend. Acad. Sci. (Paris)*, 1939, **208**, 1065.
46. Whiffen and Thompson, *J. Chem. Soc.*, 1946, 1005.
47. Coulson and Moffitt, *Phil. Mag.*, 1949, **40**, 1.
48. Josien and Fuson, *J. Amer. Chem. Soc.*, 1951, **73**, 478.
49. Hadži and Sheppard, *ibid.*, 5460.
50. Koch, *J. Chem. Soc.*, 1951, 512.
51. Lecomte, Josien and Lascombe, *Bull. Soc. Chim. France*, 1956, 163.
52. Jones, Herling and Katzenellenbogen, *J. Amer. Chem. Soc.*, 1955, **77**, 651.
53. Jones, Nolin and Roberts, *ibid.*, 6331.
54. Scrocco and Salvetti, *Boll. Sci. Fac. Chim. Ind. Bologna*, 1954, **12**, 93.
55. Marion, Ramsay and Jones, *J. Amer. Chem. Soc.*, 1951, **73**, 305.
56. Cross and Rolfe, *Trans. Faraday Soc.*, 1951, **47**, 354.
57. Bartels-Keith and Johnson, *Chem. and Ind.*, 1950, 677.
58. Richards and Burton, *Trans. Faraday Soc.*, 1949, **45**, 874.
59. Colthup, *J. Opt. Soc. Amer.*, 1950, **40**, 379.
60. Ashdown and Kletz, *J. Chem. Soc.*, 1948, 1454.
61. Pozefsky and Coggeshall, *Analyt. Chem.*, 1951, **23**, 1611.
62. Jones, Humphries, Herling and Dobriner, *J. Amer. Chem. Soc.*, 1952, **74**, 2820.
63. Jones, Ramsay, Herling and Dobriner, *ibid.*, 2828.

64. Hunsberger, Ketcham and Gutowsky, *ibid.*, p. 4839.
65. Josien and Fuson, *Compt. rend. Acad. Sci. (Paris)*, 1952, **234**, 1680.
66. Duval, Freymann and Lecomte, *Bull. Soc. Chim. (France)*, 1952, 106.
67. Bellamy, Spicer and Strickland, *J. Chem. Soc.*, 1952, 4653.
68. Haszeldine, *Nature*, 1951, **168**, 1028.
69. Barnes and Pinkney, *J. Amer. Chem. Soc.*, 1953, **75**, 479.
70. Leonard and Robinson *ibid.*, 2143.
71. Hergert and Kurth, *ibid.*, 1622.
72. Birch, *J. Chem. Soc.*, 1951, 3026.
73. Josien, Fuson, Lebas and Gregory, *J. Chem. Phys.*, 1953, **21**, 331.
74. Josien and Fuson, *Bull. Soc. Chim. (France)*, 1952, 389.
75. Bergmann and Pinchas, *Bull. Res. Council Israel*, 1952, **1**, 87.
76. Doering and Knox, *J. Amer. Chem. Soc.*, 1952, **74**, 5683.
77. *Idem*, *ibid.*, 1953, **75**, 297.
78. Doering and Hiskey, *ibid.*, 1952, **74**, 5688.
79. Nicholls and Tarbell, *ibid.*, 1953, **75**, 1104.
80. Francis, *J. Chem. Phys.*, 1951, **19**, 942.
81. Bergmann and Pinchas, *J. Chim. Phys.*, 1952, **49**, 537.
82. Lecomte, *Bull. Soc. Chim. France*, 1955, 1026.
83. Jones and Sandorfy, *Chemical Applications of Spectroscopy* (Interscience, New York), 1956.
84. Jones and Herling, *J. Org. Chem.*, 1954, **19**, 1252.
85. Lord and Miller, *Applied Spectroscopy*, 1956, **10**, 115.
86. Shigorin, *Doklady Akad. Nauk. S.S.R.*, 1954, **96**, 769.
87. Bellamy, *J. Chem. Soc.*, 1955, 4221.
88. Kagarise, *J. Amer. Chem. Soc.*, 1955, **77**, 1377.
89. Margoshes, Fillwalk, Fassel and Rundle, *J. Chem. Phys.*, 1954, **22**, 381.
90. Fuson, Josien and Shelton, *J. Amer. Chem. Soc.*, 1954, **76**, 2526.
91. Josien and Deschamps, *J. Chim. Phys.*, 1955, **52**, 213.
92. Scrocco and Liberti, *Ricerca. Sci.*, 1954, **24**, 1687.
93. Bellamy and Williams, *J. Chem. Soc.*, 1957, in press.
94. Lascombe and Josien, *Bull. Soc. Chim. France*, 1955, 1227.
95. Cole and Thornton, *J. Chem. Soc.*, 1956, 1007.
96. Josien and Lascombe, *J. Chim. Phys.*, 1955, **52**, 162.
97. *Idem*, *Compt. Rend. Acad. Sci. (Paris)*, 1954, **238**, 2414.
98. Bayliss, Cole and Little, *Aust. J. Chem.*, 1955, **8**, 26.
99. Chulanovskii, *Doklady Akad. Nauk. S.S.R.*, 1955, 101, 457.
100. Josien, Lascombe, Lecomte and Mathieu, *Compt. Rend. Acad. Sci. (Paris)*, 1955, **240**, 1982.
101. Wheland, *Resonance in Organic Chemistry* (Wiley, New York, 1955), p. 52.
102. Mecke and Noack, *Angew. Chem.*, 1956, **18**, 150.
103. Heilmann, De Gaudemaris and Arnaud, *Compt. Rend. Acad. Sci. (Paris)*, 1955, **240**, 1995.
104. Franzen, *Chem. Ber.*, 1955, **88**, 717.
105. Theus, Surber, Colombi and Schinz, *Helv. Chim. Acta*, 1955, **38**, 239.
106. Gamboni, Theus and Schinz, *ibid.*, 255.
107. Schubert and Sweeney, *J. Amer. Chem. Soc.*, 1955, **77**, 4172.
108. Tanaka, Nagakura and Kobayashi, *J. Chem. Phys.*, 1956, **24**, 311.
109. Wiberley and Bunce, *Analyt. Chem.*, 1952, **24**, 623.
110. Fuson, Josien and Cary, *J. Amer. Chem. Soc.*, 1951, **73**, 4445.
111. Josien and Fuson, *Bull. Soc. Chim. (France)*, 1952, 389.
112. Cromwell and Hudson, *J. Amer. Chem. Soc.*, 1953, **75**, 872.
113. Dickson and Page, *J. Chem. Soc.*, 1955, 447.
114. Jones, *J. Amer. Chem. Soc.*, 1953, **75**, 4839.
115. Corey, *ibid.*, 1953, **75**, 2301, 3297; 1954, **76**, 175.
116. *Idem*, *Experimentia*, 1953, **9**, 329.
117. Corey and Burke, *J. Amer. Chem. Soc.*, 1955, **77**, 5418.
118. Corey, Topie and Wozniak, *ibid.*, 5415.
119. Sandris and Ourisson, *Bull. Soc. Chim. (France)*, 1956, 958.
120. Inayama, *Pharm. Bull. Japan*, 1956, **4**, 198.
121. Kummler and Huitric, *J. Amer. Chem. Soc.*, 1956, **78**, 3369.
122. Brutcher, Roberts, Barr and Pearson, *ibid.*, 1507.

M

123. Bellamy, Thomas and Williams, *J. Chem. Soc.*, 1956, 3704.
124. Mizushima, Shimanouchi, Miyazawa, Ichishima, Kuratani, Nakagawa and Shido, *J. Chem. Phys.*, 1953, **21**, 815.
125. Daasch and Kagarise, *J. Amer. Chem. Soc.*, 1955, **77**, 6156.
126. Fuson, House and Melby, *J. Amer. Chem. Soc.*, 1953, **75**, 5952.
127. Leonard, Leitenen and Mottus, *ibid.*, 3300.
128. Alder, Schafer, Esser, Kriger and Reubke, *Ann.*, 1955, **593**, 23.
129. Bellamy and Beecher, *J. Chem. Soc.*, 1954, 4487.
130. Shigorin, *Zhur. Fiz. Khim.*, 1954, **28**, 584.
131. Park, Brown and Lacher, *J. Amer. Chem. Soc.*, 1953, **75**, 4753.
132. Eistert and Reiss, *Chem. Ber.*, 1954, **87**, 92.
133. Hunsberger, Lednicer, Gutowsky, Bunker and Tunsoig, *J. Amer. Chem. Soc.*, 1955, **77**, 2466.
134. Hadži and Sheppard, *Trans. Faraday Soc.*, 1954, **50**, 911.
135. Shaw and Simpson, *J. Chem. Soc.*, 1955, 655.
136. Bellamy and Branch, *ibid.*, 1954, 4491.
137. Bender and Figueras, *J. Amer. Chem. Soc.*, 1953, **75**, 6304.
138. Sweeney, Curran and Quagliano, *ibid.*, 1955, **77**, 5508.
139. Susz and Cooke, *Helv. Chim. Acta*, 1954, **37**, 1273.
140. Cooke, Susz and Herschmann, *ibid.*, 1280.
141. Jewell and Spur, *Ohio State Symposium* 1956, cf. *Spectrochim. Acta*, 1956, **8**, 305.
142. Bellamy and Williams, *J. Chem. Soc.*, 1957, 861.
143. Duncanson, *ibid.*, 1953, 1207.
144. Tarbell and Hoffman, *J. Amer. Chem. Soc.*, 1954, **76**, 2451.
145. Josien and Fuson, *J. Phys. Radium*, 1954, **15**, 654.
146. Jones, Sandorfy and Trucker, *ibid.*, 320.
147. Freiss and Frankenberg, *J. Amer. Chem. Soc.*, 1952, **74**, 2679.
148. Prelog, *J. Chem. Soc.*, 1950, 420.
149. Bürer and Günthard, *Helv. Chim. Acta*, 1956, **39**, 356.
150. Schubert, Sweeney and Latourette, *J. Amer. Chem. Soc.*, 1954, **76**, 5462.
151. Anet, Bailey and Robinson, *Chem. and Ind.*, 1953, 944.
152. Leonard, Fox, Oki and Chiavarelli, *J. Amer. Chem. Soc.*, 1954, **76**, 630.
153. Leonard and Oki, *ibid.*, 3463.
154. Leonard, Fox and Oki, *ibid.*, 5708.
155. Leonard, Oki and Chiavarelli, *ibid.*, 1955, **77**, 6234.
156. Leonard, Oki, Brader and Boaz, *ibid.*, 6237.
157. Leonard and Oki, *ibid.*, 6241, 6245.
158. Mottus, Schwarz and Marion, *Can. J. Chem.*, 1953, **31**, 1144.
159. Anet and Marion, *ibid.*, 1954, **32**, 452.
160. Barchewitz, Tatibouet and Souchay, *Compt. Rend. Acad. Sci. (Paris)*, 1953, **236**, 1652.
161. Yates, Ardas and Fieser, *J. Amer. Chem. Soc.*, 1956, **78**, 650.
162. Otting and Staiger, *Chem. Ber.*, 1955, **88**, 828.
163. Kurantani, Tsuboi and Shimanouchi, *Bull. Chem. Soc. Japan*, 1952, **25**, 250.
164. Tarbell, Smith and Boekelheide, *J. Amer. Chem. Soc.*, 1954, **76**, 2470.
165. Fabian, Delaroff, Poirier and Legrand, *Bull. Soc. Chim. France*, 1955, 1455.
166. Cosgrove, Daniels, Whitehead and Goulden, *J. Chem. Soc.*, 1952, 4821.
167. Pinchas, *Analyt. Chem.*, 1955, **27**, 2.
168. Heilmann, Gaudemaris and Arnaud, *Bull. Soc. Chim. France*, 1957, 112, 119.
169. Jones, Forbes and Mueller, *Can. J. Chem.*, 1957, **35**, 504.
170. Mohrbacher and Cromwell, *J. Amer. Chem. Soc.*, 1957, **79**, 401.
171. Allen, Davis, Stewart and Van Allen, *J. Org. Chem.*, 1955, **20**, 306.
172. Allen and Van Allen, *ibid.*, 323.
173. Bürer and Günthard, *Chimica*, 1957, **11**, 96.
174. Josien and Deschamps, *J. Chim. Phys.*, 1957, **54**, 885.
175. Pinchas, *Analyt. Chem.*, 1957, **29**, 334.
176. Whiffen, *private communication.*
177. Susz and Wuhmann, *Helv. Chim. Acta.*, 1957, **40**, 722, 971

CHAPTER 10

Carboxylic Acids

10.1. INTRODUCTION AND TABLE

CARBOXYLIC acids exist normally in dimeric form with very strong hydrogen bridges between the carbonyl and hydroxyl groups of the two molecules. Even in the vapour state, and in dilute solution in certain solvents, this association persists to some extent, so that the carbonyl frequencies as normally measured are considerably modified. For this reason the infra-red spectra of these materials are usually measured in the solid or liquid state. To some extent this masks the differences produced by changes in the structure immediately around the carbonyl group, so that the differentiation of αβ-unsaturated or α-halogen acids is not always as clear cut as is the case with ketones. Nevertheless it is generally true that the same factors which influence the carbonyl frequencies of ketones apply to carboxylic acids, and that the shifts are in the same directions. The carbonyl frequencies of carboxylic acids appear in much the same spectral region as aldehydes and ketones, but the acids can be identified by the study of other regions of the spectrum.

The abnormally strong hydrogen bonding in these acids is an advantage in one way, as the O–H stretching vibrations are so distorted from the normal as to be relatively characteristic, so that observations in this region give a valuable indication of the presence of carboxylic acids.

There are also a number of other regions of the spectra from which some data may be obtained, although with less certainty than from those mentioned above. There are the regions near 1400 cm.$^{-1}$, 1250 cm.$^{-1}$ and 920 cm.$^{-1}$. The origin of these bands is not clear, and each of the first two has been associated by various workers with the single bond C–O– stretching vibration. The third band probably arises from the OH deformation mode.

The study of all of these regions will generally provide a reasonably reliable identification of carboxylic acids, especially if account is taken of the intensity of the carbonyl absorption in relation to that of known acids. In addition, a limited amount of data on the immediate environment of the COOH group may sometimes be obtained from a study of the C=O frequency.

Confirmation of the identification of a carboxylic acid can be readily obtained by the examination of a salt, or of a solution of the acid in water in which ionisation has occurred. Ionisation of the acid results in equilibration of the two oxygen atoms attached to the carbon with the disappearance of the carbonyl absorption, and the appearance of two new bands near 1550 cm.$^{-1}$ and 1400 cm.$^{-1}$ arising from the symmetrical and anti-symmetrical vibrations of the COO$^-$ grouping. The addition of mineral acids to ionised aqueous solutions reduces the ionisation, and the carbonyl absorption reappears.

The identification of carboxylic acids by infra-red methods is therefore usually possible with reasonable certainty and, as will be seen, it is sometimes possible to obtain some additional data on the environment of the carboxyl group.

These correlations are listed in Table 10 and discussed in detail below.

TABLE 10

Carboxylic acid.	OH stretching vibrations (free)	3560–3500 cm.$^{-1}$ (m.)
	OH stretching vibrations (bonded)	2700–2500 cm.$^{-1}$ (w.)
C=O vibrations :		
Saturated aliphatic acids		1725–1700 cm.$^{-1}$ (s.)
α-Halogen-substituted aliphatic acids . .		1740–1720 cm.$^{-1}$ (s.)
αβ-Unsaturated acids		1715–1690 cm.$^{-1}$ (s.)
Aryl acids		1700–1680 cm.$^{-1}$ (s.)
Acids showing internal hydrogen bonding .		1670–1650 cm.$^{-1}$ (s.)
C–O-stretching vibrations or OH deformation		⌠1440–1395 cm.$^{-1}$ (w.)
vibrations		⌡1320–1211 cm.$^{-1}$ (s.)
OH. Deformation (out of plane) . . .		950–900 cm.$^{-1}$ (v.)
$-C\underset{O-}{\overset{O}{\lessgtr}}$		⌠1610–1550 cm.$^{-1}$ (s.)
		⌡1420–1300 cm.$^{-1}$ (s.)
Band progression in solid fatty acids . .		1350–1180 cm.$^{-1}$ (w.)

The special case of amino-acids, in which zwitterion structures arise, will be considered separately in the section dealing with carbon nitrogen compounds.

All correlations relate to samples examined in the solid or liquid state.

10.2. THE OH STRETCHING VIBRATION OF THE CARBOXYL GROUP

The OH stretching frequencies of acids have been extensively studied, as they are anomalous in showing no absorption in the normal free OH or bonded OH regions when examined in the solid state.

A number of aliphatic acids have been studied as vapours at various temperatures [1, 2, 52, 53] and as solutions in carbon tetrachloride and other solvents.[3–8, 54–56] The results of this work show that whereas the OH stretching absorption of the monomers lies near 3550 cm.$^{-1}$, the dimeric form gives rise to a broad absorption region with many sub-maxima, between 3000 cm.$^{-1}$ and 2500 cm.$^{-1}$. Analogous changes occur in the carbonyl region. The dimeric form is not readily broken, and even in relatively dilute solutions in carbon tetrachloride, and in the vapour state at low temperatures, bands due to both the monomer and dimer are shown.

The monomer bands under these conditions have been studied in detail by Goulden,[54] who finds an overall range from 3504 cm.$^{-1}$ in trifluoroacetic acid, the strongest studied, to 3545 cm.$^{-1}$ in *p-N*-dimethylaminobenzoic acid, which was the weakest. This dependance of the frequency upon the acid strength is a reflection of the changing inductive effects of the substituents of the carboxyl group which affects both frequencies and PK_a values. Simple linear relationships therefore connect OH frequencies and PK_a values for the separate series of aliphatic, aromatic and βγ-unsaturated acids. Some measurements were also made of the approximate extinction coefficients of the monomer bands, with the interesting result that they were found to be only about one-fifth of the values of phenols. Measurements on the relative intensities of monomer and dimer bands at various concentrations have also been used to evaluate equilibrium constants.[57]

In the liquid or solid states, however, no monomer bands occur, and Flett [9] and Shreve *et al.*[10] have confirmed that only dimers (or higher polymers) are found. The infra-red spectra of acids are therefore best determined on materials in this state, when complications due to the presence of monomer do not arise; the greater proportion of the data available on carboxylic acid frequencies therefore relates to spectra obtained on solids or liquids.

Under these conditions the examination of a very considerable number of acids has [9, 10, 55, 56, 58, 89, 91] shown that the OH absorptions occur as broad bands with a series of minor peaks over the range 3000–2500 cm.$^{-1}$. In most cases the main peak is near 3000 cm.$^{-1}$ with a main satellite band near 2650 cm.$^{-1}$. Although this is usually overlaid to some extent by the CH absorptions, the pattern is nevertheless highly characteristic. Dimerisation explains the considerable OH shift, but does not account for either the appearance of the satellite bands or for the overall breadth of the absorption. These topics have been discussed by many workers. One suggestion has been that the fundamental OH stretching mode is accompanied by a series of supplementary peaks arising from its interaction with low-frequency vibrations of the dimer involving stretching of the hydrogen bond.[3, 59-63] A closely related suggestion has been elaborated in quantum mechanical terms by Bateuv [61] and Stepanov.[62, 63] An alternative due to Fuson and Josien [58] visualises the broad peaks as arising from a series of hydrogen bonds of different discreet lengths. The whole problem has been fully discussed recently by Bratoz, Hadži and Sheppard,[55, 56] who have pointed out that there are difficulties associated with either of these explanations, particularly in respect of the lack of temperature dependence of the OH bands and in the results of deuteration studies. They go on to point out that all the observable peaks in the range can be satisfactorily identified as combination bands of lower-frequency vibrations involving the COOH group, the intensity being enhanced by Fermi resonance with the OH fundamental. For example, in the H acids the coupled C–O and OH frequencies near 1420 cm.$^{-1}$ and 1300 cm.$^{-1}$ account for the main 2700 cm.$^{-1}$ satellite. This satellite shifts to 2100 cm.$^{-1}$ in the D acids, where it corresponds to a summation of the B_u and A_g bands, which are coincident at 1050 cm.$^{-1}$. Satellite bands which are found at higher frequencies than the fundamental can also be satisfactorily explained as summation bands of one or other of these modes with the carbonyl fundamental. The problem of the great breadth of the main OH absorption is, however, not yet fully resolved.

Pauling [11] has accounted for the increased strength of the hydrogen bonds in fatty acid dimers on the basis of the large contribution of an ionic resonance structure $RC\diagdown_{OH_+ \cdots O_-}^{O^- \cdots HO^+}\diagup CR$, and this enables him to explain the greater shift in the OH frequency of these dimers over that in hydrogen-bonded alcohols in which the OH linkages are not loosened by the influence of the charges.

Since few other compounds absorb in the 2700–2500 cm.$^{-1}$ range, this is a particularly valuable region for the identification of carboxylic acids, although the bands are often weak, so that their detection in acids of high molecular weight may be difficult. The separation of these bands from the CH stretching vibrations is sufficiently great with a rock-salt prism to prevent any possibility of confusion. In general, therefore, absorption between 2700 cm.$^{-1}$ and 2500 cm.$^{-1}$ can be taken as strong evidence for the presence of a dimeric carboxylic acid, but this identification should never be made without taking account also of other regions of the spectrum, and especially of the carbonyl region. Absorption between 2700 cm.$^{-1}$ and 2500 cm.$^{-1}$ is indicative only of a strongly hydrogen-bonded OH group, and although bonds of this strength are unusual in compounds other than carboxylic acids, they do occur in a limited number of cases. Also it is possible in exceptional cases for the OH bands of intramolecularly bonded acids to occur at still lower frequencies. In potassium hydrogen maleate,[64] for example, the hydrogen atom is probably symmetrically placed between the two oxygen atoms. This compound has no strong bands which show any alteration on deuteration at frequencies above 1600 cm.$^{-1}$

Examples of other materials showing hydrogen bonds of comparable strength are found in the enolic β-diketones and similar materials [12] in which a strong chelate ring occurs. Similarly neither *o*-hydroxydiphenylsulphoxide nor α-nitroso-β-naphthol show any normal OH vibration, and this has been attributed to chelation.[13] We have also found that sulphonic acids and the organo-phosphoric acids show OH absorption in this region.[14] The carbonyl absorption of β-diketones is, however, shifted to considerably lower frequencies than ever occur with carboxylic acids, so that they are not a real complication, provided account is taken of the C=O vibrations as well as of this O–H vibration. Also chelated hydroxyl groups of this type do not normally show the band structure which is so typical of carboxylic acids.

These bands are unlikely to be confused with SH or SiH absorptions, which also appear in this region,[38] as the latter are characteristically sharp and well defined, in contrast to the broad, rather diffuse bands given by acids.

As a final check deuterium exchange can be employed when the OH band shows the expected degree of shift.[39, 55, 56] The OH stretching band of CD_3COOH is, for example, at 3125 cm.[-1] and the OD band of CD_3COOD at 2299 cm.[-1].

These characteristic OH bands can also be used to give information on the crystal structure of solid acids. Kuratani [15] has studied the infra-red dichroism of cinnamic, adipic and other acids crystallising as needles, over the wave-lengths 3570–2850 cm.[-1], and found that the absorption is stronger when the electric vector of the polarised radiation is parallel to the long axis of the needles, from which it follows that the O–H . . . O bonds are parallel to this axis.

10.3. THE C=O STRETCHING VIBRATION

10.3(a). The Influence of Physical State. The physical state in which carboxylic acids are examined has a direct effect on the carbonyl frequency. As has been mentioned, a number of workers have examined some of the simpler acids in the vapour phase,[1, 2] when, depending on the temperature, varying proportions of the monomeric and dimeric forms occur. Hartwell, Richards and Thompson [16] have examined a number of acids in this way and compared their results with those obtained from the liquids. In a typical case they found acetic acid at 20° C. as a vapour absorbed at 1735 cm.[-1] and 1785 cm.[-1], whilst at 60° C. it absorbed at 1735 cm.[-1] and 1790 cm.[-1], but then showed a considerably greater intensity in the higher frequency band, indicating a greater proportion of monomer. In the liquid state it absorbed at 1717 cm.[-1].

In dilute solutions in non-polar solvents, such as carbon tetrachloride, two carbonyl frequencies corresponding to the monomer and dimer are found. Studies on the intensity changes in these bands on dilution can be carried out in the same way as on the OH frequencies to determine equilibrium coefficients.[65] The monomer frequency measured in this way is usually a little lower than that obtained from the vapour. In trifluoroacetic acid, for example, the monomer in the vapour absorbs at 1820 cm.$^{-1}$ and falls to 1810 cm.$^{-1}$ in carbon tetrachloride.[66] With unflorinated alkyl acids the monomer frequency in carbon tetrachloride has an average value [17] of 1760 cm.$^{-1}$

In certain solvents, such as dioxane, only a single carbonyl frequency is shown. This was originally attributed to the existence of the acids as free monomers in this state.[9] However, the frequencies found in this solvent and in ether are consistently some 20 cm.$^{-1}$ below the monomer values in carbon tetrachloride,[67] and it therefore seems likely that strong solvent interaction effects are taking place. This has been confirmed by Fraenkel *et al.*,[68] who demonstrated a gradation of the frequency with the polarity of the solvent. In compounds such as pyridine, 1 : 1 and 1 : 2 complexes are formed leading to the occurrence of the monomeric carbonyl frequency accompanied by the carboxylate ion absorptions.[68]

However, the main bulk of data on the carbonyl frequencies of these acids has been obtained from the examination of the solid or liquid phases or of solutions of sufficient concentration for hydrogen bonding to persist. It is therefore the frequencies for the dimeric materials which are of value for correlation purposes. In the spectra of such materials, changes of crystal form which influence the degree of hydrogen bonding can result in marked differences in the low-frequency region, but the carbonyl frequencies are not appreciably altered. A typical case is that of the cinnamic acids. Lecomte and Guy [18] quote values of 1702 cm.$^{-1}$, 1707 cm.$^{-1}$ and 1709 cm.$^{-1}$ for the C$=$O frequency of three different forms of *cis*-cinnamic acid, and 1699 cm.$^{-1}$ for each of two forms of *trans*-cinnamic acid.

However, changes of as much of 30 cm.$^{-1}$ towards higher frequencies occur on melting due to the disruption of the strong hydrogen bonds of the crystal and their replacement by looser forms of association,[67, 89] and marked changes also occur in some instances of acids examined in pressed discs due to interaction with the alkali halide.[78]

The influence of structural changes in the immediate vicinity of the carboxyl group on the carbonyl frequencies has not been as extensively studied as in the case of ketones, and the results are not so clear cut, but nevertheless a certain amount of data is available. Barnes *et al.*[19] have given values for the C$=$O frequencies of a number of acids, and Lecomte [20] has discussed the relationship between the carbonyl frequency and its surrounding structure, on the basis of the examination of a limited number of materials. This latter aspect has been further studied by Gillette,[21] and especially by Flett,[9, 22] whilst data on individual groups of carboxylic acids have been given by a number of other workers.[23-25] The general findings are discussed below.

10.3(b). Saturated Aliphatic Acids. Saturated monobasic aliphatic acids which do not carry electron-attracting substituents absorb between 1725 cm.$^{-1}$ and 1705 cm.$^{-1}$ when examined in the solid or liquid state. This is in line with Flett's findings on some sixty carboxylic acids,[9] and agrees with the findings of the other workers mentioned and of ourselves. Sinclair, McKay and Jones [42] find the carbonyl absorption of saturated fatty acids (C_{14}–C_{21}) in solution to be 1708 cm.$^{-1}$, and the same value is obtained for unsaturated fatty acids other than $\alpha\beta$-unsaturated acids.[43] Freeman [44] quotes 1712 ± 6 cm.$^{-1}$ for this frequency in twenty-seven branched chain acids he has examined in solution. In the solid state these frequencies are a few cm.$^{-1}$ lower. Confirmatory results have been obtained by subsequent workers.[56, 67, 89, 90] Thioacetic acid [27] absorbs a little below this range at 1696 cm.$^{-1}$.

10.3(c). The Influence of α-Halogen Groups. As in the case of ketones, the substitution of α-halogen or cyano-groupings results in the carbonyl absorption shifting towards higher frequencies. α-Chloropropionic acid, for example, absorbs at 1730 cm.$^{-1}$, as against 1710 cm.$^{-1}$ for β-chloropropionic acid.[9] In 2-bromostearic acid the shift is smaller and the band is at 1716 cm.$^{-1}$, as against 1708 cm.$^{-1}$ for stearic acid.[43] The monomeric forms show a similar although smaller shift in solution. Similarly, in the vapour phase chloroacetic acid absorbs at 1794 cm.$^{-1}$, whilst acetic acid absorbs at 1785 cm.$^{-1}$. Gillette [21] observed a similar correlation for the methyl and halogen acetic acids, and found a progressive frequency rise in the carbonyl absorption through the series mono ⟶ trichloroacetic acid. Work on other types of carbonyl frequencies has indicated, however, that the shift which follows the introduction of the second and third α-halogen atoms is appreciably smaller than with the first,[70] and a similar effect is to be expected in acids. Rotational isomerism is also to be expected in mono- and di-α-halogen acids, in line with the similar effects found in ketones and in esters,[71] leading to multiple carbonyl frequencies. In this connection it is interesting to note that the liquid state spectrum of dichloroacetic acid illustrated by Bratoz *et al.*[56] shows two carbonyl bands despite the absence of any monomer as indicated by free OH bands. However, isomerism of this type would be more difficult to detect in acids, due to the complications of monomer/dimer equilibria in solution and to the fact that the acids themselves are highly polar, so the concentrations of less polar configurations may be small in the liquid state. In general, the shift found for α-halogen substitution is of the order of 20 cm.$^{-1}$, so that we would suggest the range 1740–1720 cm.$^{-1}$ for liquid and solid acids of this type as a general approximation. Acids with α-fluorine substitution are, however, likely to absorb at even higher frequencies between 1790 cm. and 1770 cm.$^{-1}$.[46, 47, 66, 72]

10.3(d). The Influence of Conjugation. In ketones αβ-unsaturation has a stronger influence on the C=O bond length than aryl substitution, and this has been attributed to the weaker double-bond character of the double bonds of the ring. With acids, however, this difference is sometimes reversed and aryl substitution then appears to have a greater effect than αβ-unsaturation.

In the series of αβ-unsaturated acids examined by Flett [9] the C=O frequency lies in the general range 1710–1700 cm.$^{-1}$, except for cinnamic acid, where the aryl group provides γδ-conjugation and the frequency falls below 1700 cm.$^{-1}$. Otherwise the effect is a slight shifting of the frequency towards the lower end of the normal frequency range. With aryl substitution, on the other hand, the C=O frequency lies between 1700 cm.$^{-1}$ and 1680 cm.$^{-1}$ and only rises above this value in substituted benzoic acids which have heavily electron-attracting nitro-groups.

However, as many of the alkyl materials were liquids, this apparent difference could be due, in part at least, to alterations in the phase rather than to some fundamental difference. Further, many cases are known of αβ-unsaturated acids which absorb in the range 1680–1700 cm.$^{-1}$. Freeman [48] has quoted a range of 1700–1692 cm.$^{-1}$ for one such series, and corresponding values have been obtained by other workers.[73, 74] It is therefore clear that both aryl and olefinic conjugation cause a frequency fall, but it is doubtful if the two can be distinguished in this way.

Extension of the conjugation beyond the αβ-position does not appreciably affect the carbonyl frequency in olefinic compounds. With acetylenic conjugation a slightly greater shift, often to below 1680 cm.$^{-1}$, is observed, but in this case extension of the conjugation to three or more acetylenic bonds causes a small frequency rise above the minimum value. This has been discussed in relation to the acidities of these compounds by Allan *et al.*[74]

10.3(e). The Influence of Chelation. Some acids are capable of forming internal hydrogen bonds, and the carbonyl frequency is reduced accordingly. Of nine acids recorded by Flett [9] as having carbonyl frequencies below 1680 cm.$^{-1}$, seven are of this type. The simplest case is that of fumaric acid, which absorbs at 1680 cm.$^{-1}$, in contrast to the normal value of 1705 cm.$^{-1}$ of maleic acid.[9] *ortho*-Hydroxybenzoic acids [8] can chelate in a similar way to the *ortho*-hydroxyacetophenones and *ortho*-hydroxybenzaldehydes, with a correspondingly large shift of the carbonyl frequency. Salicylic acid absorbs at 1655 cm.[-1], and this is comparable with the shifts experienced with the β-hydroxy-αβ-unsaturated ketones. β-Amino-αβ-unsaturated acids also show this effect, as is to be expected. 3-Amino-2-naphthoic acid absorbs at 1665 cm.[-1]. Flett,[9] and Musso[75] quote a number of other similar cases. We have also observed a case of this type with N-phenylanthranilic acid, in which the carbonyl absorption occurs at 1660 cm.[-1].

In the consideration of carbonyl frequencies of hydroxy-, amino- or ketonic acids, allowances must also be made for the possibility that ring closure has occurred with the formation of a lactone, lactam or lactol. The characteristic carbonyl frequency of the carboxylic acid then disappears. Penicillic acid[28] has been shown to be such a case, and it exists as a free acid only under certain limited physical conditions. Similarly, acetophenone *ortho*-carboxylic acid absorbs at 1732 cm.[-1]. This corresponds to a five-membered ring lactol frequency rather than that of an aryl acid. *ortho*-Formylbenzoic acid (1738 cm.[-1]) also exists as the lactol rather than as the free acid,[17] and numerous other cases are known. In some cases, such as benzil-*ortho*-carboxylic acid, both forms are known. The keto-form has absorptions at 1698 cm.[-1] and 1683 cm.[-1], corresponding to the aryl ketone and to the acid, whilst the lactol form absorbs at 1692 cm.[-1] and 1745 cm.[-1], corresponding to the aryl ketone and the five-membered ring lactol carbonyl absorption.

10.3(f). Dicarboxylic Acids. Flett[9] and Schonmann[26] have studied a number of dicarboxylic acids. Oxalic acid absorbs very strongly between 1710 cm.[-1] and 1690 cm.[-1], but in malonic acid two frequencies are shown at 1740 cm.[-1] and 1710 cm.[-1]. This inter-action effect is reduced in succinic acid, which shows only a weak band at 1780 cm.[-1], and its main carbonyl absorption at 1700 cm.[-1]. Higher members, such as adipic acid, show only a single band near 1700 cm.[-1] and this has been confirmed by Corish and Davison[67] for other longer-chain fatty acids. Phthalic acid is also normal in showing a single CO band at 1695 cm.[-1], whilst terephthalic acid absorbs at 1690 cm.[-1]. Dicarboxylic acids can therefore be regarded as being essentially normal in their carbonyl frequencies, provided the first members of the series are ignored.

Schotte and Rosenberg[76, 77] have also studied dicarboxylic acids, particularly in relation to the stereoisomerism of αα'-di-substituted compounds. Minor differences occur between the carbonyl frequencies of optically active and racemic forms— probably due to differences in crystal structure—and these enable the two to be differentiated.

10.3(g). The Intensity. Carbonyl absorptions from carboxylic acids are generally more intense than those of ketones. Cross and

Rolfe [29] quote values for the molecular extinction coefficient of 502–564 for oleic, stearic and palmitic acids as against an average value of 200 for normal saturated ketones. These determinations were made in solution in hexane, but it is clear from the values quoted for the carbonyl frequencies that the concentrations were sufficient to ensure that the acids remained in the dimeric form.

Flett [9] has also made a number of determinations of the intensities of these bands, and his results indicate a considerable degree of variation from one class of compound to another. It is probable, therefore, that the situation is similar to that with the ketones, in which each class of compound has its own frequency range and characteristic absorption intensity, but a good deal of work will be necessary before it can be established whether or not this is the case, and the absolute intensities can be used for identification purposes. Nevertheless, in the examination of an unknown compound in which a carbonyl group is postulated, the carbonyl intensity could reasonably be expected to be closely similar to that of the nearest known carboxylic acid with a similar structure around the COOH group.

The characteristic intensity of the carboxyl carbonyl group of oxidised cellulose has been used by Forziati, Rowen and Plyler [30] in the estimation of carboxyl groups in cellulose, but in this case oxidised samples of known carboxyl content were available as standards.

10.4. OTHER CHARACTERISTIC CARBOXYLIC ACID VIBRATIONS

10.4(a). Near 1400 cm.$^{-1}$. A band near 1400 cm.$^{-1}$. has been observed by Flett [9] in forty-five out of sixty carboxylic acid spectra. It is therefore less generally useful than the two correlations already discussed. The band is intrinsically weak, and this may account for its absence in some cases. We have also noted the appearance of this band in a further ten acids not listed by Flett. The overall range appears to be between 1440 cm.$^{-1}$ and 1395 cm.$^{-1}$, and such data as are available suggest that structural changes affect this band in the opposite direction to changes in the C=O frequency. Thus of six acids listed by Flett [9] as absorbing above 1430 cm.$^{-1}$, four are unsaturated or chelated, whilst of eight below 1415 cm.$^{-1}$, four have strongly electron-attracting substituents. Hadži and Sheppard [49] have also found a band within the same frequency range in fifteen carboxylic acids. These include diacetylene carboxylic acid and trichloracetic acid, and as neither the C≡C nor the CCl_3 structures could possibly have any fundamental near 1400 cm.$^{-1}$, this clearly identifies this absorption with the carboxyl group. In an attempt to establish the type of vibration involved, they have compared their spectra with those of all the corresponding deutero derivatives, and been able to show that this absorption, together with another near 1300 cm.$^{-1}$, arises from a C–O vibration coupled with an OH in-plane deformation vibration to such an extent that neither can be specifically assigned in the original acids. In the deuterated materials the interaction is much reduced and the individual absorptions can be more clearly seen. In dicarboxylic acids the corresponding band at 1435 cm.$^{-1}$ has been identified specifically with a vibration of the dimerised carboxyl group as it disappears in the molten acids,[67, 89] in which the hydrogen bonds are more randomly distributed. Possibly, the absence of this band reported in some acids is due to this cause. Francis [50] and Sinclair *et al.*[42, 43] have recently pointed out that saturated fatty acids and esters which have a methylene group adjacent to the carbonyl group, all absorb at 1410 cm.$^{-1}$, whereas no comparable band is found in αβ-unsaturated acids. They associated it therefore with a CH_2 deformation which has been modified by the adjacent CO group. This absorption is of course quite distinct from the carboxyl group absorption discussed above, and it occurs along with it in acids containing the group –CH_2COOH.[49, 67] This absorption is more intense than a normal CH_2 group, and in short-chain fatty acids it is useful in the recognition of α-chain branching. For acids of chain length less than C_{14}, the 1410 cm.$^{-1}$ band is stronger than the 1475 cm.$^{-1}$ methylene deformation absorption unless there is α-branching, when the CH_2COOH group is lost.

10.4(b). Near 1250 cm.$^{-1}$. A band near 1250 cm.$^{-1}$ appears in all the acids examined by Flett,[9] and Shreve *et al.*[10] have noted the presence of a doublet between 1280 cm.$^{-1}$ and 1250 cm.$^{-1}$ in a large number of long-chain fatty acids which they believe may be characteristic of such compounds. These results indicate that the position of this band varies widely from compound to compound, and that it can occur anywhere within the range 1320–1210 cm.$^{-1}$. It has usually been identified as being the strongest band in the spectrum between 1600 cm.$^{-1}$ and 700 cm.$^{-1}$ Thus Flett [9] lists eighteen acids as absorbing above 1280 cm.$^{-1}$, of which fourteen are aromatic and two more are unsaturated, whilst of ten absorbing below 1240 cm.$^{-1}$ six are substituted acetic acids and others, such as α-chloropropionic acid, contain electronegative substituents.

On the other hand, other workers studying saturated fatty acids and those in which any double bonds are well removed from the carboxyl group [42, 43, 44] all find this absorption very close to 1290 cm.$^{-1}$, and Hadži and Sheppard [49] quote the relatively narrow range of 1300 ± 15 cm.$^{-1}$ for this absorption in all the acids which they have examined. Freeman [44] has pointed out that in the fatty acids series this band is invariably accompanied by a second absorption at lower frequency. These two bands are remarkably consistent in their frequencies (1285 $\pm$ 5 cm.$^{-1}$ and 1235 $\pm$ 5 cm.$^{-1}$) and in their relative intensity patterns, so long as there is no chain branching nearer to the carboxyl than the δ carbon atom. With a nearer approach of the point of branching to the carboxyl group a more pronounced disturbance of these frequencies and of their intensity patterns is observed, so that in some cases the intensity of the second band is greater than that of the first. Guertin *et al.*[79] and Corish and Chapman [89] have extended this work to cover lower members of the fatty acid series with essentially similar results. This observation would appear to offer a reasonable explanation of the considerable disparity between the wide frequency ranges quoted by one group of workers and the narrow ranges given by others. It seems likely that all acids will show an absorption in the region of 1300 cm.$^{-1}$, but that in many cases it will be accompanied by a second band at lower frequencies which may be of greater intensity. The identification of the carboxyl groups with the strongest band in this region will therefore lead to a much wider frequency range than the direct search for bands close to 1300 cm.$^{-1}$. The higher frequency absorption is almost certainly derived from the coupled C–O and OH in-plane deformation modes,[49] but the origin of the second is less certain. Shreve *et al.*[10] associate their band near 1200 cm.$^{-1}$ with the C–O valence and point out that esters and similar materials also absorb near this frequency.[31] Kuratani [51] also assigns a band in trichloracetic acid to this cause on the grounds that the absorption persists in the acetate ion, but in view of the findings of Hadži and Sheppard on interaction effects these suggestions must be treated with caution until further information is available.

O'Connor *et al.*[24] also report a band in the range 1170–1150 cm.$^{-1}$ in the spectra of a large number of even-numbered carbon atom fatty acids which is not present in the corresponding ester spectra. The lower frequency suggests, however, that this is probably due to some other cause and that it is not directly related to the bands under discussion.

10.4(c). The OH Deformation Vibration of the Carboxyl Group. Davies and Sutherland [3] have suggested that in the lower fatty acids the out-of-plane deformation mode of the hydroxyl of the carboxyl group may arise near 935 cm.$^{-1}$. Shreve *et al.*[10] have found strong absorption between 939 cm.$^{-1}$ and 926 cm.$^{-1}$ in the spectra of a series of long-chain fatty acids which vanishes on esterification, and which they suggest may be tentatively assigned to this cause.

Flett [9] has observed this band in forty-three out of sixty acids, but is unable to find any precise connection between its appearance or disappearance, with its frequency or structural factors. This band is of widely varying intensity and is very weak in some instances.

This may account for its absence in certain cases. A band between 953 cm.$^{-1}$ and 844 cm.$^{-1}$ in the even-numbered C_6–C_{18} acids is also reported by O'Connor *et al.*[24] and by Sinclair *et al.*,[42] which is absent from the corresponding ethyl and methyl esters. Hadži and Sheppard find a band at 935 $\pm$ 15 cm.$^{-1}$ in all the fifteen acids they have examined. They have assigned it to the OH out-of-plane deformation mode and have shown that it exhibits the expected shift to 675 $\pm$ 15 cm.$^{-1}$ on deuteration.

It would therefore seem likely that this band is a reasonably characteristic one for carboxylic acids and that it arises from the OH deformation. As such, it would be expected to show marked changes associated with changes of state which may alter the degree of hydrogen bonding. We have observed in a limited number of cases considerable frequency shifts of this band on passing from solid to solution; sometimes this occurs to such an extent that the band is regarded as having disappeared. Bonner and Hofstadter,[1] for example, associate this band only with the dimeric material, in which they attribute it to the structure O–H . . . O. However, a considerable frequency shift also occurs on passing from melted films to nujol mulls of crystals. In the extreme case of the two polymorphic forms of stearic acid we find a shift of 48 cm.$^{-1}$ on passing from the stable to the unstable modification, and this has been confirmed by Sinclair *et al.*[42] Because of the extreme variability in the intensity of this band, it is not a particularly suitable one for the identification of acids, but it may be useful for confirmatory purposes. The frequency range is normally between 940 cm.$^{-1}$ and 900 cm.$^{-1}$, and the band is usually broad and ill-defined in compounds examined in the solid state. In solution the band does not appear at dilutions in which the acid is entirely monomeric.[49]

10.4(d). Band Progression in Fatty Acids. Long-chain fatty acids examined in the solid or crystal state exhibit a regular series of evenly spaced absorptions in the region 1350–1180 cm.$^{-1}$. Jones *et al.*[41] have pointed out that the number and appearance of these bands can afford information as to the length of the carbon chain involved. Thus lauric acid (C_{12}) shows only three regularly spaced bands in this region, the lowest being at 1195 cm.$^{-1}$. As the carbon chain lengthens the number of such bands increased and heneicosoic acid (C_{21}) shows nine such bands, the lowest being at 1184 cm.$^{-1}$. Between C_{16} and C_{21} the number of bands increased by one for each unit increase in the length of the carbon chain. Similar bands are shown by fatty acid esters and also by paraffins, although in the latter case the intensities are very much reduced. They are therefore to be associated with rocking or twisting motions of the CH_2 groups in the chains. These motions are primarily associated with the *trans* arrangement of the methylene groups such as occurs in *n*-paraffins. In consequence, anything which interferes with this arrangement modifies the spectrum in this region. Corish and Davison [67] have suggested that the virtual disappearance of these bands in molten acids is due to a continuous and random distribution of the $(CH_2)_n$ chains. The changes in structure in this region following changes of state have been fully confirmed by other workers.[80, 81, 89-92] Similarly, chain branching or the presence of double bonds tends to modify these patterns. In tetrabromostearic acid the characteristic pattern is lost, but the bands are clear and sharp in 2-bromostearic acid. A study of this region may therefore give data of some value in specific cases. It may provide, for example, a simple means of differentiating between saturated fatty acids of different chain lengths, as the spectra of these compounds as a class are otherwise largely indistinguishable. Meiklejohn *et al.*[91] have shown that there are also substantial differences between the spectra of fatty acid salts in this region which can equally well be used for identification. They have also made suggestions on the use of these absorptions for chain-length determinations.

10.5. THE IONISED CARBOXYL GROUP; SALTS

Lecomte and his co-workers have made a very extensive study of the infra-red spectra of the salts of organic acids and have examined almost a thousand such materials.[32-35] When ionisation occurs, giving the COO^- group, resonance is possible between the two C–O bonds. In consequence the characteristic carbonyl absorption vanishes and is replaced by two bands between 1610 cm.$^{-1}$ and 1550 cm.$^{-1}$ and between 1400 cm.$^{-1}$ and 1300 cm.$^{-1}$, which correspond to the anti-symmetrical and symmetrical vibrations of the COO^- structure.

Of these bands, the former is very much more characteristic, as it is generally more constant in frequency whilst many other skeletal vibrations occur in the wide range 1400–1300 cm.$^{-1}$. Lecomte's general finding has been confirmed by later workers, such as those engaged on the penicillin project,[45] and, as will be seen later, a somewhat similar state of affairs has been found to occur with aminoacids in which the zwitterion form permits resonance in the same way. Raman data [40] on numbers of carboxylic acids also indicate that salt formation results in the disappearance of the $C=O$ absorption and its replacement by a band near 1430 cm.$^{-1}$. The fact that in this case the group is identified by the symmetric vibration is in accordance with theory which requires this mode to be strong in the Raman and weak in the infra-red. The reverse is true of the asymmetric frequency, and Ehrlich [80] estimates the intensity ratio for polymeric acids in the infra-red as about 7·6 : 1.

In the solid state the two frequencies show minor variations with the nature of the metallic ion and also with the nature of the group to which the ionised carboxyl group is attached. Kagarise [83] has shown that for mono- and di-valent elements there is a linear relationship between the electro-negativity of the element and the asymmetric stretching frequency of the salt, and Stimpson [84] has also noted variations of this type. Changes in the nature of the substituent group also have marked effects, and there are, for example, well-defined differences between the characteristic frequencies of formate, acetate and oxalate ions. [85] Similarly, in substituted benzoic acids the carboxylate frequencies vary with the nature of the aromatic substituents. [84] Such differences are best studied by noting the separation between the two absorption bands, as this is more distinctive than the precise position of either. In sodium trifluoroacetate the influence of the CF_3 group is particularly marked, and the COO^- frequencies occur [86] at 1680 cm.$^{-1}$ and 1457 cm.$^{-1}$. The former is close to the normal range for un-ionised acids, but must be compared with the value of 1825 cm.$^{-1}$ shown by the unassociated free acid.

Hydrogen bonding of the carboxylate group can lead to a small reduction in the asymmetric frequency. In the salt $CF_3COONa.2CF_3COOH$, for example, [86] the bonded carboxylate ion absorbs at 1625 cm.$^{-1}$ (*as*) as compared with 1667 cm.$^{-1}$ for trifluoroacetic acid in pyridine solution. [67] In disodium ethylenediamine tetracetic acid the asymmetric carboxylate frequency of 1637 cm.$^{-1}$ is higher than in the tetrasodium salt (1597 cm.$^{-1}$). This has also been ascribed to hydrogen bonding, [85] but other factors may be involved in this special case.

In general, the spectra of fatty acid salts in the solid state show more distinctive differences than do the original acids, and Childers and Struthers [88] have made use of this in the analysis of acid mixtures of various types.

The carbonyl frequencies of ionised acids have been studied in solution by Gore, Barnes and Petersen, [36] who have used solutions in water and in heavy water, in silver chloride cells to scan the whole spectral range. In a typical case sodium acetate was found to show the COO^- absorptions near 1560 cm.$^{-1}$ and 1410 cm.$^{-1}$. Using heavy water which avoids the obscuring of the carbonyl region by the water bands, it is possible to observe the reappearance of the unionised acid, and consequently of the carbonyl group, on adding DCl, when a strong band appears at 1730 cm.$^{-1}$. This change can be reversed by the addition of NaOD. This characteristic shifting of the carbonyl frequency on passing from the un-ionised to the ionised acid is highly characteristic of carboxylic acids, and provides a neat and simple way in which the presence of such materials can be confirmed.

N

A typical use of such a method is that of Cross, Richards and Willis.[37] In studies on oxidised polythene the extent to which carboxyl groups were contributing to the total carbonyl absorption observed was assessed by a comparison of the intensity at 1550 cm.$^{-1}$ and at 1720 cm.$^{-1}$ before and after conversion of the carboxyl groups into a salt. It should be noted that these bands from acid salts are very similar to those of the nitro-group which the ionised carbonyl resembles electronically, and they arise from similar vibration modes. However, in practice there is little difficulty in differentiating the two.

10.6. BIBLIOGRAPHY

1. Bonner and Hofstadter, *J. Chem. Phys.*, 1938, **6**, 531.
2. Herman and Hofstadter, *ibid.*, p. 534.
3. Davies and Sutherland, *ibid.*, p. 755.
4. Davies, *J. Chem. Phys.*, 1940, **8**, 577.
5. Buswell, Rodebush and Roy, *J. Amer. Chem. Soc.*, 1938, **60**, 2239.
6. Klotz and Gruen, *J. Phys. and Colloid Chem.*, 1948, **52**, 961.
7. McCutcheon, Crawford and Welsh, *Oil and Soap*, 1941, **18**, 9.
8. Martin, *Nature*, 1950, **166**, 474.
9. Flett, *J. Chem. Soc.*, 1951, 962.
10. Shreve, Heether, Knight and Swern, *Analyt. Chem.*, 1950, **22**, 1498.
11. Pauling, *The Nature of the Chemical Bond* (O.U.P., 1940), p. 306.
12. Rasmussen, Tunnicliff and Brattain, *J. Amer. Chem. Soc.*, 1949, **71**, 1068.
13. Amstutz, Hunsberger and Chessick, *ibid.*, 1951, **73**, 1220.
14. Bellamy and Beecher, *J. Chem. Soc.*, 1952, 1701.
15. Kuratani, *J. Chem. Soc. Japan*, 1950, **71**, 401.
16. Hartwell, Richards and Thompson, *J. Chem. Soc.*, 1948, 1436.
17. Grove and Willis, *ibid.*, 1951, 877.
18. Lecomte and Guy, *Compt. rend. Acad. Sci. Paris*, 1948, **227**, 54.
19. Barnes, Gore, Liddel and Williams, *Infra-red Spectroscopy* (Reinhold, 1944).
20. Lecomte, *Traite de Chimie Organique*, Ed. Grignard et Baud (Masson et Cie., Paris, 1936), vol. 2, p. 143.
21. Gillette, *J. Amer. Chem. Soc.*, 1936, **58**, 1143.
22. Flett, *Trans. Faraday Soc.*, 1948, **44**, 767.
23. Bartlett and Rylander, *J. Amer. Chem. Soc.*, 1951, **73**, 4275.
24. O'Connor, Field and Singleton, *J. Amer. Oil Chem. Soc.*, 1951, **28**, 154.
25. Rao and Daubert, *J. Amer. Chem. Soc.*, 1948, **70**, 1102.
26. Schonmann, *Helv. Phys. Acta*, 1943, **16**, 343.
27. Sheppard, *Trans. Faraday Soc.*, 1949, **45**, 693.
28. Munday, *Nature*, 1949, **163**, 443.
29. Cross and Rolfe, *Trans. Faraday Soc.*, 1951, **47**, 354.
30. Forziati, Rowen and Plyler, *J. Res. Nat. Bur. Stand.*, 1951, **46**, 288.
31. Thompson and Torkington, *J. Chem. Soc.*, 1945, 640.
32. Lecomte, *Rev. Optique*, 1949, **28**, 353.
33. Duval, Lecomte and Douvillé, *Ann. Physique*, 1942, **17**, 5.
34. Douvillé, Duval and Lecomte, *Bull. Soc. chim.*, 1942, **9**, 548.
35. Duval, Gerding and Lecomte, *Rev. trav. chim.*, 1950, **69**, 391.
36. Gore, Barnes and Petersen, *Analyt. Chem.*, 1949, **21**, 382.
37. Cross, Richards and Willis, *Discuss. Faraday Soc.*, 1950, **9**, 235.
38. Colthup, *J. Opt. Soc. Amer.*, 1950, **40**, 397.
39. Herman and Hofstadter, *J. Chem. Phys.*, 1939, **7**, 460.
40. Edsall, *ibid.*, 1937, **5**, 508.
41. Jones, McKay and Sinclair, *J. Amer. Chem. Soc.*, 1952, **74**, 2575.
42. Sinclair, McKay and Jones, *ibid.*, p. 2570.
43. Sinclair, McKay, Myers and Jones, *ibid.*, p. 2578.

44. Freeman, *ibid.*, p. 2523.
45. *The Chemistry of Penicillin* (Princeton University Press, 1949), p. 382.
46. Haszeldine, *Nature*, 1951, **168**, 1028.
47. Husted and Ahlbrecht, *J. Amer. Chem. Soc.*, 1953, **75**, 1607.
48. Freeman, *ibid.*, 1859.
49. Hadži and Sheppard, *Proc. Roy. Soc.*, 1953, **A216**, 247.
50. Francis, *J. Chem. Phys.*, 1951, **19**, 942.
51. Kuratani, *J. Chem. Soc. Japan*, 1952, **73**, 758.
52. Fuson, Josien, Jones and Lawson, *J. Chem. Phys.*, 1952, **20**, 1627.
53. Josien and Fuson, *Compt. Rend. Acad. Sci. (Paris)*, 1952, **235**, 1025.
54. Goulden, *Spectrochim. Acta*, 1954, **6**, 129.
55. Bratoz, Hadži and Sheppard, *Bull. Sci. Acad. RPF. Yougoslavie*, 1953, **1**, 71.
56. *Idem, Spectrochim. Acta*, 1956, **8**, 249.
57. Harris and Hobbs, *J. Amer. Chem. Soc.*, 1954, **76**, 1419.
58. Fuson and Josien, *J. Opt. Soc. Amer.*, 1953, **43**, 1102.
59. Davies and Evans, *J. Chem. Phys.*, 1952, **20**, 342.
60. Chulanovski and Simova, *Doklady, Akad. Nauk. S.S.S.R.*, 1949, **68**, 1033.
61. Bateuv, *Izvest, Akad. Nauk. S.S.S.R., Otdel Khim. Nauk.*, 1950, 402; *ibid., Ser. Fiz.*, 1950, **14**, 429.
62. Stepanov, *J. Phys. Chem. (U.S.S.R.)*, 1945, **19**, 507; 1946, **20**, 907.
63. *Idem, Nature*, 1956, **157**, 808.
64. Cardwell, Dunitz and Orgel, *J. Chem. Soc.*, 1953, 3740.
65. Barrow and Yerger, *J. Amer. Chem. Soc.*, 1954, 5428.
66. Josien, Fuson, Lawson and Jones, *Compt. Rend. Acad. Sci. (Paris)*, 1952, **234**, 1163.
67. Corish and Davison, *J. Chem. Soc.*, 1955, 6005.
68. Fraenkel, Belford and Yankwich, *J. Amer. Chem. Soc.*, 1954, **76**, 15.
69. Barrow, *ibid.*, 1956, **78**, 5802.
70. Bellamy, Thomas and Williams, *J. Chem. Soc.*, 1955, 3704.
71. Josien and Callas, *Compt. Rend. Acad. Sci. (Paris)*, 1955, **240**, 1641.
72. Haszeldine, *J. Chem. Soc.*, 1954, 4026.
73. Harrand and Tuernal-Vatran, *Ann. Phys.*, 1955, **10**, 5.
74. Allan, Meakins and Whiting, *J. Chem. Soc.*, 1955, 1874.
75. Musso, *Chem. Ber.*, 1955, **88**, 1915.
76. Schotte and Rosenberg, *Arkiv. Kemi.*, 1956, **8**, 551.
77. Rosenberg and Schotte, *Acta. Chem. Scand.*, 1954, **8**, 867.
78. Farmer, *Chem. and Ind.*, 1955, 586.
79. Guertin, Wiberley, Bauer and Goldenson, *Analyt. Chem.*, 1956, **28**, 1553.
80. Neuilly, *Compt. Rend. Acad. Sci. (Paris)*, 1954, **238**, 65.
81. Rigaux, *ibid.*, 63, 783.
82. Ehrlich, *J. Amer. Chem. Soc.*, 1954, **76**, 5263.
83. Kagarise, *J. Phys. Chem.*, 1955, **59**, 271.
84. Stimpson, *J. Chem. Phys.*, 1954, **22**, 1942.
85. Ito and Berstein, *Can. J. Chem.*, 1956, **34**, 170.
86. Klemperer and Pimentel, *J. Chem. Phys.*, 1954, **22**, 1399.
87. Chapman, *J. Chem. Soc.*, 1955, 1766.
88. Childers and Struthers, *Analyt. Chem.*, 1955, **27**, 737.
89. Corish and Chapman, *J. Chem. Soc.*, 1957, 1746.
90. Wensel, Schiedt and Breusch, *Z. Naturforsch*, 1957, **12B**, 71.
91. Meiklejohn, Meyer, Aronovic, Schuette and Meloch, *Analyt. Chem.*, 1957 **29**, 329.
92. Vov Sydow, *Acta Chem. Scand.*, 1955, **9**, 1119.

CHAPTER 11

Esters and Lactones

11.1. INTRODUCTION AND TABLE

ESTERS have two characteristic absorptions arising from the $C=O$ and $C-O-$ groups. The carbonyl frequency is notably raised above that of normal ketones by the influence of the adjoining oxygen atom, so that differentiation of the two is usually possible. There is, however, a certain amount of overlap between, for example, unsaturated esters in which the CO frequency is lowered, and ketones such as α-halogen substituted materials in which the CO frequency is raised. It is therefore necessary to take account of the intensity of the CO band, and also of the single bond $C-O$ band which, in esters, is very strong and which can usually be differentiated from the weaker $C-C$ bands of ketones which appear in the same spectral region. A similar enhancement of the carbonyl intensity under the influence of the adjacent oxygen atom also occurs, of course, in acids; but in practice the existence of these in polymeric form in the state in which they are usually examined results in a compensating shift to a lower frequency. There is still some degree of overlapping between the carbonyl frequency ranges of esters and acids, and the $C-O$ stretching bonds also absorb in similar ranges, but, as has been shown (Chapter 10), the identification of acids from the OH region or by salt formation will usually resolve any difficulties, whilst again there are marked intensity differences in the carbonyl absorptions of the two classes.

The ester carbonyl absorption follows closely in behaviour the ketonic carbonyl band insofar as frequency shifts arising from environmental changes are concerned, and, as will be seen, the shifts are of the same order of magnitude in both cases. This applies also to ring systems in which the changes in the CO frequencies of cyclic ketones with alteration of the ring size are closely paralleled by the comparable behaviour of lactones. As the various structural factors causing frequency shifts have been fully discussed under aldehydes and ketones in Chapter 9, they will be considered in rather less detail here.

As in the case of ketones, no discussion of carbonyl frequencies of esters with nitrogen attached to the carbonyl group is included in this section, as such materials will be dealt with in Chapter 12.

The single bond $C-O$ absorption falls in the same general region as other $C-O$ stretching vibrations of unsaturated ethers and alcohols, and is not particularly significant as such, especially as the frequency shows less stability than is the case with the carbonyl absorption. However, sufficient work has been done in some cases to enable the smaller and more specific frequency ranges of individual classes of esters, such as acetates, butyrates, benzoates, etc., to be characterised, whilst certain esters show two distinct absorption bands in this region, which increases considerably the possibilities of their identification.

In the case of the acetates, a very extensive study of the structure of the C–O band of a large number of sterol acetates has enabled Jones *et al.*[1] to obtain evidence as to the stereochemical structure of C_3 acetoxy-sterols in relation to the hydrogen atom at C_5.

The correlations dealt with are shown in Table 11.

TABLE 11 *

C=O Stretching Vibrations

Normal saturated esters	1750–1735 cm.$^{-1}$
$\alpha\beta$-Unsaturated and aryl esters . . .	1730–1717 cm.$^{-1}$
Vinyl ester type compounds	1770–1800 cm.$^{-1}$
Esters with α-electronegative substituents .	1770–1745 cm.$^{-1}$
α-Keto esters	1755–1740 cm.$^{-1}$
β-Keto esters (enolic)	Near 1650 cm.$^{-1}$
Salicylates and anthranilates . . .	1690–1670 cm.$^{-1}$
γ-Keto esters and higher . . .	1750–1735 cm.$^{-1}$
δ-Lactones	1750–1735 cm.$^{-1}$
γ-Lactones, saturated	1780–1760 cm.$^{-1}$
γ-Lactones, $\alpha\beta$-unsaturated . . .	1760–1740 cm.$^{-1}$
γ-Lactones, $\beta\gamma$-unsaturated . . .	Near 1800 cm.$^{-1}$
β-Lactones	Near 1820 cm.$^{-1}$
Thio-esters, all types	Near 1675 cm.$^{-1}$

C–O– Stretching Vibrations

Formates	1200–1180 cm.$^{-1}$
Acetates	1250–1230 cm.$^{-1}$
Phenolic acetates	Near 1205 cm.$^{-1}$
Propionates and higher . . .	1200–1150 cm.$^{-1}$
Acrylates, fumarates, maleates . .	1300–1200 and 1180–1130 cm.$^{-1}$
Benzoates and phthalates . . .	1310–1250 and 1150–1100 cm.$^{-1}$

* All bands shown in this table are strong.

11.2. C=O STRETCHING VIBRATIONS IN ESTERS

11.2(a). Saturated Esters. The carbonyl frequencies of some thirty-six simple esters, including formates, acetates, butyrates, etc., were examined by Thompson and Torkington in 1945.[2] In the case of formates, which, as the first members of a series, might be expected to be anomalous, the carbonyl frequency was in the range

1724–1722 cm.$^{-1}$, but with all the others it fell very close to 1740 cm.$^{-1}$. These observations were all made on samples in the liquid state, and later, Hartwell, Richards and Thompson [3] supplemented this work with observations on a similar range of esters as vapours. They found a general raising of the frequency by about 20–30 cm.$^{-1}$ above that of the liquid phase studies, but the carbonyl frequencies still showed the same order of consistency. These workers also studied methyl acetate in nine different solvents, and found the frequency to be within the range 1756–1738 cm.$^{-1}$. This is sufficiently close to the mean value for liquids to indicate that changes from the liquid state to solution are unlikely to affect the frequency significantly.

Hydrogen bonding also has only a small effect unless resonance stabilisation occurs. Searles *et al.*[41] have shown the carbonyl shift in methanol solution is about 8 cm.$^{-1}$, which is similar to the case of ketones. With lactones the proton-accepting power can be a little greater, leading to shifts of up to 15 cm.$^{-1}$, depending upon the ring size. Henbest and Lovell [68] have also noted a few unusual instances in which hydrogen bonding takes place preferentially on the alcohol oxygen atom, and the carbonyl frequency then rises about 10 cm.$^{-1}$ above the usual value.

These general findings have been confirmed by many other workers. Hampton and Newell [4] have described the carbonyl frequencies of nineteen esters of various kinds. They note that the frequency is more subject to variation with increasing molecular complexity, but this is primarily due to known causes, such as α-halogenation or αβ-unsaturation and their value of 1738 cm.$^{-1}$, for example, for ethyl palmitate, is substantially the same as for simpler saturated materials. These workers have also given values for the molecular extinction coefficients of esters. The values show considerable variations from class to class, but within a given group they are reasonably constant and consistent. The values quoted for simple saturated esters of the type under discussion, for example, range from 569 to 610 units. Anderson and Seyfried [5] have also given data on the positions and intensities of ester carbonyl absorptions which are generally in line with these.

With more complex molecules the correlation still holds good. Rasmussen and Brattain [6] find the carbonyl frequencies of methyl pivalate, ethyl diphenyl acetate and methyl sarcosinate to be all close to 1739 cm.$^{-1}$, indicating that there is little or no inductive effect on the C=O arising from α-methyl, aryl or amino-substitution. With ethyl cyanoacetate, however, the frequency rises to 1751 cm.$^{-1}$, reflecting the influence of the C≡N group. Shreve *et al.*[7] and Sinclair *et. al.*[33,34] have examined the methyl esters of long-chain fatty acids, and find the carbonyl frequency falls in the range 1748–1739 cm.$^{-1}$, whilst a number of triglycerides absorb [7] between 1751 and 1748 cm.$^{-1}$. O'Connor *et al.*[8] report similar findings in the methyl and ethyl esters of fatty acids.

The most extensive study of ester carbonyl absorptions is that made by Jones and co-workers,[9-11, 28, 42, 43] who have investigated the carbonyl frequencies of over a hundred sterol acetates, propionates, etc. With certain exceptions which will be dealt with later, all the saturated materials absorbed in the range 1742–1735 cm.$^{-1}$, regardless of where the ester group was situated in the steroid nucleus, although there were indications that similarly substituted materials each had an even narrower range of characteristic frequencies.

As regards the intensities of these carbonyl absorptions, no detailed study has yet been made, but there is every indication that the situation will be found to be similar to that of the ketones in which the various groups of structural types, as classified by the frequencies, are found to have similar extinction coefficients within the class, but to differ from those of other classes.[12]

Indications of this are given in the work of Hampton and Newell [4] and of Anderson and Seyfried [5] referred to above. Jones *et al.*[12] have shown that five steroid aryl acetates have comparable carbonyl intensities and that they are about one and a half to two and a half times the strength of saturated ketones, whilst Stahl and Pessen [35] have found that the proportionate decrease of carbonyl absorption intensity in alkyl sebacates with progressive increases in the chain length, is so regular as to afford a possible means of differentiating between them. Cross and Rolfe [13] have also measured the extinction coefficients of a number of esters. Those of the saturated materials lie relatively close together, but that of one αβ-unsaturated ester is markedly different. The use of molecular extinction coefficients in the identification of ester groups in alkaloids has been demonstrated in the identification of ester groups in alkaloids has been demonstrated by Marion, Ramsay and Jones,[27] and additional intensity data on a small number of esters have been given by Barrow [44] and by Francis.[45] These workers confirm that there are major changes in the carbonyl intensity with change in the carbonyl function, and Barrow has suggested that these reflect changes in the resonance energies of the different systems.

11.2(b). The Influence of Conjugation. The expected lowering of the carbonyl frequency by αβ-unsaturation has been confirmed by many workers.[2-4, 6, 10, 46, 47] However, the weakening of the carbonyl bond by αβ-unsaturation is, in general, less than in the case of ketones, and the extent of the shift is of the same magnitude for aryl substitution as for a simple double bond. The distinction between these two types which is possible in ketones is not therefore possible with esters. Methyl methacrylate absorbs at 1718 cm.$^{-1}$ and propyl methacrylate [13] at 1721 cm.$^{-1}$, whilst a

series of eleven steroid benzoates [10] absorbed in the range 1724–
1719 cm.[-1]. Direct confirmation that the reduction in the frequency is due to the influence of the double bond is given by the fact
that these steroid benzoates absorbed at 1739–1735 cm.[-1] after
hydrogenation to the hexahydrobenzoate.[10] The frequency fall is
therefore of the order of 20 cm.[-1]. Further conjugation in the
$\gamma\delta$-position has little, if any, appreciable effect, and ethyl cinna-
mate,[4] for example, absorbs at 1717 cm.[-1], against 1724 cm.[-1] for
methylbenzoate.[6] Methyl esters of naphthalene and phenanthrene
carboxylic acids also absorb [30] at 1724 cm.[-1]. These values relate
to studies on liquids or solutions, and the vapour frequencies are
likely to be 20–30 cm.[-1] higher.[3]

These frequencies are, of course, subject also to other changes
arising from additional structural features. For example, the
ortho-, *meta-* and *para-*nitrobenzoates [6] absorb at 1733 cm.[-1], reflecting
a marked lessening of the influence of the aryl group. Compounds
such as ethyl $\beta\beta$-diethoxyacrylate [6] (1736 cm.[-1]), diallyl maleate [4]
(1738 cm.[-1]) and diethyl-1-2-dicyanoethane dicarboxylate [46] (1755
cm.[-1]) also show abnormally high carbonyl frequencies. These are
probably due to field effects similar to those operating in α-halogen-
ated compounds.

Conjugation with acetylenic links produces an enhanced shift,
and compounds of this type absorb [47] in the range 1720–1708 cm.[-1].

11.2(c). Vinyl Esters. One case of frequency alteration in
esters which is not paralleled in ketones is that arising from the structure CO–O–C=C. Compounds of this type show a marked enhancement of the carbonyl frequency, regardless of whether the double
bond is normal or part of an aromatic ring. Barnes *et al.*[14] noted this
effect in vinyl acetate, which absorbs at 1776 cm.[-1]. Hartwell *et al.*[3]
found a similar effect with phenyl acetate and Jones *et al.* have
reported it in steroid phenolic esters.[28] Rasmussen and Brattain [6]
have observed a further frequency shift in *ortho-*nitrobenzoyl acetate
(1786 cm.[-1]), presumably due to the influence of the nitro-group.
Other instances of this effect are given by Grove and Willis [15] and
by Walsh,[16] and it is clear that in some cases, such as phthalidylidene
acetic acid, the shift can be even greater with the carbonyl frequency
at 1800 cm.[-1]. Bellamy [48] has suggested that as vinyl acetate has
no resonance energy the normal mesomerism to forms such as

$$-C \overset{O^-}{\underset{+}{=}} OR$$ is suppressed n such cases, so that the frequency of the

carbonyl absorption is determined solely by the high electronegativity of the oxygen atom.

11.2(d). The Influence of α-Halogen Groups. The influence
of α-halogen substitution in esters is closely parallel to the cases

of ketones already discussed. A substantial rise in the carbonyl frequency follows the introduction of a CF_3 group in the α-position,[36-38, 49, 50] and compounds of this type absorb near 1790 cm.[-1]. However, studies on compounds with only one or two α-halogen atoms at first gave conflicting results. Hauptschein *et al.*[25] found an average value of 1786 cm.[-1] for the carbonyl frequencies of mono-α-fluorinated esters which is close to that for trifluoro compounds. Bender,[49] however, obtained values for the liquids ranging from 1776 to 1749 cm.[-1]. Solution studies by McBee and Christman [51] on mono-, di- and tri-fluorinated compounds showed that two carbonyl frequencies are given in some cases. This has been explained by Josien and Calas,[52] who have provided additional data and shown that rotational isomerism is involved. The nature of the effects causing frequency shifts has been discussed by Bellamy and Williams,[53] and a dipolar mechanism is probably involved. In consequence, only the halogen atom which is near in space to the carbonyl oxygen has any significant effect upon the frequency. This explains the fact that the shifts for monohalogen substituents are the same as for trihalogen ones. The values for chloracetic esters [52] illustrate this point. Methyl trichloroacetate absorbs at 1776 cm.[-1], and methyl acetate at 1750 cm.[-1]. Both the mono- and di-chloro compounds show two bands at these positions. The higher-frequency band therefore corresponds to the isomer in which one chlorine atom is close to the carbonyl oxygen atom, and the lower frequency band to a form in which it is twisted away from it. Two bands are therefore always to be expected in compounds which can show rotational isomerism of this type. However, it may not always be possible to observe both in the liquid state, as the high polarity of the liquid will favour the more polar (higher-frequency) form and increase its concentration.

In a few special cases frequency shifts of ester carbonyl group have been observed in structures with the grouping $-CO-O-CH_2-CF_3$, despite the apparent separation of the halogen atoms from the carbonyl oxygen.[50] No similar effect is found with β-fluorination on the other side of the carbonyl, and compounds with the group $CF_3CH_2CO-O-R$ show a normal ester frequency. The rise in the frequency of the first group is not well understood, but may be connected with the *cis* arrangement of esters which could allow the fluorine atoms to approach the oxygen of the carbonyl group. Similar interaction effects probably occur with substituents such as the α-nitrile group, but have not been fully studied. In 1 : 1-di-acetoxypropane the abnormal carbonyl frequency of 1761 cm.[-1] has also been attributed to a field effect.[54]

11.3. THE C=O STRETCHING VIBRATION IN DIESTERS AND KETO ESTERS

11.3(a). α-Diesters and α-Keto Esters. As in α-diketones, the degree of interaction of two adjacent CO groups appears to be very small. Dibutyloxalate [4] absorbs at 1746 cm.$^{-1}$ and methylpyruvate [17] at 1748 cm.$^{-1}$. Grove and Willis [15] report two similar cases in which the interaction effect is so small as to be hardly detectable.

11.3(b). β-Keto Esters and Related Compounds. The phenomenon of conjugate chelation has already been described in some detail in the case of diketones (Chapter 9), and essentially similar effects are observed with esters of comparable structure. Rasmussen and Brattain [6] have studied a number of esters in which this effect is found. Ethyl αα-dimethylaceto-acetate cannot enolise and in solution is normal in showing absorptions at 1718 cm.$^{-1}$ and 1742 cm.$^{-1}$ due to the ketone and ester carbonyl groups. Both ethyl-α-methylacetoacetate and ethylacetoacetate, however, show an additional band at 1650 cm.$^{-1}$, which is ascribed to the ester carbonyl group after chelation to the enolic hydroxyl group. The methyl ester also shows absorption at 1632 cm.$^{-1}$, which has been assigned [30] to the C=C linkage. On the other hand, there does not seem to be much possibility of enolisation in diethyldiacetylsuccinate, as this shows only normal ketone and ester bands. The β-diester, diethylmalonate, is essentially normal in its carbonyl frequency,[2] although in carbon tetrachloride solution some splitting into a doublet is observed.[46]

In the aromatic series *n*-butylsalicylate shows its ester absorption [6] at 1675 cm.$^{-1}$ and methylsalicylate [4] at 1684 cm.$^{-1}$; this is again ascribed to conjugate chelation. The shift is less than occurs with enolised chelate β-diketones or alkyl-β-keto esters, indicating that the chelation is not so strong. This probably reflects the weaker double-bond character of the ring linkages. The influence of chelation is clearly shown by the examination of acetylated *n*-butylsalicylate, in which the carbonyl frequency returns to 1723 cm.$^{-1}$, which is normal for an aryl ester. The acetate band is also normal and appears at 1770 cm.$^{-1}$, reflecting its vinyl ester structure.

With compounds such as methyl-10-hydroxy-9-phenanthrene carboxylate,[30] the increased degree of fixation of the ring double bonds results in stronger chelation, so that the frequency shift is increased to about 75 cm.$^{-1}$. As in the case of the corresponding ketones, the frequency shifts of chelated esters have been used to measure double-bond character in the indane series.[55]

Chelation also occurs in cyclic β-keto esters, such as derivatives of enolisable keto esters of *cyclo*hexanone and *cyclo*pentanone. Leonard *et al.*[31] and Bellamy and Beecher [56] have examined a number of such cases. Non-enolisable keto esters of *cyclo*hexanone show absorptions near 1735 cm.$^{-1}$ and 1718 cm.$^{-1}$ corresponding to the ester and ketonic carbonyl groups. However, compounds such as ethyl-*cyclo*hexanone-2-carboxylate show these bands and two others at 1656 cm.$^{-1}$ and 1618 cm.$^{-1}$ which must arise from the chelate structure of the enol form. Leonard *et al.*[31] associate the first of these new bands with the chelated carbonyl absorption and the second with the double-bond absorption. A similar effect is observed in *cyclo*pentanone derivatives, but the intensities of the bands are then much reduced.

Chelation is also to be expected in β-amino-αβ-unsaturated esters [6] by analogy with the ketones. This has been found experimentally in the case of methyl-*N*-methylanthranilate, which absorbs at 1685 cm.$^{-1}$, indicating a chelation of about the same strength as occurs with the salicylate. Removal of the chelating hydrogen atom results in reversion of the ester carbonyl frequency to 1730 cm.$^{-1}$.

11.3(c). γ- and δ-Diesters and Keto Esters. γ- and δ-Diesters do not interact to any appreciable extent. Diethylsuccinate [17] absorbs at 1733 cm.$^{-1}$, whilst phthalates usually absorb near 1730 cm.$^{-1}$. This latter value is slightly high for aryl esters, and this may be due to the fact that the electronic influence of the ring is shared between the two carbonyl groups. Ester groups even further apart show no evidence of interaction. Diethyladipate is completely normal, and absorbs at 1739 cm.$^{-1}$.

In considering γ- and δ-keto esters and similar materials the possibility of lactol formation should not be overlooked, as the ester frequencies will then appear as those of the corresponding five- or six-membered ring lactones. The characteristic frequencies of these will be discussed below. The use of the number and position of carbonyl frequencies in the identification of lactol structures has been demonstrated in a number of cases by Grove and Willis.[15]

Reference has already been made in Chapter 9 to the interference effects found with the structure –CO–C–O–CO–, as in 21-acetoxy-20–ketosteroids.[10, 54] The effect on the ester carbonyl absorption is less than that on the keto-carbonyl band and is usually of the order of + 10 cm.$^{-1}$.

11.4. C=O STRETCHING VIBRATIONS IN LACTONES, LACTOLS, ETC.

11.4(a). Six-membered Rings (δ-Lactones). The ester carbonyl group of δ-lactones occurs in the same position as in open-chain compounds. This is parallel to the case of cyclic ketones, and is to be attributed to the lack of strain in rings of this size. This correlation is quoted by Rasmussen and Brattain [18] on the basis of unpublished work, but they have also [6] given a value for δ-valero-lactone (1738 cm.[-1]). Jones *et al.*[10,42] have confirmed this correlation in a number of steroid δ-lactones, and it has also been found to hold good for a number of six-membered ring lactols by Grove and Willis.[15] Unsaturated rings of this type have not been extensively studied, but it is to be expected, by comparison with the behaviour of γ-lactones, that the carbonyl frequency will be subject to the same degrees of shift from αβ-conjugation, α-electronegative substituents or vinyl ester type unsaturation as with open-chain esters.

This correlation does not apply to lactones with two carbonyl groups in the same six-membered ring. Wasserman and Zimmerman [23] have examined mesolactide and benzilide in which the carbonyl frequencies occur between 1767 cm.[-1] and 1757 cm.[-1] and Randall *et al.*[17] quote a value of 1721 cm.[-1] for dehydracetic acid. There are compounds in which interaction effects might well be expected and are too complex for any interpretation of these shifts to be attempted.

Another factor which might be expected to lead to frequency shifts is the introduction of ring strain by the fusion of the lactone to other cyclic systems. In certain spiro-type δ-lactones of the steroid series this is certainly the case, as absorption occurs in the 1793–1786 cm.[-1] range.[42] This is a higher frequency even than the corresponding spiro γ-lactones (1781–1777 cm.[-1]), which are essentially normal. Wilder Winston and [57] have also reported carbonyl frequencies near 1764 cm.[-1] in tricyclic lactones which are believed on other grounds to be six-ring systems. However, the extent of shift will clearly depend upon the degree of additional strain, if any, which is introduced.

11.4(b). Five-membered Rings. γ-Lactones have been fairly extensively studied, and examples are now known of frequency shifts with structural changes which parallel nearly all those of open-chain esters. Whiffen and Thompson [19] in 1946 quoted the over-all range of 1800–1740 cm.[-1] for γ-lactones and noted that the frequency lay towards 1800 cm.[-1] in βγ-unsaturated materials. Richards and Thompson,[20, 21] confirmed this and reported four fully saturated γ-lactones as absorbing at 1740 cm.[-1]. Later work has, however, tended to show that the carbonyl frequency of γ-lactones is actually rather higher than this value,[18, 6, 10, 15] and that a shift occurs as in the case of five ring ketones. Rasmussen [6] finds 1770 cm.[-1] for γ-valerolactone and Jones 1780–1778 cm.[-1] for steroid γ-lactones. This value has also been confirmed by Grove and Willis,[15] by Woodward and Kovach [22] and by Marion *et al.*,[27] and it is supported by the values obtained for αβ- and βγ-unsaturated γ-lactones, in which the frequency shifts are of the order to be expected from a normal value of about 1770 cm.[-1]. αβ-Unsaturated γ-lactones would then be expected to absorb about 20 cm.$^{-1}$ lower than the saturated materials at 1750 cm.$^{-1}$, and this has been confirmed by Grove and Willis,[15] who have examined a number of aromatic lactols such as acetophenone-*ortho*-carboxylic acid, the lactol of benzil-*ortho*-carboxylic acid, phthalide and a number of similar products. With unsaturation βγ to the carbonyl group of five-membered ring lactones, the vinyl ester type of structure is produced, and the frequency consequently rises to near 1800 cm.$^{-1}$. A typical case is that of βγ-angelica lactone, which absorbs at 1799 cm.$^{-1}$, and 3-methylenephthalide and phthalidylidene acetic acid [15] absorb at 1780 cm.$^{-1}$ and 1800 cm.$^{-1}$, respectively. Woodward and Kovach [22] regard 1792 cm.$^{-1}$ as characteristic of enol lactones which have this structure. In instances in which one of the double bonds is exocyclic it is possible for both types of conjugation to occur together. In proto-anemonin and its homo derivative an αβ-conjugated γ-lactone system occurs which has also a vinyl ether structure due to the presence of an exocyclic double bond on the γ carbon atom. These compounds [58] absorb in the liquid state at 1776 cm.$^{-1}$. In the converse case,[59] in which the vinyl ether system is in the ring and the αβ conjugation is exocyclic, the corresponding frequency is 1750 cm.$^{-1}$.

Another case of frequency shifts in γ-lactones is presented by γ-acetoxy-γ-valerolactone, in which the lactone carbonyl frequency occurs [6] at 1797 cm.$^{-1}$. This effect is not understood, but a number of similar cases of frequencies near 1800 cm.$^{-1}$ from γ-lactones with electronegative substituents in the γ-position have been reported by Brügel and his associates.[60]

Chelate systems can also occur in certain cases. Rasmussen and Brattain [6] have observed this in α-acetyl-γ-butyrolactone, which has the β-keto ester structure. The non-enolised form gives rise to bands at 1773 cm.$^{-1}$ (five-membered ring lactone) and 1718 cm.$^{-1}$ (ketone), but there is also a band at 1656 cm.$^{-1}$, which the authors attribute to a chelated carbonyl group similar to those observed in open-chain products. Halogen substitution in the α-position also raises the carbonyl frequencies. In the extreme case, perfluoro-butyrolactone absorbs at 1873 cm.$^{-1}$ due to the influence of the fluorine atoms.[29]

Other factors which might be expected to influence these carbonyl frequencies are ring strain arising from fused-ring systems and hydrogen bonding effects. However, in contrast to the behaviour of δ-lactones, tri- and tetra-cyclic γ-lactones absorb normally [61] near 1770 cm.$^{-1}$, and this is true also of spiro-type steroid γ-lactones.[42] Hydrogen bonding, on the other hand, appears to have rather more effect upon both γ- and δ-lactones than it has upon the corresponding esters, and shifts of up to 15 cm.$^{-1}$ can occur from this cause.[41]

11.4(c). Four-membered Rings. These have not been studied to any extent, and are very uncommon. The Raman spectrum of β-butyrolactone has been obtained by Taufen and Murray [32] and shows a band at 1818 cm.$^{-1}$. The spectrum of β-propionolactone in the infra-red has been studied by Searles *et al.*,[41] and this compound absorbs at 1841 cm.$^{-1}$ in carbon tetrachloride solution. These values confirm the expectation that the increased ring strain will result in a further shift towards higher frequencies.

11.5. THIOL ESTERS

Only a very limited amount of data is available on thiol esters, but Rasmussen and Brattain [18] have studied a number of simple open-chain thiol esters in which the carbonyl frequencies occurred at 1675 cm.$^{-1}$ for both saturated, α-amino- and αβ-unsaturated materials. It would seem, therefore, that the structural factors which cause carbonyl frequency shifts in normal esters do not do so in thiol esters. This is emphasised by the constant carbonyl frequencies of fluorinated thiol esters (1680 cm.$^{-1}$), and has been attributed to the greater relative polarisability of the sulphur atom.[25, 29]

The spectrum of an unsaturated γ-thiolactone has also been shown [24] to absorb near 1670 cm.$^{-1}$.

11.6. C–O STRETCHING VIBRATIONS

11.6(a). General. The C–O stretching mode gives rise to strong absorption bands in the region 1300–1000 cm.$^{-1}$ in acids, alcohols, ethers and esters. As a skeletal mode it is much less stable in position than the corresponding carbonyl vibration, and it is very sensitive to changes in the mass and nature of the attached groups. Despite its very considerable intensity, the band is often difficult to recognise, as it occurs in a region of the spectrum where many strong bands commonly occur. Moreover, it is not to be expected that a band will arise from a pure C–O stretching motion, and the movements of other atoms are undoubtedly involved. Fowler and Smith [62] have studied a series of esters and concluded that no bands in this region can be unequivocally assigned. Nevertheless, useful data can be obtained from this region by a study of the most intense bands, which are the most likely to be primarily associated with the oxygen function.

Formates, acetates, butyrates and other simple esters have been studied in some detail by Thompson and Torkington,[2] who were able to show that the strongest band, which commonly occurs near 1200 cm.$^{-1}$, was relatively constant in frequency in each group, whilst in each case there was one other strong band in the 1200–1000 cm.$^{-1}$ range which was more subject to frequency shift following changes in the nature of the alcohol residue. The first of these they assigned tentatively to the C–O band contiguous to the carbonyl group, and its intensity has been studied in some detail by Francis [45] and by Russell and Thompson.[63] The second, more variable band was assigned to the C–O link of the alcohol residue. Later workers have found that $\alpha\beta$-unsaturated esters show two strong bands in the 1300–1100 cm.$^{-1}$ region, whilst others have been able to employ the C–O' frequencies for the study of steric effects in steroid molecules. In view of the variations from class to class, these correlations will be considered individually.

11.6(b). Formates. Methyl formate has its strongest band in the 1250–1050 cm.$^{-1}$ region at 1214 cm.$^{-1}$, falling to 1195 cm.$^{-1}$ in ethyl formate and to 1185 cm.$^{-1}$ in higher homologues.[2, 63] Disregarding the first member of the series, this band is likely to occur in the range 1200–1180 cm.$^{-1}$, but the frequency will almost certainly be influenced by conjugation in phenolic formates and similar materials. The extent to which this will occur is not known, so that this correlation and, indeed, all those relating to the C–O stretching mode, must be applied with caution. Jones *et al.*[1] have confirmed the presence of the 1180 cm.$^{-1}$ band in two sterol formates. Formates also show a second absorption of much lower intensity [63] in the range 1161–1151 cm.$^{-1}$.

11.6(c). Acetates. Acetates have been much more fully studied than other esters. Thompson and Torkington [2] found a characteristic band near 1245 cm.$^{-1}$ in the lower eight acetates up to butyl acetate, and the band did not change in position in the branched-chain isomers. Jones *et al.*[1, 65] have recently examined the position of this band in over one hundred 3-acetosteroids with most interesting results. Firstly, the complete group of spectra confirmed that a very strong band was present in this region in all the acetates studied. In many cases it was a single band, when it occurred in the range 1247–1236 cm.$^{-1}$; in other cases splitting into three components with bands between 1250 cm.$^{-1}$ and 1200 cm.$^{-1}$ was found. Correlation of these findings with the known structures of the sterols revealed that the single-band structure was shown by all those compounds in which the C_3 acetate group and the C_5 hydrogen atom were in the *trans*-configuration and also in those compounds from which the C_5 hydrogen atom was absent and a Δ^5-double bond was present. Similarly the triplet structure was found in all cases in which these two groups were in the *cis*-configuration. Each of the *trans*- and *cis*-forms have of course two stereoisomers, but these are readily differentiated by precipitation of the alcohol with digitonin, which determines the configuration at C_3. This method therefore provides a means of establishing the relative configurations of the C.3-hydroxy- and the C_5-hydrogen atom of any given steroid. The complication of the single-band structure being shown also by the Δ^5-sterols is not a real difficulty, as the presence of the double bond can be readily identified spectroscopically. The method is not, however, applicable to compounds with elements or groups other than hydrogen at C_5. Comparable results have been obtained by other workers both in sterols [39, 64] and in decanol acetates.[40]

The authors suggest that the origin of this differentiation may lie in the possibility that the *cis*-compounds showing multiple bands may be able to exist as a mixture of labile isomers resulting from hindered rotation about the C–O band of the acetate group. However, this is rendered somewhat improbable by the finding of Allsop *et al.*[66] that no similar phenomenon occurs in triterpenoid-3-acetates in which both equatorial and axial substitution leads to only a single band at 1243 cm.$^{-1}$ This must be attributed to the presence in these cases of the *gem* dimethyl group at the C_4 carbon, but they point out that this in itself would not prevent rotational isomerism taking place. Doubling of the 1250 cm.$^{-1}$ band also occurs in simple acetates in solution.[63]

Jones *et al.*[1] have also examined three steroid acetates in which ring I is fully aromatic. As is to be expected, this results in a shift of the C–O stretching frequency, and the strongest band in this region is now found near 1205 cm.$^{-1}$ The position of the C–O absorption in these, and in saturated steroid acetates, is inversely tied to that of the carbonyl absorption, and a simple linear relation connects the two.[65]

The second absorption arising from acetates occurs in the 1060–1000 cm.$^{-1}$ range, and is much more difficult to identify owing to its weaker intensity. However, it can be identified with reasonable certainty in steroid and triterpenoid acetates, and like the 1250 cm.$^{-1}$ absorption, it is then valuable in assigning the steric configuration. Thus Rosenkrantz and Skrogstrom [64] and Jones and Herling [65] have shown that the precise position of this band within this range can be used to differentiate axial and equatorial configurations, and in general the band appears to follow closely the behaviour of the related OH band found in the hydroxy steroid compounds in the same region. A similar differentiation can also be achieved in the triterpene series,[66] although it is interesting to note that in this case the direction of shift on passing from an axial to an equatorial configuration appears to be the opposite to that which occurs in the sterols.

11.6(d). Propionates, Butyrates and Higher Homologues. Thompson and Torkington [2] quote the following mean values for the C–O stretching modes of the series of simpler higher esters which they have examined:

Propionates 1190 cm.$^{-1}$, normal butyrates 1190 cm.$^{-1}$, *iso*butyrates 1200 cm.$^{-1}$, and *iso*valerates 1195 cm.$^{-1}$

The frequencies found within each group were very consistent, and comparable values have been quoted by Kendall *et al.*[67] for higher members of the series. They list the following as characteristic: adipates 1175 cm.$^{-1}$, ricinoleates 1174 cm.$^{-1}$, 2-ethylhexoates 1168 cm.$^{-1}$, laurates 1163 cm.$^{-1}$, oleates, 1172 cm.$^{-1}$, sebacates 1172 cm.$^{-1}$, stearates 1174 cm.$^{-1}$, citrates 1183 cm.$^{-1}$ and benzoates 1280 and 1120 cm.$^{-1}$. Apart from the last, the distinction between the others is probably too fine to be of much value, but it strongly supports the correlation of this band with an ester frequency. Shreve *et al.*[7] have commented on the position of the C–O– vibration in the methyl esters of long-chain fatty acids, in which they find a common pattern of three bands near 1250 cm.$^{-1}$, 1205 cm.$^{-1}$ and 1175 cm.$^{-1}$ which they associate with the C–O linkage, and this has been confirmed by Sinclair *et al.*[33] The band near 1175 cm.$^{-1}$ is, however, the strongest in each case, so that the assignment is generally in agreement with the earlier correlations.

A somewhat similar pattern is found[7] in triglycerides, but in this case the absorption pattern is of a strong band near 1163 cm.$^{-1}$ flanked by weaker bands near 1250 cm.$^{-1}$ and 1110 cm.$^{-1}$. It is therefore reasonable to expect a strong band to be present between 1250 cm.$^{-1}$ and 1160 cm.$^{-1}$ in esters higher than propionates provided, of course, there are no other interfering structures present such as αβ-unsaturation either of the C–O– link or the C=O group.

11.6(e). αβ-Unsaturated Esters. Only a limited number of spectra of esters of this type are available in the literature, and no systematic study of this group has been published. Colthup[26] indicates that acrylates, fumarates, maleates, benzoates and phthalates all give two strong bands in the approximate regions 1310–1250 cm.$^{-1}$ and 1200–1100 cm.$^{-1}$, although he does not quote any data. However, we can confirm that both benzoates and phthalates show two strong and usually recognisable bands between 1300 cm.$^{-1}$ and 1250 cm.$^{-1}$ and 1150 cm.$^{-1}$ and 1100 cm.$^{-1}$ which are often helpful in identifying these groups. Jones *et al.*[1] report finding a strong band at 1270 cm.$^{-1}$ in five steroid benzoates which also supports this correlation.

11.7. BIBLIOGRAPHY

1. Jones, Humphries, Herling and Dobriner, *J. Amer. Chem. Soc.*, 1951 **73**, 3215.
2. Thompson and Torkington, *J. Chem. Soc.*, 1945, 640.
3. Hartwell, Richards and Thompson, *ibid.*, 1948, 1436.
4. Hampton and Newell, *Analyt. Chem.*, 1949, **21**, 914.
5. Anderson and Seyfried, *ibid.*, 1948, **20**, 998.
6. Rasmussen and Brattain, *J. Amer. Chem. Soc.*, 1949, **71**, 1073.
7. Shreve, Heether, Knight and Swern, *Analyt. Chem.*, 1950, **22**, 1498.
8. O'Connor, Field and Singleton, *J. Amer. Oil Chem. Soc.*, 1951, **28**, 154.
9. Jones, Humphries and Dobriner, *J. Amer. Chem. Soc.*, 1949, **71**, 241.
10. *Idem, ibid.*, 1950, **72**, 956.
11. Jones and Dobriner, *Vitamins and Hormones* (N.Y. Academic Press, 1949, 294.

o

12. Jones, Ramsay, Keir and Dobriner, *J. Amer. Chem. Soc.*, 1952, **74**, 80
13. Cross and Rolfe, *Trans. Faraday Soc.*, 1951, **47**, 354.
14. Barnes, Gore, Liddel and Williams, *Infra-red Spectroscopy* (Reinhold, 1944).
15. Grove and Willis, *J. Chem. Soc.*, 1951, 877.
16. Walsh, *Trans. Faraday Soc.*, 1947, **43**, 75.
17. Randall, Fowler, Fuson and Dangl, *Infra-red Determination of Organic Structures* (Van Nostrand, 1949).
18. Rasmussen and Brattain, *The Chemistry of Penicillin* (Princeton Univ. Press, 1949), p. 404.
19. Whiffen and Thompson, *J. Chem. Soc.*, 1946, 1005.
20. Richards and Thompson, *C.P.S. Reports*, 442, 511.
21. *Idem, The Chemistry of Penicillin* (Princeton Univ. Press, 1949), p. 386.
22. Woodward and Kovach, *J. Amer. Chem. Soc.*, 1950, **72**, 1019.
23. Wasserman and Zimmerman, *ibid.*, p. 5787.
24. Hurd and Kreuz, *ibid.*, p. 5543.
25. Hauptschein, Stokes and Nodiff, *ibid.*, 1952, **74**, 4005.
26. Colthup, *J. Opt. Soc. Amer.*, 1950, **40**, 397.
27. Marion, Ramsay and Jones, *J. Amer. Chem. Soc.*, 1951, **73**, 305.
28. Jones, Humphries, Herling and Dobriner, *ibid.*, 1952, **74**, 2820.
29. Hauptschein, Stokes and Grosse, *ibid.*, p. 1974.
30. Hunsberger, Ketcham and Gutowsky, *ibid.*, p. 4839.
31. Leonard, Gutowsky, Middleton and Peterson, *ibid.*, p. 4070.
32. Taufen and Murray, *ibid.*, 1945, **67**, 754.
33. Sinclair, McKay and Jones, *ibid.*, 1952, **74**, 2570.
34. Sinclair, McKay, Myers and Jones, *ibid.*, 2578.
35. Stahl and Pessen, *ibid.*, 5487.
36. Haszeldine, *Nature*, 1951, **168**, 1028.
37. Husted and Ahlbrecht, *J. Amer. Chem. Soc.*, 1953, **75**, 1607.
38. Rappaport, Hauptschein, O'Brien and Filler, *ibid.*, 2695.
39. Fürst, Kuhn, Scotoni and Günthard, *Helv. Chim. Acta*, 1952, **35**, 951.
40. Dauben, Haerger and Freeman, *J. Amer. Chem. Soc.*, 1953, **74**, 5206.
41. Searles, Tamres and Barrow, *J. Amer. Chem. Soc.*, 1953, **75**, 71.
42. Jones and Herling, *J. Org. Chem.*, 1954, **19**, 1252.
43. Jones and Sandorfy, *Chemical Applications of Spectroscopy* (Interscience, New York), 1956.
44. Barrow, *J. Chem. Phys.*, 1953, **21**, 2008.
45. Francis, *ibid.*, 1951, **19**, 942.
46. Felton and Orr, *J. Chem. Soc.*, 1955, 2170.
47. Allan, Meakins and Whiting, *ibid.*, 1874.
48. Bellamy, *ibid.*, 4221.
49. Bender, *J. Amer. Chem. Soc.*, 1954, **75**, 5986.
50. Filler, *ibid.*, 1376.
51. McBee and Christman, *ibid.*, 1955, **77**, 755.
52. Josien and Calas, *Compt. Rend. Acad. Sci. (Paris)*, 1955, **240**, 1641.
53. Bellamy and Williams, *J. Chem. Soc.*, 1957, 4294.
54. *Idem, ibid.*, 1957, 861.
55. Hunsberger, Lednicer, Gutowsky, Bunker and Tunsoig, *J. Amer. Chem. Soc.*, 1955, **77**, 2466.
56. Bellamy and Beecher, *J. Chem. Soc.*, 1954, 4487.
57. Wilder and Winston, *J. Amer. Chem. Soc.*, 1955, **76**, 5598.
58. Grundmann and Kober, *ibid.*, 2332.
59. Brügel, Dury, Stengel and Suter, *Angew. Chem.*, 1956, **68**, 440.
60. Brügel, Stengal, Reicheneder and Suter, *ibid.*, 441.
61. Berson, *J. Amer. Chem. Soc.*, 1954, **76**, 4975.
62. Fowler and Smith, *J. Opt. Soc. Amer.*, 1953, **43**, 1054.
63. Russell and Thompson, *J. Chem. Soc.*, 1955, 479.
64. Rosenkrantz and Skrogstrom, *J. Amer. Chem. Soc.*, 1955, **77**, 2237.
65. Jones and Herling, *J. Amer. Chem. Soc.*, 1956, **78**, 1152.
66. Allsop, Cole, White and Willis, *J. Chem. Soc.*, 1956, 4868.
67. Kendall, Hampton, Hausdorff and Pristera, *App. Spectroscopy*, 1953, **7**, 179.
68. Henbest and Lovell, *J. Chem. Soc.*, 1957, 1965.

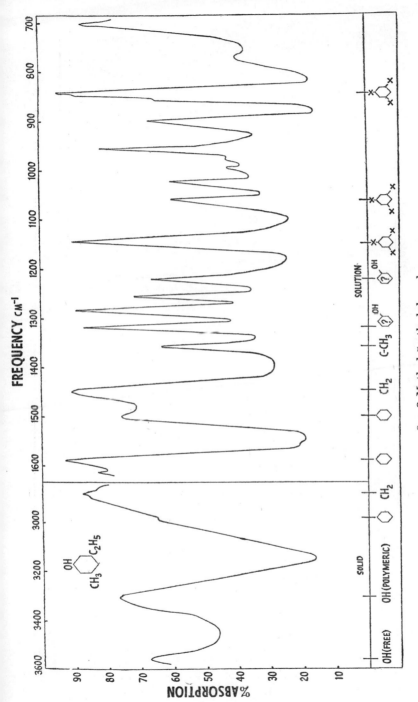

8. 3-Methyl-5-ethylphenol

193

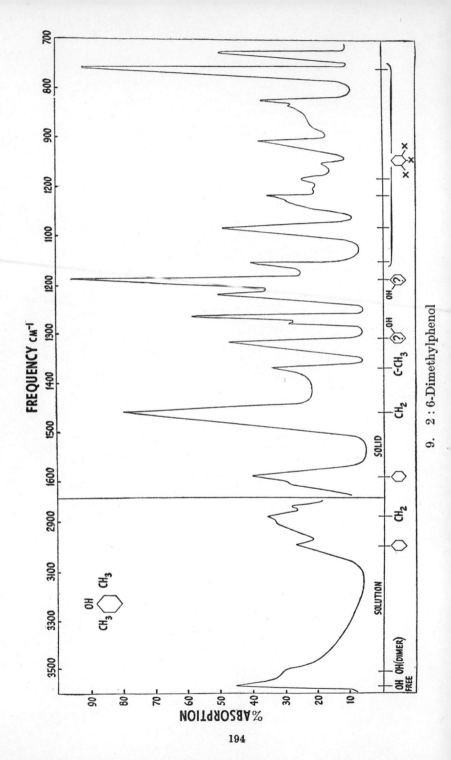

9. 2 : 6-Dimethylphenol

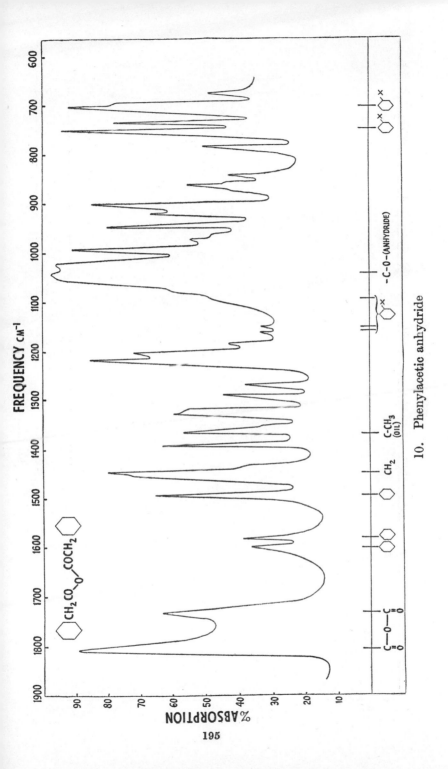

10. Phenylacetic anhydride

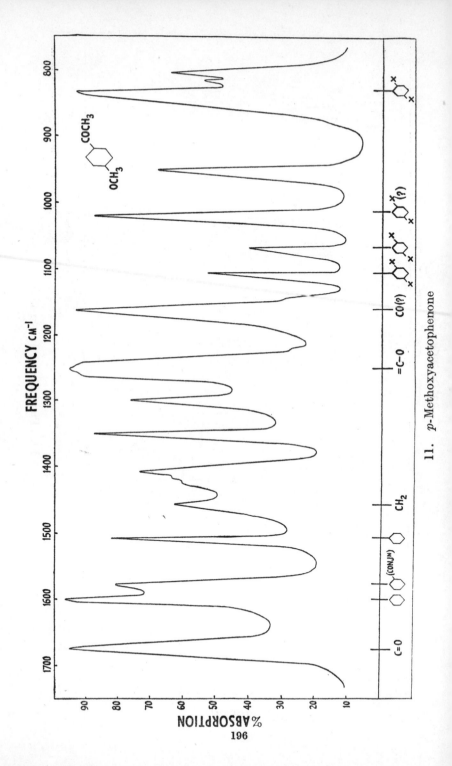

FREQUENCY cm⁻¹

11. *p*-Methoxyacetophenone

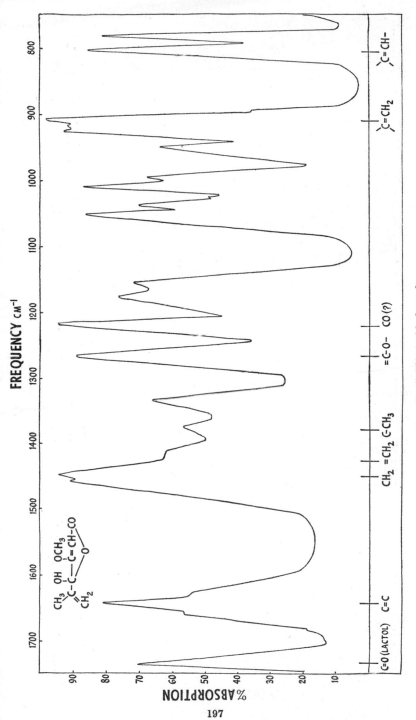

12. Penicillic acid (lactol)

197

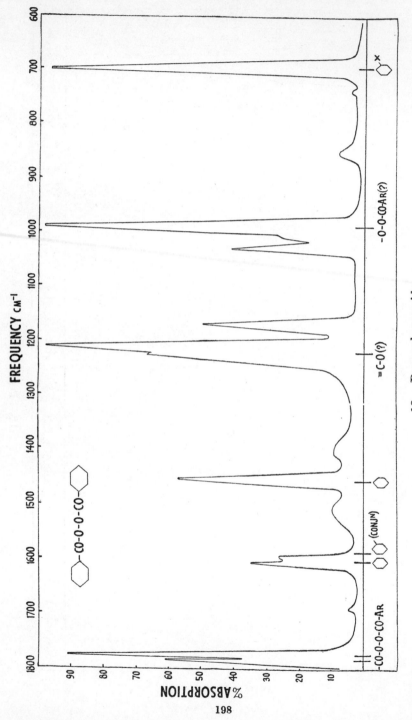

13. Benzoyl peroxide

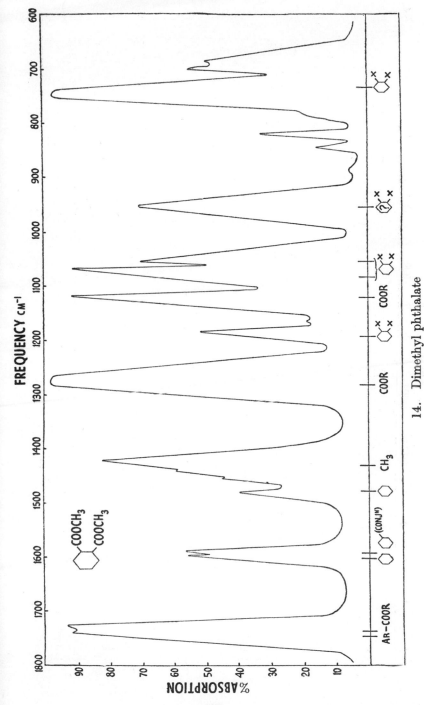

14. Dimethyl phthalate

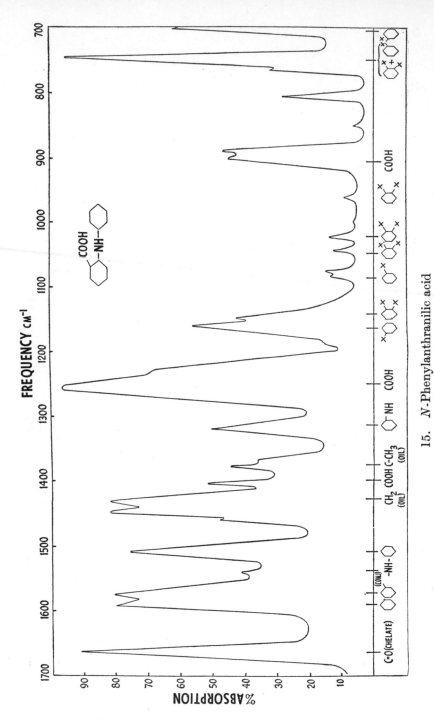

15. *N*-Phenylanthranilic acid

PART III

VIBRATIONS INVOLVING MAINLY CARBON–NITROGEN AND NITROGEN–HYDROGEN LINKAGES

CHAPTER 12

Amides, Proteins and Polypeptides

12.1. INTRODUCTION AND TABLE

PRIMARY and secondary amides can theoretically exist in either a keto or enol form, R–CO–NH– or R–C(OH)=N–, each of which would probably be stabilised by resonance with a dipolar form such as R–C$\overset{O^-}{=}$NH$^+$– or R–C$\overset{OH^+}{-}$N$^-$–. Hantzsch [1] did in fact postulate the enolic form for a number of simple amides on the basis of ultraviolet absorption spectra, whereas X-ray measurements [2] indicate that in the solid state these compounds exist as ring polymers, and that the occurrence of an enolic form is very unlikely. This is further supported by chemical evidence such as the fact that 2-hydroxypyridines exist wholly in the lactam form, despite the potential stabilisation which would be afforded to the lactim by the resonance of the ring. [70] Dipole-moment data lead to a similar conclusion, [71-73, 106] and the infra-red evidence from both amides and hydroxypyridines fully supports the ketonic structure.

In consequence all amides can be expected to show a carbonyl absorption, the frequency of which will be influenced to some extent by the dipolar structure with which it can resonate. It will also be affected to a lesser extent by the nature of the R group adjacent to the carbonyl. This absorption is termed the amide I band and is common to all types of amide, including cyclic forms. Its frequency is, however, markedly affected by hydrogen-bonding effects, so that considerable shifts can occur on passing from the solid to solution. This applies with even greater force to the other characteristic amide bands, so that in correlation work on amides and related materials particular attention must be paid to the physical state in which the material is examined.

In addition to the carbonyl absorption, primary and secondary amides show characteristic bands originating in NH modes which, taken together with the first, are usually sufficient to characterise an amide grouping with reasonable certainty. Primary amides show two NH stretching modes corresponding to the asymmetric and symmetric motions of the hydrogen atoms, whilst secondary amides usually show only a single absorption, the position of which depends on whether the compound exists in the cis- or trans-form. Most secondary amides show frequencies corresponding to both forms in solution, although that from the trans-isomer predominates in nearly all cases.[74] Again, hydrogen bonding effects give rise to considerable shifts in the solid state, and absorptions from both free and bonded NH vibrations can often be observed together in concentrated solutions. The position of the bonded NH absorptions varies also with the nature of the hydrogen bonds concerned, and there are, for example, differences between the NH frequencies of secondary amides bonded in the *cis-* and *trans*-forms. With many secondary amides a second NH absorption is found at lower frequencies, whilst with more complex materials such as polypeptides and proteins, multiple absorptions occur in this region. Di-ketopiperazine, for example, in the solid state shows five bands, all of which are believed to be associated with NH stretching modes. The interpretation of these complex absorptions will be considered separately in the section dealing with polypeptides and proteins. It should be noted, however, that marked differences exist between the behaviour of OH and NH groups with changes of state. For example, *N*-ethyl acetamide and similar materials [75, 76] show a progressive change in the NH frequency with increasing concentration, in contrast to the more discreet shifts of the OH absorptions. This has led various workers to suggest that differences in mechanism may be involved. It has been suggested, for example, that proton transfer may take place in amides,[77] although it is difficult to see how this could fail to lead to the existence of keto-enol forms. An alternative suggestion, due to Cannon,[76, 78] is that dipolar interactions between the $^-OCN^+$ groups play a more considerable part than direct hydrogen bonds in some secondary amides.

The NH_2 deformation mode in primary amides is to be expected in the 1600 cm.$^{-1}$ region, and the absorption which is found here in all such compounds (amide II band) is generally ascribed to this cause. However, secondary amides also exhibit a strong characteristic band at rather lower frequencies, the origin of which is the subject of much controversy. It has been variously assigned as an NH deformation mode, a C–N stretching mode and as a mixed vibration involving both types of motion. In our present state of knowledge none of the proposed explanations is able to explain satisfactorily all the observed facts but, whatever its origin may be, the consistent appearance of this band in all non-cyclic secondary amides has proved to be extremely valuable in correlation work. The band is accompanied in secondary amides by a weaker absorption (Amide III), near 1300 cm.$^{-1}$. This is found in both cyclic and open-chain compounds. In primary amides it falls near 1400 cm.$^{-1}$ and is assignable to the C–N stretching mode.

Changes in the C=O frequencies of amides corresponding to ring strain, occur in lactams with small rings, and the frequency is also altered by fusion of the lactam ring with another cyclic structure in which the nitrogen atom loses its attached hydrogen atom. There are also differences in the hydrogen-bonded NH stretching modes of

TABLE 12

NH *Stretching Modes*

Primary amides (free NH)	Near 3500 cm.$^{-1}$ and 3400 cm.$^{-1}$ (m.)	
„ (bonded NH) . . .	Near 3350 cm.$^{-1}$ and 3180 cm.$^{-1}$ (m.	
Secondary amides (free NH) (*trans*-) . .	3460–3400	cm.$^{-1}$) (m.)
„ „ (*cis*-). . .	3440–3420	cm.$^{-1}$ (m.)
„ (bonded NH) (*trans*-) . .	3320–3270	cm.$^{-1}$ (m.)
„ „ (*cis*-) . .	3180–3140	cm.$^{-1}$ (m.)
„ „ (*cis*- and *trans*-)	3100–3070	cm.$^{-1}$ (w.)

CO *Absorption* (*Amide I*)

Primary amides .	Solid, near 1650 cm.$^{-1}$. Dilute solutions, near 1690 cm.$^{-1}$ (s.)
Secondary amides .	Solid, 1680–1630 cm.$^{-1}$. Dilute solution, 1700–1670 cm.$^{-1}$ (s.)
Tertiary amides .	Solid and dilute solutions, 1670–1630 cm.$^{-1}$ (s.)
Cyclic amides .	(*a*) Large rings, near 1680 cm.$^{-1}$ (solution) (s.)
	(*b*) γ-Lactams (1) Unfused, near 1700 cm.$^{-1}$ (s.)
	„ (2) Fused, 1750–1700 cm.$^{-1}$
	(*c*) β-Lactams (1) Unfused, 1760–1730 cm.$^{-1}$ (solution) (s.)
	„ (2) Fused (to thiazolidine rings), 1780–1770 cm.$^{-1}$ (solution) (s.)

NH$_2$ *Deformation* (*Amide II*)

Primary amides only	1650–1620 cm.$^{-1}$ (solid) (s.), 1620–1590 cm.$^{-1}$ (solution) (s.)

Amide II

Secondary, non-cyclic amides only .	1570–1515 cm^{-1} (solid) (s.), 1550–1510 cm.$^{-1}$ (solution) (s.)

Amide III

Secondary amides only	Near 1290 cm.$^{-1}$ (m.)

NH *Deformation* (*Amide V*)

Bonded secondary amides only . . .	Near 720 cm.$^{-1}$ (m.) broad.

Other Correlations (*Amide IV and VI Absorptions*)

Secondary amides only	Near 620 cm.$^{-1}$ and 600 cm.$^{-1}$
Primary amides	1420–1400 cm.$^{-1}$ (m.)

cyclic compounds, due to the fact that in these the amide group must exist in the *cis*-form.

In addition, the substitution of other functional groups in the immediate vicinity of the amide link often gives rise to marked spectral changes. The spectra of compounds containing the CO–NH–CO structure, for example, are sufficiently different from those of normal amides to enable them to be differentiated. Urethanes and anilides correspond more closely with normal amides, but in the substituted ureas the interpretation of the 1600 cm.$^{-1}$ region becomes extremely difficult due to the complexity of the NH absorptions. Insofar as it can be recognised, however, the amide carbonyl absorption appears at a normal frequency. Amido-acids have been considered elsewhere (Chapter 13) on account of the affinities they show to amino-acids.

Other characteristic absorptions of secondary amides have been described at lower frequencies, but are of less diagnostic value. These include the out-of-plane NH deformation [79] frequency which occurs near 700 cm.$^{-1}$ and is exceptionally broad in the spectra of solids and concentrated solutions. This has been termed the Amide V absorption by Mizushima *et al.*[80] Assignments of Amide IV and Amide VI bands at still lower frequencies have also been made. These are essentially skeletal vibrations, and they have been discussed further by Miyazawa.[81]

These correlations are listed in Table 12 on p. 205.

12.2. NH STRETCHING VIBRATIONS

12.2(a). Primary Amides. In dilute solutions simple primary amides show two free NH stretching absorptions near 3500 cm.$^{-1}$ and 3400 cm.$^{-1}$, and so are clearly similar to normal amines. Acetamide [3] in dilute chloroform solution, for example, absorbs at 3538 cm.$^{-1}$ and 3420 cm.$^{-1}$

A number of workers [4-9, 82] have studied these absorptions in both the solid state and in solution. The most detailed study is by Cleverley,[83] who has listed both the frequencies and intensities of the free and bonded NH bands of a wide range of amides in chloroform solution. The length and nature of the alkyl side-chain have little effect on these frequencies, which occur in essentially the same positions throughout.

In solutions of moderate concentration both free and bonded absorptions appear and a complex pattern results. *N*-octanamide, for example, in chloroform has its free NH$_2$ absorptions at 3530 and 3415 cm.$^{-1}$, but shows additional bands at 3498, 3345, 3300 and 3182 cm.$^{-1}$. This suggests that different types of association are occurring simultaneously. In the solid state the pattern simplifies again, and two broader NH peaks are found near 3350 and 3180 cm.$^{-1}$.

12.2(b). Secondary Amides. In very dilute solutions simple secondary amides studied under low resolution show only one band in the 3460–3420 cm.$^{-1}$ range.[4, 5, 6, 7] This frequency is much too low to correspond to a hydroxyl absorption, so that in this case the evidence for the keto-structure is strong. Under conditions of high resolution this band can be split into two components in many cases. Amides such as γ-butyrolactam and δ-valerolactam, which can exist only in the *cis*-form, show only one band in the range 3440–3420 cm.$^{-1}$, whilst others such as benzanilide, which has a *trans*-configuration, show a single band at slightly higher frequencies (3460–3440 cm.$^{-1}$). The twin bands shown by most secondary amides have therefore been assigned to the *cis*- and *trans*-rotational isomers,[74] and it becomes possible to estimate the relative proportions of the two by a comparison of their relative intensities. In normal secondary amides such as *N*-methylacetamide the *trans*-form predominates to the extent of 95%, but in sterically hindered compounds, such as *N*-tert.-butylphenylacetamide, the *cis*-form is present to the extent of approximately 70%. In the solid state the absorption frequency is determined largely by the type of hydrogen bonding involved, and in some cases, especially with dipeptides, polypeptides and proteins, two or, in some cases, multiple absorptions are found. With open-chain secondary amides the main NH absorption occurs near 3270 cm.$^{-1}$ in the solid state,[4, 6, 7, 88] In solution both free and bonded NH absorptions are shown, and the frequency of the latter depends very much upon the nature of the solvent and upon the concentration employed.[75, 76, 82] In solids the band is near 3280 cm.$^{-1}$, whilst in solution in carbon tetrachloride it ranges in the case of *N*-ethylacetamide from 3372 to 3309 cm.$^{-1}$, depending on the concentration.[75, 76] This is generally accepted as evidence that variations in the length of the polymer chain are taking place.

The assignment of these bands to a bonded NH absorption is supported by deuteration work, and by work on simple amines under conditions in which NH . . . O=C hydrogen bonds are formed. On exchange of the NH hydrogen atom for D by D_2O treatment, the 3280 cm.$^{-1}$ band in a number of simple secondary amides has been shown to shift to 2450 cm.$^{-1}$, which is the expected position for the corresponding ND vibration.[5, 9] Under conditions of suitable resolution this band can again be resolved into a doublet corresponding to the *cis*- and *trans*-forms. In addition, diphenylamine absorbs near 3320 cm.$^{-1}$ under conditions which permit an intermolecular NH . . . O=C bond to be formed.[4] In dilute solution diphenylamine absorbs at 3430 cm.$^{-1}$, and in the solid state this is replaced by a broader band at 3380 cm.[1], due to the formation of NH . . . N hydrogen bonds. In solutions to which *NN*-diethylacetamide is added, however, the frequency falls to 3320 cm.$^{-1}$, indicating

P

that the NH . . . O=C bond is considerably stronger and that it is not very far removed from the observed frequency in solid secondary amides. Mizushima *et al.*[84] have carried out related studies in which the proton-accepting and donating powers of amides are compared with those of phenol and of aniline, and concluded that their proton-donating properties are about equal to those of alcohols and greater than those of amines.

In addition to the main 3280 cm.$^{-1}$ absorption, a number of secondary amides absorb more weakly at 3080 cm.$^{-1}$. This band is also associated with NH modes and, like the 3280 cm.$^{-1}$ band, it vanishes in dilute solution and is replaced by a single absorption at 3420 cm.$^{-1}$. This band is of particular interest in the spectra of polypeptides and proteins, in which it almost always occurs, and will therefore be dealt with in the following section, but the fact that it also occurs in many simple secondary amides should not be overlooked. Both these absorptions occur in comparable positions also in thioamide structures.[85]

Cyclic lactams and related products are similar to the open-chain materials in dilute solutions,[6, 10, 16] and absorb near 3420 cm.$^{-1}$. However, in the condensed phase the band near 3280 cm.$^{-1}$ is not shown, but is replaced by another at 3175 cm.$^{-1}$. In solution this band occurs at 3220 cm.$^{-1}$, and the frequency is independent of concentration.[75] This suggests that only a dimeric species is present in such cases. These materials also show the 3080 cm.$^{-1}$ band, which is usually more intense than in open-chain amides. The differences between the NH frequencies of these two types of amide in the condensed phase have led Darmon and Sutherland [6,10] to suggest that the 3290 cm.$^{-1}$ absorption is d ue to amides which ar hydrogen bonded in the *trans*-form I

I.

whereas the 3175 cm.$^{-1}$ absorption arises from the *cis* arrangement such as in II or III.

II.   or   III.

The fact that the 3175 cm.$^{-1}$ band is observed only in cyclic lactams in which the *cis*-configuration must exist, provides strong support for this view, particularly as there is now a good deal of evidence available from both infra-red and dipole moment studies which confirms that open-chain amides exist predominantly in the *trans*-configuration.[73, 74, 86, 87]

At one time it was suggested that the 3080 cm.$^{-1}$ band might also be associated mainly with the *cis* type of bridge,[6, 7] but later work has indicated that other factors are operative in this case, and this view is not now generally held.[10, 11, 12, 90] When examining spectra for the presence of the 3080 cm.$^{-1}$ band it should be borne in mind that aromatic compounds generally, including anilides, absorb in this region due to the stretching motions of the ring hydrogen atoms.

12.3. THE AMIDE I BAND (THE CARBONYL ABSORPTION)

12.3(a). General. All amides show a strong absorption band near 1640 cm.$^{-1}$ when examined in the solid state. In NN-di-substituted materials there is no question but that this derives from the carbonyl absorption, as enolic forms are not possible. The fact that the absorption is at an appreciably lower frequency than the carbonyl absorption of normal ketones must be due to the resonance effect with the ionic form. This is enhanced by the strong association effects in the solid state, and the corresponding vapours absorb at considerably higher frequencies. Formamide, for example,[89] absorbs at 1740 cm.$^{-1}$ as a vapour, falling to 1709 cm.$^{-1}$ in dilute solution in chloroform. Similarly, N-methyl[90] and N-ethylacetamide[75] absorb in the 1720–1715 cm.$^{-1}$ range as vapours, fall to near 1700 cm.$^{-1}$ in dilute solutions, and to 1650 cm.$^{-1}$ in the liquids. These values suggest that the contribution of the ionic form is relatively small in the vapour state. In NN-disubstituted amides in which hydrogen bonding is impossible it is nevertheless likely that strong dipolar association effects play some part in the low frequencies found in the solid state.[76] In simple or N-mono-substituted amides this band could also be interpreted as being due to the C=N stretching motion of the enolic form, as this group also absorbs in this region. However, a number of convincing arguments can be produced which indicate that the assignment to the carbonyl group in all cases is much more probable. Thus the frequency shifts shown by this band on the substitution of electrophilic groups on the nitrogen atom are in the direction which would be expected for a band originating in a carbonyl group and opposite to that which would be expected for a C=N vibration.[4, 9] Similarly, the considerable frequency shifts accompanying changes of state are more readily explained on the basis of the breaking or formation of hydrogen bonds on the carbonyl group, whilst there is also the point that if the amide I band is assigned to the C=N group of the enol form, no other groups remain to which the amide II band of primary and secondary amides can be assigned. This evidence, coupled with the fact that the undoubted carbonyl group of NN-disubstituted amides does in fact absorb at comparatively low frequencies, provides strong support for the ketonic structure of the amide group generally, and the assignment of this band to the CO group is now agreed by all workers in this field, although it is generally accepted that the frequency contains some small contribution from C–N stretching modes.

The precise location of the amide I band is determined by the presence or absence of any substituents on the nitrogen atom and by their electronegativity, by the inclusion of the amide group in a strained ring, by the presence of α-halogen atoms in some cases, and particularly by the physical state in which the samples are examined. All these cases are considered individually below. The special cases such as –CO–NH–CO– and O–CO–NH– structures are not included in the immediate discussion, but are considered collectively later.

12.3(b). Primary Amides. R–CO–NH₂. Simple primary amides examined in the solid state absorb near to 1650 cm.$^{-1}$. No precise range can be given, as the number of samples examined is not large, and interest has focused mainly on the secondary amides in connection with studies on proteins and on penicillin. However, a sufficient number have been examined by various workers [4, 5, 9, 25, 29] to substantiate the correlation. Acetamide appears to be an exception in absorbing at 1694 cm.$^{-1}$ in the solid state,[5] despite the fact that X-ray evidence indicates association in this form. This amide I absorption is subject to considerable alteration on change of state in which hydrogen bonding is broken,[4, 5, 13–15, 25] and is also liable to variations in solution depending on the polarity of the solvent employed.[4] Thus five unsubstituted amides examined by Richards and Thompson [4] in dilute solution in dioxane all absorbed close to 1690 cm.$^{-1}$, in contrast to the 1650 cm.$^{-1}$ value found for the corresponding solids. In concentrated solutions the frequency appeared at some intermediate value depending on the dilution. Thus hexoamide absorbs at 1655 cm.$^{-1}$ in the solid state, at 1668 cm.$^{-1}$ in concentrated solutions and at 1680 cm.$^{-1}$ in dilute solution (chloroform). The corresponding values of 1692 cm.$^{-1}$ and 1672 cm.$^{-1}$ given for this absorption band in dioxan and in methanol [4] indicate the degree of frequency shift likely to be associated with alterations in the type of solvent employed. In chloroform solution all the amides $CH_3(CH_2)_nCONH_2$[91] from $n = 1$ to $n = 10$ absorb consistently at 1679 cm.$^{-1}$. The influence of α-halogen substitution has not been studied in detail, but Haszeldine [65] reports upward frequency shifts in fully fluorinated amides, and trichloroacetamide absorbs [91] in chloroform solution at 1732 cm.$^{-1}$.

12.3(c). Secondary Amides (N-mono-substituted Amides) (Open-chain). Until recently, the great majority of studies on secondary amides have been concerned only with their examination in the solid state. Randall *et al.*[5] list the frequencies of some seventy-six such compounds they have examined in this way, mainly in connection with work on penicillin, and many of the results have been conveniently summarised in *The Chemistry of Penicillin*.[9] Simple N-mono-substituted amides,[4, 5, 9] in this state, show the amide I band very close to 1640 cm.$^{-1}$. Richards and Thompson [4] have pointed out, however, that electrophilic substituents on the nitrogen atom can give rise to an increase in this frequency up to 1680 cm.$^{-1}$. This is confirmed by Lacher *et al.*[66] and by Gierer,[92] who have also studied N-chlorinated compounds which show elevated frequencies. Similar effects are observed in the numerous compounds examined by Randall *et al.*,[5] who also found the same effect in very complex amides in which the molecular size and shape would reduce the tendency to complete orientation within the crystal. In dilute solution in inert solvents the carbonyl frequency rises to about 1680 cm.$^{-1}$ for simple monosubstituted amides and up to 1700 cm.$^{-1}$ for anilides and similar products.[4, 5, 9] On the other hand, as is to be expected, the highly complex, and therefore less oriented amides do not show any appreciable shifts in frequency following a change of state. Penicillin, for example, absorbs at 1681–1667 cm.$^{-1}$ in dilute solution and at 1667 cm.$^{-1}$ in the solid state.[9] This failure to show any frequency shift similar to that of simple amides was one of the main difficulties in the initial identification of the amide group in penicillin, and this was resolved only by the demonstration that other complex amides, known to contain the CO–NH– link, showed a similar behaviour. A further complication with complex amides is the fact that differences in crystal form apparently exert a considerable influence on the carbonyl frequencies in some cases. The amide band of sodium benzyl penicillin, for example, occurs near 1700 cm.$^{-1}$ in the crystalline form and near 1667 cm.$^{-1}$ in the amorphous form,[9] whilst there is a further shift to 1650 cm.$^{-1}$ in the free acid.

In view of all these complex effects it is not possible to develop any precise correlations of the amide I band as determined from the solid state, with structure surrounding the carbonyl group. It can be stated that all the neutral amides examined show this band in the over-all range 1680–1630 cm.$^{-1}$, but that, except for some simple amides, no deduction as to the nature of the amide environment can safely be drawn from observations of the exact position of the CO frequency. It might, for example, be expected that the compound $Ph-CO-NH-CH_3$ would show the amide I band at a lower frequency than does $PhCH_2-CO-NH-C_2H_5$ owing to the influence of ring conjugation. In fact there is no significant difference between them [5] and both absorb at 1649 cm.[-1]. Presumably, therefore, any changes due to conjugation are counterbalanced or masked by the effects of crystal packing. The influence of conjugation on amide carbonyl frequencies does not appear to have been studied in open-chain materials, but the effects of α-halogen substitution have been studied by several workers, and their results have been discussed by Bellamy and Williams.[93] Unlike α-halogen ketones, the introduction of a single α-halogen atom does not alter the carbonyl frequency significantly,[94] owing to the fact that the halogen atom takes up a *gauche*-configuration in relation to the carbonyl oxygen. With di- and tri-substituted products, however, a nearer approach of the halogen to the oxygen becomes possible and elevated frequencies are found.[88, 91, 95] Alkyl trifluoromethyl amides of the type CF_3CONHR, for example, absorb in the range 1698–1718 cm.[-1] in the solid state.

The frequency range quoted for solids is limited specifically to neutral products, since amides in which a carboxyl group is also present are anomalous and usually show the amide I band at considerably lower frequencies. The ethyl ester of hippuric acid, for example, absorbs in the normal range at 1650 cm.[-1], whereas the free acid [5] has the amide I band at 1597 cm.[-1]. Randall *et al.*[5] have pointed out that amongst the many amido-acids of this type they have examined, only the α-amido-acids absorb below 1618 cm.[-1], whereas those which are differently substituted absorb between 1680 cm.[-1] and 1618 cm.[-1], the great majority being at the lower end of this range.

More recently a number of simpler mono-substituted amides have been examined as vapours and in various solvents. As mentioned above, the vapour carbonyl frequencies are much closer to those of ketones and suggest that the contribution of the ionic form is quite small under these conditions. In solution the frequency varies with both the nature of the solvent and the concentration studied. The free, carbonyl absorption of *N*-ethyl acetamide, for example, ranges from 1687 to 1663 cm.[-1] over a series of solvents even at concentrations at which hydrogen bonding effects are precluded.[75] At higher concentrations the frequency varies continuously with the concentration, reflecting the changing strengths of the intermolecular bonds.[76, 90] Effects of this type again limit the possibilities of obtaining structural data from the precise frequency shown.

12.3(d). Tertiary Amides. *NN'*-Di-substituted amides are incapable of forming hydrogen bonds, and the carbonyl absorption band is consequently not much influenced by changes in state or in the complexity of the molecule. The band usually falls near 1650 cm.$^{-1}$ unless a phenyl group is substituted on to the nitrogen atom, when it is raised to 1690 cm.$^{-1}$. As with acetanilides, this is due to the competitive effect of the ring for the lone pair electrons of the nitrogen atom. In consequence, the contribution of the ionic form of the amide is reduced and the carbonyl frequency is raised. A similar effect may account for the high frequencies shown by *N*-nitrosoamides, which absorb near 1740 cm.$^{-1}$ in solution,[96] although alternative explanations are possible in this case. Gierer [92] points out that the inverse effect occurs in dimethyl urea, in which the ionic character of the carbonyl is reinforced by the second nitrogen atom so that in the solid state the frequency falls to 1610 cm.$^{-1}$. The consistency of this frequency in solution refers, of course, to non-polar solvents, and in those in which bonding can occur there is an appreciable lowering of the carbonyl frequency. *NN*-Diethylacetamide, for example, absorbs at 1647 cm.$^{-1}$ in dioxane solution, but this falls to 1615 cm.$^{-1}$ in methanol.[4] Randall *et al.*[5] quote an overall range of 1667–1631 cm.$^{-1}$ for this absorption on the basis of eleven materials of this type they have examined, and the values quoted by Richards and Thompson [4] are in agreement with this. As with the secondary amides, this correlation does not always hold when carboxyl groups are substituted elsewhere in the molecule. *l*-*N*-Phenacetylproline, for example, absorbs at 1590 cm.$^{-1}$ in the solid state. In other cases such as *N*-phenacyl-*N*-phenylglycine the carbonyl absorption appears at the top of the normal range in the ester, and very close to the bottom in the free acid.[5] Letaw and Gropp [88] have shown that, as in the case of secondary amides, marked frequency shifts follow the introduction of more than a single halogen atom at the α-position. In this case all the dihalogen-substituted compounds studied showed two carbonyl absorptions in solution, which is consistent with the suggestion that rotational isomerism is involved.

12.3(e). Lactams. The carbonyl absorption of lactams is normal in unstrained rings of six or more carbon atoms, but it shifts towards higher frequencies in smaller rings due to ring strain. This resembles the state of affairs in the lactones, except that in this case an additional variable is introduced by the possibility of their being parts of a fused system of rings with a tertiary nitrogen atom.

Six or more membered Rings. Not very much has been done in this field, but such evidence as exists indicates that the carbonyl absorptions of amide groups included in large ring systems are essentially similar to normal amides.[9] In six-membered ring systems Edwards and Singh [98] find secondary lactams to absorb at 1665 cm.$^{-1}$ in chloroform solution, whilst tertiary systems absorb near

1637 cm.[-1]. The fusion of an additional ring did not in these cases alter the frequency appreciably. They have also made the interesting observation that $\alpha\beta$ unsaturation does not lower the carbonyl frequency of such systems but appears to raise it a little, although the situation is complicated by the appearance of additional bands at lower frequencies. Nevertheless, such behaviour is not unexpected, as in non-planar rings it will not be possible for both the C–N and C–C= links to achieve coplanarity with the carbonyl bond.

Further conjugation is found in systems such as the pyrollidones and quinolones, which have been studied by several groups.[98-101] The spectra are in general more complex, but they give a clear indication that not only 2-hydroxy- but also 4-hydroxypyridines exist in the lactam form. Similar effects occur in pyrimidines, in which there is evidence that a lactam carbonyl frequency occurs in 2- and 4-hydroxy compounds which is absent from the corresponding methoxy derivatives.[102, 103]

Some amino-acid anhydrides containing two secondary amide links in the same six-membered ring have been studied by Brockmann and Musso [107] and appear to be essentially normal.

As regards larger ring systems the carbonyl frequency appears to be essentially unaltered, and occurs near 1670 cm.[-1] in solution. Thus seven-,[85, 104] eight-[104] and nine-membered [18] ring systems have been examined by different workers. Schiedt [105] has studied even larger systems in which he makes the additional observation that in rings of nine or more members the amide II absorption is also found, although it is absent from smaller cyclic systems. This is significant, as dipole moment studies have recently shown that the *trans*-form is favoured in ring systems of this size.[114]

Five-membered Rings. Only a limited number of simple γ-lactams have been studied, although more data are available on heterocyclic systems such as oxazalones, etc.

γ-Butyrolactam [5] absorbs in the liquid state and in solution [75, 85] at 1700 cm.[-1], and at 1754 cm.[-1] in the vapour phase,[85] whilst a series of fused γ-lactams examined in connection with penicillin studies, indicated that the carbonyl group has a frequency of about 1750–1700 cm.[-1] with the greater proportion lying towards the lower end of this range.[9, 64]

Four-membered Rings. In view of the interest in penicillin a much greater number of β-lactams of various types have been studied. In all, seventeen unfused β-lactams have been examined by British and American workers,[9] and the carbonyl absorption found to be within the range 1760–1730 cm.[-1] (in solution). In samples examined in the solid state the overall range was somewhat wider, but shifts on passing from one state to another were often not large. With fused β-lactams coupled to thiazolidine rings the frequency was raised considerably, and in the three examples studied it lay in the narrow range 1780–1770 cm.$^{-1}$ in solution. In the solid state the absorptions were only a few cm.$^{-1}$ less. This value compares with the 1779 cm.$^{-1}$ band which is assigned to the β-lactam group of penicillin, and it is interesting to note how this value falls to 1739 cm.$^{-1}$ in desthiopenicillin in which the β-lactam ring remains, but in which it is no longer fused to the thiazolidine ring.

Subsequent to this work a considerable number of β-lactams have been examined by Sheehan [19-24] and co-workers in connection with synthetic studies. Their findings essentially confirm those of the earlier workers, although they have noted that the substitution of two COOR groups on the α-carbon to the amide nitrogen results in a high-frequency shift into the 1770 cm.$^{-1}$ region in unfused β-lactams, so that it is clear that fusion is not the only factor involved. Furthermore, they have found that fused thiazolidine β-lactams exhibit an even greater CO shift into the 1800 cm.$^{-1}$ region following oxidation of the sulphur atom of the thiazolidine ring to the sulphone. The fact that a change in a grouping so far removed from the carbonyl group results in so big a shift indicates the need for caution in the interpretation of CO frequencies in this region. It emphasises also that the correlations developed for fused β-lactams are based solely on β-lactam/thiazolidine structures, and will not necessarily be applicable directly to any other type of fused ring system.

12.3(f). The Intensity of the Amide I Band. The great majority of studies on amides have been carried out on samples in the solid state, so that not much is known about factors which may influence the intensity of the carbonyl absorption. Richards and Burton [26] have made a few measurements on the extinction coefficients of some simple amide CO absorptions and found some consistency, but Lenormant [27, 29] states that the intensities are subject to considerable variation, and points out that in *N*-ethylbenzamide the CO band at 1650 cm.$^{-1}$ is appreciably weaker than the amide II band at 1560 cm.$^{-1}$. A similar reversal of the normal intensity pattern occurs in *N*-methylbenzamide, whilst there is a progressive reversal of the intensity pattern of the amide I and II bands throughout the series acetamide, chloroacetamide, dichloroacetamide, trichloroacetamide.[28] However, it is not clear whether this arises from an absolute variation in the intensity of the CO absorption in these cases or from changes in the intensity of the amide II band with which it is compared. Lenormant [27] also points out that the intensity of the CO band can be altered by changes in the alkalinity of the solutions. Jones and Cleverley [91] have made some intensity studies on *N*-alkyl amides and obtained fairly consistent extinction coefficients of 600–800, but the changes in polarity of the carbonyl link which accompany changes of state or of solvent will clearly have a great effect and make work of this kind very difficult. Nevertheless, further work in this field is clearly desirable in view of its considerable importance in polymer studies.

12.4. THE AMIDE II BAND

Primary and secondary amides show a second strong band in the 1600–1500 cm.$^{-1}$ region which is absent from the spectra of tertiary amides and also from those of cyclic lactams under normal conditions. The origins of this band are not definitely established, nor is it clear whether the same cause is responsible in the two cases. Nevertheless, the band is referred to generally as the amide II band.

12.4(a). Primary Amides. RCONH$_2$. All primary amides show a second band of weaker intensity very close to the main carbonyl absorption. Usually its intensity is about half to one-third that of the CO absorption, and it lies on the low-frequency side in the range 1650–1620 cm.$^{-1}$ (solids).[4, 5, 9] Randall *et al.*[5] state that, on occasion, it falls on the high-frequency side of the carbonyl absorption, but this effect is not illustrated in any of the spectra of simple amides which they reproduce. In such cases it would be difficult to differentiate between band-shifts and intensity inversion. In some instances the two bands fall so close together in the spectrum of materials examined as solids that only a single band appears. However, owing to the fact that the two bands show frequency shifts in opposite directions following changes of state, the presence of both can be established in this way. Phenacetamide, for example, seems to have a single broad band at 1645 cm.$^{-1}$ in the solid state which is resolved into two bands at 1678 cm.$^{-1}$ and at 1580 cm.$^{-1}$ in dilute solution.[5]

The results of the various workers in this field [4, 5, 9] indicate that the band occurs in the 1650–1620 cm.$^{-1}$ region in the solid state, falling to 1620–1590 cm.$^{-1}$ in dilute solution. In chloroform solution all primary amides CH$_3$(CH$_2$)$_n$CONH$_2$ show this band at 1590–1588 cm.$^{-1}$, with an ε_{max} of 180–210 for all values of n from 1 to 10.[91] The nature of the R group in the RCONH$_2$ structure does not materially affect this frequency, and cyanacetamide, for example, absorbs at 1620 cm.$^{-1}$ (solid). The direction of the frequency shift following the breaking of hydrogen bonds is such as to suggest that a deformation mode is involved, and most authors are agreed that this absorption arises from an NH$_2$ bending motion similar to that shown by simple amines in this region. However, while this conclusion can be tentatively accepted, it should be remembered that some form of C–N interaction such as has been suggested for the secondary amides is also a possibility, and the vibration may be a mixed one, in which, however, the NH deformation is likely to be the predominant factor.

12.4(b). Secondary Amides. RCONHR. The amide II absorption band shown by all secondary amides in the region of 1550 cm.$^{-1}$ (solids) is the centre of much controversy. The many arguments put forward to explain this band cannot be discussed very fully here, but in view of the importance of this assignment in protein studies, a brief account of the main suggestions is given below.

12.4(c). The Origin of the Amide II Band in Secondary Amides. One commonly accepted explanation of this band is that it arises from the NH deformation mode, and that it is therefore similar in origin to the amide II band of unsubstituted amides. This view is supported by its absence in tertiary amides,[4, 9] by the weakening of the band on deuteration,[9, 10, 58] by the directions of frequency shift that accompany changes of state and by polarisation studies which indicate that an in-plane NH deformation is involved.[35] However, this simple explanation is not entirely satisfactory for a number of reasons. It is pointed out, for example, that it does not account for the absence of this absorption in cyclic lactams with less than nine-membered rings. This is not perhaps a very serious objection in itself, as it has been shown by dipole moment studies that smaller ring systems of this type have a *cis*-configuration whilst larger ones are *trans*.[114] In the associated state in which the majority of these studies were made the NH stretching frequency of *cis*-forms is about 100 cm.$^{-1}$ lower than in the *trans*-forms, so that an appreciably higher deformation frequency would be expected. In *cis*-systems the amide II band would be expected to approach very close to the amide I band, and may coincide with it. Nevertheless, other relevant objections remain, as the band is also absent from Raman spectra and the deuteration results are ambiguous, as changes occur in several regions as well as the 1130 cm.$^{-1}$ region in which the ND frequency would be expected.

The most popular of the alternative explanations offered has been the assignment of this band to a C–N stretching motion in which the C–N link has considerable double-bond character due to its resonance with the carbonyl group.[5, 28] This is supported to some extent by deuteration data and is consistent with the results of X-ray work,[34, 67] but has other defects in that it does not account for the absence of the band in tertiary amides, or for the polarisation results.

A third explanation due to Lenormant [27–31] has revived the two-molecular-state theory in a modified form. In this, both amide I and II bands are attributed to carbonyl vibrations. The first arises from the normal keto form and the second from a polar modification associated as a dimer. This theory has been seriously weakened by Gierer's observations [92] that the amide II band persists in vapours when only unassociated molecules are present.

These discordant views have been reconciled, at least in part, by Frazer and Price,[59, 108] who pointed out that it is an over-simplification to consider any single motion of a pair of atoms of the –CO–NH– system in isolation. The double-bond character and charge distribution of both the C=O and C–N links change during the vibration itself, thereby affecting the frequencies of other vibrations of the group. Coupling between these bonds leads to an asymmetric OCN mode (amide I) and a symmetric frequency. The latter then couples with the NH deformation mode. Accordingly, they assign the amide II band as a mixed vibration, which can best be described as an out-of-phase combination of OCN and NH vibrations in which the angular displacement of the hydrogen atom plays the greater part. The corresponding in-phase mode, which has primarily a C–N stretching character, is assigned to the amide III band (see below) and occurs near 1290 cm.$^{-1}$. This view that mixed vibrations are involved has won almost general acceptance, although Mizushima *et al.*[80] prefer to reverse the assignments and regard the amide II band as having more C–N than NH character. In this they have been followed by Becher *et al.*,[111, 112] who have interpreted the results of deuteration studies of dimethyl and methylene ureas along similar lines. Gierer [92] prefers to regard the amide II band as arising from mixing of NH and N–CH$_3$ modes in N-methyl-acetamide, but this is open to a number of serious objections.[90, 109]

The assignment to mixed frequencies does, however, enable the results of deuteration to be explained in a much more satisfactory manner than hitherto, and there can be little doubt that an explanation along these lines is the correct one. Nevertheless, some minor discrepancies remain whichever view is taken of the nature of the mixed modes. For example, Abbott and Ambrose [109] point to difficulties in explaining the results of deuteration of acetanilide along the lines of Frazer and Price's picture, while Mizushima *et al.*[80] themselves point to some discrepancies in their interpretation of the deuteration results. Once it is accepted that both C–N and N–H motions are involved in the amide II and amide III absorptions, it is perhaps somewhat academic to go very deeply into which of them plays the larger part in any one absorption. However, in so far as the amide II band is concerned the results of Mecke *et al.*[85, 110] on thioamides would appear to offer strong support to the views of Frazer and Price. In thioamides the amide II band near 1550 cm.$^{-1}$ is not only strong but is also present in the smaller ring cyclic lactams; on deuteration it moves by almost exactly the predicted amount, establishing it as a pure NH motion. The amide III band, on the other hand, is stationary near 1290 cm.$^{-1}$. It would not therefore seem unreasonable to assume that in normal amides which also have a good deal of C=N character the NH deformation frequency is not very far removed from 1550 cm.$^{-1}$ and that by interaction with the OCN mode it is re-established near this point.

12.4(d). The Frequency Range of the Amide II Band. The position of the amide II absorption in N-mono-substituted amides has been studied by many workers. Richards and Thompson [4] have given the spectra of a substantial number, whilst Randall et al.[5] give details of the band position in 72 mono-substituted amides. The results of several other groups of workers who find comparable results have also been summarised.[9] The frequency range found by these workers is 1570–1515 cm.$^{-1}$ for materials examined in the solid state, a considerable proportion of which absorb near the mean value of 1540 cm.$^{-1}$. Richards and Thompson [9] have shown that electrophilic substituents on the nitrogen atom give a small frequency shift towards longer wave-lengths in some cases, but in N-chloromethyl acetamide the amide II band appears to be absent.[92] Apart from this no specific studies have been made which attempt to relate the band position with the nature of the environment of the amide group. This is partly because the changes following solution and change of state are quite large and would tend to mask any minor differences arising in this way. The presence of carboxyl groups elsewhere in the molecule has not the same marked effect on the amide II absorption as it has on the amide I band, and the direction of any resulting shift is variable. For example, hippuric acid and methylphenaceturate both absorb at 1555 cm.$^{-1}$ (solids), whilst ethyl hippurate and phenaceturic acid both absorb [5] at 1530 cm.$^{-1}$.

In solution the amide II band shifts towards lower frequencies within the range 1650–1510 cm.$^{-1}$; thus methylphenaceturate absorbs at 1555 cm.$^{-1}$ in the solid state, at 1535 cm.$^{-1}$ when molten, and at 1517 cm.$^{-1}$ in dilute solution.[5] This shift to lower frequencies on the breaking of hydrogen bonds is in the opposite direction to that which occurs with absorptions arising from stretching modes, such as the OH and NH absorptions near 3300 cm.$^{-1}$, but is in the direction to be expected from changes in deformation frequencies. As in the case of the amide I band, the extent of the shift on passing from the solid state to dilute solution is influenced by the complexity of the molecule itself. In the complex materials in which considerations of geometry may inhibit the full formation of hydrogen bonds in the crystal lattice, the shifts observed on solutions are small. The 1515 cm.$^{-1}$ band of solid benzyl-penicillin, for example, does not alter appreciably in position on solution. Typical examples of frequency shifts on change of state are given by N-methylacetamide (1565 cm.$^{-1}$ liquid, 1534 cm.$^{-1}$ solution, 1490 cm.$^{-1}$ vapour [87, 90-92]) and by α-chloro-N-methylacetamide [94] (1565 cm.$^{-1}$ solid, 1550 cm.$^{-1}$ liquid, 1515 cm.$^{-1}$ vapour). However, in general, remarkably few data are available on the characteristic frequencies of this absorption in dilute solutions or in the vapour phase.

As indicated earlier, this absorption is absent from cyclic lactams and similar products,[9, 28] but occurs in the related thiolactams. The frequency shows similar variations with state as before. In thiovalerolactam, for example, the amide II band shifts from 1572 to 1513 cm.[-1] on passing from the solid to the vapour phase.[85]

12.5. OTHER CORRELATIONS

12.5(a). Primary Amides. Randall *et al.*[5] have noted the presence of a band in the range 1418–1399 cm.[-1] in all unsubstituted amides they have examined, which is absent from the spectra of *N*-substituted amides. They assign this to the C–N stretching absorption, and regard this as supporting their assignment of the amide II band to a similar origin. However, the number of simple amides they have examined is rather limited, and this correlation has not been discussed by other workers.

For identification work the correlation must in any case be of limited value, in view of the fact that absorption in this region is not specific. We have noted a weak absorption in this region in many nitrogenous non-amides such as diphenylamine, but this does not afford any support for the original assignment, as there is no reason to suppose that the C–N bond has any considerable double-bond character in these compounds.

12.5(b). The Amide III Band. This absorption band occurs in secondary amides [80, 90, 108] in the region 1305–1200 cm.[-1], and is usually notably weaker than either of the amide I or II bands. It is almost certainly due to a mixed vibration involving OCN and N–H modes, and this aspect has already been discussed in relation to the amide II band above. The amide III absorption in normal amides is sensitive to deuteration changes, indicating mixing, but in thioamides it is essentially unchanged, and is then wholly attributable to a C–N mode.[85] Changes of state result in marked shifts in normal amides, but, as is to be expected, these are notably reduced in the thio-derivatives. This band has only recently been positively identified as a characteristic secondary amide absorption, and has not as yet been studied in any great detail.

12.5(c). Skeletal Vibrations. Low-frequency absorptions, termed by Mizushima *et al.*[80] the amide IV and amide VI bands, have been identified in secondary amides near 620 cm.[-1] and near 600 cm.[-1] respectively.[80, 81] They have their origins in skeletal modes, and are of limited use for characterisation purposes.

12.5(d). The Out-of-plane NH Deformation Mode. A characteristic feature of proteins and of secondary amides is an ill-defined absorption with a maximum near 700 cm.[-1]. On deuteration the intensity of this band falls and a new band appears near 530 cm.$^{-1}$. This change by a factor of 1·36 is almost exactly what would be expected for a pure NH deformation mode, and thus characterises this absorption.[79]   On dilution the band weakens, and in secondary amides eventually vanishes altogether at high dilution. It is therefore clearly connected with the associated form of these compounds, and precisely similar bands, behaving in the same way, are observed in thioamides.[85]   The free γ NH frequency corresponding to this mode is not well defined. In N-methyl-acetamide it is assigned at 648 cm.$^{-1}$ in dilute solution,[80] and in eneral it falls below the rock-salt region.

12.6. AMIDES CONTAINING SPECIALISED STRUCTURES

12.6(a). Compounds Containing the Group CO–NH–CO.

The group CO–NH–CO does not commonly occur in open-chain products, but it is found in many cyclic materials, such as hydantoin succinimide and the purines and related products. The possibilities of tautomerism of certain of the uracils and pyrimidines will be discussed in Chapter 16 and will not be dealt with here. The remaining materials show a single, bonded amide NH absorption in the 3200 cm.$^{-1}$ region, and from the limited number examined [5] the absorption would appear to be similar to that of cyclic lactams occurring at lower frequencies than in open-chain products.

The carbonyl absorptions of these materials [5] appear as two widely separated bands in the regions 1790–1720 cm.$^{-1}$ and 1710–1670 cm.$^{-1}$. The first of these is assigned to the 4-position carbonyl group, as it persists in compounds in which the CO in the 2-position is replaced by C=S. The second could arise from C=N vibrations, but is assigned to the 2-position carbonyl, as it persists in compounds in which the NH group is replaced by N–CH$_3$.

The change from NH to NCH$_3$ compounds does not give rise to any appreciable carbonyl shifts, and as the solid and solution spectra are closely parallel, it is assumed that there is not much hydrogen bonding in the solid state.[5] However, it is difficult to reconcile this conclusion with the low frequencies reported for the NH stretching band in the solid state and in dilute solutions, and more work in this field would appear desirable.

With cyclic compounds containing three carbonyl groups, those immediately adjacent to the NH group behave as above, whilst the third shows a normal CO absorption. The spectra of six trialkyl pyr-rolidine triones examined by Skinner and Perkins [32] show absorptions at 1786 cm.$^{-1}$, 1724 cm.$^{-1}$ and 1667 cm.$^{-1}$. The absorption at 1724 cm.$^{-1}$ is attributed to the CO group in the 3 position.

12.6(b). Compounds Containing the Group R–NH–CO–OR.

In compounds of this type the carbonyl absorption responsible for the amide I band is likely to be lowered in frequency by the NH group as in normal amides, but the C–O–R residue will exert an influence in the opposite direction, as it does in the case of esters the carbonyl absorption of which is higher than that of ketones. This expectation is realised in practice, at least as far as the urethanes examined by Randall *et al.*[5] and the carbamates examined by ourselves are concerned. The amide I band of a series of urethanes falls [5] in the range 1736–1700 cm.$^{-1}$, whilst a small series of variously substituted carbamates show this band in the range 1710–1690 cm.$^{-1}$. The amide II band appears at the normal position in the NH compounds, and this may be regarded as affording some slight supporting evidence for the predominance in the amide II band of the NH deformation rather than the OCN link, which might be expected to be more influenced by the change from C–N–C– to C–N–O–. Urethane itself absorbs at 1618 cm.$^{-1}$, corresponding to the amide II absorption of an unsubstituted amide, whilst the NN-di-substituted products show no band in this region. The simple N-mono-substituted urethanes [5] and carbamates show their NH stretching absorption for the solid products in the 3300–3250 cm.$^{-1}$ region, which is normal for open-chain amides.

This same residue occurs in cyclic systems, such as the oxazolones, which have been studied by Gompper and Herlinger [115] and compared with the corresponding thioketo compounds. The carbonyl frequency then falls near 1750 cm.$^{-1}$, and the amide III absorption is raised to 1380 cm.$^{-1}$.

12.6(c). Anilides Ph–NHCOR. The substitution of an aromatic residue on the amide nitrogen does not have any very significant influence on the spectrum, apart from raising the frequency of the amide I band due to the carbonyl group by a small amount. Richards and Thompson [4] found the CO band of a series of anilides to be at 1700 cm.$^{-1}$ in dilute solution, and this value was further increased to 1715 cm.$^{-1}$ in compounds in which the substituents on the ring increase their electron attracting properties. The amide II band appeared to be much less subject to alteration in this way, and only small shifts to lower frequencies could be detected. Gierer [92] records essentially similar results for a series of acetanilides with different ring substituents. In the solid state the arylamides show the CO absorption at rather higher frequencies than alkylamides. The spectra of a considerable range of anilides of fatty acids have been recorded by Dijkstra and De Jonge.[116]

The NH stretching absorptions are normal for open-chain amides and occur near 3270 cm.$^{-1}$ (solid), but the identification of any possible additional absorption in the 3070 cm.$^{-1}$ region is prevented in this case by the CH aromatic absorptions which fall in the same region.

12.6(d). Substituted Urea Derivatives –NHCONH– etc. The spectra of urea derivatives have been examined by Thompson, Nicholson and Short,[25] by Randall *et al.*,[5] by Boivin and Boivin,[117, 118] and by Becker.[111, 112] However, it is not possible to interpret the results fully, as the spectra are often complex and the possibilities of the existence of various dipolar and enolic forms are considerable. However, the CO absorption appears near 1660 cm.$^{-1}$ in fully substituted ureas, and a band in this region is also shown by the mono- and di-substituted products which can reasonably be assigned to the same cause. The NH absorptions are, however, more complex. Both acetyl and phenacetyl urea show absorption at 1634 cm.$^{-1}$ which might be assigned to the NH_2 deformation,[5] but there is no sign of any corresponding band at lower frequencies which might be expected from the substituted NH group. Deuteration studies on dimethyl urea and methylene ureas have been helpful in assigning the appropriate amide bands,[111, 112] and data are also available on the thioureas for comparison.[85, 110] Nevertheless, the interpretation of these complex spectra remains a matter of great difficulty. Gompper *et al.*[115] have discussed the characteristic frequencies of the NH–CO–N– grouping in cyclic systems.

12.6(e). Compounds Containing the Group R–CO–NH–N–. These compounds appear to be little affected by the presence of the additional nitrogen atom, and the spectrum of diformylhydrazine, for example, does not differ very greatly from that of other secondary amides.[80] In cyclic systems, such as pyrazolones, however, it is much more difficult to identify the characteristic amide frequencies due to the multiplicity of bands which occur.[119, 120]

12.7. POLYPEPTIDES AND PROTEINS

12.7(a). General. The possibility that infra-red methods would throw some light on the problem of the structures of proteins and similar materials was appreciated by a number of relatively early workers in this field.[13-15, 36-40] These workers were able to show that proteins exhibited a common pattern of bands, including those at 3300 cm.$^{-1}$ due to hydrogen-bonded NH groups, and the amide I and II bands in the 1600–1500 cm.$^{-1}$ region, whilst the remainder of the spectrum was largely determined by the nature of the component amino-acids. In addition, the weak band near 3080 cm.$^{-1}$ was noted by some workers and assigned tentatively to an additional NH absorption.[40] However, in recent years a stimulus has been given to this work by the development of polarised radiation techniques which enable the internal orientation of certain groupings to be studied. Coupled with advances in the methods of preparation of simple model polypeptides and of improved methods for the purification of proteins themselves, this work is now beginning to yield valuable

Q

results which have been reviewed by Sutherland [121] and by Elliott.[122]

In addition, studies have been made on very simple peptides containing only a few amino-acid residues. In the simpler members the characteristic peptide pattern is dominated by the influence of the zwitterion structures which are undoubtedly present. For this reason they have been discussed separately below, although the results are nevertheless also directly relevant to the discussion which follows on the characteristic frequencies of larger polypeptides.

12.7(b). Simple Peptides. The spectra of simple peptides have been investigated by a number of workers.[25, 41, 123–127] In dipeptides such as glycyl-glycine the influence of the zwitterion structure is greatest and the spectrum is more complex than in the higher members of the series. This compound is known from X-ray studies to exist in the zwitterion form with an open-chain structure.[34] It has NH absorptions at 3300 cm.$^{-1}$, 3080 cm.$^{-1}$, 1630 cm.$^{-1}$, 1575 cm.$^{-1}$, 1540 cm.$^{-1}$ and 1240 cm.$^{-1}$, as indicated by the shifting of these bands on deuteration.[25, 41] The first two correspond to NH stretching absorptions, whilst the 1540 cm.$^{-1}$ band is the normal amide II band which may be an NH deformation. The 1630 cm.$^{-1}$ and 1575 cm.$^{-1}$ bands have parallels in the amino-acid I and II bands and may be associated with the NH_3^+ grouping. The carbonyl group of the peptide link absorbs normally at 1655 cm.$^{-1}$, and there are strong bands at 1608 cm.$^{-1}$ and at 1400 cm.$^{-1}$ which probably correspond to the COO^- group. Edsall has found a similar 1400 cm.$^{-1}$ absorption in the Raman spectrum.[42] A weak band near 1680 cm.$^{-1}$ in the infra-red has been found by both the main groups of workers in this field, which is tentatively assigned to the CO of the un-ionised carboxyl group. There is, however, a discrepancy here, as Edsall *et al.*[42] find this band in the Raman spectrum at 1740 cm.$^{-1}$. The assignment is, however, supported by the spectra of the lower polyglycines. Ascending through the series to hexa- and polyglycine the influence of the zwitterion structure becomes progressively less, so that the 1400 cm.$^{-1}$ band (which is the stronger of the two COO^- vibrations) eventually vanishes, whilst the 1680 cm.$^{-1}$ band is retained. Thompson *et al.*[25] report the latter as being strengthened in the higher members, whilst Blout and Linsley [41] say that it is diminished in intensity. This is probably a difference only in words, in that if the band is in fact due to the un-ionised COOH group, its absolute intensity will fall progressively as the chain length and the molecular weight increase, whilst its relative intensity per COOH group will increase due to the increasing proportion of un-ionised carboxyl groups.

None of the polyglycines shows absorption higher than 3330 cm.$^{-1}$, indicating that all the NH groups are capable of hydrogen bonding in the crystal state. The 3300 cm.$^{-1}$ band showed a regular and stepwise increase in intensity relative to the CH_2 absorption with increases in molecular weight, with a tendency towards a limiting value for the absorption ratios as the number of CH groups approached that of the amide links.[41] This affords strong evidence for the assignment to the NH-bonded stretching mode. The 3080 cm.$^{-1}$ band, on the other hand, did not behave in this way, although its correlation with the NH structure is definitely established by deuteration when it vanishes and is replaced by two bands [41] at 2530 and 2480 cm.$^{-1}$. The remaining characteristic absorptions of the higher peptides took on more and more the appearance of the typical protein spectrum as the chain length was increased and the influence of the zwitterion diminished. All the polyglycines absorbed at 1015 cm.$^{-1}$ $\pm$ 10 cm.$^{-1}$, and this may be a characteristic of the diglycine structure,[41] particularly as it is not found in glycyl-alanine or in any other polypeptides in which two glycine residues are not directly linked.[127] Polypeptides from single amino-acids tend to resemble proteins in their spectra as soon as the number of residues is three or more [109] and then exhibit the typical amide absorptions, such as the amide II, III and V bands referred to above.[127] Polyproline and polysarcosine [124] are, of course, somewhat different, as they lack NH links.

Mixed polypeptides have also been studied by both groups of workers.[25, 41] The overall pattern is similar to that of the polyglycines, but a few interesting differences have been noted. In particular, many of the glycine–leucine peptides show absorptions at 3400 cm.$^{-1}$ and 3520 cm.$^{-1}$ in addition to the 3300 cm.$^{-1}$ and 3080 cm.$^{-1}$ absorptions. This clearly indicates the presence of unbonded NH_2 groupings and suggests that the crystal packing of these materials is such that it is not possible for all the terminal NH_2 groups to enter into hydrogen bonding. Interesting results have also been obtained from a study of variations in the optical forms of the amino acids used in their preparation. When more than one asymmetric carbon is present, marked spectral changes follow in some cases. Thus the spectrum of *dl*-glycyl-alanine is identical with that of the *ld*-compound, but differs markedly from the *dd*- or *ll*-forms, which are themselves identical. Similarly, *lll*-trialanine is identical with the *ddd*-form, but shows distinct differences from a mixed isomer preparation.[123] These differences are centred mainly in the NH stretching and the amide I and II absorptions, and are connected with the steric differences introduced. Elliott [126] has also reported small differences between the active and meso forms of polypeptides such as polyglycine, polyalanine, etc. These are more pronounced in the α-folded forms than in the β modifications, but in the former they are still small and amount to shifts of about 9 cm.$^{-1}$ in the carbonyl absorption. A number of simple peptides have also been examined in heavy water solution by Lenormant *et al.*,[62, 128] who have followed the change in the carbonyl and NH_2 absorption following alterations in the pH of the solution. Parallel studies on larger molecules have been made by Ehrlich and Sutherland.[129, 130] These have established that the band at 1550 cm.$^{-1}$ contains contributions from both the COO^- and the amide II absorptions. In consequence, the changes in the state of ionisation which occur on denaturation of such materials will affect this absorption independently of any accompanying configurational changes.

Acetylated compounds with no residual NH_2 or COOH groups have also been studied.[25, 43, 131, 132] The spectra in these cases are much more like those of the polyamides in the 3080 cm.$^{-1}$ and 1600 cm.$^{-1}$ region. In studies on compounds such as acetylglycine-*N*-methyl-amide, Mizushima and co-workers[8, 43, 63, 68] have reported the persistence of a band near 3330 cm.$^{-1}$, in addition to the free NH absorption at 3450 cm.$^{-1}$, in dilute solution in carbon tetrachloride. Further, more detailed, studies[44, 132, 137] have shown that both inter- and intra-molecular bonding can lead to absorption at this point, so the interpretation of structure from this region is very difficult. In acetylproline -*N*-methylamide the molecules all assume a folded configuration in carbon tetrachloride, but in chloroform, in which the tendency to hydrogen bonding is reduced, a second configuration can arise, capable of intermolecular bonding. This tendency is increased in acetyl piperidine α-carboxylic acid *N*-methylamide,[132] in which steric effects reduce further the tendency to intramolecular hydrogen bonds. In dilute solution in carbon tetrachloride this material exhibits absorption at 3390 cm.$^{-1}$ assigned to intramolecular bonds, accompanied by another band at 3367 cm.$^{-1}$ due to intermolecular links. This evidence is indicative of the difficulty in assigning 3280 cm.$^{-1}$ absorption of proteins wholly to *trans*-intermolecular bonding.

12.7(c). The NH Stretching Band near 3330 cm.$^{-1}$. The band centred near 3330 cm.$^{-1}$ is certainly due to a bonded NH structure, as shown by deuteration and polarisation studies. As with the simpler peptides, there has been much discussion as to whether this band can be regarded as arising wholly from a *trans*-type hydrogen bond between chains or whether intramolecular bonds are involved, or both. It has been shown that poly-γ-benzyl-α-glutamate does not absorb at 3450 cm.$^{-1}$ in dilute chloroform solution, indicating that all the NH groups are able to bond within the molecule itself. In contrast, polycarbobenzoxy-*dl*-lysine, which has NH and CO groups in both the main and the side-chains, does absorb at 3450 cm.$^{-1}$ under these conditions, indicating that the polypeptide chains are then effectively isolated.[11, 49, 51] The folding of the chains in solution may be different from that in the solid state, but it does afford evidence that in the α folded form the hydrogen bonds of the peptide links are intramolecular in this case. On the other hand, Shigorin *et al.*,[133-135] on the basis of studies with polycaprolactams and similar products, assign the 3300 cm.$^{-1}$ absorption wholly to intermolecular bonding, and associate the weaker absorption near 3200 cm.$^{-1}$ with intramolecular association. As with the simpler peptides, it is probable that both types of association give rise to absorption near 3300 cm.$^{-1}$. Thus both poly-γ-benzyl-*l*-glutamate [136] and poly-α-*l*-glutamic acid [137] can be prepared in two distinct modifications which differ in the directions of orientation of the NH group. One is probably a coiled α-form with intramolecular bonds, and the other is an open or random form. Both absorb close to 3300 cm.$^{-1}$. Similarly, nylon and other large synthetic polymers in which intramolecular bonding is improbable also absorb near this point. The interpretation of changes in intensity in this band, such as those which follow denaturation,[45] is therefore very difficult.

As mentioned earlier, the 3300 cm.$^{-1}$ absorption is accompanied [50] by a weaker absorption near 3200 cm.$^{-1}$. This is assigned by Shigorin *et al.*[133, 135] to intramolecular association only, but their evidence for this would not appear to be conclusive in view of the data quoted above and of the fact that both α- and β-keratins absorb at this point.[135]

12.7(d). The NH Stretching Band near 3080 cm.$^{-1}$. Originally this band was assigned as being due to intramolecular hydrogen bonds of the NH group additional to the interchain bonds which give rise to the 3330 cm.$^{-1}$ absorption.[6, 7] Later work has, however, indicated that other factors are involved. The fact that this band becomes progressively weaker in nylon as the temperature is raised, without any shift in frequency, is evidence that it is a weaker bond than that responsible for the 3330 cm.$^{-1}$ band, despite its lower frequency. Many different suggestions have been made as to the origin of this band. For example, it has been suggested that interactions in the crystal state are responsible,[12] that it arises from " twinning " *cis* intermolecular bonds,[134] from *cis-* and *trans*-modifications, from combination tones of the NH frequency with low-frequency fundamentals of the associated forms, or that together with the 3300 cm.$^{-1}$ band it represents the normal NH modes of a sequence of coupled oscillators. The most recent discussion of this problem assigns this band as an overtone of the amide II absorption in accordance with earlier suggestions by Badger.[82]

It will be seen that no simple explanation of the bands in this region is possible at present, especially as some of the simpler compounds, such as diketopiperazine, which might be expected to afford a useful lead, are in fact more complex and show multiple absorptions.

12.7(e). The Amide I and II Bands. The amide I and II absorptions appear in all polypeptides and proteins. The majority of these materials absorb in the normal 1650 cm.$^{-1}$ and 1550 cm.$^{-1}$ regions, but minor differences occur amongst them which may to some extent reflect changes in the hydrogen bonding pattern. The cyclic peptide gramicidin,[47] for example, absorbs at 1610 cm.$^{-1}$ and 1513 cm.$^{-1}$. The influence of changes in the type of bonding on these absorption frequencies is very well brought out in studies on the folded and extended forms of the same materials, carried out in conjunction with work on dichroism and X-ray patterns.[46, 52, 54] Poly-*l*-glutamic benzyl ester shows the amide CO absorption as a single band at 1658 cm.$^{-1}$, and X-ray evidence indicates that it exists wholly in the α-form. In low-molecular-weight preparations, however, it exists in a random form or in some uncoiled state, and the amide I absorption then occurs [136] near 1630 cm.$^{-1}$. The counterparts of these forms have been observed in solution.[113] The methyl ester, however, shows two bands at 1658 cm.$^{-1}$ and at 1628 cm.$^{-1}$, of which the latter shows no orientation. When cast from formic acid, in what is believed to be the β form, only the 1629 cm.$^{-1}$ component is shown. Similarly, two amide II frequencies at 1527 cm.$^{-1}$ and 1550 cm.$^{-1}$ correspond to the β and α forms. Hurd *et al.*[69] have also been able to observe carbonyl shifts in synthetic polypeptides following differences in their method of preparation which they ascribe to the existence of α and β forms, and Krimm [138] has suggested that the differences in the carbonyl frequencies may arise from differences in the angles formed by the O . . . H–N– hydrogen bonds. This is, however, disputed by Cannon,[78] who prefers to regard them as arising from different degrees of interaction of the $^-$OCN$^+$ dipoles.

The position of these bands may therefore give some indication of the molecular form, but in the solid state other factors also may be involved. For example, on raising the temperature of nylon, frequency shifts of the CO and NH bands occur which are very similar to those described for a change from the α to β form, although there is strong evidence that nylon retains the extended β form under these conditions.[48] Similarly, an absorption in the 1625 cm.$^{-1}$ region in chitin has been tentatively assigned to an amide CO group which is hydrogen bonded to an OH group.[55] The interpretation of the amide II frequencies is also fraught with considerable difficulties. Marked changes in these bands occur, for example, on deuteration as well as on change of configuration,[128, 139, 140] whilst the presence of the ionised carboxyl absorption in the same region can also lead to confusion. In many proteins the amide II absorption is in part overlaid by the ionised carboxyl band, so changes which occur in this region with changes of state may only reflect

the alteration in the COO⁻ group on moving away from the iso-
electric point.[128, 129, 130, 137] The interpretation of group frequencies
in this region therefore calls for great caution.

Some useful data on proteins can also be obtained from the
overtone region, especially as it then becomes possible to work in
the presence of liquid water. These absorptions also show dichroism,
but it must not necessarily be assumed that this will be always in
the same direction as the parent fundamental, and many of the bands
in this region are combination bands arising from more than one
fundamental. Thus a band near 4600 cm.$^{-1}$ in many proteins was
originally identified with the carbonyl absorption [53] as it shifts with
alterations of the helical form and is present in polymethylmeth-
acrylate but absent in polyethylene. However, this has recently
been shown by Hecht and Wood [141] to be a combination band of
$2\nu CO$ with the 1250 cm.$^{-1}$ absorption. These workers have also
elucidated the origins of a number of other high-frequency absorptions of this type, and Frazer [142] has also discussed assignments in
this region and the significance of the results of dichroic studies.

12.8. INFRA-RED DICHROISM IN PROTEIN STUDIES

The use of polarised infra-red for studying the orientation of
specific groupings within a crystal or oriented film has now been in
vogue for several years. It consists simply in passing polarised radiation through the sample in two directions at right angles and observing
the intensity changes which occur in certain bands. In this way the
orientation of individual groups in relation to the whole can be
studied. This method, which was applied by Glatt *et al.* to proteins
in 1947,[56, 57] has since been extensively used by others in this field,
and a substantial body of evidence has been built up which indicates
that differentiation between the folded (α) and extended (β) forms of
proteins and polypeptides is possible in this way.[46, 49–51, 59, 61, 125]
Useful reviews of this technique have recently been given by
Elliott [122] and by Bamford *et al.*[17]

Ambrose, Elliot and Temple [46] studied the NH stretching absorptions of oriented polyglutamic esters, α- and β-keratins, and oriented
myosin and tropomyosin. In all cases in which the material is
believed to exist in the folded α-form the NH stretching bands at
both 3310 cm.$^{-1}$ and 3060 cm.$^{-1}$ showed parallel dichroism, whereas
they were markedly perpendicular in feather keratin, which is the
β form. Similar findings in respect of the polyglutamic ester were
reported by Ambrose and Hanby.[51] This excludes the possibility
that the dichroism is shown by side-chain NH groups, as these are
absent from this material. This work was later extended to studies on
the C=O stretching and NH deformation modes,[49, 52] which, in addition to frequency shifts, were found to show changes in their direction

of orientation on change of form. Polyglutamic ester, for example, in the α-form shows strong parallel dichroism. No orientation in the β-form could be obtained, but the CO absorption in a similar co-polymer material showed a complete alteration from the parallel to perpendicular dichroism with a change of form.

The NH deformation modes behave similarly, and in this case the α-form has perpendicular dichroism and the β-form parallel dichroism. Similar data can also be obtained from the 4810 cm.$^{-1}$ band, which arises from a combination of the NH stretch and amide II absorptions.[56, 141] The technique has also been applied to the study of simple secondary amides in crystals.[33, 109]

This interpretation of the results in which only a single form of hydrogen bond is proposed for α-keratin and similar structures was criticised by Darmon and Sutherland [6] as an over-simplification, and they point out that the attachment of numerical values to dichroic ratios is hazardous in view of the discrepancy between the small dichroic ratios found for NH in α-keratin and nylon and the large ratio to be expected.[6]

The need for caution in the interpretation of polarisation studies is indicated by the recent work of Fraser and Price.[59] They point out that the transition moment of the carbonyl stretching mode responsible for the amide I absorption will be displaced from the CO direction due to interaction with the C–N vibration, and to an orbital following effect. They have calculated the dichroism of an oriented poly-peptide in which the chains have the configuration of Pauling and Corey [60] with a 3·7 residue helix, and have shown that if allowance is made for a displacement of the CO transition moment by 20° towards the NO, the dichroic value obtained is very close to that observed experimentally.[54] The objection to the 3·7 helix based on polarisation studies [61] cannot therefore be maintained.

12.9. BIBLIOGRAPHY

1. Hantzsch, *Ber.*, 1931, **64**, 661.
2. Senti and Harker, *J. Amer. Chem. Soc.*, 1940, **62**, 2008.
3. Davies, *Discuss. Faraday Soc.*, 1950, **9**, 325.
4. Richards and Thompson, *J. Chem. Soc.*, 1947, 1248.
5. Randall, Fowler, Fuson and Dangl, *Infra-red Determination of Organic Structures* (Van Nostrand, 1949).
6. Darmon and Sutherland, *Nature*, 1949, **164**, 440.
7. Astbury, Dalgliesh, Darmon and Sutherland, *ibid.*, 1948, **162**, 596.
8. Mizushima, Shimanouchi and Tsuboi, *ibid.*, 1950, **166**, 406.
9. *The Chemistry of Penicillin* (Princeton University Press, 1949), p. 390.
10. Darmon, *Discuss. Faraday Soc.*, 1950, **9**, 325.
11. Elliot and Ambrose, *Nature*, 1950, **165**, 921.
12. Sutherland, *Discuss. Faraday Soc.*, 1950, **9**, 274.
13. Buswell, Rodebush and Roy, *J. Amer. Chem. Soc.*, 1938, **60**, 2444.
14. Buswell, Downing and Rodebush, *ibid.*, 1940, **62**, 2759.
15. Buswell and Gore, *J. Phys. Chem.*, 1942, **46**, 575.
16. Tsuboi, *Bull. Chem. Soc. Japan*, 1949, **22**, 215.

17. Bamford, Brown, Elliott, Hanby and Trotter, *Proc. Roy. Soc.*, 1953, **141B**, 49.
18. Witkop, Patrick and Rosenblum, *J. Amer. Chem. Soc.*, 1951, **73**, 2641.
19. Sheehan and Bose, *ibid.*, 1950, **72**, 5158.
20. *Idem, ibid.*, 1951, **73**, 1761.
21. Sheehan, Hill and Buhle, *ibid.*, p. 4373.
22. Sheehan and Corey, *ibid.*, p. 4756.
23. Sheehan and Laubach, *ibid.*, p. 4752.
24. Sheehan and Ryan, *ibid.*, p. 4367.
25. Thompson, Nicholson and Short, *Discuss. Faraday Soc.*, 1950, **9**, 222.
26. Richards and Burton, *Trans. Faraday Soc.*, 1949, **45**, 874.
27. Lenormant, *Discuss. Faraday Soc.*, 1950, **9**, 319.
28. *Idem, Bull. Soc. chim.*, 1948, **15**, 33.
29. *Idem, Ann. Chim.*, 1950, **5**, 459.
30. Lenormant and Chouteau, *J. Physiol.*, 1949, **A203**, 41.
31. Chouteau and Lenormant, *Compt. rend. Acad. Sci. (Paris)*, 1951, **232**, 1479.
32. Skinner and Perkins, *J. Amer. Chem. Soc.*, 1950, **72**, 5569.
33. Sandeman, *Proc. Roy. Soc.*, 1955, **A232**, 105.
34. Hughes and Moore, *J. Amer. Chem. Soc.*, 1949, **71**, 2618.
35. Elliot, Ambrose and Temple, *J. Chem. Phys.*, 1948, **16**, 877.
36. Stair and Coblentz, *J. Res. Nat. Bur. Stand.*, 1935, **15**, 295.
37. Wright, *J. Biol. Chem.*, 1939, **127**, 137.
38. Bath and Ellis, *J. Phys. Chem.*, 1941, **45**, 204.
39. Lenormant, *Compt. rend. Acad. Sci. (Paris)*, 1945, **221**, 58.
40. Darmon and Sutherland, *J. Amer. Chem. Soc.*, 1947, **69**, 2074.
41. Blout and Linsley, *ibid.*, 1952, **74**, 1946.
42. Edsall, Otvos and Rich, *ibid.*, 1950, **72**, 474.
43. Mizushima, Shimanouchi, Tsuboi, Sugita, Kato and Kondo, *ibid.*, 1951, **73**, 1330.
44. Mizushima, Shimanouchi, Tsuboi and Souda, *ibid.*, 1952, **74**, 270.
45. Uzman and Blout, *Nature*, 1950, **166**, 862.
46. Ambrose, Elliot and Temple, *ibid.*, 1949, **163**, 859.
47. Klotz, Griswold and Gruen, *J. Amer. Chem. Soc.*, 1949, **71**, 1615.
48. Sutherland and Tanner, *Ohio Symposium on Molecular Spectroscopy*, 1951.
49. Elliot and Ambrose, *Discuss. Faraday Soc.*, 1950, **9**, 324.
50. Holliday, *ibid.*, p. 325.
51. Ambrose and Hanby, *Nature*, 1949, **163**, 483.
52. Hanby, Waley and Watson, *J. Chem. Soc.*, 1950, 3239.
53. Ambrose, Elliot and Temple, *Proc. Roy. Soc.*, 1951, **A206**, 192.
54. Ambrose and Elliot, *ibid.*, 1951, **A205**, 47.
55. Darmon and Rudall, *Discuss. Faraday Soc.*, 1950, **9**, 251.
56. Glatt and Ellis, *J. Chem. Phys.*, 1948, **16**, 551.
57. Glatt, *ibid.*, 1947, **15**, 880.
58. Pauling, Corey and Branson, *Proc. U.S. Nat. Acad. Sci.*, 1951, **37**, 205.
59. Fraser and Price, *Nature*, 1952, **170**, 490.
60. Pauling and Corey, *Proc. U.S. Nat. Acad. Sci.*, 1951, **37**, 235.
61. Bamford, Brown, Elliot, Hanby and Trotter, *Nature*, 1952, **169**, 357.
62. Lenormant and Chouteau, *Compt. rend. Acad. Sci. (Paris)*, 1952, **234**, 2057.
63. Mizushima, Shimanouchi, Tsuboi, Sugita, Kurosaki, Mataga and Souda, *J. Amer. Chem. Soc.*, 1952, **74**, 4639.
64. Wasserman, Precopio and Liu, *ibid.*, p. 4093.
65. Haszeldine, *Nature*, 1951, **168**, 1028.
66. Lacher, Olsen and Park, *J. Amer. Chem. Soc.*, 1952, **74**, 5578.
67. Yakel and Hughes, *ibid.*, 6302.
68. Mizushima, Shimanouchi, Tsuboi, Sugita, Kurosaki, Matoga and Souda, *ibid.*, 1953, **75**, 1863.
69. Hurd, Bauer and Klotz, *ibid.*, 624.
70. Wheland, *Resonance in Organic Chemistry* (Wiley, New York, 1956), p. 410.
71. Smith, *Electric Dipole Moments* (Butterworths, London, 1955), p. 241.
72. Bates and Hobbs, *J. Amer. Chem. Soc.*, 1951, **73**, 2151.
73. Worsham and Hobbs, *ibid.*, 1954, **76**, 206.

74. Russell and Thompson, *Spectrochim. Acta*, 1956, **8**, 138.
75. Klemperer, Cronyn, Maki and Pimentel, *J. Amer. Chem. Soc.*, 1954, **76**, 5846.
76. Cannon, *Mikrochem. Acta*, 1955, 555.
77. Oshida, Ooshika and Miyasaka, *J. Phys. Soc. Japan*, 1955, **10**, 849.
78. Cannon, *J. Chem. Phys.*, 1956, **24**, 491.
79. Kessler and Sutherland, *ibid.*, 1953, **21**, 570.
80. Miyazawa, Shimanouchi and Mizushima, *ibid.*, 1956, **24**, 408.
81. Miyazawa, *J. Chem. Soc. Japan*, 1956, **77**, 321, 619.
82. Badger and Rubakava, *Proc. Nat. Acad. Sci. U.S.*, 1954, **40**, 12.
83. Cleverley, quoted in *Chemical Applications of Spectroscopy* (Interscience, New York, 1956), p. 515.
84. Mizushima, Tsuboi, Shimanouchi and Tsuda, *Spectrochim. Acta*, 1955, **7**, 100.
85. Mecke and Mecke, *Chem. Ber.*, 1956, **89**, 343.
86. Mizushima, *Structure of Molecules and Internal Rotation* (Academic Press, New York, 1954), p. 117.
87. Mizushima, Shimanouchi, Nagakura, Kuratani, Tsuboi, Baba and Fujioka, *J. Amer. Chem. Soc.*, 1950, **72**, 3490.
88. Letaw and Gropp, *J. Chem. Phys.*, 1953, **21**, 1621.
89. Evans, *ibid.*, 1954, **22**, 1228.
90. Davies, Evans and Lumley Jones, *Trans. Faraday Soc.*, 1955, **51**, 761.
91. Jones and Cleverley, quoted in *Chemical Applications of Spectroscopy* (Interscience, New York, 1956), p. 522.
92. Gierer, *Z. Naturforsch*, 1953, **8B**, 644, 654.
93. Bellamy and Williams, *J. Chem. Soc.*, 1957, 4294.
94. Mizushima, Shimanouchi, Ichishima, Miyazawa, Nakagawa and Araki, *J. Amer. Chem. Soc.*, 1956, **78**, 2038.
95. Robson and Reinhart, *J. Amer. Chem. Soc.*, 1955, **77**, 498.
96. White, *ibid.*, 6008.
97. Edwards and Singh, *Can. J. Chem.*, 1954, **32**, 683.
98. Ramirez and Paul, *J. Amer. Chem. Soc.*, 1955, **77**, 1035.
99. Scheinker and Resnikow, *Doklady. Akad. Nauk. S.S.S.R.*, 1955, **102**, 109.
100. Scheinker and Pomerantsev, *Zhur. Fiz. Khim.*, 1956, **30**, 79.
101. Gibson, Kynaston and Lindsey, *J. Chem. Soc.*, 1955, 4340.
102. Brown and Short, *ibid.*, 1953, 168.
103. Tanner, *Spectrochim. Acta*, 1956, **8**, 9.
104. Brügel, *Private communication*.
105. Schiedt, *Angew Chem.*, 1954, **66**, 609.
106. Kotera, Shibata and Sorve, *J. Amer. Chem. Soc.*, 1955, **77**, 6187.
107. Brockmann and Musso, *Chem. Ber.*, 1956, **89**, 241.
108. Frazer and Price, *Proc. Roy. Soc.*, 1953, **141B**, 66.
109. Abbott and Ambrose, *ibid.*, 1956, **234A**, 247.
110. Mecke, Mecke and Luttringhaus, *Zeit. Naturforsch.*, 1955, **10B**, 367.
111. Becher and Griffel, *Naturweiss*, 1956, **43**, 467.
112. Becher, *Chem. Ber.*, 1956, **89**, 1593.
113. Doty, Holtzer, Bradbury and Blout, *J. Amer. Chem. Soc.*, 1954, **76** 4493.
114. Huisgen and Walz, *Chem. Ber.*, 1956, **89**, 2616.
115. Gompper and Herlinger, *ibid.*, 2825.
116. Dijkstra and De Jonge, *Rec. trav. chim.*, 1956, **75**, 1173.
117. Boivin and Boivin, *Can. J. Chem.*, 1954, **32**, 561.
118. Boivin, Bridges and Boivin, *ibid.*, 242.
119. Gargon, Boivin and Paquin, *ibid.*, 1953, **31**, 1025.
120. Gargon, Boivin, McDonald and Yaffe, *ibid.*, 1954, **32**, 823.
121. Sutherland, *Advances in Protein Chemistry*, 1952, **7**, 291.
122. Elliott, *J. App. Chem.*, 1956, **8**, 341.
123. Ellenbogen, *J. Amer. Chem. Soc.*, 1956, **78**, 363, 366, 369.
124. Berger, Kurtz and Katchalski, *ibid.*, 1954, **76**, 5552.
125. Elliott and Malcolm, *Trans. Faraday Soc.*, 1956, **52**, 528.
126. Elliott, *Proc. Roy. Soc.*, 1954, **A221**, 104.
127. Asai, Tsuboi, Shimanouchi and Mizushima, *J. Phys. Chem.*, 1954, **59**, 322.

128. Lenormant and Blout, *Nature*, 1953, **172**, 770.
129. Ehrlich and Sutherland, *ibid.*, 671.
130. *Idem, J. Amer. Chem. Soc.*, 1954, **76**, 5268.
131. Mizushima, Tsuboi, Shimanouchi, Sugita and Yoshimoto, *ibid.*, 1954, **76**, 2479.
132. Mizushima, Tsuboi, Shimanouchi and Asai, *ibid.*, 1954, **76**, 6003.
133. Mikhailov, Shigorin and Makar'eva, *Doklady. Acad. Nauk. S.S.S.R.*, 1952, **87**, 1009.
134. Shigorin, Mikhailov and Makar'eva, *ibid.*, 1954, **94**, 711.
135. Shigorin, Mikhailov and Klyuyeva, *Zhur. Fiz. Khim.*, 1956, **30**, 1591.
136. Blout and Asadourian, *J. Amer. Chem. Soc.*, 1955, **78**, 955.
137. Blout and Idelson, *ibid.*, 1956, **78**, 497.
138. Krimm, *J. Chem. Phys.*, 1955, **23**, 1371.
139. Lenormant and Blout, *Bull. Soc., Chim. Fr.*, 1954, 859.
140. Lenormant, *Trans. Faraday Soc.*, 1956, **52**, 549.
141. Hecht and Wood, *Proc. Roy. Soc.*, 1956, **A235**, 174.
142. Frazer, *J. Chem. Phys.*, 1956, **24**, 89.
143. Cannon, *Spectrochim. Acta*, in press.

CHAPTER 13

Amino-acids, their Hydrochlorides and Salts, and Amido-acids

13.1. INTRODUCTION AND TABLE

EDSALL'S studies on the Raman spectra of amino-acids provided the first direct optical evidence [1, 2] for the dipolar structure of these materials, and his findings have been fully confirmed by similar later studies.[3-5] The first infra-red studies were made by Freymann, Freymann and Rumpf [6] working in the overtone region on the NH stretching frequencies, and they also obtained evidence for the presence of a quaternary nitrogen atom in the neutral amino-acids. Further data in the fundamental region were obtained by a number of other workers, mostly in studies in the 3000 cm.[-1] region.[7-10] Wright [11, 12] was also amongst the early workers in this field, and he was the first to point out that the spectrum of the racemic form of cystine in the solid state differs from that of either of the pure optical isomers. This fact has been fully substantiated by later workers on other amino-acids,[13, 14] and it appears to be true also of meso-tartaric acid.[15] Some fifty pairs of d- and l-forms of amino-acids have been studied by Koegel et al.[32] As with the polypeptides examined by Ellenbogen,[33] the individual d- and l-isomers have identical spectra, but these can differ appreciably from those of the racemate. When two asymmetric carbon atoms are present, as in normal and allo-forms, differences become possible between the spectra of the optical isomers. Brockmann and Musso,[34] and Erhart and Hey [35] report similar findings.

More recently, interest in amino-acids has been stimulated by work on protein hydrolysates, and also by the studies undertaken in connection with the penicillin problem. The spectra of a large number of amino-acids have now been described by several groups of workers,[17-23, 33, 34] and a number of correlations have been defined by which amino-acids and their hydrochlorides can be identified. These are as follows:

(a) The NH stretching region. No bands in the normal 3500–3300 cm.[-1] range are shown, but instead an absorption appears near 3070 cm.[-1] due to the NH_3^+ group. This correlation probably holds also for hydrochlorides, but not for the N-substituted amino-acids such as sarcosine or proline in which only the NH_2^+ group is involved. With salt formation the NH_2

group reappears without a charge and normal NH stretching bands are shown, unless chelation occurs, as in metal glycinates.

(b) An absorption corresponding to the ionised carbonyl group appears in amino-acids of all types and in their salts. In the corresponding hydrochlorides this band disappears and is replaced by a typical carbonyl absorption. In α-amino-acid hydrochlorides this carbonyl absorption is displaced about 20 cm.$^{-1}$ towards higher frequencies under the influence of the NH_3^+ group.

(c) Two characteristic bands in the 3000–2000 cm.$^{-1}$ region are shown by most but not all amino-acids, whilst their hydrochlorides show an almost continuous series of bands between 3030 cm.$^{-1}$ and 2500 cm.$^{-1}$.

(d) In addition to the ionised carboxyl group absorption, two other bands appear in the 1600–1500 cm.$^{-1}$ region, one or more of which must be associated with the NH_3^+ group. These bands are absent from NH_2^+ type amino-acids, as is the case with the corresponding stretching vibrations. Amino-acid hydrochlorides containing the NH_3^+ group also show these two bands.

(e) In addition, many amino-acids absorb near 1300 cm.$^{-1}$ and many hydrochlorides near 2000 cm.$^{-1}$, but the origin of these absorptions is not known.

These correlations form a comprehensive basis for the identification of amino-acids as a class, and this can be supplemented in a number of ways, particularly by the observation of the changes in NH, $C\!\!<^O_{O^-}$ and $C{=}O$ frequencies which occur in hydrochlorides and salts. Studies in solution in water and in heavy water have also been valuable in this connection.[24, 30] It is also possible to use antimony trichloride as a solvent for special purposes.[36]

The presence of sulphur or other functional groups does not appear to affect the validity of these assignments.[13, 18, 32] Dicarboxylic mono-amino-acids behave as expected in showing a carbonyl absorption in addition to the ionised carboxyl and NH_3^+ absorptions,[13] and ornithine[22] and other diamino-carboxylic acids show free NH_2 absorptions in addition to those of a typical amino-acid, but compounds of this complexity have not been very fully studied. The number of carbon atoms separating the NH_2 and COOH groups does not appear to affect the existence of these materials in dipolar form. Randall *et al.*[17] find ε-aminocaproic acid to be a typical amino-acid in this respect and Gaümann and Günthard have obtained similar results with other amino-acids with widely separated functional groups.[29] Lenormant[13] has also shown the persistence of the NH_3^+

absorptions in $NH_2(CH_2)_{10}COOH$ and similar compounds, and Despas *et al.*[37] report similar findings.

With aromatic acids the presence of the aromatic ring absorptions in the 1600–1500 cm.$^{-1}$ region complicates the spectrum a good deal, but nevertheless β-phenylalanine, tyrosine and similar products appear to be essentially normal.[13, 17] Anthranilic acid, on the other hand, shows normal carboxyl and amine absorptions slightly modified by the internal hydrogen bond, and so does not behave as a typical amino-acid. The absence of the zwitterion form in this case may be associated with the hydrogen bond effect.

Substitution of alkyl groups on the nitrogen atom of primary amino-acids gives rise to compounds such as sarcosine which cannot take on more than the NH_2^+ structure. These continue to show the ionised carboxyl absorption, but adequate correlations have not been worked out for the NH_2^+ vibrations, owing to the limited number of compounds available.

TABLE 13

NH_3^+ *Vibrations.*   (NH$_2$ Amino-acids and their hydrochlorides.   Not in salts)

   NH_3^+ stretching frequencies   .   3130–3030 cm.$^{-1}$ (m.)

   NH_3^+ deformation frequencies   Amino-acid 1, 1660–1610 cm.$^{-1}$ (w.).
                                     (Hydrochlorides down to 1590 cm.$^{-1}$)
                                     Amino-acid 2, 1550–1485 cm.$^{-1}$ (m.)

NH *Vibrations.*   Amido-acids, 3390–3260 cm.$^{-1}$.   (Esters lower) (m.)

COOH *Frequencies*

   Ionic carboxyl (all types of amino-acids and salts but not hydrochlorides), 1600–1560 cm.$^{-1}$ (s.)
   Normal acid carbonyl (un-ionised).   Hydrochlorides
       1754–1720 cm.$^{-1}$ α-amino-acids (s.)
       1724–1695 cm.$^{-1}$ α-amido-acids (s.)
       1730–1700 cm.$^{-1}$ β, γ, and lower amino-acids (s.)

The Region 3000–2000 *cm.*$^{-1}$

   Amino-acids, 2760–2530 cm.$^{-1}$ (w.)
                2140–2080 cm.$^{-1}$ (w.) } Present in most, but not all cases
   Amino-acid hydrochlorides .   .   A series of almost continuous bands, 3030–2500 cm.$^{-1}$ (w.)
   Amido-acids, 2640–2360 cm.$^{-1}$.} Present in most, but not all
                1945–1835 cm.$^{-1}$.} cases (w.)

Other Correlations (Amino-acids).   A band near 2000 cm.$^{-1}$ is shown by most amino-acid hydrochlorides (w.)
   A band near 1300 cm.$^{-1}$ is shown by most amino-acids and their derivatives (m.)

Other Correlations (Amido-acids)

   Amide I (CO) α-acids, 1620–1600 cm.$^{-1}$.   Other acids, 1650–1620 cm.$^{-1}$ (s.)
   Amide II, 1570–1500 cm.$^{-1}$ (s.)

N-acyl substitution results in compounds which combine some of the characteristic features of amino-acids and of amides. Their spectra show a number of distinctive features, some of which are similar to those of amino-acids, so that they are more conveniently considered here than under amides. In common with amides, however, the positions of key bands in these compounds are prone to alteration following changes of state, and it is important that comparisons should be made only between materials examined in comparable states. The differences associated with the spectra of solid and liquid esters have been employed by Randall *et al.*[17] for their identification. These compounds do not exist as zwitterions, and therefore show NH and CO frequencies and the amide I and II bands. Like the amino-acids, they also show absorptions in the 3000–2000 cm.$^{-1}$ region. Dipeptides and similar products also containing the NH_3^+ group are dealt with separately in Chapter 12.

The correlations to be discussed are summarised in Table 13. In all cases the ranges quoted relate to materials examined in the solid state as this is the condition in which these materials are usually studied.

13.2. NH_3^+ STRETCHING VIBRATIONS

No absorption in the usual NH stretching region 3500–3300 cm.$^{-1}$ is shown by any amino-acid or hydrochloride.[10, 11, 12, 17, 18, 19] Instead a single band appears in the 3130–3030 cm.$^{-1}$ region. Both Freymann and Freymann [10] and Thompson *et al.*[19] have reported an absorption near 3070 cm.$^{-1}$ in a number of amino-acids which they have assigned to the NH_3^+ stretching mode, and although Randall *et al.*[17] have not commented on this correlation, their data have been re-examined by Fuson *et al.*,[18] who found that all the thirteen amino-acids they examined absorbed in the 3130–3030 cm.$^{-1}$ range. Fuson *et al.*[18] have also given data on an additional five amino-acids which they found to absorb in this region. Finally, Koegel *et al.*[32] observe this band in the very extensive series of amino-acids they have studied. It is almost certainly due to the asymmetric NH_3^+ stretching mode, and the corresponding symmetric frequency is probably amongst the bands found between 3000 and 2000 cm.$^{-1}$

Although hydrochlorides can reasonably be expected to absorb similarly, there is not very much information available on this point. The simple amine hydrochlorides of butylamine [37] and methylamine [38] absorb here, and Thompson *et al.*[19] find a 3100 cm.$^{-1}$ band in glycine ester hydrochloride, whereas the sodium salt of phenylglycine with an uncharged NH_2 group shows a normal amine absorption near 3370 cm.$^{-1}$. Gore *et al.*[24] have confirmed the presence of a band near 3000 cm.$^{-1}$ in a solution of glycine in heavy water containing DCl. On the other hand, an examination of the amino-acid hydrochloride spectra published by Randall *et al.*[17] indicates that seven compounds containing the NH_3^+ structure and three with the NH_2^+ structure do not show any absorption in this range, whereas five others with the NH_3^+ structure absorb within the limits 3145–3049 cm.[-1]. This clearly indicates the need for further work on this subject, as, if it were to be substantiated that amino-acid hydrochlorides do not absorb here, it would throw doubt on the assignment of this absorption to the NH_3^+ group. However, for recognition purposes the fact remains that all the neutral amino-acids so far examined in this region do show absorption, and the correlation can therefore be applied for identifications with reasonable reliability. NH_3^+ stretching frequencies also occur in co-ordination compounds such as the cobalt amines, and these have been studied by a number of workers.[39-45] However, in these cases the charge on the nitrogen atom is substantially smaller, and the asymmetric and symmetric frequencies occur near 3300 cm.[-1] and 3150 cm.[-1] respectively. This correlation will of course apply only to amino-acids which are capable of taking up the NH_3^+ structure. *N*-substituted amino-acids such as *N*-phenyl-glycine, sarcosine or proline can only have the NH_2^+ group, which probably absorbs at much lower frequencies. The limited number of such compounds studied precludes any correlation being made, but studies on the hydrochlorides of secondary amines [38, 46] indicate that absorption from the NH_2^+ stretching mode may be expected somewhere near 2700 cm.[-1]. The NH^+ frequency may well be lower still, and Lord and Merrifield [31] have reported values of 2425 cm.[-1] for the hydrochlorides of a few tertiary amines examined in the solid state.

13.3. NH_3^+ DEFORMATION VIBRATIONS. "AMINO-ACID BANDS" I AND II

As indicated in Table 13, all amino-acids capable of possessing the NH_3^+ structure, and their hydrochlorides, show at least one, and probably two, characteristic bands in the 1600–1500 cm.[-1] region in addition to any ionic carboxyl absorption.[13, 17-19] The first of these, in the 1660–1610 cm.[-1] range, is often weak, and in some cases appears only as a shoulder on the main ionic carboxyl absorption. The second characteristic band is usually more intense, but the absolute intensity appears to be variable.[17] It appears in the overall range 1550–1485 cm.[-1]. The origin of these bands is not clear, but the fact that they are probably associated with the NH_3^+ deformation is indicated by their absence in salts and in *N*-substituted amino-acids [13, 17] and by their presence in the hydrochlorides. Lenormant [13] attributes the second band to the NH_3^+ deformation and does not attempt to assign the first, whereas Randall *et al.*[17] assign the first to NH_3^+ and do not assign the second. It has been suggested that the two frequencies arise from symmetric and asymmetric NH_3^+ deformations, both of which would be infra-red active, and this seems very likely. In primary amine hydrochlorides [38] and in complex amines,[41, 44, 47-49] however, the NH_3^+ structure shows much stronger splitting, and deuteration studies [39] indicate that the second absorption occurs near 1300 cm.$^{-1}$.

"*Amino-Acid I.*" As regards the first of these bands, all the mono-amino- mono-carboxylic-acids examined by Randall *et al.*,[17] show this band, as do the additional five acids examined by Fuson *et al.*,[18] and in the great majority of cases it falls within the narrower range 1640–1610 cm.$^{-1}$. The extended range has, however, been quoted to cover compounds such as *dl*α-amino-caproic acid,[17] which absorbs at 1658 cm.$^{-1}$, and a few other amino-acids which Lenormant similarly found to absorb in the 1640–1600 range. In general, Lenormant's findings [13] follow closely those of Randall *et al.*,[17] but he has not been able to detect this band in all cases. Similarly, Thompson, Nicholson and Short [19] illustrate this band only in some cases, and Klotz and Gruen [20] do not comment upon it in relation to their spectra. However, the band is observed in only a few exceptional instances in the fifty amino-acids studied by Koegel *et al.*,[32] despite the fact that many of them duplicate the compounds of Randall and of Lenormant. This may reflect the inherent weakness of the band in some cases and the differing film thicknesses used, but it may also be associated with differences in the crystal form examined. In this connection it is clear from Lenormant's detailed values that this band, together with the ionic carboxyl absorption, is one of those most affected by changes in the optical form, and the band shifts associated with this may be sufficient to mask the weaker NH_3^+ absorption. Brockmann and Musso [34] also note the appearance of this band in racemates, although it cannot be identified in the separate *d*- and *l*-forms. They associate this with differences in the hydrogen bridging arrangements in the crystals.

Whilst, therefore, it appears to be likely that that all amino-acids capable of NH_3^+ formation will show absorption in this range, the possibility of it being very weak, or of it being masked by the ionic carboxyl absorption if this occurs at a high frequency, cannot be overlooked.

The probable position of NH_2^+ deformations in acids such as sarcosine cannot be predicted on the available evidence. *dl*-Proline [13] absorbs at 1653 cm.$^{-1}$ and sarcosine [17] at 1645 cm.$^{-1}$, but *N*-phenyl-glycine shows no band in this region.

Hydrochlorides with the NH_3^+ structure show a similar absorption. The number of compounds examined is appreciably less, but Randall

R

et al.[17] quote a range of 1610–1590 cm.[-1] for the compounds they have examined, whilst Lenormant's [13] values are in general agreement. The detection of this absorption is considerably simplified in this case by the suppression of the ionic carboxyl absorption in the same region.

"*Amino-acid II.*" There is more general agreement on the occurrence of this band, which is usually considerably stronger than the first. It is reported as being present in the range given, in all the NH_3^+ acids and hydrochlorides examined by Randall *et al.*,[17] Fuson *et al.*,[18] Thompson *et al.*,[19] Klotz and Gruen [20] and other workers.[22, 32, 34] It is absent from the spectra of salts,[13] and this supports the assignment to NH_3^+ deformations. As indicated above, however, its intensity is variable to some extent, although it is usually strong. Koegel *et al.*[32] find this band close to 1515 cm.[-1] in almost all the fifty compounds they have studied. However, it is absent from the spectrum of *isovaline* and shows doubling in some other amino-acids, such as $\alpha\beta$-diamino-propionic and -butyric acids. In hydroxy-acids the band shows an interesting progression towards higher frequencies as the OH group is brought successively nearer to the NH_3^+. In hexahomoserine it is at 1504 cm.[-1], rising to 1522 cm.[-1] in pentahomoserine. In homoserine itself it appears at 1538 cm.[-1], and in serine it vanishes, being presumably superimposed [34] on the COO^- absorption at 1600 cm.[-1]. The band is absent from NH_2^+ type amino-acids such as sarcosine, proline and the compound $CH_3NH(CH_2)_{10}COOH$,[13] but in secondary amine hydrochlorides this absorption occurs [46] near 1600 cm.[-1], so it may be coincident with the ionised carboxyl absorption. As before, the number of hydrochlorides examined is considerably less, but the band persists in all those reported. The disappearance of the band on salt formation provides a convenient method of confirmation of identifications based upon it.

13.4. COOH VIBRATIONS

13.4(a). The Ionised Carboxyl Group. The position of the absorption bands of the ionised carboxyl group are fairly well established (Chapter 10.5) following the work of Lecomte,[25] and Raman studies on both normal acid salts and amino-acids, by Edsall.[1-5] Two absorptions corresponding to the asymmetric and symmetric modes occur near 1550 cm.[-1] and 1410 cm.[-1]. The former is usually more easy to identify in infra-red spectra, as many other absorptions can occur in the same region as the second band.

Amino-acids follow completely this expected pattern in that the neutral acids and their salts all show absorptions near 1600 cm.[-1] which can be assigned to the ionic carboxyl absorption.[13, 17-22, 32, 34, 50] All the various workers in this field are agreed on this assignment, which is supported by the large number of amino-acid spectra they have examined. Thompson *et al.*[19] have proposed the narrow range 1600–1590 cm.$^{-1}$, but this is obviously too restricted in the light of the results of other workers. Fuson *et al.*[18] follow Randall *et al.*[17] in proposing the range 1600–1560 cm.$^{-1}$, and this is sufficiently wide to cover all the acids examined by these groups except sarcosine,[17] which absorbs at 1616 cm.$^{-1}$. All the values quoted by Lenormant [13] also fall within this range, although, as already noted, the illustrated spectrum of $NH_2(CH_2)_{10}COOH$ (for which compound no values are quoted) suggests that the COOH frequency lies above 1650 cm.$^{-1}$. This last compound may be exceptional in that the much greater chain length than usual gives rise to different possibilities in crystal packing.

This absorption vanishes on formation of the quaternary hydrochloride in which the ionisation of the carboxyl group is suppressed. This is confirmed by both Randall *et al.*[17] and by Lenormant.[13] In some cases the band appears to persist in the hydrochloride spectra illustrated by Klotz and Gruen,[20] but this is probably due to the presence of the " amino-acid I band" due to the NH_3^+ group which these workers did not identify, but which is more clearly seen when the ionic carboxyl absorption is suppressed. The spectral changes following the change of the ionic carboxyl to the non-ionic form have been elegantly demonstrated by Gore *et al.*[24] working with glycine in water and in heavy water solution. In neutral solution the ionic carboxyl absorption is shown (1610 cm.$^{-1}$ and 1400 cm.$^{-1}$) which is replaced by the carbonyl absorption at 1740 cm.$^{-1}$ on the addition of DCl. On the addition of NaOD the original ionic absorptions reappear at approximately the original positions (1590 cm.$^{-1}$, 1400 cm.$^{-1}$).

Lenormant [28] has also examined some amino-acids in heavy water solution and has noted that the ionic absorption of alanine occurs at 1618 cm.$^{-1}$ in neutral solution and at 1570 cm.$^{-1}$ in alkaline solution. In contrast to this, β-alanine absorbs near 1618 cm.$^{-1}$ under both conditions.

This correlation is applicable to all types of amino-acids, regardless of whether or not the amine group has the NH_2^+ or NH_3^+ structure. A similar effect is reported in pyridine betaine,[26] although in this case the absorption occurs as high as 1652 cm.$^{-1}$.

With non-crystalline preparations it is sometimes possible for both the ionised and un-ionised carboxyl absorptions to appear,[21] and this is a source of possible confusion in work of this kind. The effect is not, however, common.

The second absorption arising from the ionic carboxyl group is less easy to identify in the infra-red, where its intensity is appreciably lower than the 1600 cm.$^{-1}$ band, but it appears clearly in many

Raman spectra.[5] Although many amino-acids do in fact absorb in this region, the assignment of any particular individual band to this mode is extremely difficult. Fuson *et al.*[18] have found bands near 1400 cm.$^{-1}$ and 1406 cm.$^{-1}$ in a series of aryl cysteines, one of which, they suggest, may be associated with the ionised carbonyl absorption, and Koegel *et al.*[32] have also identified this absorption as occurring at 1408 cm.$^{-1}$ in the vast majority of the amino-acids they have studied. Ehrlich and Sutherland [50] have also identified a band at 1410 cm.$^{-1}$ in *N*-methyl succinamic acid with the COO$^-$ symmetric mode. In view of the weakness of this absorption in the infra-red, however, great care is required for its positive identification.

13.4(b). The Un-ionised Carboxyl Absorption. The normal carbonyl absorption of the COOH group appears only in hydrochlorides in the amino-acid series, except in the case of dicarboxylic mono-amino-acids in which both the ionic and non-ionic forms appear.

Randall *et al.*[17] have commented upon the abnormally high-frequency range which they find for this absorption (1754–1724 cm.$^{-1}$), which overlaps to some extent the frequency range of normal esters. However, Edsall [5] has pointed out that in Raman work, abnormal frequencies in the 1750–1740 cm.$^{-1}$ range occur only in the α-amino-acids, and that the remainder absorb normally in the 1730–1700 cm.$^{-1}$ range. Consideration of the spectral data of Randall *et al.*[17] and of Lenormant [13] confirm that this is true also for the infra-red spectra. The great majority of the compounds examined by Randall *et al.*,[17] for example, are α-amino-acids absorbing in the higher frequency range, whereas δ-amino-*n*-valeric acid hydrochloride is shown as absorbing at 1701 cm.$^{-1}$.

This general effect of an elevation of the frequency by about 20 cm.$^{-1}$ in α-amino-acids is not surprising, and must reflect the influence of the NH$_3^+$ Cl$^-$ grouping on the C=O bond length of the adjacent carbonyl group. A similar effect is shown by halogen substitution in acids and ketones, whereas β-halogen substituents are sufficiently far removed from the carbonyl group to be without effect on its frequency.

This correlation should also be applicable to the hydrochlorides of NH$_2^+$ type acids, but, as in previous cases, not much information is available. Sarcosine hydrochloride again appears to be slightly abnormal in showing its carbonyl absorption at 1757 cm.$^{-1}$, but both proline and *N*-phenylglycine hydrochloride absorb at 1730 cm.$^{-1}$. Histidine hydrochloride absorbs at 1706 cm.$^{-1}$ and ornithine dihydrochloride [13] at 1739 cm.$^{-1}$. As far as the limited data available allow, therefore, it seems reasonable to assume that the correlation is obeyed by this type of compound.

13.5. THE REGION 3000–2000 CM.⁻¹

Thompson *et al.*[19] have drawn attention to the presence of a weak, but definite band near 2100 cm.⁻¹ in the spectra of the simple amino-acids which is absent from the spectrum of phenylglycine sodium salt or from *p*-aminophenylacetic acid. This suggests its association with the zwitterion structure. Randall *et al.*[17] had earlier noted a similar effect and drawn attention to the presence of two bands in this region in the spectra of most but not all amino-acids. The fact that amine hydrochlorides generally absorb in this region supports the suggestion that the NH_3^+ structure may be involved. The bands have considerable diagnostic value, as they occur in a relatively clear spectral region, but they do not appear in all cases. Fuson *et al.*[18] have studied this data and supplemented it with their own observations. They find one or two bands in the range 2760–2530 cm.⁻¹ in ten out of thirteen cases studied by Randall *et al.*[17] and in a further five cases examined by themselves. Similarly, another band occurs in the range 2140–2080 cm.⁻¹ in eleven out of thirteen cases studied by Randall *et al.*[17] and in three out of five cases studied by themselves. Koegel *et al.*[32] find a band at 2128 cm.⁻¹ in all the α-amino-acids they have studied, including many which are branched at the α-carbon atom. They also find absorption at 2564 cm.⁻¹ in all these cases except aminocaproic acid. However, the position becomes more complex when other polar groups are introduced. In ornithine, for example, the 2128 cm.⁻¹ band is absent. It appears at this point in hexahomoserine and shows a progressive fall in frequency as the chain length is reduced. In serine it appears at 2033 cm.⁻¹. This is parallel with the behaviour of the NH_3^+ deformations of this series, and clearly identifies this band with an NH_3^+ stretching absorption. Other anomalous cases are aspartic acid (2062 cm.⁻¹ and 1905 cm.⁻¹) and aminoadipic acid (1923 cm.⁻¹). Whilst therefore it is clear that characteristic frequencies exist in this region which are connected with the NH_3^+ stretching modes, they must be employed with caution for anything more complex than simple amino-acids.

Hydrochlorides of amino-acids, along with other types, exhibit an almost continuous series of band of moderate intensity between 3030 cm.⁻¹ and 2500 cm.⁻¹.[17]

13.6. OTHER CORRELATIONS (AMINO-ACIDS)

Randall *et al.*[17] have noted the presence of a band near 2000 cm.⁻¹ in NH_3^+ type amino-acid hydrochlorides which is absent from the NH_2^+ series, but no interpretation has been attempted and no other data are available.

In addition, Klotz and Gruen [20] have noted a persistent band near

1300 cm.$^{-1}$ in the spectra of the amino-acids they have examined, and a band in the range 1335–1300 cm.$^{-1}$ of medium intensity is shown in almost all the published spectra of amino-acids covering this range.[12, 17, 18, 19, 22]   Koegel et al.[32] report bands at 1370 cm.$^{-1}$ and 1316 cm.$^{-1}$ in all the simpler amino-acids they have studied, and it is interesting to note that the symmetric NH_3^+ deformation frequency has been assigned near this point in complex amines.[39]

Josien and Fuson [27] have noted an intense band in the range 1232–1215 cm.$^{-1}$ in amido-acids, amino-acid hydrochlorides and in dicarboxylic amino-acids. The occurrence of this band in circumstances in which the COOH group is un-ionised suggests a correlation with the C–O stretching or the C–OH bending vibration of the carboxyl group, and it will be recalled that many carboxylic acids absorb near 1250 cm.$^{-1}$ (Chapter 10). This is therefore a second possible region for confirmation of the presence of the COOH group. Despas et al.[40] have also associated bands in the 1250–1100 cm.$^{-1}$ and the 1000–900 cm.$^{-1}$ ranges with NH_3^+ absorptions, but it is difficult to see which modes would be likely to be involved, as the rocking motions lead to absorption at lower frequencies.

Another possible correlation relates to the 880 cm.$^{-1}$ region in which many amino-acids show absorption. Fuson et al.[18] suggest very tentatively that a deformation mode of the ionic carboxyl grouping may be involved, but analogy with the complex amines suggests that the NH_3^+ rocking mode is a more probable assignment.

13.7. AMINO-ACID SALTS

Amino-acids can, of course, form basic and acidic salts, and the frequencies arising in hydrochlorides have already been discussed above. Salt formation through the carboxyl group in long-chain amino-acids removes the zwitterion character, and the amino-group then shows the normal NH_2 absorptions of a primary amine. However, in α-amino-acids a different situation arises, as the amino-group can co-ordinate to many metals by donation of its lone-pair electrons. Compounds of this type are of considerable biological importance, and they have been studied by many workers.[51-54] The metal glycinates are compounds of this type, but their spectra are complicated by the presence of additional bands due to water of crystallisation. However, they exhibit typical NH_2 stretching frequencies near 3250 cm.$^{-1}$ and 3130 cm.$^{-1}$. These are higher than the corresponding hydrochloride frequencies, which is consistent with the concept of lone-pair donation by the nitrogen atom. The ionised carbonyl frequencies appear at the usual positions. This has been interpreted as indicating a fully ionic bond between the oxygen and metal atoms, although this implies a degree of equivalence between the two oxygen atoms of the carboxyl group which it is difficult to reconcile with the square coplanar configuration assigned to many of these chelates, such as copper. Rosenberg [54] has carried out low-temperature studies on chelates of glycine and leucine when a sharpening of the absorption bands takes place. In the leucine series, which is not hydrated, the NH_2 stretching frequencies rise to near 3350 cm.$^{-1}$ and 3250 cm.$^{-1}$; but the COO^- absorption remains near 1600 cm.$^{-1}$. It is also possible to differentiate between such compounds as the *cis-* and *trans-*forms of platinum glycine complexes by taking advantage of the minor differences which occur in the NH_2 absorptions in the two cases.

13.8. AMIDO-ACIDS

13.8(a). NH Vibrations. Fuson *et al.*[18] have analysed the results of Randall *et al.*[17] in addition to their own and have shown that in solid compounds the NH stretching vibration falls in the range 3390–3260 cm.$^{-1}$. This covers fifteen α-amido-acids studied by Randall *et al.* and a further ten samples examined by themselves. On formation of esters in which the hydrogen bonding possibilities are reduced, this frequency increases, and is then closer to the normal range. Micheel and Schleppinghoff [16] also find values of 3350 cm.$^{-1}$ in a series of *N*-acetyl amino-acids.

13.8(b). The Region 3000–2000 cm.$^{-1}$. Like the amino-acids, the amido-acids show in many cases broad and rather weak absorption bands in this region. An analysis by Fuson *et al.*[18] of the published data indicates that a band in the range 2640–2360 cm.$^{-1}$ occurs in twenty-three out of twenty-six cases, whilst another in the range 1945–1835 cm.$^{-1}$ occurs in sixteen out of twenty-six cases. These bands, which are sometimes multiple, are probably combination bands of some sort, and the fact that they do not invariably occur reduces their value. However, it is important to remember in the interpretion of the spectra of unknowns that amido-acids, in addition to amino-acids and hydrochlorides, may show absorptions in this region. Micheel *et al.*[16] also comment on the presence of a band between 2600 and 2500 cm.$^{-1}$ in all their materials. This is probably a characteristic carboxylic acid frequency and corresponds to the absorption near 2650 cm.$^{-1}$ which is found in dimeric carboxylic acids (Chapter 10).

13.8(c). The Carboxyl Group Absorption. The carboxyl absorption of these materials in the solid state is normal [17, 18] and falls in the range 1724–1695 cm.$^{-1}$, except for hippuric acid, which absorbs at 1740 cm.$^{-1}$, and *N*-chloroacetyl *dl*-serine, which absorbs at 1730 cm.$^{-1}$. Randall *et al.*[17] suggest that this band occurs at frequencies above 1695 cm.$^{-1}$ for α-acids, and below this for others, but the number of amido-acids other than α-acids they have studied is not large. Of these several absorb at 1695 cm.$^{-1}$, whilst others, such as ε-benzamido caproic acid, absorb at 1698 cm.$^{-1}$. It is doubtful, therefore, whether this fine distinction can be sustained. Solution results in shifts of 30–60 cm.$^{-1}$ towards higher frequency in dilute solutions.[18]

13.8(d). The Amide I and II Absorptions. The location of the amide I band at or below 1620 cm.$^{-1}$ is regarded by Randall *et al.*[17] as being characteristic of the α-amido-acids, as others absorb on the high-frequency side. In general this is well supported by their own findings (1620–1600 cm.$^{-1}$ in twelve out of fifteen cases) and by those of Fuson *et al.*,[18] and Micheel and Schleppinghoff.[16] However, this rule cannot be applied inflexibly. Fuson *et al.* find *dl*-acetyl cystine to absorb as low as 1587 cm.$^{-1}$, whilst *dl*-phenacetyl-β-phenylalanine [17] absorbs as high as 1665 cm.$^{-1}$. In solution this band again shows appreciable shifts to higher frequencies (1700–1680 cm.$^{-1}$).

The amide II band is essentially normal and falls in the range 1570–1500 cm.$^{-1}$ for the twenty-five compounds studied by the two main groups of workers.[17, 18] The shifts on solution are appreciably smaller than in the first case and are in the opposite direction. The frequency range found is approximately 1530–1510 cm.$^{-1}$ and the values of Fuson *et al.*[18] are in agreement with this. Micheel *et al.*[16] do not comment on this absorption in their compounds.

13.8(e). Other Correlations. The presence of a band at or near 1225 cm.$^{-1}$ in many amido-acids and also in amino-acid hydrochlorides has been suggested as a possible aid in their identification.[18, 27] This is a COOH band, probably originating in a C–O stretching or OH deformation mode and its significance in identification work has been discussed in the section dealing with carboxylic acids.

13.9. BIBLIOGRAPHY

1. Edsall, *J. Chem. Phys.*, 1936, **4**, 1.
2. *Idem, ibid.*, 1937, **5**, 225, 508.
3. Edsall and Scheinberg, *J. Chem. Phys.*, 1940, **8**, 520.
4. Edsall, *J. Amer. Chem. Soc.*, 1943, **65**, 1767.
5. Edsall, Otvos and Rich, *ibid.*, 1950, **72**, 474.
6. Freymann, Freymann and Rumpf, *J. Phys. Radium*, 1936, **7**, 30.
7. Heintz, *Compt. rend. Acad. Sci. (Paris)*, 1935, **201**, 1478.
8. Lenormant, *ibid.*, 1946, **222**, 1432.
9. Duval and Lecomte, *Bull. Soc. Chim. France*, 1943, **10**, 187.
10. Freymann and Freymann, *Proc. Indian Acad. Sci.*, 1938, **8**, 301.
11. Wright, *J. Biol. Chem.*, 1937, **120**, 641.
12. *Idem, ibid.*, 1939, **127**, 137.
13. Lenormant, *J. Chim. Phys.*, 1946, **43**, 327.
14. Sutherland, *Discuss. Faraday Soc.*, 1950, **9**, 319.
15. Lecomte, unpublished work quoted in Reference 13 above.
16. Micheel and Schleppinghoff, *Chem. Ber.*, 1955, **88**, 763.
17. Randall, Fowler, Fuson and Dangl, *Infra-red Determination of Organic Structures* (Van Nostrand, 1949.)

18. Fuson, Josien and Powell, *J. Amer. Chem. Soc.*, 1952, **74**, 1.
19. Thompson, Nicholson and Short, *Discuss. Faraday Soc.*, 1950, **9**, 222.
20. Klotz and Gruen, *J. Phys. Colloid. Chem.*, 1948, **52**, 961.
21. *The Chemistry of Penicillin* (Princeton University Press, 1949), p. 407.
22. Larsson, *Acta Chem. Scand.*, 1950, **4**, 27.
23. Kuratani, *J. Chem. Soc. Japan.*, 1949, **70**, 453.
24. Gore, Barnes and Petersen, *Analyt. Chem.*, 1949, **21**, 382.
25. Duval, Lecomte and Douvillé, *Annals de Physique*, 1942, **17**, 5.
26. Rasmussen and Brattain, *J. Amer. Chem. Soc.*, 1949, **71**, 1073.
27. Josien and Fuson, *Compt. rend. Acad. Sci. (Paris)*, 1951, **232**, 2016.
28. Lenormant, *ibid.*, 1952, **234**, 1959.
29. Gäumann and Günthard, *Helv. Chim. Acta*, 1952, **35**, 53.
30. Lenormant, *J. Chim. Phys.*, 1952, **49**, 635.
31. Lord and Merrifield, *J. Chem. Phys.*, 1953, **21**, 166.
32. Koegel, Greenstein, Winitz, Birnbaum and McCallum, *J. Amer. Chem. Soc.*, 1955, **77**, 5708.
33. Ellenbogen, *ibid.*, 1956, **78**, 363, 366, 369.
34. Brockmann and Musso, *Chem. Ber.*, 1956, **89**, 241.
35. Erhart and Hey, *ibid.*, 2124.
36. Lacher, Croy, Kianpour and Park, *J. Phys. Chem.*, 1954, **58**, 206.
37. Despas, Khaladji and Vergoz, *Bull. Soc. Chim. Fr.*, 1953, 1105.
38. Bellanato and Barcelo, *Anales. Fiz. Quim.*, 1956, **52B**, 469.
39. Powell and Sheppard, *J. Chem. Soc.*, 1956, 3108.
40. Chatt, Duncanson and Venanzi, *ibid.*, 1956, 2712.
41. Hill and Rosenberg, *J. Chem. Phys.*, 1956, **24**, 1219.
42. Beattie and Tyrrell, *J. Chem. Soc.*, 1956, 2849.
43. Caglioti, Silvestrom, Sartori and Scrocco, *Ricerca. Sci.*, 1956, **26**, 1743.
44. Pentland, Lane and Quagliano, *J. Amer. Chem. Soc.*, 1956, **78**, 887.
45. Fujita, Nakamoto and Kobayashi, *ibid.*, 3295.
46. Heacock and Marion, *Can. J. Chem.*, 1956, **34**, 1782.
47. Merritt and Wiberley, *J. Phys. Chem.*, 1955, **59**, 55.
48. Barrow, Kreuger and Basolo, *J. Inorg. Nuclear Chem.*, 1956, **2**, 340.
49. Mizushima, Nakagawa and Quagliano, *J. Chem. Phys.*, 1956, **25**, 1367.
50. Ehrlich and Sutherland, *J. Amer. Chem. Soc.*, 1954, **76**, 5268.
51. Sweeney, Curran and Quagliano, *ibid.*, 1955, **77**, 5508.
52. Sen, Mizushima, Curran and Quagliano, *ibid.*, 211.
53. Svatos, Curran and Quagliano, *ibid.*, 6159.
54. Rosenberg, *Acta Chem. Scand.*, 1956, **10**, 840.

CHAPTER 14

Amines and Imines

14.1. INTRODUCTION AND TABLE

PRIMARY amines can be identified by the presence of two absorption bands in the NH stretching region arising from the symmetric and asymmetric vibrations of the hydrogen atoms. In some cases a third band is shown in this region due to hydrogen bonding effects. Hydrogen bonding results in a shift towards lower frequencies in all cases, but the bonds are considerably weaker than those of OH groups, so that the bands are sharper and are not shifted to anything like the same extent. Unfortunately there is a good deal of overlapping between the OH and NH vibrations in this region, so that differentiation is not always possible. Frequency shifts of the NH stretching vibration occur also in structures such as amines and hydrochlorides in which the amine group is charged (NH_3^+). These cases are considered separately.

Primary amines also show an NH_2 deformation absorption near 1650 cm.$^{-1}$, and, like the stretching mode, this is subject to frequency shifts on hydrogen bonding. Deuteration is a useful aid in recognising these absorptions. In addition to these, a characteristic band can often be identified in aromatic amines, which is probably a C–N stretching absorption. There is also an absorption in the low-frequency region corresponding to the external deformation of the NH_2 group, but its position in relation to the structural environment has not been adequately defined.

Secondary amines show only a single NH stretching band in the 3500–3200 cm.$^{-1}$ region, which is also subject to small changes on hydrogen bonding, and imines absorb in very much the same region. The NH deformation in these compounds is too weak to be of any real value for identification purposes, although there appears to be an enhancement of the intensity in a limited number of cases; thus the NH deformation may be responsible for the amide II band shown by all secondary amides, but this latter assignment is still a a matter of controversy (Chapter 12). As with primary amines, C–N linkages of aromatic compounds can be identified, whereas the corresponding aliphatic materials show weaker absorptions which are more variable in position.

Tertiary amines are extremely difficult to identify spectroscopically. The C–N stretching band in aromatics can be identified in some cases, but there is no satisfactory correlation for aliphatic materials.

The possibility of identification of the CH_3–N group is also discussed.

The correlations discussed are listed in Table 14 below.

TABLE 14

NH *Stretching Absorptions*

Primary amines. Two bands	.	.	3500–3300 cm.$^{-1}$ (m.)
Lowered on hydrogen bonding or in the solid state.			
Secondary amines. One band	.	.	3500–3300 cm.$^{-1}$ (m.)
Imines. One band .	.	.	3400–3300 cm.$^{-1}$ (m.)

NH *Deformation Frequencies*

Primary amines .	.	.	.	1650–1590 cm.$^{-1}$ (s.-m.)
Secondary amines	.	.	.	1650–1550 cm.$^{-1}$ (v.w.)

C–N *Vibrations*

Aromatic amines.	Primary	.	.	1340–1250 cm.$^{-1}$ (s.)
	Secondary	.	.	1350–1280 cm.$^{-1}$ (s.)
	Tertiary .	.	.	1360–1310 cm.$^{-1}$ (s.)
Aliphatic amines	.	.	.	$\begin{cases} 1220\text{–}1020 \text{ cm.}^{-1} \text{ (m.-w.)} \\ \text{Near } 1410 \text{ cm.}^{-1} \text{ (w.)} \end{cases}$

14.2. NH STRETCHING VIBRATIONS

14.2(a). General. The occurrence of an absorption band near 3500 cm.$^{-1}$ in primary amines was first noted by Coblentz,[1] and the fact that this was of general occurrence and was to be associated with the N–H stretching vibration was established by Bell,[2-5] and by Ellis,[6-7] who examined a considerable number of compounds and were able to show that the absorption was present in all primary and secondary amines, but absent from tertiary materials. The resolution of the instruments available to these workers was, however, not sufficiently good to enable their values for individual frequencies to be of much direct value. Since that time there have been a good number of publications dealing with individual amines and with hydrogen bonding effects in certain cases, but no comprehensive studies appear to have been carried out on groups of compounds, other than the special cases of amides and amino-acids, with a view to determining the relationship between the precise frequency found and the structure of the molecule as a whole. Furthermore, the possibility of utilising the scattered data available for this purpose is limited by the fact that only a very small proportion of it relates to determinations made with lithium or calcium fluoride prisms, and the resolution given by rock-salt in this region is insufficient to show up clearly the small frequency differences which probably do exist between different classes of amines.

14.2(b). Primary Amines. Primary amines in dilute solution in non-polar solvents give two absorption bands in the region

3500–3300 cm.$^{-1}$. The first of these, which is due to the asymmetric stretching mode, is usually found near 3500 cm.$^{-1}$, and the second, which arises from the corresponding symmetrical mode, near 3400 cm.$^{-1}$. Both of these are subject to small changes with alteration of the polarity of the solvent, and to rather larger changes in concentrated solutions in which intermolecular association can occur. Intramolecular bonding also lowers these frequencies, as will be seen from the discussion of hydrogen bonding effects below.

This assignment rests mainly upon the examination of single compounds such as methylamine [8-9, 46] and of aniline,[10-12, 47-48] both of which have been extensively studied. The former absorbs at 3470 and 3360 cm.$^{-1}$ and the latter at 3481 cm.$^{-1}$ and 3395 cm.$^{-1}$. Califano and Moccia [47] have studied the two NH stretching frequencies of a series of substituted anilines under high resolution. They found that each of these frequencies is a direct function of the reactivity of the compound as measured by Hammet σ values. This agrees with earlier suggestions by Richards [14] and Flett,[15] who attempted to relate the NH frequencies to the basicity of the amines. Within a related series this is probably sound, but Fuson et al.[13] have pointed out that, in secondary amines at least, the differences resulting from structural changes, such as those between diphenylamine and pyrrole, are sufficiently great to mask this effect. An alternative approach to the infra-red determination of basicities is that of Searles et al.,[49] who have measured the OD shifts of deuteromethanol in different amines. Studies have also been made on aminoanthraquinones,[16] naphthylamines,[17] and aminopyridines.[50-52] Although made at lower resolution, these are in good agreement with the ranges quoted.

A substantial amount of high-resolution data is also available on metallic co-ordination compounds in which a primary amine acts as an electron donor. Compounds such as (L, *am* PtCl$_2$), where L is one of a series of ligands and *am* is a primary or secondary amine, have been studied in solution by Chatt, Duncanson and Venanzi.[53,54]

Bellamy and Williams [55] have recently reviewed the high-resolution data available. They point out that as both the asymmetric and symmetric stretching frequencies depend basically upon the same force constant, they must be directly related to each other. Over a range of sixty-four primary amines for which reliable data are available, they find that the equation $\nu_{sym} = 345 \cdot 53 + 0 \cdot 876 \, \nu_{as}$ is obeyed in all cases with a standard deviation of $4 \cdot 8$ cm.$^{-1}$. This is a valuable diagnostic relationship for free NH$_2$ frequencies, particularly as it is applicable also to co-ordination compounds in which these frequencies are lowered by as much as 200 cm.$^{-1}$. However, as they point out, the relationship must be expected to fail in situations in which one NH link is bonded and the other is not, as in the dimeric complexes described by Chatt *et al.*[54] or in compounds such as anthranilic acid. In some solid co-ordination compounds, however, the equality between the NH links is restored and the relation is again obeyed. This therefore offers a sensitive method for the detection of non-equivalent NH links in primary amines.

Only a limited amount of work has been done on the intensity relationships of these bands, although Califano and Moccia [86] have studied the aromatic series in some detail. Vampiri [56] has made the interesting observation that the total absorption intensity of primary amines in the 3600–3300 cm.$^{-1}$ region is approximately double that of the corresponding secondary amines.

Very little is known of the likely absorption frequencies of NH_2 groups attached to other elements than carbon, although the special case of hydrazine has been examined by several workers. The latest study by Giguère and Liu [18] reported bands for the vapour state at 3350 cm^{-}.^{1}, 3325 cm.$^{-1}$ and 3314 cm.$^{-1}$, which agrees also with the range quoted. 1-1-Dimethylhydrazine has also been studied by Shull *et al.*[57]

14.2(c). Secondary Amines and Imines. Secondary amines show only a single NH stretching absorption in dilute solution, although a second band at low frequencies is sometimes shown at higher concentrations when hydrogen bonding effects occur.

As before, the data on which this correlation is based are widely scattered and of unequal value. Fuson *et al.*[13] have determined accurately the free NH absorptions of indole, pyrrole, carbazole and diphenylamine as 3491 cm.$^{-1}$, 3496 cm.$^{-1}$, 3483 cm.$^{-1}$ and 3433 cm.$^{-1}$ respectively. Richards and Burton [33] confirm the latter figure and quote also 3430 cm.$^{-1}$ for methyl- and ethyl-anilines. Marion, Ramsay and Jones [34] quote a range of 3480–3440 cm.$^{-1}$ for a series of secondary amines associated with alkaloids, and comment that the band persists in piperidine and related structures, but is much reduced in intensity, and in some cases cannot be detected in chloroform solution. Heacock and Marion [58] have observed a similar low-intensity effect with pyrrolidine and piperazine in chloroform. They quote a range of 3380–3205 cm.$^{-1}$ for a series of bases of this type, but these refer to the free bases which are associated. Witkop [35, 41, 42] and Mirone and Vampiri [45] have also examined a number of indole derivatives, and found values in the range 3472–3378 cm.$^{-1}$. In ethylene-imine [20] the NH vibration frequency is 3341 cm.$^{-1}$. Randall *et al.*[19] have quoted an overall range of 3500–3050 cm.$^{-1}$ for the free NH vibration, but in fact most of the spectra on which this is based were determined on solid materials, and it is doubtful whether the normal free NH absorption ever occurs much below 3300 cm.$^{-1}$.

The most detailed studies of secondary amines are due to Russell and Thompson,[59] who have examined both the intensity and frequency of this band in a wide range of compounds. Both were found to be very sensitive to the nature of the surrounding structure. In aliphatic secondary amines the frequency falls in the range 3310–3350 cm.$^{-1}$ with low intensity. In alkylaryl amines the frequency rises sharply to near 3450 cm.$^{-1}$ and the intensity increases by a factor of 50. In pyrrole, indole and similar compounds the frequency is as high as 3490 cm.$^{-1}$ and the intensity is again much enhanced. In this series, at least, the observed intensity would seem to have considerable diagnostic value. Marked variations in both frequency and intensity have also been noted by Barr and Haszeldine [60] in NH groups with fluorine substituents at the α-carbon atom. The NH frequency of *bis*-2-2-2-trifluorodimethyl-amine, for example, is 3460 cm.$^{-1}$, and the extinction coefficient is about 50 times greater than that of dimethylamine itself. The spectra of secondary arylamines have also been studied by Salimov and Tatevskii.[74]

The imino group = NH appears to have a somewhat narrower frequency range for the free NH absorption, as is to be expected from the fact that the structure about the NH group is almost always the group –C=NH. Colthup [21] quotes an overall range of 3400–3300 cm.$^{-1}$ for imines with this structure, but little or no information is available in the literature generally. Pickard and Polly [61] have quoted frequencies of near 3200 cm.$^{-1}$ for a number of these ketimines, but these probably relate to samples examined in the condensed phase. Randall *et al.*[19] and Lieber, Levering and Patterson [22] have given spectra for a considerable number of substituted guanidines, but the interpretation of their spectra is complicated by the presence of other NH groups in these compounds. In addition, a large number of aminopyrimidines have been examined by Brownlie [23] and by Short and Thompson,[24] but whilst it is possible that many of these exist in the imido-form, the complex tautomerism which these compounds can undergo makes any correlation difficult.

14.3. HYDROGEN BONDING IN AMINES

Intermolecular and/or intramolecular hydrogen bonding effects are shown by most amines under suitable conditions. As with the hydroxyl group, no attempt will be made to review all the work—especially in the overtone region—which has been carried out in this connection, as a number of excellent reviews already exist,[25, 26, 62] but a general indication of the conditions under which frequency shifts may be expected, and of the extent to which they are likely to occur, is given below.

14.3(a). Intermolecular Hydrogen Bonds. In the condensed phase hydrogen bonding occurs with amines causing a small fall in the frequency, which is usually considerably less than 100 cm.$^{-1}$. This has given rise to discussion as to whether true hydrogen bonding is involved, as frequency changes of this order might well arise from changes of state due to the possibilities of interaction of hydrogenic vibrations in neighbouring molecules in the solid state. However, solution studies at high resolution by Fuson *et al.*[13] have demonstrated that intermolecular bonding of the type originally suggested by Gordy[27] and by Thompson and Harris[28] probably does occur in pyrrole and related compounds. Typical shifts in the low-frequency region observed by Fuson *et al.*[13] on passing from liquids or highly concentrated solutions to very dilute solutions were approximately 80–90 cm.$^{-1}$ in pyrrole and indole, 70 cm.$^{-1}$ for carbazole and 30 cm.$^{-1}$ for diphenylamine. The exact difference in any one case depends, of course, on the solvent and the concentration, as the shift in the bonded absorption is slightly less in the more dilute solution, whilst the free NH position varies somewhat with the polarity of the solvent.[13] The changes which take place in the intensity and position of the NH band in pyrrole in different solvents at various concentrations have been studied by several groups of workers.[63-68] Whilst no conclusive solution has been reached, it is at least highly probable that genuine hydrogen bonding rather than dipolar association takes place with this compound at high concentrations. However, in the case of aniline, Bellamy and Williams[55] point out that their relationship is obeyed by the NH frequencies of the pure liquid, which suggests that hydrogen bonding is not taking place. This is also supported by the progressive shifts towards lower frequencies which accompany an increase in the concentration of solutions, whereas in pyrrole a second absorption appears under these conditions.

NH groups are also capable of interacting with alcohols[29] and with ketonic groups,[30] although the shifts are again small. Sutherland[30] has indicated that, in general, association with ketonic groups gives absorption in the range 3320–3240 cm.$^{-1}$ and with other nitrogen atoms within the range 3300–3150 cm.$^{-1}$. In view of the difficulty in assigning any precise frequency ranges to the free NH vibrations in amines, it is not possible to do more than indicate the approximate range of 3400–3100 cm.$^{-1}$ for associated NH absorptions of this type. The possibility of the simultaneous occurrence of absorptions corresponding to both the free and bonded NH absorption should not be overlooked. Thus Flett has noted that solid β-naphthylamine and 2-aminoanthraquinone show three absorption peaks in the NH region,[16] and we have found a similar effect with *ortho-* and *meta-*chloranilines, *p*-phenylenediamine, *p*-nitraniline and other amines.

Pyrrole and other secondary amines at suitable concentrations show two absorptions.[13] There is a danger of confusion in the second case, with the two free NH bands of primary amines, but this can be avoided by studies at other concentrations. In any case, the broadening of the low-frequency band is usually a sufficient indication that a hydrogen bond is involved.

14.3(b). Intramolecular Bonds. In alcohols the commonest case of intramolecular bonding arises with conjugated systems containing the group $\underset{\text{O}}{\text{C}}-\text{C}=\underset{\text{OH}}{\text{C}}$, such as salicylic acid and acetylacetone.

This finding is repeated in amines in which a similar conjugated system favours the formation of internal bonds. In such cases, however, shifts observed in the NH frequencies are not usually large, indicating a considerably weaker bond, although the shifts in the carbonyl absorption are a good deal greater than would be expected from this. For example, in methyl N-methylanthranilate the carbonyl frequency of 1685 cm.$^{-1}$ indicates the presence of a strong hydrogen bond, whilst the NH frequency of 3361 cm.$^{-1}$ is not appreciably different from its usual position in intermolecular bonding.[31] However, the fact that such chelation is occurring is indicated by the carbonyl frequency of methyl N-N-dimethylanthranilate which reverts to the normal ester value of 1730 cm.$^{-1}$. Hathway and Flett [17] have obtained somewhat similar findings for a series of nitronaphthylamines. In 2-nitro-1-naphthylamine in dilute solution the asymmetrical NH frequency is raised from 3486 cm.$^{-1}$ in α-naphthylamine to 3528 cm.$^{-1}$, whilst the symmetrical NH frequency falls at the same time from 3412 cm.$^{-1}$ to 3378 cm.$^{-1}$. A smaller fall is observed in the case of 1-nitro-2-naphthylamine. In both these cases alteration in the N=O frequency near 1340 cm.$^{-1}$ afforded confirmation of chelation. However, bonding was found to be weak or absent in 3-nitro-2-naphthylamine and 8-nitro-1-naphthylamine in which the NH frequencies were virtually the same as in the naphthylamines themselves. The former case is attributed to the reduced double-bond character of the 2 : 3-double bond of naphthalene, whilst in the second case the absence of the conjugated double bond apparently prevents the formation of a chelated bond, despite the fact that the amino- and nitro-groups are actually closer together in the compound than in the 1-nitro-2-amino-material. Chelation also occurs in 1-aminoacridine, in 8-aminoquinoline [40] and in certain amino-azo compounds,[75] but the frequency changes are small.

Cromwell et al.[32] have found that β-amino-αβ-unsaturated ketones show similar chelation effects, but in this case a considerable shift of the NH frequency is reported, as no NH bands could be observed in the materials examined, and it was concluded that they were coincident with the CH stretching bands near 3000 cm.$^{-1}$. The position is further complicated in these cases by their observation that a smaller but still appreciable carbonyl shift occurs in four compounds in which the amino-group is fully substituted and unable to form hydrogen bonds. The suggestion has been made that in these cases the structure $R-\overset{\underset{|}{O^-}}{C}=C-\overset{\underset{||}{\diagdown N^+}}{C}-R$ may contribute appreciably to the ground state, and it is possible that a contribution from similar resonant forms rather than hydrogen bonding accounts also for the small shifts observed in the NH frequencies in the cases quoted earlier, in which the NH shifts are so much smaller than would be expected in relation to the shifts in the carbonyl absorption. Flett [16] has suggested an explanation along these lines to account for the small NH shifts observed in 1-amino- and 1 : 4-diamino-anthra-quinones, and in this case the suggestion is supported by the fact that 2-amino-anthraquinone exhibits the same phenomenon of carbonyl shift. However, there is a possibility of ambiguity in the assignment of the C=O frequencies in these cases, as the NH_2 deformation is to be expected in the same region.

14.4. NH DEFORMATION VIBRATIONS

14.4(a). Primary Amines. The situation in respect of our knowledge of NH deformations has recently been discussed by Suther-land,[30] who has pointed out that it is very unsatisfactory. There is general agreement that the NH_2 internal deformation mode occurs in the range 1650–1590 cm.$^{-1}$ in simple amines, but this is based on an extremely limited number of compounds, such as methylamine,[8, 9, 46] aniline,[10–12] hydrazine [18] and substituted hydrazines,[36] and a small number of long-chain amines.[69] There is, however, much more data available on the simple amides in which the NH_2 deformation in this region has been fully studied by many workers (see Chapter 12), and these provide some indirect supporting evidence for this assignment, although this evidence is weakened to some extent by the con-troversy as to whether the corresponding band in secondary amides does in fact arise from the NH deformation mode at all. Deuteration work has, however, strengthened the case for regarding this absorp-tion in primary amides and amines as being due to NH deformations, although a number of bands at longer wave-lengths are also affected. However, a band in the 1650–1590 cm.$^{-1}$ range appears in almost all the spectra of primary amines we have been able to trace in the literature, and also in a considerable number of such materials we have examined ourselves. The exceptions are largely certain aro-matic materials in which the NH deformation absorption is obscured by the aromatic ring vibration near 1600 cm.$^{-1}$. Thus *ortho*-chloro-aniline shows only a single strong band at 1613 cm.$^{-1}$, whereas the

S

meta-substituted compound absorbs strongly at 1613 cm.$^{-1}$ and at 1597 cm.$^{-1}$. However, a few other cases are known. For example, the appearance of a band at 1650 cm.$^{-1}$ in most amino-substituted pyrimidines is regarded as evidence for their existence in the amino- rather than the imino-form, but 2-methyl-4 : 6-dimethoxy-5-aminopyrimidine, which must exist as a primary amine, has no band in this region.[24, 37] The correlation also appears to hold good for thioamide structures. Thioxamide, for example, absorbs at 1600 cm.$^{-1}$.

In the absence of more precise data it is not possible to relate movements of this band within the given frequency range with any structural features. As a deformation mode this absorption moves to higher frequencies on bonding,[37] but the shifts are often not sufficient to take the absorption out of the overall range quoted. Primary amides have been studied particularly in this connection, and in a typical case the NH deformation of hexoamide is given as 1635 cm.$^{-1}$ in the solid state, falling to 1595 cm.$^{-1}$ in very dilute solution.[38]

Primary amines should also show absorptions at longer wavelengths due to the external deformations of the NH_2 group, but very little is known of these. Most primary amines show broad absorptions in the range 900–650 cm.$^{-1}$ which alter in shape and frequency with alterations in the degree of hydrogen bonding, and which are therefore presumed to correspond to vibrations of this type. However, although assignments have been made for this vibration in a few single molecules,[8, 9, 46] there are no data available which could be usefully employed in analytical work.

14.4(b). Secondary Amines. The NH deformation absorption, which is a strong to medium intensity band in primary amines, is usually extremely weak in secondary aliphatic amines, so that it frequently cannot be detected at all with the film thicknesses normally employed. With secondary aromatic amines the position is confused to some extent by the presence of the ring C=C stretching absorptions in the same region, coupled with the fact that in certain cases these become intensified when a nitrogen atom is directly attached to the ring.[31] This has led to a good deal of confusion in connection with characteristic frequencies for the anilido structure. Thus Witkop and Patrick [39] have quoted a band at 1613 cm.$^{-1}$ as being typical of the structural element C_6H_5–N–C$\leqslant$, where C does not have a double bond. In the spectra of a number of indole derivatives which they quote to illustrate this point only a single band is shown in this region, and this is presumably the aromatic band; nevertheless in the spectrum of methyl ketol, which is also given and which does have a double bond at C, this band is notably weakened in intensity. However, the same authors have also put forward [35, 41, 42] a second correlation which describes a strong band in the 1639–1600 cm.⁻¹ range as being "characteristic of anilino structures in general and of indolenines in particular". The structure Ph–N=C–, which they associate particularly with this band, contains of course the C=N link, which is also to be expected to absorb in this region, or, when conjugated, to interact with the aromatic ring vibrations.

Randall *et al.*[19] have also discussed the "anilino" structure and given correlations for it, but these seem to be essentially similar to those of the normal aromatic system coupled with an intensification of a third band at 1610–1590 cm.⁻¹ which is normally weak or absent. This effect is therefore very similar to that of ring conjugation (Chapter 4).

However, whilst some aromatics examined as thin mulls seem to show no additional band in this region, others, such as phenyl-β-naphthylamine and methyl-*N*-methylanthranilate,[31] do show some differences from the disubstituted amines. Hadži and Skrbljak [70] have recently reinvestigated this question using deuteration techniques. Their results show clearly that there is indeed an additional weak absorption in the 1510 cm.⁻¹ region in aromatic secondary amines. This is an NH deformation mode which is coupled with the lower-frequency C–N stretching mode. However, in some instances, such as methyl aniline, it is superimposed on the ring vibrations and is difficult to identify. In thioamides the band is clearly marked and has much greater intensity.[71–73]

In aliphatic secondary amines this band is too weak to be detected readily. In cyclic bases, for example, only the normal aromatic absorptions are found in this region unless salt formation occurs.[58] Similarly, Barr and Haszeldine [74] could not identify this band in dimethyl or diethylamine, although a band near 1500 cm.⁻¹ was traced in some fluorinated derivatives. Imines with the structure –C=NH are similar to other secondary amides in that any NH deformation absorption shown is extremely weak, but of course they also show an absorption in the same region corresponding to the terminal C=N linkage.

14.5. C–N STRETCHING VIBRATIONS

14.5(a). Aromatic Amines. Colthup [21] has given the following correlation for aromatic amines. A strong band appears as follows:

Primary, 1340–1250 cm.⁻¹; Secondary, 1350–1280 cm.⁻¹; Tertiary, 1360–1310 cm.⁻¹.

These are based on his own unpublished work, and no publications have dealt in detail with these particular correlations. However, its persistence in the same approximate frequency range in all three types indicates that these must be C–N stretching vibrations the frequency of which is largely determined by the aromatic character of the carbon atom. This interpretation is also that of Barnes et al.,[44] who put forward this correlation in more general terms.

Colthup's findings are fully supported by the spectra of about forty aromatic amines of various types which we have in our files, and also by the spectra of a number of anilino-derivatives of phosphorus containing the structure P–NH–Ar.[43] The frequency appears to shift slightly within the ranges given with different types of ring substitution, but insufficient data are available for the evaluation of the extent of these effects. The intensity of these bands appears to be rather variable, some being relatively strong and others of not more than medium intensity. This may also be associated with some differences in substitution or other structural features. Lieber et al.[22] have also found these bands in a series of thirteen tetrazoles of various types. More recently Hadži [70] has studied the effects of deuteration upon this absorption in aniline derivatives. The band near 1260 cm.$^{-1}$ moves to near 1350 cm.$^{-1}$. This identifies it with a C–N stretching mode, which in the hydrogen compounds is lowered in frequency by coupling with the NH deformation frequency.

14.5(b). Aliphatic Amines. Colthup [21] has also indicated correlations for aliphatic amines with absorptions in the 1220–1020 cm.$^{-1}$ range. These presumably correspond to C–N stretching frequencies of non-conjugated links, and the bands are often of low intrinsic intensity. Because of this, and of the rather wide frequency range in which they occur along with so many other skeletal vibrations, these correlations are not of much direct value, except in providing confirmatory evidence in some cases. In methylamine this band occurs [46] at 1044 cm.$^{-1}$.

In unsaturated tertiary amines it is possible to differentiate between $\alpha\beta$- and $\beta\gamma$-unsaturation by observing the frequency changes which occur in the 1600–1700 cm.$^{-1}$ region on salt formation.[87]

14.6. THE CH₃–N GROUP

The deformation mode of the CH_3 group attached to a nitrogen atom could be expected to give an absorption band of reasonably characteristic frequency similar to that of the CH_3–C absorption which occurs at 1375 cm.$^{-1}$. In this case, however, alterations in the substituents on the nitrogen atom might have a greater influence on the frequency. This vibration in simple molecules appears to occur in the 1460–1430 cm.$^{-1}$ region. Examination of the spectra of a range of more complex materials containing this group indicates that whilst many of them show absorption near 1430 cm.$^{-1}$, in others the band, if it occurs at all, is indistinguishable from the main CH deformation vibration. The band is not strong, and the usefulness of the correlation is further diminished by the fact that a considerable proportion of other nitrogen-containing compounds appear also to show weak bands in the region 1430–1400 cm.$^{-1}$. Dimethylamino-compounds such as dimethylamine and bisdimethylaminofluorophosphine oxide do not show any behaviour comparable with that of *iso*propyl derivatives in showing any splitting of this band into two components of equal intensity. It must therefore be concluded that, despite the constant frequency shown by the CH_3 deformation mode when attached to carbon, silicon and a number of other elements, the corresponding NCH_3 vibration is too weak in intensity or too variable in position to afford any useful correlation.

14.7. THE GROUPS NH_3^+, NH_2^+ AND NH^+

Amine derivatives with positively charged nitrogen atoms commonly occur in salts, in co-ordination compounds involving ammonia and in zwitterion structures. The latter have been discussed in the previous chapter, and will not be reconsidered here.

14.7(a). NH_3^+ Absorptions. These occur in complex amines and in primary amine hydrochlorides. In the former series they have been studied by many workers.[53, 54, 76-83] The charge on the nitrogen atom is appreciably smaller than in hydrochlorides, so that the frequencies are nearer to those of normal amines. A few such compounds studied in solution show stretching frequencies near 3380 cm.$^{-1}$ and 3280 cm.$^{-1}$. However, most studies have been made on solids in which intermolecular bonding effects lower the range to 3350–3150 cm.$^{-1}$ and sometimes lead to a multiplicity of bands. The NH_3 deformation (*as.*) frequency occurs, as in primary amines, near 1600 cm.$^{-1}$, the symmetric mode near 1300 cm.$^{-1}$ and the NH_3 rocking frequency near 800 cm.$^{-1}$. These have been confirmed by deuteration studies.

Hydrochlorides of simple primary amines have been little studied, but appear similar to those of amino-acids. Methylamine hydrochloride, for example, absorbs at 3075 cm.$^{-1}$ and at 2972 cm.$^{-1}$, and has an NH deformation band [84] at 1617 cm.$^{-1}$. In hydroxylamine hydrochloride the NH bonds are more strongly associated and are assigned [84] at 2955 cm.$^{-1}$ and 2667 cm.$^{-1}$.

14.7(b). NH_2^+ Absorptions. A large number of co-ordination compounds containing aniline derivatives, methylamine and other amines have been studied by Chatt *et al.*[53] in the high-frequency region. In dilute solution these behave like normal primary amines in that the relationship of Bellamy and Williams [55] is obeyed, but the influence of the electron donation is shown by the substantial reductions which take place in the NH stretching frequencies. These occur about 200 cm.$^{-1}$ lower than the same bands in aniline. Further reductions accompany hydrogen bonding in concentrated solutions and in solids. The NH_2 deformations of compounds of this type have been studied by Mizushima *et al.*,[81] and are more nearly normal.

The hydrochlorides of secondary bases have been examined by Heacock and Marion,[58] who found a complex series of absorptions between 2800 cm.$^{-1}$ and 2000 cm.$^{-1}$. This was especially marked in aromatics, in which three or four bands recurred between 2780–2600 cm.$^{-1}$, in addition to others at lower frequencies. On deuteration these bands become attenuated, indicating that an NH motion is involved. Out of seventeen salts studied, fifteen had a band in the range 2760–2690 cm.$^{-1}$, all absorbed between 1620 cm.$^{-1}$ and 1560 cm.$^{-1}$ (NH_2 deformation), and all absorbed near 800 cm.$^{-1}$ (NH_2 rock). Barcello *et al.*[84] report similar findings for dimethylamine hydrochloride.

14.7(c). NH$^+$ Absorptions. In trimethylamine hydrochloride the NH$^+$ stretching band [84] is at 2735 cm.$^{-1}$. In salts of pyridine, indolene and Shiff's bases the group C=NH^{+-} absorbs at 2500–2325 cm.$^{-1}$. However, when no other hetero-atom is in the vicinity of the NH$^+$ group, a second band appears between 2200 cm.$^{-1}$ and 1800 cm.$^{-1}$. Witkop [85] has discussed the diagnostic applications of this effect.

14.8. BIBLIOGRAPHY

1. Coblentz, *Investigations of Infra-red Spectra* (Carnegie Institute, 1905).
2. Bell, *J. Amer. Chem. Soc.*, 1925, **47**, 2192.
3. *Idem. ibid.*, p. 3039.
4. *Idem. ibid.*, 1926, **48**, 813.
5. *Idem. ibid.*, p. 818.
6. Ellis, *J. Amer. Chem. Soc.*, 1927, **49**, 347.
7. *Idem. ibid.*, 1928, **50**, 685.
8. Cleaves and Plyler, *J. Chem. Phys.*, 1939, **7**, 563.
9. Bailey, Carson and Daly, *Proc. Roy. Soc.*, 1939, **A173**, 339.
10. Buswell, Downing and Rodebush, *J. Amer. Chem. Soc.*, 1939, **61**, 3252.
11. Gordy, *ibid.*, 1937, **59**, 464.
12. Williams, Hofstadter and Herman, *J. Chem. Phys.*, 1939, **7**, 802.
13. Fuson, Josien, Powell and Utterback, *ibid.*, 1952, **20**, 145.
14. Richards, *Trans. Faraday Soc.*, 1948, **44**, 40.
15. Flett, *ibid.*, p. 767.
16. *Idem. J. Chem. Soc.*, 1948, 1441.
17. Hathway and Flett, *Trans. Faraday Soc.*, 1949, **45**, 818.
18. Giguère and Liu, *J. Chem. Phys.*, 1952, **20**, 136.
19. Randall, Fowler, Fuson and Dangl, *Infra-red Determination of Organic Structures* (Van Nostrand, 1949).
20. Hoffman, Evans and Glockler, *J. Amer. Chem. Soc.*, 1951, **73**, 3028.
21. Colthup, *J. Opt. Soc. Amer.*, 1950, **40**, 397.
22. Lieber, Levering and Patterson, *Analyt. Chem.*, 1951, **23**, 1594.
23. Brownlie, *J. Chem. Soc.*, 1950, 3062.
24. Short and Thompson, *ibid.*, 1952, 168.
25. Pauling, *The Nature of the Chemical Bond* (Oxford University Press, 1950).
26. Hunter, Price and Martin, *Report on the Symposium on the Hydrogen Bond* (Institute of Chemistry, 1950).
27. Gordy, *J. Chem. Phys.*, 1939, **7**, 167.

28. Thompson and Harris, *J. Chem. Soc.*, 1944, 301.
29. Baker, Davies and Gaunt, *ibid.*, 1949, 24.
30. Sutherland, *Discuss. Faraday Soc.*, 1950, 9, 274.
31. Rasmussen and Brattain, *J. Amer. Chem. Soc.*, 1949, 71, 1073.
32. Cromwell, Miller, Johnson, Frank and Wallace, *ibid.*, p. 3337.
33. Richards and Burton, *Trans. Faraday Soc.*, 1949, 45, 874.
34. Marion, Ramsay and Jones, *J. Amer. Chem. Soc.*, 1951, 73, 305.
35. Witkop, *ibid.*, 1950, 72, 614.
36. Axford, Janz and Russell, *J. Chem. Phys.*, 1951, 19, 704.
37. Thompson, Nicholson and Short, *Discuss. Faraday Soc.*, 1950, 9, 222.
38. Richards and Thompson, *J. Chem. Soc.*, 1947, 1248.
39. Witkop and Patrick, *J. Amer. Chem. Soc.*, 1951, 73, 713.
40. Short, *J. Chem. Soc.*, 1952, 4584.
41. Witkop and Patrick, *J. Amer. Chem. Soc.*, 1951, 73, 1558.
42. *Idem. ibid.*, p. 2188.
43. Bellamy and Beecher, *J. Chem. Soc.*, 1952, 1701.
44. Barnes, Gore, Stafford and V. Zandt Williams, *Analyt. Chem.*, 1948, 20, 402.
45. Mirone and Vampiri, *Atti accad. Nazl. Lincei Rend. Classe Sci. fis. mat. e. Nat.*, 1952, 12, 405.
46. Barcello and Bellanato, *Spectrochim. Acta*, 1956, 8 27.
47. Califano and Moccia, *Gazz. Chim.*, 1956, 86, 1014.
48. Richtering, *Z. Phys. Chem.*, 1956, 9, 393.
49. Searles, Tamres, Block and Quarterman, *J. Amer. Chem. Soc.*, 1956, 78, 4917.
50. Angyal and Werner, *J. Chem. Soc.*, 1952, 2911.
51. Shigorin, Danyushevskii and Gold'farb, *Izvest. Akad. Nauk. S.S.S.R. Otdel khim Nauk.*, 1956, 120.
52. Costa, Blasina and Sartori, *Z. Phys. Chem.*, 1956, 7, 123.
53. Chatt, Duncanson and Venanzi, *J. Chem. Soc.*, 1955, 4461.
54. *Idem, ibid.*, 1956, 2712.
55. Bellamy and Williams, *Spectrochim. Acta*, 1957, 9, 341.
56. Vampiri, *Gazz. Chim.*, 1954, 84, 1087.
57. Shull, Wood, Aston and Rank, *J. Chem. Phys.*, 1954, 22, 1191.
58. Heacock and Marion, *Can. J. Chem.*, 1956, 34, 1782.
59. Russell and Thompson, *J. Chem. Soc.*, 1955, 483.
60. Barr and Haszeldine, *ibid.*, 1955, 4169.
61. Pickard and Polly, *J. Amer. Chem. Soc.*, 1954, 76, 5169.
62. Hunter, *Progress in Stereochemistry*, Vol. 1 (Butterworth, London, 1954), p. 224.
63. Josien and Fuson, *J. Chem. Phys.*, 1954, 22, 1169.
64. Fuson and Josien, *J. Phys. Radium*, 1954, 15, 652.
65. Josien and Fuson, *J. Chem. Phys.*, 1954, 22, 1264.
66. Mirone and Fabbri, *Gazz. Chim.*, 1956, 86, 1079.
67. Tuomikoski, *Mikrochem. Acta*, 1955, 505.
68. *Idem, J. Phys. Radium*, 1955, 16, 347.
69. Despas, Khaladji and Vergoz, *Bull. Soc. Chim. Fr.*, 1953, 1105.
70. Hadži and Skrbljak, *J. Chem. Soc.*, 1957, 843.
71. Hadži, *ibid.*, 847.
72. Mecke and Mecke, *Chem. Ber.*, 1956, 89, 343.
73. Mecke, Mecke and Luttinghaus, *Zeit. Naturforsch.*, 1955, 10B, 367.
74. Salimov and Tatevskii, *Doklady Akad. Nauk. S.S.S.R.*, 1957, 112, 890.
75. Bagratishvili, *ibid.*, 1954, 96, 753.
76. Powell and Sheppard, *J. Chem. Soc.*, 1956, 3108.
77. Duval, Duval and Lecomte, *Compt. Rend. Acad. Sci. (Paris)*, 1947, 224, 1632.
78. Beattie and Tyrell, *J. Chem. Soc.*, 1956, 2849.
79. Hill and Rosenberg, *J. Chem. Phys.*, 1956, 24, 1219.
80. Mizushima, Nakagawa and Quagliano, *ibid.*, 1956, 25, 1367.
81. Mizushima, Nakagawa and Sweeney, *ibid.*, 1956, 25, 1006.
82. Svatos, Curran and Quagliano, *J. Amer. Chem. Soc.*, 1955, 77, 6159.
83. Barrow, Kreuger and Basolo, *J. Inorg. Nuclear Chem.*, 1956, 2, 340.

84. Bellanato and Barcello, *Anales. real Soc. Espan. fis. y. quim. Madrid,* 1956, **52B**, 469.
85. Witkop, *Experimentia,* 1954, **10**, 420.
86. Califano and Moccia, *Gazz. Chim.,* 1957, **87**, 58.
87. Leonard and Gash, *J. Amer. Chem. Soc.,* 1954, **76**, 2781.

CHAPTER 15

Unsaturated Nitrogen Compounds

15.1. INTRODUCTION AND TABLE

THE data available on unsaturated nitrogen-containing compounds are extremely variable. The position of the C≡N stretching vibration in nitriles has been extensively studied and is clearly defined; the influence of conjugation or of halogen substitution is also known. Similarly, azides can be recognised without undue difficulty by the characteristic N≡N absorption. The number of compounds studied in this case is still relatively small, but the position of the band near 2140 cm.$^{-1}$ leaves little room for doubt that it originates in a triple-bond vibration. It is interesting to note that inorganic azides also show this band clearly.

The double-bond vibrations, C=N and N=N, are less well defined. The approximate positions of the absorptions due to each are known, but little is known of factors influencing the position or intensity. In conjugated cyclic compounds the C=N vibration appears to be subject to frequency shifts which are much greater than any shown by the corresponding C=C vibrations, so that considerable caution is required in the interpretation of the spectra of compounds containing such structures. The correlations discussed are listed in Table 15.

TABLE 15

C≡N *Stretching Vibrations*	
Saturated alkyl nitriles . . .	2260–2240 cm.$^{-1}$ (s.)
αβ-Aryl nitriles	2240–2220 cm.$^{-1}$ (s.)
αβ-Unsaturated alkyl nitriles . .	2235–2215 cm.$^{-1}$ (s.)
Isocyanates	2275–2240 cm.$^{-1}$ (s.)
C=N *Stretching Vibrations*	
Open-chain compounds . . .	1690–1640 cm.$^{-1}$ (v.)
Open-chain αβ-unsaturated compounds .	1660–1630 cm.$^{-1}$ (v.)
Conjugated cyclic compounds . .	1660–1480 cm.$^{-1}$ (v.)
N=N *Stretching Vibrations* . .	1630–1575 cm.$^{-1}$ (v.)
–N=C=N–	2155–2130 cm.$^{-1}$ (s.)
N≡N *Stretching Vibrations* (Azides) .	$\begin{cases} 1340\text{–}1180 \text{ cm.}^{-1} \text{ (w.)} \\ 2160\text{–}2120 \text{ cm.}^{-1} \text{ (s.)} \end{cases}$

15.2. THE –C≡N STRETCHING VIBRATION

15.2(a). General. Infra-red absorption from nitriles is to be expected in the triple-bond region 2300–2000 cm.$^{-1}$, but until recently only isolated examples of compounds of this type have been studied. However, Reitz and Sabathy [1,2] and Reitz and Skrabel [3] studied the Raman spectra of monomeric nitriles and found values of 2245 cm.$^{-1}$ for aliphatic nitriles, 2229 cm.$^{-1}$ for aromatic nitriles and 2220 cm.$^{-1}$ for conjugated compounds.

Subsequent infra-red determinations indicated that these values were approximately correct for infra-red spectra also. Snyder and Eliel [4] in 1948 published the spectra of two nitriles, one of which was conjugated and the other was not, and although frequencies were not given, it was apparent from the spectra that the conjugated system was absorbing about 30 cm.$^{-1}$ lower than the other. Marvel *et al.* [5,6] studied the monomers and dimers of acetyl and benzoyl nitriles and found values of 2235 cm.$^{-1}$ for the monomer and 2256 cm.$^{-1}$ for the dimer in which conjugation with the CO group was lost. The dimer of 2-cyano-1 : 3-butadiene was also studied. This contains two CN groups, only one of which is conjugated. This showed two peaks at 2220 cm.$^{-1}$ and 2243 cm.$^{-1}$.

Other isolated observations on this frequency include phosphoryl cyanides,[7] which absorb at 2232 cm.$^{-1}$, and hydrogen cyanide, which has been studied as a mixture of the ^{12}C and ^{13}C istopes.[8] The C≡N frequencies found were 2213 cm.$^{-1}$ and 2157 cm.$^{-1}$, respectively, which is within 1 cm.$^{-1}$ of the theoretical value for this shift.

The most intensive study of nitriles which confirms and amplifies all these results is that of Kitson and Griffith,[9] who have examined the spectra of some seventy different nitriles in an attempt to relate the observed frequency shifts with the molecular structure.

These workers have found that in thirty-four saturated mono- and di-nitriles (excluding malononitrile) the C≡N frequency lies between 2260 cm.$^{-1}$ and 2240 cm.$^{-1}$, and in a further seventeen unsaturated but not conjugated nitriles the frequencies were within the same range. Twelve further nitriles in which the C≡N was conjugated with a double bond (excluding fumaronitrile) have a strong band between 2232 cm.$^{-1}$ and 2218 cm.$^{-1}$, and four compounds with nitrile groups of both types exhibit both absorptions. Similarly with aromatic compounds, those in which the C≡N group was directly attached to the ring (twelve compounds) absorbed in the range 2240–2221 cm.$^{-1}$, whilst two others, in which the C≡N group was separated from the ring by methylene groups, showed the normal frequencies of 2254 and 2248 cm.$^{-1}$. As is to be expected, the nature of other ring substituents affects the frequency to some extent, but the range given includes the absorption shown by compounds with either electron repelling or electron attracting substituents. These results have been supplemented by further work by Felton and Orr [35] and by Skinner and Thompson,[36] who have also studied numerous nitriles with similar results.

From this it is clear that the C≡N group can be identified with reasonable certainty in the infra-red provided the intensity is sufficient. A limited amount of additional data can also be obtained as to conjugation, and the behaviour of C≡N groups in this respect resembles closely that of the carbonyl group, which has been more extensively studied. There are, however, significant differences. Thus, whilst the presence of α-fluorine atoms raises the nitrile frequency, as with carbonyl compounds, the direct attachment of chlorine lowers it. Perfluoroalkyl nitriles absorb at 2275 ± 5 cm.$^{-1}$, and in $CF_2=CFCN$ the frequency (2255 cm.$^{-1}$) is again raised relative to vinyl cyanide.[37] However, cyanogen chloride absorbs at 2214 cm.$^{-1}$, which contrasts with the elevated carbonyl frequency of phosgene. In aryl nitriles the influence of the aromatic ring is enhanced by the presence of a para-$N(CH_3)_2$ group,[38] leading to slightly lower frequencies. This is similar to the behaviour of the acetophenones.

As regards malononitrile and fumaronitrile mentioned above as being the two exceptions to these correlations, they are both cases in which some interaction between the C≡N groups is to be expected, and a similar discrepancy exists in the case of the C=O frequencies of the corresponding carboxylic acids. They are not therefore significant in so far as the general applicability of these correlations is concerned. Another apparent exception is diazoguanidine cyanide, which is reported by Lieber et al.[13] to absorb at 2126 cm.$^{-1}$. This large shift is much greater than would be expected from the -N=N- conjugation.

The above correlations, of course, are not applicable to compounds of the type -N≡C which are iso-nitriles. The number of such compounds examined is very few, but the C≡N triple bond of this type [11] probably absorbs in the range 2180–2120 cm.$^{-1}$. McBride and Beachell [29] have recently compared the spectra of a limited number of nitriles and iso-nitriles. The former absorb in the ranges given, depending upon the nature of the substituents, but the alkyl iso-nitriles absorbed between 2183–2144 cm.$^{-1}$ and the aryl derivatives near 2145 cm.$^{-1}$. They also observed a new band near 1592 cm.$^{-1}$ in the spectra of the iso-nitriles which is absent from those of the nitriles. There is, however, no band in this region in methyl iso-cyanide which has been studied by Williams.[39] In this compound the N≡C absorption occurs at 2166 cm.$^{-1}$.

15.2(b). Intensities of C≡N Bands. The intensity of the nitrile absorption band has also been studied by Kitson and Griffith.[9] They find a marked variation in intensity in various types of nitrile, so that the band varies from very strong to undetectable. In general, the band is strong in compounds containing C, H and N only, and in such compounds its strength is a function of the proportion of nitrile groups in the molecule, so that the intensity of each $C\equiv N$ group can be regarded as being essentially the same in all cases. Conjugation also has some effect, and Cross and Rolfe [12] have reported the 2250 cm.$^{-1}$ band of benzonitrile as being about twice the intensity of either of two non-conjugated materials.

The introduction of an oxygenated group into the molecule results in a "quenching" of the $C\equiv N$ absorption intensity to a remarkable extent, and its effect is greater when the oxygen-containing group is attached to the same carbon atom as the nitrile. In acetone cyanhydrin, for example, the $C\equiv N$ intensity is about a third of the normal and in *dl-* and *meso*-diacetyl cyanhydrin the nitrile band was weak but detectable. In the corresponding acetoxy-compounds it could not be detected at all.

This study illustrates well the scope and limitations of the infra-red method for the study of this particular group. Where a band appears in the spectrum the $C\equiv N$ group can be identified with certainty, and some data on conjugation can also be obtained. Provided closely parallel compounds are used as standards, it is possible to estimate the $C\equiv N$ content in this way. Magat *et al.*[10] have estimated the $C\equiv N$ group in nylon-like polymers, using adiponitrile as their intensity standard.

On the other hand, the absence of any strong absorption in this region cannot be taken as evidence for the absence of $C\equiv N$ groups unless oxygen is known to be absent, whilst intensity measurements cannot be used to estimate $C\equiv N$ groups in an unknown product, as the arbitrary selection of a standard could lead to large errors if it did not happen to be closely similar to the product under examination.

The intensity of the $C\equiv N$ absorption, and also the half-band width shows very wide variations with structure. These are very much greater than the corresponding frequency shifts, so it should be possible to make use of these properties with advantage in diagnostic work. For example, Felton and Orr [35] have noted that the nitrile absorption intensity in a compound such as 3-methyl-but-2-eno-nitrile is more than ten times greater than in acetonitrile. The most detailed studies are due to Skinner and Thompson [36] and to Sensi and Gallo.[40] With alkyl cyanides the intensities lie in the range $2{\cdot}0$–$3{\cdot}2 \times 10^{-8}$, but all aromatic nitriles have much higher values, which depend in part on the nature and positions of the ring substituents and are probably connected with changes in the resonance energies. $\alpha\beta$-Unsaturated compounds show similar frequencies to aromatic nitriles, but their intensity behaviour is markedly different, and the bands are a good deal weaker. Marked changes in $C\equiv N$ intensities also follow the introduction of polar groups at the α-position.

15.3. *ISO*CYANATES AND CARBODIMIDES

15.(3)a. *iso*Cyanates. This class of compound has been studied by Davison [42] and by Hoyer.[41] Davison studied ten *iso*cyanates and found a very intense absorption at 2269 cm.$^{-1}$ $\pm$ 6 cm.$^{-1}$. This is unaltered by changes of state and by conjugation. The intensities of this band in two aromatic *iso*cyanates were assessed as being over 100 times that of the corresponding band in alkyl cyanides which absorb in the same region, so that differentiation should be possible in this way. These findings have been fully confirmed by Hoyer.[41] More than forty *iso*cyanates have been studied by this worker, who finds both alkyl and aryl compounds to absorb in the range 2274–2242 cm.$^{-1}$, with the majority near 2270 cm.$^{-1}$. No clear distinction was traceable between conjugated and non-conjugated compounds, but the high intensity of this band was confirmed. In 1-cyano-3-*iso*cyanato-propane, for example, the N=C=O absorption at 2272 cm.$^{-1}$ could be clearly differentiated from the much weaker nitrile absorption on the low-frequency side. Phenyl *iso*cyanate is anomalous in showing a doublet at 2278 cm.$^{-1}$ and 2260 cm.$^{-1}$. The 2270 cm.$^{-1}$ absorption of *iso*cyanates corresponds to the asymmetric stretching mode of the N=C=O group, and in theory a weaker symmetric frequency is to be expected near 1350 cm.$^{-1}$. This has been identified at 1377 cm.$^{-1}$ in methyl *iso*cyanate by Eyster and Gillette.[25] If a positive identification could be made it would make the differentiation of *iso*cyanates from nitriles much simpler. Unfortunately this second band is too weak to be recognised [42] with any certainty, and is liable to be hidden by the methyl and methylene absorptions which occur in this region.

15.3.(b) Carbodimides. Compounds of this class contain the structure R–N=C=N–R and have been little studied. Khorana [43, 45] has studied a very limited number of examples and noted absorption at 2150 cm.$^{-1}$. A more detailed study of both frequency and intensity has been made by Meakins and Moss.[44] Nine carbodimides were examined by these authors, and all showed a very intense absorption in the range 2152–2128 cm.$^{-1}$ accompanied in three instances by a much weaker combination band at lower frequencies. Little frequency or intensity differences was found between alkyl and aryl derivatives. The intensity of the band was assessed by a variety of methods, and the extinction coefficient ε^a was of the order of 1400. This is some $2\frac{1}{2}$ times as strong as a normal ketonic carbonyl absorption.

15.4. THE –C=N– STRETCHING VIBRATION

15.4(a). General. A good deal of work has been done on the position of the –C=N– stretching absorption in various classes of compounds, and the situation has been reviewed in detail by

Fabian, Legrand and Poirier.[46] The band remains a difficult one to identify, however, owing to the considerable changes in intensity which follow changes in its environment. Also, the information available on the effects of conjugation in ring systems is often conflicting and indecisive. This is partly due to the fact that in many of the compounds studied the conjugation is with C=C links and the frequencies of the two are so close that, in ring systems at least, it is doubtful whether either can be regarded as retaining its individual character. For this reason Randall *et al.*[14] prefer to identify groups of bands in the 1600–1500 cm.$^{-1}$ region as being characteristic of particular structures such as thiazoles, rather than to assign individual bands. A useful list of references to heterocyclic ring frequencies of this type has been compiled by Jones and Sandorfy.[47] In pyridine and similar aromatic compounds the individuality of the C=N absorption is, of course, completely lost, and systems of this type will be considered separately in the section on heterocyclic aromatic materials (Chapter 16).

A second difficulty in the identification of C=N absorptions arises from the fact that much of the early work on this link has been carried out in connection with studies on penicillin, so that the compounds examined often contained amide groups, amine groups and aromatic ring systems, all of which are liable to give absorptions in the same spectral region as the C=N group.

As will be seen from the following discussion, C=N absorption in open-chain systems or in non-conjugated ring systems occurs within the range 1690–1640 cm.$^{-1}$, and the influence of conjugation is usually small. With conjugated cyclic systems the position is much less clear, and the C=N absorptions have been assigned as being within the range 1660–1480 cm.$^{-1}$. In acyclic compounds and cyclic materials without internal conjugation, Barnes *et al.*[15] assigned the C=N absorption to the 1650 cm.$^{-1}$ region, and this assignment has been fully confirmed by later work, especially by the large volume of work carried out on the penicillin project, which has not been fully published, but which has been summarised by Thompson, Brattain, Randall and Rasmussen.[16] This concludes that the C=N absorption occurs near 6·0 μ (1667 cm.$^{-1}$) as judged from oxazines, oxazolines, oximes and imines. This is confirmed by Fabian *et al.*,[46] who assign the overall range of 1674–1665 cm.$^{-1}$ to non-conjugated compounds of the type R–CH=N–R, with a slight lowering in some cases when one of the carbon substituents carries a branched chain. Oximes also follow this assignment reasonably well.

Acetoxime, for example, absorbs at 1675 cm.$^{-1}$, *cyclo*hexanone oxime at 1669 cm.$^{-1}$ and *cyclo*pentanone oxime [12] at 1684 cm.$^{-1}$. The slight rise on passing from a six-membered ring to a five-membered ring recalls the similar rise in the C=O frequency of *cyclo*pentanone over that of *cyclo*hexanone, and may be due to ring strain. Form-aldoxime and acetone oxime have been studied in some detail by Califano and Lüttke,[48] whilst Palm and Werbin [49] have studied a range of geometric isomers. In the solid state unconjugated oximes absorb close to 1640 cm.$^{-1}$ and are unaffected by the geometric form. However, this frequency is influenced by intermolecular association, and the frequencies in dilute solution are somewhat higher. Fabian *et al.*,[46] who also take account of Raman data, quote the overall range of 1684–1652 cm.$^{-1}$ for oximes in solution.

Imines also appear to be very similar. Picard and Polly [50] quote 1640–1633 cm.$^{-1}$ for non-conjugated compounds. However, this probably refers to samples in the condensed phase, and higher values would be expected in solution, when they would probably fall within the 1680–1660 cm.$^{-1}$ range. Baguley and Elvidge [51] quote a solid-state frequency of 1664 cm.$^{-1}$ for an exocyclic $=$NH bond attached to a five-membered ring, which would be expected to be raised a little above the normal value. When one or more NH groups are attached to the carbon atom of the C$=$N link, as in guanidines and related materials, it becomes more difficult to identify the C$=$N links with any certainty. In general, the frequencies appear to be slightly higher than usual. Lieber, Levering and Patterson [13] quote an overall range of 1689–1657 cm.$^{-1}$ for compounds of this type, but Pickard and Polly find a wide variation between 1718 and 1590 cm.$^{-1}$. Non-conjugated C$=$N links in oxazolones also occur [17] within the range 1683–1668 cm.$^{-1}$. Provided therefore that the C$=$N link is not conjugated and carries no charge on the nitrogen atom, the stretching frequency in unstrained compounds of all types may be expected in the overall range 1680–1650 cm.$^{-1}$, with somewhat lower values in the solid state. Departures from this will be found, however, particularly in the guanidines and in strained-ring systems. In pyrazolones, for example,[52] the C$=$N frequency can rise to 1700 cm.$^{-1}$. However, when the nitrogen atom of the C$=$N bond is so substituted that it is able to take on a more polar character the characteristic frequency alters considerably. Goulden [30] quotes limits of 1659–1510 cm.$^{-1}$ for a series of compounds of this type, and the metallic chelates of some oximes have also been found to show considerable variations in their C$=$N frequencies.[31] The direction of frequency shift in such cases depends in part on the nature of the charge on the nitrogen atom. In N$^+$$=$C compounds, for example, the frequencies are raised a little above the normal, and Leonard *et al.*[53, 54] have made use of this in the differentiation of αβ-unsaturated tertiary amines by observing the high C$=$N$\overset{+}{\diagdown}$ frequencies which occur when salt formation allows tautomerism to take place.

The influence of conjugation on this frequency is very similar to the case of the C=C frequency, although the shifts are a little less. Acetylazine [19] with two C=N bands in conjugation absorbs at 1664 cm.$^{-1}$, but with crotonaldehyde azine [19] the interpretation is more complex, as there are two C=C groups as well as two C=N links. However, here also the strongest band is at 1650 cm.$^{-1}$. Similarly, α-furylazine absorbs at 1635 cm.$^{-1}$. When aromatic rings form the conjugating system, the effect is again small. The C=N frequency in solution then falls in the overall range [45] 1660–1630 cm.$^{-1}$, with slightly lower values for solids and associated compounds such as the aromatic aldoximes. The presence of a second aromatic ring on the other side of the C=N link leads to a concentration of the observed frequencies near the lower end of this range. The influence of aryl conjugation on the C=N absorption in oxazolones has also been extensively studied in connection with the penicillin programme. The general finding of the American group of workers in this field [17] was that non-conjugated oxazolones absorbed in the range 1683–1668 cm.$^{-1}$ and that this was only lowered to 1657–1641 cm.$^{-1}$ by aromatic-type conjugation. Similar values were obtained by the British group,[18] who also found that even in oxazolones in which the aromatic conjugation was coupled with C=C conjugation on the opposite side of the C=N link, C=N absorption occurred in the range 1672–1634 cm.$^{-1}$, despite the fact that other ring vibrations were considerably altered.

15.4(b). Conjugated Cyclic Systems. As has been indicated above, the C=N absorptions of conjugated cyclic systems cannot readily be considered in isolation, as they interact with other double bonds to a much greater extent than is the case with acylic materials. Furthermore, in such systems extensive shifts of both C=C and C=N absorptions can occur, so that it is then difficult to differentiate between the two, and it is preferable to consider the group of absorptions as a whole in relation to the particular structural unit.

A typical case is that of the thiazoles. Randall *et al.*[14] have examined seven examples of this type of compound and found absorptions in the range 1634–1570 cm.$^{-1}$ and 1538–1493 cm.$^{-1}$ which they regard as being typical of the thiazole structure. Similarly benzthiazoles give two bands in the range 1647–1513 cm.$^{-1}$ and 1529–1473 cm.$^{-1}$. Cases such as these recall the similar vibration effects in aromatic systems, and it is clearly necessary to regard the system as a single unit for correlation purposes. The triazines and related compounds have been studied by Roosens [20] and are somewhat similar cases. In the thiazolines studied by Otting and Drawert [55] the C=N frequency of unconjugated compounds occurs near 1640 cm.$^{-1}$ and falls to near 1610 cm.$^{-1}$ (solid state) with aromatic conjugation. However, conjugation with a C=C link leads to multiple frequencies, and up to four bands are then found. Of these, those near 1640 cm.$^{-1}$ and 1570 cm.$^{-1}$ are attributed to the asymmetric and symmetric stretching frequencies of the system $-C=C-C=N$.

A second class of $C=N$ conjugated ring compounds is that in which the conjugation results in a total suppression of the absorption bands. Such cases have been reported by Lieber *et al.*[13] for a number of tetrazoles in which neither a $C=N$ nor an $N=N$ absorption could be detected, although a strong absorption occurs at 1626 cm.$^{-1}$ in a single triazole which they have examined, which they attribute to the $C=N$ linkage.

Clearly, therefore, the application of $C=N$ correlations to conjugated cyclic systems can be undertaken only after the examination of a series of closely related materials, and until considerably more work has been done in this field, they cannot safely be applied to the identification of this group in unknown products.

15.4(c). The Intensity of $C=N$ Absorptions. The intensity of the $C=N-$ absorption varies widely with the nature of the attached group. Cross and Rolfe [12] have noted that in oximes it is extremely weak, but even then varies by a factor of two in non-conjugated compounds. On the other hand, Goulden [30] noted that in imino-thioethers the $-C=N-$ absorption was relatively strong, whilst in $N:N'$-dimethylbenzamide it is extremely strong.[56] Fabian and Legrand [56] have compared the extinction coefficients of the $-C=N-$ absorptions in various systems. In a compound such as N-propylidene propylamine the ε value in carbon tetrachloride is 140. Replacement of one or both alkyl groups by aromatic rings raises this value slightly to 180. On the other hand, oximes such as *cyclo*hexanone oxime have an ε value of 20 under these conditions, falling to less than 8·5 in the oxime of acetophenone.

The substitution of a sulphur atom on to the carbon of the double bond raises the extinction coefficient to 218 (conjugated 270), whilst nitrogen has an even greater effect. Values ranging from $\varepsilon = 365$ to 880 are quoted for variously substituted benzamidines. Oxygen attached to the double bond at the carbon atom also has a very marked effect, and methyl N-phenyl benzimidate has an ε value of 670.

Whilst extinction coefficients have not the precision of intensity measurements based on band areas, the relative orders of magnitude are clearly so widely different that intensities measured in this way will give useful information as to the immediate environment of the $-C=N-$ bond.

15.5. THE $-N=N-$ STRETCHING VIBRATION

Not very much is known of the characteristics of infra-red absorption bands arising from the $-N=N-$ linkage. By analogy with

T

the –C≡N– and C≡C groups any such band might be expected to appear in the 1600 cm.$^{-1}$ region, but it would be likely to be weak unless conjugated and might well be absent in symmetrical structures.

Herzberg [21] quotes azomethane as having a strong Raman absorption at 1575 cm.$^{-1}$ which is assigned to the –N=N– stretching vibration, and Lieber, Levering and Patterson [13] have found absorptions in the range 1631–1613 cm.$^{-1}$ in four azo-compounds, although their identification is weakened by the fact that two of their compounds show two bands in this region, as C=N groups are also present and the differentiation between the two is not easy. These workers have also given the spectra of a number of tetrazoles which do not appear to show any –N=N– absorptions, despite the presence of this group. Le Fevre *et al.*[60] have also investigated the cyclic –N=N– frequencies in formazans. We have examined a small number of aromatic diazo-compounds, but in no case have we observed any clear-cut bands in the expected region, other than those arising from the conjugated aromatic system itself. As these compounds all showed some degree of symmetry, it is possible that the –N=N– absorptions were too weak to be observed, or, alternatively, they may well be merged with the stronger C=C ring absorptions. The same difficulty has been encountered by Le Fèvre *et al.*,[34,57] who have studied many aromatic diazo-compounds. They find common absorptions at 1406 ± 14 cm.$^{-1}$ and at 1577 ± 8 cm.$^{-1}$, and although they assign the latter to the –N=N– link they point out that it could well arise from ring vibrations. The possible interference of the latter clearly limits the usefulness of the –N=N– correlation, which would be likely to find its main application in the study of azo-dyes. The same difficulty was encountered by Dolinsky and Jones,[58] who were unable to identify either of the 1577 cm.$^{-1}$ and 1408 cm.$^{-1}$ absorptions in aromatic azo-compounds. They did, however, make the interesting observation that *ortho*-hydroxy or aminoazo-compounds were abnormal and different from the *p*-substituted compounds, which led them to conclude that zwitterion structures involving the –N=$\overset{+}{\text{N}}$H– structure were involved. Hadži [59] had investigated this further using deuteration techniques. He found that complex mixtures of tautomers involving the hydrazones are formed in this way, whilst compounds such as 4-phenylazo-1-naphthol and the *o*-methyl derivative of 1- and 4-phenylazophenol exist as true –N=N– compounds. He was, however, unable to identify any characteristic –N=N– frequency in any of these compounds.

The weak intensity of the –N=N– band, and the fact that it probably arises in the 1600 cm.$^{-1}$ region along with aromatic absorptions, therefore appear to preclude any useful correlation for this group. In the azoxy-compound hexafluoroazoxymethane the $\ce{>C-N=N-C<}$ group shows [61] the $N=N$ absorption at 1570 cm⁻¹, with the $N \rightarrow O$ band at 1270 cm.⁻¹.

There is also a possibility that a characteristic frequency for the skeleton $-C-N=N-C$ may exist, as Tetlow [23] has shown that both *cis*- and *trans*-azobenzenes show absorption at 927 cm.⁻¹ which is absent from hydrazobenzene, and that this band shows a Christiansen filter effect only in the *trans*-form, which may indicate its association with a skeletal group along the direction of maximum polarisability.

15.6. THE DIAZO GROUP

Diazomethane is a linear molecule with the structure $CH_2=N=\overset{+}{N}$ and absorbs at 2101 cm.⁻¹. The assignment of this to the stretching frequency is supported by fundamental studies on two diazo-cyanides.[32, 33] More recently diazonium salts have been investigated by Aroney *et al.*[62] and by Whetsel *et al.*[63] Altogether a total of over fifty aryl diazonium salts have been studied by these groups. Aroney *et al.*[62] find the characteristic $-CN_2{}^+$ frequency at 2261 cm.⁻¹ with a range of about ± 20 cm.⁻¹. Whetsel[63] *et al.* confirm these figures but extend the range slightly. These latter workers studied the influence of both the anion and the diazonium cation on this frequency. Changes in the former produce only negligible shifts, but ring substitution by groups with strong electron-attracting properties has a marked effect. Diazonium salts of *p*-nitro-aniline, for example, absorb at 2294 cm.⁻¹, whereas the corresponding *p*-diethylamino-derivatives absorb at 2151 cm.⁻¹. In the extreme case of diazophenol the frequency falls to 2110 cm.⁻¹. However, Le Fevre *et al.*[64] have recently shown that both diazo-phenols and diazonaphthols exist in fact as quinone diazides, so the frequency fall due to the increased resonance is readily understood on this basis. The range found for compounds of this type was 2173–2014 cm.⁻¹, depending upon the nature and positions of other ring substituents.

The high frequency of this absorption is typical of $X=X=X$ structures, and it cannot therefore always be readily differentiated from *iso*cyanates and similar materials. However, the recognition of this band in the spectrum of the naturally occurring azaserine has recently led to its successful synthesis.[65]

15.7. AZIDES

Azides can be readily identified by the strong $N=N=N$ asymmetric stretching absorption which occurs with great consistency close to 2130 cm.⁻¹. The corresponding symmetric vibration is at considerably lower frequency, and is not only much weaker, but is also much more variable in position, so that it is of relatively little use for analytical purposes.

The spectrum of hydrazoic acid has been examined by Eyster,[24] who has assigned the band at 2141 cm.$^{-1}$ to the $N{=}N{=}N$ asymmetric vibration and that at 1269 cm.$^{-1}$ to the corresponding symmetric mode. Methyl azide has also been fully studied,[25] and the corresponding bands in this case are at 2141 cm.$^{-1}$ and 1351 cm.$^{-1}$.

A systematic study of azides as a group has been made by Sheïnker and Syrkin,[26] who examined the Raman spectra of sodium azide and six other materials. They found a strong band in all cases in the range 2167–2080 cm.$^{-1}$ and a second weaker one in the range 1343–1177 cm.$^{-1}$. In accordance with the earlier work these were assigned to the asymmetric and symmetric vibrations respectively. It should be noted, however, that some inorganic azides have a simple linear structure so that the symmetric frequency is not found in the infra-red. In ammonium azide crystals, for example, only the 2050 cm.$^{-1}$ band is shown and the symmetric band is absent.[66]

Further confirmation of these findings has come from Boyer [27] and also from Lieber, Levering and Patterson.[13] Boyer studied the addition of hydrazoic acid to conjugated systems and examined the infrared spectra of the products. Ten azides in all were examined, and all showed strong absorptions near 2128 cm.$^{-1}$. The frequency did not appear to be particularly sensitive to environmental changes, and 1-phenyl-1-azido-2-nitroethane, for example, absorbed at the same frequency as triazoacetone.

Lieber *et al.*[13] repeated earlier work on sodium azide and examined five others not previously studied. They reported a relatively strong band in all cases in the range 2151–2128 cm.$^{-1}$ with a second weaker and more variable band near 1282 cm.$^{-1}$. In the light of this later work it would seem probable that Sheïnker and Syrkin [26] have quoted a wider range for the asymmetrical vibration than is likely to be found in normal practice, and that this absorption can normally be expected within the range 2160–2120 cm.$^{-1}$. This is, of course, essentially similar to the diazo-, *iso*cyanate and similar groups.

The Raman spectra of inorganic azides have been examined by Kahovec and Kohlrausch.[28] Their results agree with the infra-red data in showing only a small frequency range for a variety of cations.

15.8. BIBLIOGRAPHY

1. Reitz and Sabathy, *Monatsh.*, 1938, **71**, 100.
2. *Idem, ibid.*, p. 131.
3. Reitz and Skrabel, *ibid.*, 1937, **70**, 398.
4. Snyder and Eliel, *J. Amer. Chem. Soc.*, 1948, **70**, 1857.
5. Marvel, Brace, Miller and Johnson, *ibid.*, 1949, **71**, 34.
6. Marvel and Brace, *ibid.*, p. 37.

7. Holmstedt and Larsson, *Acta Chem. Scand.*, 1951, **5**, 1179.
8. Richardson and Bright-Wilson, *J. Chem. Phys.*, 1950, **18**, 155.
9. Kitson and Griffith, *Analyt. Chem.*, 1952, **24**, 334.
10. Magat, Chandler, Faris, Reith and Salisbury, *J. Amer. Chem. Soc.*, 1951, **73**, 1031.
11. Mellon, *Analytical Spectroscopy* (Wiley, 1950).
12. Cross and Rolfe, *Trans. Faraday Soc.*, 1951, **47**, 354.
13. Lieber, Levering and Patterson, *Analyt. Chem.*, 1951, **23**, 1594.
14. Randall, Fowler, Fuson and Dangl, *Infra-red Determination of Organic Structures* (Van Nostrand, 1949).
15. Barnes, Gore, Liddel and Van Zandt Williams, *Infra-red Spectroscopy* (Reinhold, 1944).
16. Thompson, Brattain, Randall and Rasmussen, *The Chemistry of Penicillin* (Princeton University Press, 1949), p. 382.
17. Rasmussen and Brattain, *ibid.*, p. 400.
18. Thompson, *ibid.*, p. 387.
19. Blout, Fields and Karplus, *J. Amer. Chem. Soc.*, 1948, **70**, 194.
20. Roosens, *Bull. Soc. Chim. (Belg.)*, 1950, **59**, 377.
21. Herzberg, *Infra-red and Raman Spectra of Polyatomic Molecules* (Van Nostrand, 1945), p. 357.
22. Crawford, Fletcher and Ramsay, *J. Chem. Phys.*, 1951, **19**, 406.
23. Tetlow, *Research*, 1950, **3**, 187.
24. Eyster, *J. Chem. Phys.*, 1940, **8**, 135.
25. Eyster and Gillette, *J. Chem. Phys.*, 1940, **8**, 369.
26. Sheïnker and Syrkin, *Izvest. Akad. Nauk. S.S.S.R. Ser. Fiz.*, 1950, **14**, 478.
27. Boyer, *J. Amer. Chem. Soc.*, 1951, **73**, 5248.
28. Kahovec and Kohlrausch, *Mh. Chem.*, 1947, **77**, 180.
29. McBride and Beachell, *J. Amer. Chem. Soc.*, 1952, **74**, 5247.
30. Goulden, *J. Chem. Soc.*, 1953, 997.
31. Duyckaerts, *Bull. Soc. Roy. Sci. Liége*, 1952, **21**, 196.
32. Sheppard and Sutherland, *J. Chem. Soc.*, 1947, 453.
33. Anderson, Le Fèvre and Savage, *ibid.*, 443.
34. Le Fèvre, O'Dwyer and Werner, *Chem. and Ind.*, 1953, 378.
35. Felton and Orr, *J. Chem. Soc.*, 1955, 2170.
36. Skinner and Thompson, *ibid.*, 1955, 487.
37. Weiblen, *Fluorine Chemistry*, Vol. 2 (Academic Press, New York, 1954).
38. Lippert and Vogel, *Zeit. Phys. Chem.*, 1956, **9**, 133.
39. Williams, *J. Chem. Phys.*, 1956, **25**, 656.
40. Sensi and Gallo, *Gazz. Chim.*, 1955, **85**, 224, 235.
41. Hoyer, *Chem. Ber.*, 1956, **89**, 2677.
42. Davison, *J. Chem. Soc.*, 1953, 3712.
43. Khorana, *Can. J. Chem.*, 1954, **32**, 261.
44. Meakins and Moss, *J. Chem. Soc.*, 1957, 993.
45. Khorana, *Chem. Reviews*, 1953, **53**, 145.
46. Fabian, Legrand and Poirier, *Bull. Soc. Chim. Fr.*, 1956, 1499.
47. Jones and Sandorfy, *Chemical Applications of Spectroscopy* (Interscience New York, 1956), p. 534.
48. Califano and Lüttke, *Zeit. Phys. Chem.*, 1956, **6**, 83.
49. Palm and Werbin, *Can. J. Chem.*, 1953, **31**, 1004.
50. Pickard and Polly, *J. Amer. Chem. Soc.*, 1954, **76**, 5169.
51. Baguley and Elvidge, *J. Chem. Soc.*, 1957, 709.
52. Gagon, Boivin, McDonald and Yaffe, *Can. J. Chem.*, 1954, **32**, 823.
53. Leonard and Gash, *J. Amer. Chem. Soc.*, 1951, **76**, 2781.
54. Leonard, Thomas and Gash, *ibid.*, 1955, **77**, 1552.
55. Otting and Drawert, *Chem. Ber.*, 1955, **88**, 1469.
56. Fabian and Legrand, *Bull. Soc. Chim. Fr.*, 1956, 1461.
57. Le Fevre, O'Dwyer and Werner, *Austral. J. Chem.*, 1953, **6**, 341.
58. Dolinsky and Jones, *J. Assoc. Off. Agric. Chem.*, 1954, **37**, 197.
59. Hadži, *J. Chem. Soc.*, 1956, 2143.
60. Le Fevre, Sousa and Werner, *Austral. J. Chem.*, 1956, **9**, 151.
61. Jander and Haszeldine, *J. Chem. Soc.*, 1954, 919.
62. Aroney, Le Fevre and Werner, *ibid.*, 1955, 276.

63. Whetsel, Hawkins and Johnson, *J. Amer. Chem. Soc.*, 1956, **78**, 3360.
64. Le Fevre, Sousa and Werner, *J. Chem. Soc.*, 1954, 4686.
65. Fusari, Frohardt, Ryder, Haskell, Johanessen, Elder and Bartz, *J. Amer. Chem. Soc.*, 1954, **76**, 2878.
66. Dows, Whittle and Pimentel, *J. Chem. Phys.*, 1955, **23**, 1475.

CHAPTER 16

Heterocyclic Aromatic Compounds

16.1. INTRODUCTION AND TABLE

THERE is a reasonably close analogy between the ring vibrations of benzene and those of pyridine and quinoline, but there are considerable differences in the hydrogen deformation vibrations. However, the out-of-plane hydrogen deformation vibrations appear to be like those of benzene compounds containing an additional substituent. An α-mono-substituted pyridine, therefore, behaves like an *ortho*-di-substituted aromatic compound in this respect. Since no very considerable numbers of pyridines or quinolines have been examined, none of these generalisations should be applied without suitable reservations or confirmatory work on similar compounds.

The pyrimidines and purines have been more extensively studied on account of their intrinsic interest as important biological compounds. The compounds studied, however, have been primarily the hydroxy- and amino-derivatives which may be capable of existence in more than one form. In any case, until more data are available on whether these compounds exist in a form which contains a heterocyclic aromatic-type ring, the results so far obtained cannot be utilised for more general studies. The more limited data available on other types of pyrimidines indicate that these also are related to

TABLE 16

Pyridines and Quinolines

CH stretching vibrations . .	Near 3020 cm.$^{-1}$ (s.)
C=C and C=N stretching vibrations	1660–1590 cm.$^{-1}$ (sometimes doubled on low-frequency side) (m.)
„ „ „	Near 1500 cm.$^{-1}$
Ring vibrations; CH deformations .	Near 1200 cm.$^{-1}$ (s.)
„ „ „ .	1100–1000 cm.$^{-1}$ (s.)
„ „ „ .	900–650 cm.$^{-1}$ (s.)
„ „ „ .	Near 710 cm.$^{-1}$ (additional to the band above) (s.)

Pyrimidines

CH stretching vibrations . .	3060–3010 cm.$^{-1}$ (s.)
C=C, C=N stretching vibrations .	1580–1520 cm.$^{-1}$ (m.)
Ring vibrations; CH deformations .	$\begin{cases} 1000\text{–}960 \text{ cm.}^{-1} \text{ (m.)} \\ 825\text{–}775 \text{ cm.}^{-1} \text{ (m.)} \end{cases}$

benzene where the C–H stretching and ring vibrations are concerned but that, as expected, there are considerable differences in the positions of the hydrogen deformation modes. The correlations discussed are listed in Table 16.

16.2. PYRIDINES AND QUINOLINES

16.2(a). General. Not much is known of the characteristic absorptions of aromatic heterocyclic systems. Kline and Turkevitch [1] and Corrsin *et al.*[21] have shown that the ring vibrations of pyridine are closely parallel to those of benzene, but that the hydrogen deformation vibrations are widely different, and where they can be recognised at all they are mostly found to shift to lower frequencies on passing from benzene to pyridine. Fully and partially deuterated [23] pyridines have also been studied in some detail. Cannon and Sutherland [2] have discussed possible correlations following their examination of β- and γ-picolines and 2 : 6-lutidine, and the spectrum of α-picoline has been given by Freiser and Glowacki,[3] and is also included in the A.P.I. series of spectra. The spectra of the picolines have also been discussed by Roberts and Szwarc.[4] In addition, data on substituted pyridine derivatives over parts of the spectral range have been given by Marion, Ramsay and Jones [5] in connection with studies on alkaloids, by Coulson, Hales and Herington [6] in connection with water estimations, and by Densham, Langston and Gough [8] in connection with pyridine estimations. Quinolines have been little studied, but the spectrum of *iso*quinoline is included in the A.P.I. series, and Hannan, Lieblich and Renfrew [7] have published the spectra of five quinoline thiols. Shindo and Ikekawa [26] have discussed the out-of-plane CH deformation frequencies in substituted pyridines, and Tallent and Siewers [27] the CH stretching vibrations.

The reasonably close analogy between the ring vibrations of pyridine and benzene derivatives, which is evident from this work, justifies to some extent the tentative correlations which have been put forward and which are discussed below, but in any application of these correlations the fact that they are based on only a very limited number of derivatives—mostly alkyl derivatives—should not be overlooked.

16.2(b). CH Stretching Vibrations. The limited data available confirm the reasonable expectation that the C–H stretching modes of pyridines and quinolines will be essentially similar to those of benzene. Pyridine and the picolines all show CH absorptions in the range 3070–3020 cm.$^{-1}$,[1, 4, 5, 6] which appear as a series of multiple absorptions under high resolution.[25, 27] The positions and numbers of these vary somewhat with the substitution involved, but the observed frequencies are in each case very close to those of the benzene homologues. Marion *et al.*[5] have noted a band near 3030 cm.$^{-1}$ in anabasine which is absent from the spectrum of piperidine and which is assigned to the C–H stretching mode of the pyridine ring. We also find some bands near 3030 cm.$^{-1}$ in a series of quinoline derivatives, but this is to be expected in view of the presence of the carbocyclic ring. As in the case of benzene, other weaker bands are also shown in this region, although very little is known about them. Pyridine, for example,[6] appears to have a small absorption as high as 3420 cm.$^{-1}$ which is in the NH stretching frequency region. On the low-frequency side many heterocyclic compounds absorb [27] in the 2830–2790 cm.$^{-1}$ range. This is not found with benzene derivatives, and may be a useful indication in some instances. However, it should be remembered that many oxygenated compounds, such as di*iso*propyl ether absorb near here also.

16.2(c). C=C and C=N Vibrations. Interactions between the C=C and C=N vibrations of the pyridine ring appear to occur in a very similar way to benzene, giving rise to two bands about 100 cm.$^{-1}$ apart which are at slightly lower frequencies than those of benzene. In many cases the higher-frequency band is accompanied by a second band on the low-frequency side.[2] This is not apparently associated, as in the case of benzene, with external conjugation of the ring, but its appearance is often very similar to the bands from such a structure, so that it is easy in the examination of heterocyclic compounds to confuse the bands of pyridine derivatives with those of conjugated aromatics.

Pyridine itself absorbs at 1580 cm.$^{-1}$ and 1570 cm.$^{-1}$, and at 1485 cm.$^{-1}$. The spectra of the picolines and 2 : 6-lutidine show absorption in the 1600–1590 cm.$^{-1}$ range [2] and near to 1500 cm.$^{-1}$, and various alkaloids containing pyridine or quinoline rings [5] also absorb between 1600 cm.$^{-1}$ and 1560 cm.$^{-1}$. Anabasine, for example, absorbs at 1592 cm.$^{-1}$ and 1576 cm.$^{-1}$, and these bands are absent from the spectrum of piperidine. The positions of these absorptions in a series of alkyl pyridines have also been studied by Shindo and Ikekawa [26] and by Cook and Church,[41] who have commented on the changes in the relative intensities which follow alterations in the positions of the substituent groups. These are, however, not sufficiently large to have much diagnostic value.

In the case of quinoline and *iso*quinoline more complex interactions are possible, *iso*quinoline itself shows three bands between 1600 cm.$^{-1}$ and 1500 cm.$^{-1}$, whilst a number of dimethylquinolines which we have examined show complex absorption patterns of four bands in this region. The pattern is essentially that of pyridine, with one or more additional bands superimposed in most cases. 8-Hydroxy-quinoline shows its major bands at 1577 cm.$^{-1}$ and 1495 cm.$^{-1}$ with much weaker peaks at 1563 cm.$^{-1}$ and 1504 cm.$^{-1}$. The quinoline thiols discussed by Hannan *et al.*[7] generally show a relatively simple pair of bands near 1600 cm.$^{-1}$, but in all these cases except one the possibility of tautomerism to the thio-ketone form exists. In the single exception in which the thiol group is substituted it is interesting to note that a more complex pattern of four strong bands is shown between 1600 cm.$^{-1}$ and 1500 cm.$^{-1}$.

16.2(d). Ring Vibrations and Hydrogen Deformations. Assignment of Pyridine and Quinoline Substitution. A number of bands have been noted which appear to persist throughout the series of substituted pyridine derivatives which may be of some assistance in recognising this type of structure. Cannon and Sutherland [2] have pointed out that pyridine, and the derivatives they have examined, show a strong band near 1200 cm.$^{-1}$ and another between 1100 cm.$^{-1}$ and 1000 cm.$^{-1}$. The spectrum of 2-methylpyridine in the A.P.I. series is similar in showing absorptions at 1240 cm.$^{-1}$ and 1043 cm.$^{-1}$, the latter being particularly strong. These are either ring vibrations or hydrogen deformation modes, so that the correlation cannot be expected to apply to the quinoline series. None of the substituted quinolines we have examined shows any strong absorptions in these regions.

The remaining characteristic region is that between 900 cm.$^{-1}$ and 700 cm.$^{-1}$ in which CH deformations occur. It has been shown in the case of benzene substitution that the strongest band in this region originates in the out-of-plane vibrations of the unsubstituted hydrogen atoms of the ring, and that the principal factor determining the frequency is the number of such free hydrogen atoms which are adjacent to one another. A similar effect can be expected in pyridine derivatives, so that pyridine with five free hydrogen atoms would be similar in this region to a mono-substituted benzene, whilst for example γ-picoline, which has two pairs of free hydrogen atoms, should be similar to a *para*-di-substituted benzene. As far as can be determined from the limited data, this expectation is realised in practice. Thus pyridine [2] absorbs at 750 cm.$^{-1}$, α-picoline [3] at 755 cm.$^{-1}$, β-picoline at 790 cm.$^{-1}$ and γ-picoline at 800 cm.$^{-1}$, corresponding to mono-, *ortho-*, *meta-* and *para*-substituted benzenes respectively. A series of eight variously substituted ethyl pyridines and nineteen substituted methyl pyridines have also been shown to follow this correlation with slightly wider divergencies.[26] Cook *et al.*[41] report similar findings and note also that characteristic patterns appear in the 2080–1650 cm.$^{-1}$ region as with benzene systems.

The 710 cm.$^{-1}$ band does not appear in the spectra of quinoline compounds. On the other hand, the CH out-of-plane deformation correlation still appears to hold good if each ring is considered separately. Thus both 2 : 6- and 2 : 7-dimethylquinolines have only two adjacent free hydrogen atoms in each of the two rings. Both compounds absorb very strongly at 831 cm.$^{-1}$ and 835 cm.$^{-1}$, respectively (corresponding to *para*-substituted aromatics). In addition, both show a second weaker band in the 900–850 cm.$^{-1}$ region which might possibly be associated with the vibration of the remaining isolated ring hydrogen atom.

2 : 3- and 2 : 4-Dimethylquinolines contain four free hydrogen atoms in the carbocyclic ring and only one in the heterocyclic ring. These show their strongest bands in this region at 755 cm.$^{-1}$ and 758 cm.$^{-1}$ (corresponding to *ortho*-substitution), respectively. They also both absorb in the 900–850 cm.$^{-1}$ range. *iso*Quinoline (A.P.I. spectrum) is similar in showing its strongest band in this region at 745 cm.$^{-1}$, which could be assigned to the four hydrogens of the carbocyclic ring. In this case a second strong band occurs at 829 cm.$^{-1}$ which could arise from the two adjacent free hydrogen atoms of the heterocyclic ring, whilst absorption at 864 cm.$^{-1}$ may be associated with the single free hydrogen atom. 8-Hydroxyquinoline should, on this basis, be similar to *meta*-substituted aromatics, containing three free adjacent hydrogen atoms in each ring. Although the spectrum is more complex in this region than those of the alkyl derivatives, the strongest band, nevertheless, occurs as expected at 780 cm.$^{-1}$. A band in the region 780–740 cm.$^{-1}$ is also shown by a considerable number of quinazolines and quinazolones.[20]

The apparent ease with which the quinoline derivatives comply with these correlations is surprising, but the close agreement of the six compounds listed with the expected absorption pattern is unlikely to be a coincidence. However, it should be remembered that, as in the case of the aromatic compounds, substitution by strongly polar groupings will materially alter these CH frequencies.

16.2(e). Hydroxy and Amino Pyridines and Quinolines. The constitution of compounds such as 2-hydroxypyridines are of interest from the point of view of the possible tautomeric pyridone structures. Dipole-moment evidence provides strong support for the view that the pyridone form is favoured exclusively, and this has been fully substantiated by infra-red studies by a number of workers.[28–31] Thus not only 2-hydroxy- but also 4-hydroxypyridine exists in this form, as do many related quinoline derivatives.

With aminopyridines, on the other hand, there is little or no evidence of imine formation. 2-Aminopyridine[32] in dilute solution absorbs at 3500 cm.$^{-1}$ and 3410 cm.$^{-1}$, and is thus very similar to aniline; 4-aminopyridine is similar.[33] Bellamy and Williams[34] have shown that these, and the corresponding frequencies of other heterocyclic amines,[35] follow the relationship which connects the asymmetric and symmetric stretching frequencies of primary amines so that there can be little doubt that this is the preferred structure.

16.3. PYRIMIDINES AND PURINES

16.3(a). General. A good deal of work has been carried out on pyrimidines owing to their biological importance as components of nucleic acids. However, owing to the many tautomeric forms in which it is possible to write the structures of some substituted pyrimidines—including some in which the aromatic character of the ring is completely lost—it has not yet proved possible to develop satisfactory correlations for the recognition of this particular class of compounds, and attention has been directed more to the elucidation of the actual structures present.

The first publications of spectra of pyrimidines are due to Blout and Fields,[9-11] who characterised the spectra of a number of nucleic acids, purines and pyrimidines, and showed that it was probable that uracil existed in the keto form. This particular finding was supported by Lacher, Campion and Park,[12] who examined uracil, 5-chlorouracil and thymine in the overtone region. Blout and Mellors [13] also explored the possibilities of the direct application of infra-red spectra to tissue samples. Brownlie, Sutherland and Todd [14] used infra-red methods to demonstrate the occurrence of hydrogen bonding in certain glycosidaminopyrimidines, but their observations were confined to the carbonyl absorption region. The spectra of a number of pyrimidines and purines have also been collected by Randall *et al.*,[15] whilst spectra in antimony trichloride have been given by Lacher *et al.*[36]

More recently a very large number of substituted pyrimidines have been studied by many workers.[16-18, 22, 37, 38] The general findings will be discussed below, but, as indicated above, the possibilities of prototropic change prohibit the formulation of characteristic correlation rules at present.

16.3(b). CH Stretching Vibrations. By analogy with pyridine and benzene, C–H stretching vibrations are to be expected in pyrimidine and its derivatives, which will give rise to absorptions near 3050 cm.$^{-1}$. Short and Thompson [18] have found a group of bands at this point in pyrimidine itself, and absorption in this region is also shown in the great majority of the spectra of substituted pyrimidines which they illustrate. However, in tri-substituted pyrimidines with only one free ring hydrogen atom the bands are very weak, and no absorption is to be expected from this cause in the tetra-substituted materials. Brownlie [16] also notes the occurrence of absorption between 3650 cm.$^{-1}$ and 3100 cm.$^{-1}$ in nine tri-substituted pyrimidines and its absence in tetra-substituted materials.

16.3(c). C=C and C=N Vibrations. In a fully aromatic

pyrimidine system absorptions can be expected between 1600 cm.[-1] and 1500 cm.[-1] arising from interaction effects of the ring double bonds. Pyrimidine [16,17,18] itself shows two bands, at 1570 cm.[-1], and at 1610 cm.[-1] [18] or 1650 cm.[-1] [15], which probably arise from this cause. Brownlie [16] reports finding absorptions in the 1640–1620 cm.[-1] and the 1580–1560 cm.[-1] regions in all the twenty-four substituted pyrimidines he has examined, except two which show only a single absorption at 1590 cm.[-1]. Blout and Fields [11] have made similar assignments on a number of pyrimidines. However, whilst there is no doubt that the lower-frequency band is a characteristic ring vibration, the assignment of the first to this cause is more doubtful, as most of Brownlie's compounds contained amino-groups the deformation mode of which might well be expected in the 1650–1600 cm.[-1] region. This is supported by the spectra given by Short and Thompson [18] of a series of substituted pyrimidines which do not contain OH or NH_2 groups, all of which show only a single band in the region 1580–1520 cm.[-1]. Tanner [38] and Montgomery [37] both find bands near 1650 cm.[-1] in aminopyrimidines, but point out that these could well originate in NH_2 deformation modes. The hydroxy-pyrimidines are also not suitable for the development of correlations for ring vibrations of this type, as they may exist in the tautomeric keto form, in which the double-bond absorptions of the ring would be expected to be different from the fully aromatic systems. As the bulk of the pyrimidines so far examined are either amino- or hydroxy-derivatives, the assignment of the ring double-bond vibrations cannot at present be made with any certainty.

16.3(d). Ring Vibrations. Short and Thompson [18] have drawn attention to the fact that a series of chloro-substituted and ethoxy-substituted pyrimidines which they have examined all absorb near 900 cm.[-1] and near 810 cm.[-1]. The former is assigned to a ring vibration, and the latter is thought to be due to this also, although the possibility that it is a CH deformation mode cannot be excluded. Bands near these frequencies are illustrated in the great majority, but not all of the spectra of the thirty-nine amino- and hydroxy-derivatives given in their paper. Similarly, Brownlie [16] has found a band in the range 1000–960 cm.[-1] in all the pyrimidines he has examined, although for reasons which are not very clear he assigns this to a $C–NH_2$ bending vibration. He also finds a band in the 825–775 cm.[-1] range in all cases, which he assigns to CH deformations in the di- and tri-substituted pyrimidines and to a skeletal vibration in the tetra-substituted materials.

The persistence of these bands in so many differently substituted compounds is unlikely to be coincidental, but the correlations are not likely to be of any great value until the structure of the amino- and hydroxy-pyrimidines has been finally established, when the reasons for the non-appearance of these bands in a few isolated cases may be elucidated.

16.3(e). Hydroxy- and Amino-Pyrimidines. It has been indicated above that the structure of the amino- and hydroxy-pyrimidines for which tautomeric possibilities exist is still a matter of controversy, and the infra-red evidence itself is not without ambiguity. Thus in the 3000 cm.[-1] region the overlapping of the frequency ranges of the bonded OH and NH absorptions introduces certain difficulties, whilst in the 1600 cm.[-1] region absorption can arise from NH deformations, carbonyl vibrations and vibrations of ring double bonds.

This controversy cannot be discussed in detail here, but the conclusions of the various workers can be summarised as follows. Brownlie [16] interprets his infra-red data as supporting the existence of these compounds in the imino and enolic forms, whilst Thompson, Nicholson and Short [17] prefer the ketonic structure for the hydroxy-derivatives and the imino-structure for the amino-derivatives. Short and Thompson [18] have reviewed all the data and suggested that the balance of evidence favours a ketonic structure for the 2- and 4-hydroxypyrimidines, and possibly also for the 2 : 4-dihydroxy-derivatives, whilst in 4 : 6-dihydroxypyrimidine one keto and one enolic group may be present. Tanner [38] has studied many di- and tri-hydroxypyrimidines, and his findings in general support the view that substitution in the 4-position leads to ketonic structures, whilst hydroxy groups at positions 5- or 6- tend to retain their original character. Amino groups are thought in general to exist in the non-tautomeric form. Short and Thompson [18] point out, however, that the electronic effects of different substituents may influence the tautomerism in any single case. Their conclusions have been further supported by the ultra-violet and infra-red data of Brown and Short.[22]

16.4. OTHER HETEROCYCLIC STRUCTURES

A number of quinazolines, quinazolones and quinazolinediones have been examined by Culbertson *et al.*[20] These show three bands termed quinazoline I, II, III bands at 1628–1618, 1581–1566 and 1517–1478 cm.[-1]. All of these are sharp and relatively strong, and obviously arise from ring vibrations. These compounds have not been further characterised. As regards the triazines, the difficulties associated with the interpretation of the spectra of tautomeric pyrimidines apply with equal force to compounds such as cyanuric acid, melamine, etc., and considerably less is known of their structure. Roosens [19] has published the spectra of cyanuric acid, cyanuric chloride and of melamine free-base and hydrochloride. We have ourselves examined these, and also ammeline, thioammeline and ammelide, but there are insufficient data available to permit any correlations to be formulated or any positive indications obtained as to the structure of these materials. A typical illustration of the uncertainties introduced in the interpretation of the spectra in the 1700–1500 cm.$^{-1}$ region is given by ammeline and by thio-ammeline. Both ammeline and ammelide absorb strongly at 1715 cm.$^{-1}$, and this appears to be strong evidence for their existence in the keto form. However, thio-ammeline absorbs equally strongly at 1695 cm.$^{-1}$, and in this case the absorption must be due to a displaced NH or ring vibration. No useful correlations for this group of compounds are therefore possible at present.

Otting [39] has recently studied 1 : 3 : 4-triazole and tetrazole, and shown that both possess considerable aromatic character. Diazines have been studied by Ito *et al.*,[40] who have commented on the differences between the absorption frequencies of pyrazine, pyrimidine and pyridazine. For example, the last two absorb at 1565 cm.$^{-1}$, but pyrazine has no band above 1490 cm.$^{-1}$ apart from the CH stretching frequency of 3054 cm.$^{-1}$. Aromatic-type, seven-membered heterocyclic ring systems have also been studied by Dimroth and Lenke,[24] and the spectra of a number of 5-amino-tetrazoles have been given by Finnegan *et al.*,[25] although no correlations are discussed.

16.5. BIBLIOGRAPHY

1. Kline and Turkevitch, *J. Chem. Phys.*, 1944, **12**, 300.
2. Cannon and Sutherland, *Spectrochimica Acta*, 1951, **4**, 373.
3. Freiser and Glowacki, *J. Amer. chem. Soc.*, 1948, **70**, 2575.
4. Roberts and Szwarc, *J. Chem. Phys.*, 1948, **16**, 981.
5. Marion, Ramsay and Jones, *J. Amer. Chem. Soc.*, 1951, **73**, 305.
6. Coulson, Hales and Herington, *J. Chem. Soc.*, 1951, 2125.
7. Hannan, Lioblich and Renfrew, *J. Amer. Chem. Soc.*, 1949, **71**, 3733.
8. Densham, Langston and Gough, *J. Chem. Soc.*, 1952 2433.
9. Blout and Fields, *Science*, 1948, **107**, 252.
10. *Idem. J. Biol. Chem.*, 1949, **178**, 335.
11. *Idem. J. Amer. Chem. Soc.*, 1950, **72**, 479.
12. Lacher, Campion and Park, *Science*, 1949, **110**, 300.
13. Blout and Mellors, *ibid.*, p. 137.
14. Brownlie, Sutherland and Todd, *J. Chem. Soc.*, 1948, 2265.
15. Randall, Fowler, Fuson and Dangl, *Infra-red Determination of Organic Structures* (Van Nostrand, 1949).
16. Brownlie, *J. Chem. Soc.*, 1950, 3062.
17. Thompson, Nicholson and Short, *Discuss. Faraday Soc.*, 1950, **9**, 222.
18. Short and Thompson, *J. Chem. Soc.*, 1952, 168.
19. Roosens, *Bull. Soc. Chim. (Belg.)*, 1950, **59**, 377.
20. Culbertson, Decius and Christensen, *J. Amer. Chem. Soc.*, 1952, **74**, 4834.
21. Corrsin, Fox and Lord, *J. Chem. Phys.*, 1953, **21**, 1170.
22. Brown and Short, *J. Chem. Soc.*, 1953, 331.
23. Anderson, Bak, Brodersen and Rastrup-Andersen, *J. Chem. Phys.*, 1955, **23**, 1047.
24. Dimroth and Lenke, *Chem. Ber.*, 1956, **89**, 2608.
25. Finnegan, Henry and Olsen, *J. Amer. Chem. Soc.*, 1955, **77**, 4420.
26. Shindo and Ikekawa, *Pharm. Bull. Japan*, 1956, **4**, 192.

27. Tallent and Siewers, *Analyt. Chem.*, 1956, **28**, 953.
28. Gibson, Kynaston and Lindsey, *J. Chem. Soc.*, 1955, 4340.
29. Ramirez and Paul, *J. Amer. Chem. Soc.*, 1955, **77**, 1035.
30. Scheinker and Resinkow, *Doklady, Akad. Nauk. S.S.S.R.*, 1955, **102**, 109.
31. Scheinker and Pomerantsev, *Zhur. Fiz. Khim.*, 1956, **30**, 79.
32. Shigorin, Danyushevskii and Gold'farb, *Izvest. Akad. Nauk. S.S.S.R.,*
    Otdel Khim. Nauk., 1956, 120.
33. Costa, Blasina and Sartori, *Z. Phys. Chem.*, 1956, **7**, 123.
34. Bellamy and Williams, *Spectrochim. Acta*, 1957, **9**, 341.
35. Angyal and Werner, *J. Chem. Soc.*, 1952, 2911.
36. Lacher, Bitner, Emery, Sefel and Park, *J. Phys. Chem.*, 1955, **59**, 615.
37. Montgomery, *J. Amer. Chem. Soc.*, 1956, **78**, 1928.
38. Tanner, *Spectrochim. Acta*, 1956, **8**, 9.
39. Otting, *Chem. Ber.*, 1956, **89**, 2887.
40. Ito, Shimada, Kuraishi and Mizushima, *J. Chem. Phys.*, 1956, **25**, 597.
41. Cook and Church, *J. Phys. Chem.*, 1957, **61**, 458.

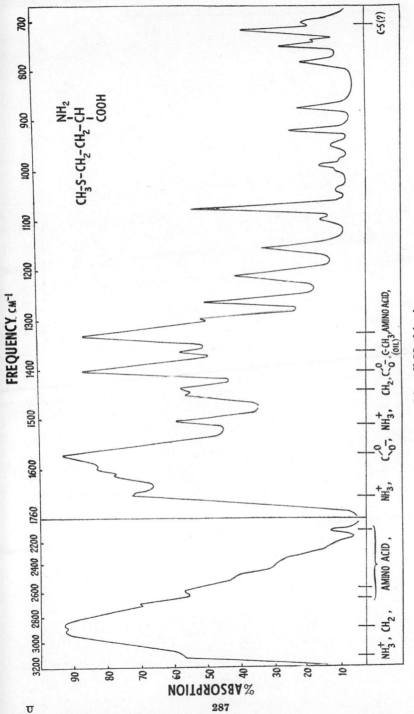

16. *dl*-Methionine

287

17. α-Naphthylamine

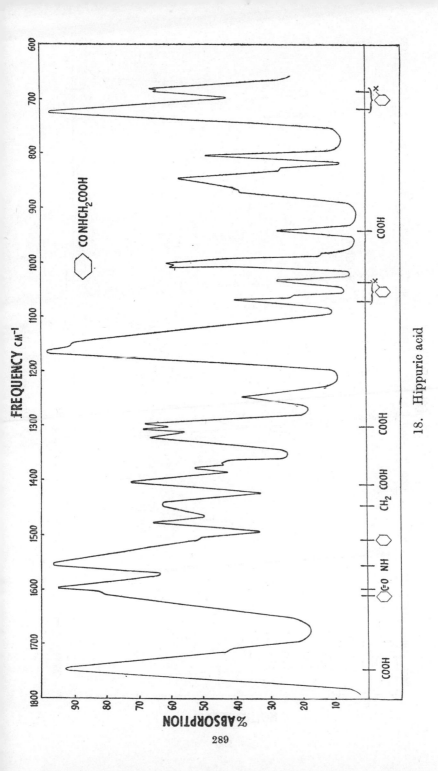

18. Hippuric acid

19. Phenylacetamide

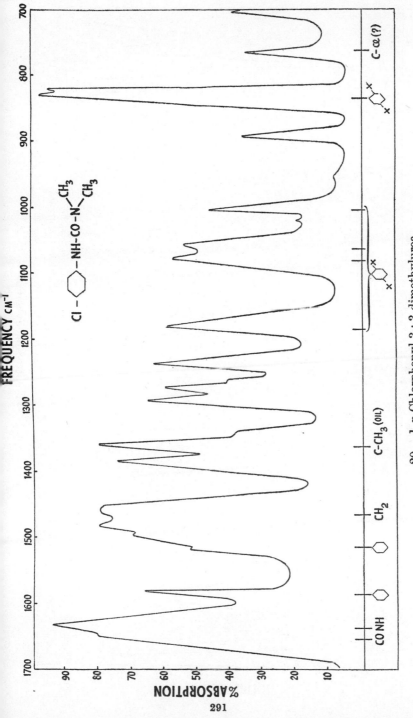

FREQUENCY CM⁻¹

Cl — $\bigcirc$ — NH-CO-N $\overset{CH_3}{\underset{CH_3}{<}}$

20. 1-p-Chlorphenyl-3 : 3-dimethylurea

291

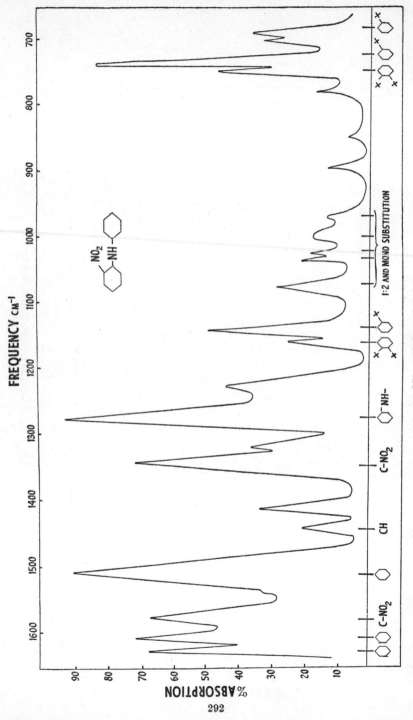

21. 2-Nitrodiphenylamine

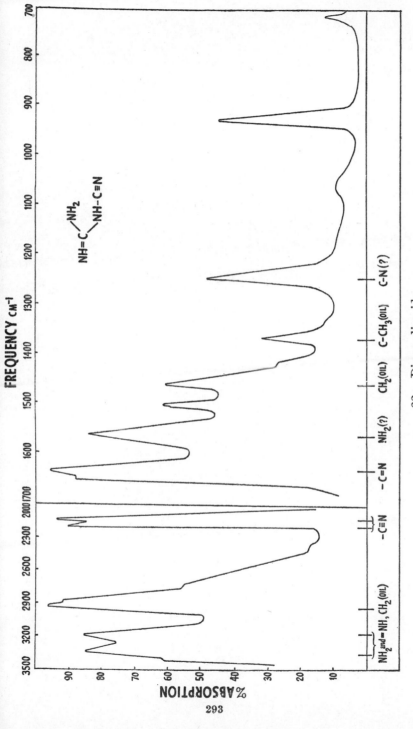

22. Dicyandiamide

293

PART IV

VIBRATIONS INVOLVING OTHER ELEMENTS; GROUPS OF INORGANIC ORIGIN

CHAPTER 17

Nitro- and Nitroso-compounds, Nitrates and Nitrites

17.1. INTRODUCTION AND TABLE

IN this chapter compounds containing the grouping $R-NO_2$, $R-NO$, or NO_3^- are considered, together with the amine oxides. In compounds such as the oximes, in which the N–O link has a purely single bond character, the frequency which arises [34] is variable in position and the vibration is probably coupled. In these circumstances this particular nitrogen–oxygen frequency has not been considered further.

Compounds containing the $R-NO_2$ group are covalent nitro-compounds, covalent nitrates and nitramines. Each of these three classes exhibits two extremely strong absorption bands in the 1650–1500 cm.$^{-1}$ and 1350–1250 cm.$^{-1}$ regions corresponding to the asymmetric and symmetric stretching valence vibrations of the NO_2 group. The frequencies at which these bands occur are sensitive to changes in the nature of the R group, so that, although there is some overlapping, it is often possible to differentiate between the three main classes. In addition, there is some evidence of characteristic absorptions occurring in the low-frequency ranges due to skeletal or deformation modes.

The valence vibration bands are not materially affected by changes of state, except in a few cases in which hydrogen bonding on to the NO_2 group can occur. The shifts involved are not in any case sufficient to take the absorption out of the ranges quoted. In the low-frequency region, however, very considerable changes often occur with nitro-compounds following changes of state or of crystal form, so that considerably less reliance can be placed upon any results from this region.

With compounds containing the $R-N=O$ group only a single band in the 1600 cm.$^{-1}$ region would be expected, but in nitrites this is almost always double, due to the co-existence of *cis-* and *trans-*forms. By a study of the relative intensities of these two bands it is often possible to obtain some data on the nature of the hydrocarbon residue R in $R-O-N=O$ structures. In compounds in which the nitroso-group is attached directly to carbon or nitrogen, the position of the $N=O$ absorption has been more difficult to determine, partly owing to the ease of dimerisation of certain compounds of this class. However, the appropriate group frequencies now appear to be reasonably well defined. In nitrites two additional useful frequencies are found in the low-frequency region, but this is not so in the case of nitroso-compounds.

Ionic nitrates have a strong band centred near 1380 cm.$^{-1}$ and a medium intensity band near 800 cm.$^{-1}$ which enable them to be characterised.

The correlations discussed are listed in Table 17 below.

TABLE 17

R·NO$_2$.	(*a*) Valence vibrations
	$\quad$ –C–NO$_2$ 1570–1500 cm.$^{-1}$, 1370–1300 cm.$^{-1}$ (aromatics, sometimes higher in alkyl compounds)
	$\quad$ –O–NO$_2$ 1650–1600 cm.$^{-1}$, 1300–1250 cm.$^{-1}$
	$\quad$ –N–NO$_2$ 1630–1550 cm.$^{-1}$, 1300–1250 cm.$^{-1}$
	(*b*) Vibrations in the low-frequency region 800–500 cm.$^{-1}$
R–N=O.	(*a*) Valence vibrations N=O
	$\quad$ –O–N=O 1681–1610 cm.$^{-1}$ (two bands)
	$\quad$ $>$C–N=O 1600–1500 cm.$^{-1}$ (s.)
	$\quad$ $_2$N–N=O 1500–1430 cm.$^{-1}$ (s.)
	$\quad$ Amine oxides 1300–1200 cm.$^{-1}$ (s.)
	(*b*) Other characteristic vibrations
NO$_3^-$.	1410–1340 cm.$^{-1}$ and 860–800 cm.$^{-1}$

17.2. NITRO-COMPOUNDS

17.2(a). The Group C–NO$_2$. Barnes *et al*[1] noted in 1944 that the NO$_2$ grouping gives rise to absorptions in the 1550 cm.$^{-1}$ and 1340 cm.$^{-1}$ regions, and this correlation is confirmed by Raman data [2] and by studies on the simpler nitro-paraffins.[3,4] The correlation has been extended by Colthup,[5] who indicates that the C–NO$_2$ compounds absorb at different frequencies from those containing the O–NO$_2$ group. In recent years this correlation has been placed on a much sounder footing by detailed studies on the influence of environment on the vibrations of the CNO$_2$ group, and the effects of conjugation, α-halogen substitution and other changes of environment are now known.

Early work on simple alkyl nitro-compounds [3,4] indicated that whilst nitromethane absorbed at 1580 cm.$^{-1}$ and 1375 cm.$^{-1}$, higher homologues showed the asymmetric absorption at somewhat lower frequencies. This has been fully substantiated by later studies. Haszeldine [24] repeated the earlier work of Smith [4] *et al.* and added some further compounds. The overall ranges for simple alkyl derivatives were 1567–1550 cm.$^{-1}$ (*as.*) and 1379–1368 cm.$^{-1}$ (*s.*). These values probably relate to the liquid state, but changes on solution are relatively small in this series. Brown,[25] and Kornblum

Ungnade and Smiley [26] have each examined about thirty-five alkyl nitro-compounds with essentially similar results. Primary and secondary compounds RCH_2NO_2 and $R_1R_2CHNO_2$ absorb in the ranges 1565–1545 cm.$^{-1}$ and 1383–1360 cm.$^{-1}$. In general, the primary compounds absorb at slightly higher frequencies than the others, but the differences given by Brown (8 cm.$^{-1}$ (*as.*) and 6 cm.$^{-1}$ (*s.*)) are within the overall spread to be expected from this series, and are not highly significant. On the other hand, a marked fall in both frequencies occurs in tertiary nitro-compounds R_3CNO_2 which absorb in the ranges 1545–1530 cm.$^{-1}$ and 1358–1342 cm.$^{-1}$. These can therefore be differentiated from primary and secondary alkyl nitro-bodies. As the multiple bonds concerned in these vibrations are not directly attached to the ring, the influence of ring strain in cyclic nitro-compounds is very small. Nitro*cyclo*hexane and nitro*cyclo*pentane, for example, behave as typical secondary alkyl nitro-compounds and absorb near the lower ends of the appropriate ranges.[25, 26] In 1-methyl-2-nitro*cyclo*propane there is a marked fall [25] in both frequencies (1538 cm.$^{-1}$ and 1357 cm.$^{-1}$), but this probably reflects the conjugation effect of the *cyclo*propane ring rather than the influence of strain.

Conjugation of the nitro-group by attachment to an ethylenic double bond leads to a fall in both frequencies similar to that shown by the carbonyl absorption. Shechter and Sheppard,[27] for example, find that 2-methyl-1-nitropropene absorbs at 1515 cm.$^{-1}$ and 1350 cm.$^{-1}$, whereas 2-methyl-3-nitropropene absorbs at 1555 cm.$^{-1}$ and 1366 cm.$^{-1}$. This has been confirmed also by Brown,[25] who finds the ranges 1524 ± 4 cm.$^{-1}$ and 1353 ± 6 cm.$^{-1}$ for monoalkyl nitroethylenes and slightly lower values of 1515 ± 4 cm.$^{-1}$ and 1346 ± 9 cm.$^{-1}$ for di- and tri-alkylnitroethylenes.

α-Halogen substitution has a marked effect upon nitro-group frequencies, which are similar in this respect to carbonyl compounds. In this case, however, whilst the asymmetric frequency is raised considerably the symmetric frequency is lowered by about the same amount. In extreme cases this leads to the appearance of these bands in the region normally associated with $-O-NO_2$ groupings. The effect is, of course, most marked in the fully halogenated nitromethanes. Chlorpicrin has been studied by several workers [8, 24, 28] and absorbs at 1625 cm.$^{-1}$ and at 1311 cm.$^{-1}$. In the trifluoro-derivative it is interesting to note that the shifts are slightly less [28, 29] (1620 cm.$^{-1}$, 1315 cm.$^{-1}$), whereas a further rise might have been expected. In the tribromo-derivative [28] the shift is again smaller (1606 cm.$^{-1}$ and 1311 cm.$^{-1}$). The effects of mono- and di-halogen substitution are parallel. Both Brown [25] and Haszeldine [24] have examined a number of compounds of this type, and it would seem that a single α-chlorine atom alters the frequencies to 1575 ± 5 cm.$^{-1}$ and 1348 ± 6 cm.$^{-1}$, while two α-chlorine atoms lead to ranges of 1587 cm.$^{-1} \pm 10$ cm.$^{-1}$, and 1332 cm.$^{-1} \pm 5$ cm.$^{-1}$. Although fewer data are available on nitro-compounds with other α-electronegative groups, it would seem likely that similar effects will occur. In compounds with the *gem*-dinitro group, for example,[25] the frequencies fall near 1580 cm.$^{-1}$ and 1330 cm.$^{-1}$, and Haszeldine has also noted a similar effect in one instance in which a COOEt group is substituted in the α-position.

Aromatic nitro-compounds have been studied by many workers, and although there has been a good deal of overlapping in the compounds studied, there has been some disagreement over the mean frequencies to be expected. Thus Francel [6] places these bands near 1530 cm.$^{-1}$ and 1360 cm.$^{-1}$, and this is supported by the data of Lothrop et al.[7] Brown [25] lists the frequencies of twelve compounds as falling in the ranges 1527 ± 16 cm.$^{-1}$ and 1348 ± 11 cm.$^{-1}$, Randle and Whiffen [30] quote average values (twenty-three compounds) of 1518 cm.$^{-1}$ and 1349 cm.$^{-1}$ and Kross and Fassel [31] (thirty-four compounds) 1523 cm.$^{-1}$ and 1344 cm.$^{-1}$. The latter workers have also shown that the frequency shifts which accompany a change of state from the solid to solution in a non-polar solvent are very small. These differences between average values are not real and merely reflect the sensitivity of the nitro-group frequencies to the other ring substituents, so that the mean values obtained depend to a large extent on the types of compounds studied. In *p*-dinitrobenzene, for example, the *as.* frequency is 1560 cm.$^{-1}$, whereas in sodium *p*-nitrophenoxide [31] it is 1501 cm.$^{-1}$. Similarly, replacement of the methyl group of nitrotoluene by the electron-donating $N(CH_3)_2$ group alters the NO_2 group frequencies [32] from 1527 cm.$^{-1}$ and 1350 cm.$^{-1}$ to 1506 cm.$^{-1}$ and 1332 cm.$^{-1}$. Franck, Hormann and Scheibe [33] have recently related the observed asymmetric stretching frequencies to broad classifications of substituents. Their measurements were made in pressed discs which might involve some displacements from the usual solid-state frequencies, as in carboxylic acids, but the relative magnitudes of the shifts are not likely to be affected, and their data agree well with other workers. They assign normal and coplanar aromatic nitro-group frequencies to the range 1548–1520 cm.$^{-1}$. This is the expected range, being somewhat higher than the corresponding compounds with ethylenic conjugation. The presence of a strong electronegative group in the *para*-position, or of a large group in the *ortho*-position which tends to throw the nitro-group out of the plane of the ring, leads to higher frequencies in the range 1565–1540 cm.$^{-1}$, whereas electron donor groups in the *ortho*- or *para*-positions result in lower frequencies 1525–1490 cm.$^{-1}$. These authors do not comment on the symmetrical frequencies, but these would be expected to be displaced from the mean of about 1350 cm.$^{-1}$ to about the same extents and directions. In compounds containing two or more nitro-groups which, because of their positions, are influenced to different extents by the substituents, multiple frequencies are found. In 1 : 3-*bis*methylamino-2 : 4 : 6-trinitrobenzene,[33] for example, absorptions occur at 1554 cm.$^{-1}$ and 1538 cm.$^{-1}$, and weak peaks also occur at 1508 cm.$^{-1}$ and 1493 cm.$^{-1}$.

In our own laboratories we have also noted instances in which both the nitro-group frequencies are doubled. This occurs in situations in which one nitro-group remains coplanar whilst another is twisted out of the plane of the ring under the influence of steric effects. This reduces the degree of aromatic conjugation and a new, higher-frequency band appears. Multiple peaks can also occur in poly-nitro-aromatics in which hydrogen bonding can occur. However, the size of the frequency shifts which might originate in this way are relatively small, and do not materially affect the overall ranges proposed.

One other possible correlation for alkyl nitro-compounds relates to the CH_2 and CH_3 frequencies of adjacent methyl or methylene groups. Kornblum *et al.*[26] have noted a band at 1379 cm.$^{-1}$ in all the primary nitro-compounds they have studied, even when a methyl group is absent. This band is additional to the NO_2 frequency itself, and almost certainly originates in the CH_2 deformation frequency of the perturbed methylene group. This is similar to the characteristic frequency shown by the group CH_2COOH in acids. In secondary alkyl nitro-compounds several bands occur in this region in addition to the nitro-group frequency itself. Brown [25] has also made some observations in this region. He finds that in simple nitro alkanes the symmetrical NO_2 stretching frequency and the asymmetrical methyl deformation frequency are superimposed at 1379 cm.$^{-1}$. However, when the methyl group is attached to the same carbon atom as the nitro-group two frequencies appear at 1395 cm.$^{-1}$ and 1370 cm.$^{-1}$. Similarly, the structure $(CH_3)_2CNO_2$ is characterised by strong bands at 1397 cm.$^{-1}$, 1374 cm.$^{-1}$ and at 1351 cm.$^{-1}$.

17.2(b). Covalent Nitrates –O–NO₂.

17.2(b). Covalent Nitrates –O–NO$_2$. Raman evidence [3] indicates that in covalent nitrates the asymmetric and symmetric NO_2 frequencies are split farther apart and occur near 1640 cm.$^{-1}$ and 1260 cm.$^{-1}$. Only a limited amount of information is available, but some results have been published on nitrocellulose [9] and on nitroglycerine.[10, 23] We have, ourselves, records for eight compounds such as *iso*propyl nitrate, ethylene glycol dinitrate, and penta-erythritol tetranitrate, which contain this grouping, and in these the asymmetric frequency falls within the range 1650–1610 cm.$^{-1}$ and the symmetric frequency within the range 1300–1250 cm.$^{-1}$. This is in line with early studies of Lecomte and Mathieu [35] on simple alkyl nitrates, and Kumler [36] has quoted values of 1656 cm.$^{-1}$ for the asymmetric stretching frequency in some nitrates of enol esters. The most extensive study in this field is due to Brown,[25] who has examined twenty-one nitrate esters and finds the characteristic stretching frequencies in the ranges 1639 $\pm$ 13 cm.$^{-1}$ and 1279 $\pm$ 7 cm.$^{-1}$.

17.2(c). Covalent Nitramines –N–NO$_2$. The nitramines show the asymmetric NO$_2$ frequency at much the same position as the C–NO$_2$ compounds, whereas the symmetric absorption is displaced towards lower frequencies. In this case, however, the nature of the adjoining structure appears to have a more marked influence on the frequency range, perhaps due to the greater possibilities of changes in the electronic structure of the nitrogen atoms to which the nitro-group is attached. Lieber *et al.*[11] have examined seventeen *N*-nitro-compounds of various types. In fourteen of these the symmetric NO$_2$ vibration is reasonably constant within the range 1315–1260 cm.$^{-1}$, whilst the exceptions (which absorb at higher frequencies) are either acid or salt forms in which the structure N=$\overset{+}{N}$=O$_2^-$ might be expected to have a marked influence. The asymmetric frequencies, on the other hand, fall in a wider range, and appears to be more influenced by the nature of the substituents. Nitroguanidine and related compounds with alkyl substituents absorb between 1634 cm.$^{-1}$ and 1605 cm.$^{-1}$, whilst arylguanidines and nitrourea absorb in the range 1587–1575 cm.$^{-1}$. Polynitramines and salts of 5-nitroaminotetrazole absorb between 1563 cm.$^{-1}$ and 1547 cm.$^{-1}$. Kumler [37] has also found values between 1655 cm.$^{-1}$ and 1620 cm.$^{-1}$ for the asymmetric frequency in nitroguanidines. Salyamon and Yaroslaviskii [38] have shown that nitramines exist preferentially in the form RNHNO$_2$ rather than in the alternative RN=NOOH structure, from studies in the overtone region, and the same laboratories [39] have made Raman studies on nitramine salts which show the symmetric stretching frequency rises to near 1400 cm.$^{-1}$ in these compounds.

Our own experience is confined to polynitramines of various types (ten in all) which follow the above classification and show the NO$_2$ absorptions in the ranges 1587–1530 cm.$^{-1}$ and 1292–1260 cm.$^{-1}$. This is presumably the region of absorption for nitramines generally, except for the cases of nitroguanidines, and ureas in which alternative prototropic forms are possible which might absorb at higher frequencies.

17.2(d). The Intensities of the R–NO$_2$ Stretching Absorptions. In all the above cases the two valence vibration absorptions of the NO$_2$ group are extremely strong bands. However, there are considerable variations in the absolute intensity from compound to compound, and the increase in the intensities on passing from mono-nitro-aromatics to di- and poly-nitro-materials is not linear with the molar NO_2-group concentration. This applies even to closely related compounds, so that, for example, the extinction co-efficient of each nitro-group is about 80 per cent higher in diethylene glycol dinitrate than in nitroglycerine.[10] The intensities of these absorptions cannot therefore be used for determining the proportion of NO_2 groups in unknown compounds. In general, the asymmetric absorption is appreciably more intense than the symmetric band. This is similar to the case of the ionised carboxyl group with which the nitro-group is isoelectronic. However, this is not an invariable rule, and in some instances both bands appear to be of comparable intensity. Marked alterations in the band shapes of both nitro-group absorptions occur in situations in which the nitro-group is subject to steric hindrances. In *ortho*-nitrotoluene, for example, the half-band width of the symmetric absorption is a little more than twice that of the corresponding band in *p*-nitro-toluene.[40] This may have useful diagnostic applications, although the absolute intensities of the two bands as determined from area measurements show very little change.

17.2(e). Low-frequency Absorptions of the RNO_2 Group. Absorption bands in the low-frequency region are to be expected from skeletal vibrations and from deformation modes involving the RNO_2 group. In alkyl nitrites Tarte [12, 13, 22] has found a band of almost constant frequency near 800 cm.$^{-1}$ which he assigns to the N–O stretching mode. However, the examination of our spectra of alkyl nitrates indicates that a similar band is present only in a few cases, and that this is subject to considerable shifts with changes of state. With nitramines we have noticed the occurrence of a band of medium intensity in the region 790–770 cm.$^{-1}$ and a band in this range occurs also in all but two of the N-nitro-compounds examined by Lieber *et al.*[11] There is probably some significance in these observations, but the correlation can only be regarded as being an extremely tentative one which might occasionally be used for confirmatory work.

In alkyl nitro-compounds the C–N absorption has been tentatively identified by Haszeldine [24] with a strong to medium absorption in the range 920–830 cm.$^{-1}$. Randle and Whiffen [30] have also suggested that the C–N mode in aromatic nitro-compounds may be responsible for a commonly found band near 850 cm.$^{-1}$. This suggestion has been discussed further by Brown [24] and by Kross and Fassel.[31] Brown points out that the bond order of the C–N link, and so its frequency, is likely in any case to be subject to wide variations on passing from one type of compound to another,

x

while Kross and Fassel [30] have attempted to identify the C–N mode by deuteration studies on nitrobenzene. Only two bands, other than the invariant ring and NO_2 absorptions, are substantially unaffected. These are at 850 cm.$^{-1}$ (partly overlapped by out-of-plane CH frequencies in *para*-substituted compounds) and at 1300 cm.$^{-1}$, and of these they regard the latter as the most likely to be associated with the C–N mode. The frequent occurrence of strong absorptions in the low-frequency region near 850 cm.$^{-1}$ and sometimes near 750 cm.$^{-1}$ is, however, a feature of aromatic nitro-compounds, which should not be forgotten when attempts are made to recognise ring-substitution arrangements by the δ-CH frequencies in this region.

17.3. R–N=O STRETCHING VIBRATIONS

In compounds such as nitrosyl chloride and bromide [14] the N=O frequency falls near 1800 cm.$^{-1}$, but this is clearly higher than the normal value, due to the shortening of the N=O distance under the influence of the halogen atom. In nitrites there is a good deal of evidence that the N=O valence vibration occurs near 1660 cm.$^{-1}$. Nitroso-compounds show rather more variable N=O frequencies, but usually absorb in the 1600–1500 cm.$^{-1}$ range. Nitrosamines absorb at still lower frequencies, usually below 1500 cm.$^{-1}$.

17.3(a). Nitrites –O–N=O. Tarte [12, 13, 22] has shown that in fifteen nitrites which he has examined the N=O frequency appears as a double band in the ranges 1681–1653 cm.$^{-1}$ and 1625–1613 cm.$^{-1}$. These are attributed respectively to the *trans-* and *cis-*forms of the nitrite structure. The frequencies show a remarkably steady stepwise fall as the size of the attached group is increased, the highest being with methyl nitrite at 1681 cm.$^{-1}$ and 1625 cm.$^{-1}$ and the lowest with amyl nitrite at 1653 cm.$^{-1}$ and 1613 cm.$^{-1}$. These ranges have been confirmed by similar studies by Haszeldine *et al.*[41, 42] on a small number of alkyl nitrites. In the case of 2 : 2 : 2-trifluoroethyl nitrite, the absorption band is shifted to 1736 cm.$^{-1}$ (*trans*) and 1695 cm.$^{-1}$ (*cis*), which is a remarkable shift in view of the distance along the chain of the fluorine atoms from the N=O link. The effect is probably due to the steric arrangement, and somewhat related phenomena have been observed in certain β-fluorinated esters.

The overall relative intensities of these bands afford a clear indication of the type of substitution involved, since the proportions of *cis-* and *trans-*forms vary between the different classes of nitrite. Thus, on determining the ratio of the extinction coefficients of the *trans-* and *cis-*forms, the original value of 1 : 1 in methyl nitrite rises to 2 : 3 in ethyl nitrite and reaches a stable value of 3 : 3·5 in the higher primary nitrites. In the secondary nitrites, however, this ratio is increased to 6 : 10 and in tertiary nitrites, in which the proportion of the *cis*-form is necessarily much reduced, it increases again to 40 : 1.

The intensities in this region are considerable, and the nitrite bands are described as having an intensity rarely met with in the infra-red.

17.3(b). Nitroso-Compounds $>$C–NO. The assignment of the –N=O stretching frequency in nitroso-compounds has been a matter of some difficulty, which arises mainly from the ease with which primary and secondary nitroso-compounds pass over into the oximes, and from the fact that the tertiary compounds dimerise readily. Thompson, Nicholson and Short [15] originally suggested that this frequency fell in the 1400–1300 cm.$^{-1}$ range, whilst Brownlie [16] assigned it as being near 1650 cm.$^{-1}$ on the basis of some nitrosopyrimidenes which he examined. More recently this problem has been studied extensively by Lüttke [43-45] and by Tarte,[46] and the situation is becoming clearer.

Lüttke has studied the changes in the spectrum which occur with time when primary and secondary nitroso-compounds are volatilised. In the cases of nitrosomethane and nitroso*cyclo*hexane, for example, absorptions appear at 1564 cm.$^{-1}$ and 1558 cm.$^{-1}$ which can be associated with the –N=O frequency. These bands rapidly diminish in intensity on standing and new bands appear, so that in a relatively short time the spectra are those of formaldoxime and of *cyclo*hexanone oxime respectively. In solution these compounds exist preferentially as dimers, and nitrosomethane, for example, absorbs near 1290 cm.$^{-1}$ in this form.

In tertiary nitroso-compounds $R_1R_2R_3CN=O$ the possibilities of oxime formation are eliminated. In these compounds also dimerisation is common in the solid state or in solution, but it is usually possible to identify the monomeric frequencies in dilute solution and in the vapour state. However, many of the compounds of this type studied by Tarte [46] and by Lüttke [32] contain one or more halogen atoms as the R groups, and this leads to a further complication in that field effects similar to those found in α-halogenated ketones are to be expected, which depend upon the molecular configuration. Doubling of the N=O absorption is therefore found in mono- and di-α-halogenated compounds, and the identification of this with the rotational isomerism has been confirmed. This effect also leads to an elevation of the frequency as in the corresponding carbonyl compounds. Nitroso*cyclo*hexane, for example, absorbs at 1558 cm.$^{-1}$, whilst 1 : 4-dichloro-1 : 4-dinitroso-*cyclo*hexane absorbs [43] at 1570 cm.$^{-1}$. In general, the N=O absorption appears to be particularly sensitive to the nature of its environment, falling as low as 1495 cm.$^{-1}$ in 2 : 4 : 6-trimethylnitrosobenzene and rising to 1620 cm.$^{-1}$ in CCl_3NO. In this latter compound it is interesting to note that the frequency is higher than that of the corresponding trifluoro-derivative,[29, 47] which suggests that induction and field effects are not the only factors operating in this case and that mesomerism involving double-bonded halogen links also plays an important part. In this connection it is perhaps significant that, unlike the carbonyl group in similar circumstances, the $N=O$ group frequency rises steadily as more and more halogen atoms are attached at the α-position.

In general, aromatic nitroso-compounds absorb near 1500 cm.$^{-1}$, tertiary aliphatic materials at higher frequencies near 1550 cm.$^{-1}$ and α-halogenated compounds at still higher frequencies up to 1620 cm.$^{-1}$. In the latter cases the bands are frequently doubled due to rotational isomerism. The $>C–N=O$ characteristic frequency would seem therefore to be reasonably well established by these studies. An alternative suggestion for this group frequency involving the 1380–1340 cm.$^{-1}$ region has been put forward by Nakamoto and Rundle,[48] but these workers did not study the 1600–1500 cm.$^{-1}$ region, which would appear to be the more probable position in view of the above work. Indirect support for the higher-frequency range is also provided by the comparison of carbonyl and $N=O$ frequencies in similarly substituted compounds by Bellamy and Williams.[49] This allows the approximate group frequency to be derived from the frequencies of ketones and indicates a value in the 1600 cm.$^{-1}$ region.

17.3(c). Nitrosamines –N–N=O. Early studies by Earl *et al.*[17] suggested that the $N=O$ absorption in N-nitroso-compounds occurred near 1400 cm.$^{-1}$. This was supported by Raman data,[18] but alternative assignments in the 1600–1500 cm.$^{-1}$ region were suggested for nitrosoguanidines and similar compounds studied by Lieber *et al.*[11] Although the total number of compounds of this type which have been studied remains relatively small, the positions of the characteristic $N=O$ absorption is now becoming clearer.

Haszeldine *et al.*[41, 42, 50] and Tarte[46, 50] have each examined small numbers of these compounds in various states, and although the earlier studies[41] gave rise to some doubt as to whether dimerisation occurred in the liquid state, this has now been satisfactorily resolved.[50] There is general agreement that in the monomeric state the $N=O$ frequency of dialkylnitrosamines occurs near 1490 cm.$^{-1}$ in the vapour. In solution in carbon tetrachloride this falls to near 1450 cm.$^{-1}$, and a small further fall occurs in the liquid state. The frequencies corresponding to the dimeric state arise near 1310 cm.$^{-1}$. Insufficient data are yet available for any accurate ranges to be laid down, but in normal alkyl nitrosamines these absorptions usually fall with 10 cm.$^{-1}$ of the value quoted. No data are available

on α-fluorinated compounds, but it is interesting to note that
N-nitroso-*bis*-2-2-2-trifluoroethylamine shows its N=O frequency
in the vapour state [42] at 1550 cm.$^{-1}$. This is a considerable shift for
a situation in which the fluorine atoms are so far removed from
the N=O link, but it may be that the geometric arrangement of the
molecule leads to their being relatively close in space despite the
number of intervening linkages. Elevated $\rangle$N–N=O frequencies
have also been reported in the case of amides which are nitrosated
on the nitrogen atom. White [51] has studied a number of compounds of this type and assigned the N=O absorptions to the
1527–1515 cm.$^{-1}$ region. These materials also show elevated
carbonyl frequencies corresponding to esters rather than to amides,
so that it is quite possible that considerable dipolar interactions
are taking place in this series also. The higher frequencies for
nitrosoguanidines suggested by Lieber *et al.*[11] may also arise by a
similar mechanism, but too little is yet known of the general behaviour of material to enable any firm conclusions to be drawn.

    17.3(d). Other Characteristc Absorptions of R–N=O Groups.
In the lower-frequency regions a few bands have been reported
which arise primarily from skeletal frequencies but which may be
useful in some cases for confirmatory evidence. Tarte,[12, 13, 22] for
example, has made some useful suggestions on alkyl nitrites.

    All the fifteen nitrites he has examined exhibit absorption in the
814–751 cm.$^{-1}$ range which he ascribes to the fundamental ν_{N-O}
vibration, and there is also a pair of bands in the 691–617 cm.$^{-1}$ and
625–565 cm.$^{-1}$ ranges which is assigned to the –O–N=O deformation
of *cis*- and *trans*-forms. Despite the rather wide frequency ranges
typical of skeletal vibrations, these assignments may well be valuable in confirming the presence of nitrite groups, and in both cases
the intensities are reasonably high. In addition, bands corresponding
to combinations of these fundamentals have been characterised at
2300–2250 cm.$^{-1}$ ($\delta_{ONO} + \nu_{N=O}$), near 2500 cm.$^{-1}$ ($\nu_{N-O} + \nu_{N=O}$) and
the first harmonic of $\nu_{N=O}$ at 3300–3200 cm.$^{-1}$. In the case of
nitrosoamines he has identified [46] related absorptions corresponding
to the N–N stretching and N–N=O deformations. These occur
near 1050 cm.$^{-1}$ and 660 cm.$^{-1}$ respectively. The second is therefore not much altered from the corresponding O–N=O mode.
The presence of the former absorption has also been confirmed by
Haszeldine in some compounds.[41, 42]

    No other useful absorptions have been identified in the cases of
–C–N=O compounds, although the C–N stretching mode has been
associated with a strong diffuse band near 1100 cm.$^{-1}$.

    17.3(e). Amine Oxides. Amine oxides also contain a multiple
bonded N–O system, and can conveniently be considered under
this heading. Costa [52-54] and his co-workers have studied this

absorption in pyridine *N*-oxide and a variety of substituted derivatives. In the original oxide it leads to an absorption band at 1270 cm.$^{-1}$ in non-polar solvents, but this appears to be very sensitive to the electrical character of substituent groups. Strong electron donors lower this frequency appreciably and *p*-methoxy-*N*-pyridine oxide [52] absorbs at 1238 cm.$^{-1}$. *p*-Hydroxy- and amino-groups are even more effective,[53] and the band in the latter case appears to be near 1200 cm.$^{-1}$. With strong electron-accepting substituents the effect is reversed, and in the *p*-nitro-derivative [52] the N $\rightarrow$ O absorption occurs at 1304 cm.$^{-1}$. A small number of tertiary amine oxides have also been studied by Mathis-Noel., Wolf and Gallais.[55] In this series the N $\rightarrow$ O band is assigned to the 970–950 cm.$^{-1}$ region. This is a very considerable shift from the corresponding assignment in the pyridine series, but the absorption would be expected to move to lower frequencies when the multiple bond character is minimised.

The *N*-oxides of pyrimidines have also been examined and compared with the pyridine *N*-oxides by Wiley and Slaymaker.[58] The N $\rightarrow$ O absorptions occur in the 1300–1255 cm.$^{-1}$ range in both series. One interesting feature of this work is the considerable differences which these workers find between the spectra of the picoline *N*-oxides. α- and β-Picoline oxides are similar to pyridine oxide and absorb between 1264 and 1260, but the γ-picoline oxide absorbs at 1290 cm.$^{-1}$.

Compounds related to amine oxides occur in the azoxy series

$$\overset{\displaystyle O}{\overset{\uparrow}{-N}}=N-$$

which contain the linkage –Ṅ=N–. Witkop and Kissman [56] have examined a small number of such compounds and noted a common absorption band in the 1310–1250 cm.$^{-1}$ region. They associate this with the N $\rightarrow$ O link, but are careful to point out that the aromatic C–N stretching absorption is to be expected in the same region. Jander and Haszeldine [57] have studied hexafluoroazoxymethane, which absorbs at 1282 cm.$^{-1}$ and 1256 cm.$^{-1}$. In view of the close parallel with the amine oxides, this would therefore appear to be a likely assignment for the N $\rightarrow$ O absorption is azoxy-compounds.

17.4. IONIC NITRATES

The nitrate ion has four fundamental modes of vibration, all of which are observable in the infra-red in suitable cases, but only two are normally sufficiently intense to be used for identification purposes. These are the ν_3 and the ν_2 vibrations, which absorb near 1390 cm.$^{-1}$ and 800 cm.$^{-1}$.

Strong bands near these frequencies are shown by inorganic

nitrates such as ammonium, thallium, barium and lead nitrates,[19, 20] whilst the 1390 cm.[-1] absorption has also been observed in many Raman spectra.[21] With organic nitrates the bands occur [5] in the overall ranges 1410–1340 cm.[-1] and 860–800 cm.[-1], and this is supported by the spectra of a number of compounds, such as guanidine nitrate, examined by Lieber *et al.*,[11] and also by the data from a very limited number of compounds we have examined ourselves. The high-frequency band is always considerably stronger than the other, which is rarely more than of medium intensity.

In Raman work on inorganic solutions it has been shown [21] that the v_3 vibration splits into two distinct bands at high concentrations, giving frequencies up to 1500 cm.[-1] on one side (Th) and down to 1315 cm.[-1] on the other (Al). This is the basis for a suggestion that there is a change of form of the ionic nitrate group at such concentrations. However, the frequencies do not fall outside the 1410–1345 cm.[-1] range until extremely high concentrations are reached, and it is extremely doubtful whether any serious departure from this correlation will arise in organic nitrates from any similar cause.

17.5. BIBLIOGRAPHY

1. Barnes, Gore, Liddel and Williams, *Infra-red Spectroscopy* (Reinhold, 1944).
2. Hibben, *The Raman Effect and its Chemical Applications* (Reinhold, 1939).
3. Nielsen and Smith, *Ind. Eng. Chem. (Anal.)*, 1943, **15**, 609.
4. Smith, Pan, and Nielsen, *J. Chem. Phys.*, 1950, **18**, 706.
5. Colthup, *J. Opt. Soc. Amer.*, 1950, **40**, 397.
6. Francel, *J. Amer. Chem. Soc.*, 1952, **74**, 1265.
7. Lothrop, Handrick and Hainer, *ibid.*, 1951, **73**, 3581.
8. Randall, Fowler, Fuson and Dangl, *Infra-red Determination of Organic Structures* (Van Nostrand, 1949).
9. Nikitin, *Zh. Fiz. Khim.*, 1949, **23**, 786.
10. Pinchas, *Analyt. Chem.*, 1951, **23**, 201.
11. Lieber, Levering and Patterson, *Analyt. Chem.*, 1951, **23**, 1594.
12. Tarte, *Bull. Soc. Chim. (Belg.)*, 1951, **60**, 227.
13. *Idem, ibid.*, p. 240.
14. Burns and Bernstein, *J. Chem. Phys.*, 1950, **18**, 1669.
15. Thompson, Nicholson and Short, *Discuss. Faraday Soc.*, 1950, **9**, 222.
16. Brownlie, *J. Chem. Soc.*, 1951, 3062.
17. Earl, Le Fèvre, Pulford and Walsh, *ibid.*, 1951, 2207.
18. Barredo and Goubeau, *Z. anorg. Chem.*, 1943, **251**, 2.
19. Newman and Halford, *J. Chem. Phys.*, 1950, **18**, 1276.
20. *Idem, ibid.*, p. 1291.
21. Mathieu and Lounsbury, *Discuss. Faraday Soc.*, 1950, **9**, 196.
22. Tarte, *J. Chem. Phys.*, 1952, **20**, 1570.
23. Pristera, *Analyt. Chem.*, 1953, **25**, 844.
24. Haszeldine, *J. Chem. Soc.*, 1953, 2525.
25. Brown, *J. Amer. Chem. Soc.*, 1955, **77**, 6341.
26. Kornblum, Ungnade and Smiley, *J. Org. Chem.*, 1956, **21**, 377
27. Shechter and Sheppard, *J. Amer. Chem. Soc.*, 1954, **76**, 3617.
28. Mason and Dunderdale, *J. Chem. Soc.*, 1956, 754.
29. Jander and Haszeldine, *ibid.*, 1954, 912.
30. Randle and Whiffen, *ibid.*, 1952, 4153.
31. Kross and Fassel, *J. Amer. Chem. Soc.*, 1956, **78**, 4225.
32. Lippert and Vogel, *Z. Phys. Chem.*, 1956, **9**, 133.

33. Franck, Hormann and Scheibe, *Chem. Ber.*, 1957, **90**, 330.
34. Palm and Werbin, *Can. J. Chem.*, 1953, **31**, 1004.
35. Lecomte and Mathieu, *J. Chim. Phys.*, 1942, **39**, 57.
36. Kumler, *J. Amer. Chem. Soc.*, 1953, **75**, 4346.
37. *Idem, ibid.*, 1954, **76**, 814.
38. Salyamon and Yaroslaviskii, *Sbornik Statei Obschiy. Khim.*, 1953, **2**, 1325.
39. Salyamon and Bobovich, *ibid.*, 1332.
40. Conduit, *Private Communication.*
41. Haszeldine and Jander, *J. Chem. Soc.*, 1954, 691.
42. Haszeldine and Mattinson, *ibid.*, 1955, 4172.
43. Lüttke, *Zeit. Electrochem.*, 1957, **61**, 302.
44. *Idem, J. Phys. Radium*, 1954, **15**, 633.
45. Schindler, Lüttke and Holleck, *Chem. Ber.*, 1957, **90**, 157.
46. Tarte, *Bull. Soc. Chim. Belges*, 1954, **63**, 525.
47. Mason and Dunderdale, *J. Chem. Soc.*, 1956, 759.
48. Nakamoto and Rundle, *J. Amer. Chem. Soc.*, 1956, **78**, 1113.
49. Bellamy and Williams, *J. Chem. Soc.*, 1957, 863.
50. Haszeldine and Jander; Tarte, *J. Chem. Phys.*, 1955, **23**, 979.
51. White, *J. Amer. Chem. Soc.*, 1955, **77**, 6008.
52. Costa and Blasina, *Z. Phys. Chem.*, 1955, **4**, 24.
53. Costa, Blasina and Sartori, *ibid.*, 1056, **7**, 123.
54. Sartori, Costa and Blasina, *Gazz. Chim.*, 1955, **85**, 1085.
55. Mathis-Noel, Wolf and Gallais, *Compt. Rend. Acad. Sci. (Paris)*, 1956, **242**, 1873.
56. Witkop and Kissman, *J. Amer. Chem. Soc.*, 1953, **75**, 1975.
57. Jander and Haszeldine, *J. Chem. Soc.*, 1954, 919.
58. Wiley and Slaymaker, *J. Amer. Chem. Soc.*, 1957, **79**, 2233.

CHAPTER 18

Organo-phosphorus Compounds

18.1. INTRODUCTION AND TABLE

IT is only within the last few years that the infra-red spectra of organo-phosphorus compounds have been studied on any scale, but the widespread use of these compounds in commerce as insecticides, oil additives, plasticisers, etc., coupled with the possibilities of studying phosphate metabolism in nucleic acids, lecithins and similar products, has recently stimulated a good deal of work in this field, and a

TABLE 18

Phosphorus–Oxygen Links

(a) P=O (free) . . .	1350–1250 cm.$^{-1}$ (exceptionally lower, down to 1175 cm.$^{-1}$) (s.)	
P=O (hydrogen bonded)	1250–1150 cm.$^{-1}$ (v.s.)	
(b) P–O–C (aromatic) . .	1240–1190 cm.$^{-1}$ (s.)	
(c) P–O–C (aliphatic) . .	1050–990 cm.$^{-1}$ (v.s.) (exceptionally lower)	
(d) P–O–Ethyl . . .	1170–1150 cm.$^{-1}$ (w.) (also given by P–O–Ar)	
(e) P–O–Methyl . .	1180 ± 10 cm.$^{-1}$ (w.)	
(f) P–O–P . . .	970–940 cm.$^{-1}$	
(g) P–OH	2700–2560 cm.$^{-1}$ (broad and shallow)	

Phosphorus–Hydrogen Links

P–H	2440–2350 cm.$^{-1}$ (m.)

Phosphorus–Carbon Links

(a) P–Phenyl . . .	1450–1435 cm.$^{-1}$ (m.)
(b) P–Alkyl . . .	No useful correlations
P–CH$_3$ . . .	1320–1280 cm.$^{-1}$

Phosphorus–Sulphur Links

P=S	840–600 cm.$^{-1}$ (v.-w.)

Phosphorus–Nitrogen Links

(a) P–NH$_2$ and P–NH– .	Normal for NH$_2$ and NH structures
(b) P–N–	Near 715 cm.$^{-1}$. Doubtful

Phosphorus–Halogen Links

(a) P–Cl	580–440 cm.$^{-1}$ (s.)
(b) P–F	885–810 cm.$^{-1}$ (s.)

Ionic Phosphate Groups

Aryl substituents . .	1090–1040 cm.$^{-1}$
Alkyl substituents . .	1180–1150 cm.$^{-1}$ (s.) and near 1080 cm^{-1}.

number of correlations are now available. These have been summarised in correlation charts for: (a) inorganic phosphorus links,[22] and (b) organo phosphorus compounds [23] by Corbridge.

A full list of the correlations which have been proposed is given in Table 18. It should be stated at once, however, that not all of these are of equal value, and that, whilst many of them are based upon the examination of large numbers of compounds, others are only very tentative correlations based on a few compounds or on compounds of a limited type.

The basis of each of these correlations is discussed below, and some indication is given of the degree of reliability which the correlation may be expected to show.

18.2. P=O STRETCHING VIBRATIONS

Meyrick and Thompson [1] were the first to examine the infra-red and Raman spectra of a number of organo-phosphorus compounds, and as a result of studies on five phosphonates they suggested that the moderately intense band shown in all cases in the 1260–1250 cm.$^{-1}$ region originated in the P=O stretching vibration. This assignment was supported by Raman data on $POCl_3$ [2] (in which the P=O vibration occurs at 1295 cm.$^{-1}$) and on other phosphites and phosphonates.[3]

This work was extended and amplified by Gore [4] and by Daasch and Smith,[5] who independently studied considerable numbers of phosphonates and phosphates. Gore [4] was able to show that the suggestion of the 1250 cm.$^{-1}$ region for this vibration was reasonably in accord with theory, as the application of Gordy's rule would indicate a frequency of 1300–1100 cm.$^{-1}$, depending on the P–O bond length used. Furthermore, he examined a considerable number of phosphates and compared them with the corresponding thiophosphates. In each case the most obvious point of difference was the presence of a band in the 1300–1250 cm.$^{-1}$ region in the phosphates. This finding was fully confirmed by Daasch and Smith,[5] who also obtained evidence that the frequency of this vibration was largely determined by the number of electronegative substituents on the phosphorus atom. In compounds with three electronegative substituents, such as phosphates or fluorphosphonates, the P=O frequency was in the approximate range 1310–1275 cm.$^{-1}$, falling to 1275–1250 cm.$^{-1}$ in compounds with only two electronegative substituents, such as hydrogen and alkyl phosphonates. With phosphinates and similar materials, absorptions near 1240 cm.$^{-1}$ were found, whilst in the extreme cases of triphenyl- and trimethyl-phosphine oxides the frequencies fell to 1190 cm.$^{-1}$ and 1176 cm.$^{-1}$, respectively. The latter two compounds are also of interest in illustrating the apparent lack of influence of the conjugation of the aromatic rings on the P=O frequencies. In general, the correlation of this band with the P=O group was established by comparison with the corresponding phosphites and similar trivalent phosphorus compounds in which this group is absent.

This correlation was further confirmed by Bellamy and Beecher [6, 7, 8] working mainly on phosphates and phosphonates, and has also been supported by the work of Holmstedt and Larsson,[9] Bergmann, Littauer and Pinchas,[10] Harvey and Mayhood,[24] Maarsen,[25] Emeleus *et al.*[26, 27] and Thomas.[28] The spectra of several naturally occurring phosphorus compounds have also been examined by a number of workers.[18-21]

This correlation can, therefore, be regarded as being firmly established, and in our own laboratories we have the spectra of over a hundred compounds containing the P=O group which absorb in the 1300–1250 cm.$^{-1}$ region. This is accordingly the frequency range quoted in Table 1, but it should be appreciated that frequencies on either side of this range will be found on occasion. As indicated above, the P=O frequency is primarily dependent upon the electronegativity of the substituent groups, so that with strongly electronegative substituents the frequency rises sharply. Trifluorophosphine oxide, for example,[29] absorbs at 1404 cm.$^{-1}$. At the other end of the scale substituents, such as carbon or hydrogen, directly attached to the phosphorus atom can lead to frequencies lower than the range quoted. Thomas [28] has studied this absorption in 250 organo-phosphorus compounds and quotes an overall range of 1350–1175 cm.$^{-1}$ (in the absence of hydrogen bonding) which gives some indication of the expected extremes.

The electronegativity dependence of this absorption has been put on a quasi-quantitative basis by Bell *et al.*[30] They have shown that for the halogen-substituted phosphine oxides there is a linear relation between the sum of the halogen electronegativities and the phosphoryl frequency. This has been extended to the derivation of effective group electronegativities for other substituents which appear to be of fairly general application. In some instances, such as in OR groups, the effective electronegativity so derived is close to that to be expected from an oxygen substituent, but anomalies arise with OH and NH_2 substituents which have lower values, presumably due to hydrogen bonding. With compounds in which nitrogen is attached to the phosphorus, more recent data [24] also indicate that the effective electronegativity of nitrogen substituents is lower than they have suggested. For example, there is a fall of 57 cm.$^{-1}$ on passing from $(EtO)_3PO$ to $(NEt_2)_3PO$. In these cases it would seem likely that lone-pair electrons of the nitrogen atoms are influencing the frequency in some way independently of the direct inductive effect.

The P=O frequency is also subject to shifts of 50–80 cm.$^{-1}$ when the molecule contains OH or NH groups with which the P=O group is able to form hydrogen bonds.[5, 7, 8, 26, 27] The bonding is exceptionally strong in the case of OH compounds, as shown by the accompanying large frequency shift of the OH stretching vibration (see later). In addition to undergoing a low-frequency shift, the intensity of the P=O vibration is considerably increased. This is not commonly the case with hydrogen-bonded carbonyl groups, except for compounds of the type –CO–C=C(OH)–, in which the resonant structure is responsible for the intensity increase. It is probable that a similar resonance structure of the group $P{\displaystyle \atop \diagdown} {O \atop OH}$ is responsible for the observed intensity increase in this case also.

Hydrogen bonding of this type appears to be limited to hydroxy- and amino-compounds, and the P=O frequency of hydrogen phosphonates, for example, is normal. There is, indeed, evidence from heats of mixing etc. that many other types of organo-phosphorus compounds show association effects,[11] but the P=O group may not be involved, as its infra-red frequency is relatively constant. On steric grounds it would appear to be difficult for the hydroxy-group in these compounds to form an intramolecular hydrogen bond, and it is more probable that association in these cases is through dimer formation, as with carboxylic acids. However, the association is extremely strong, and in the few cases which have been studied in dilute solutions in non-polar solvents, the shifted P=O frequency persists, but is accompanied also, in many cases, by a second absorption corresponding to the unbonded P=O vibration.[7] With the amino compounds, however, the bonds are usually intermolecular, and the NH and P=O frequencies revert to normal in dilute solution. One interesting application of this correlation is in the demonstration that dialkyl hydrogen phosphites exist wholly in the phosphonate form:

$$P{\diagup OH \atop \diagdown OR}^{\displaystyle OR} \longrightarrow P{\diagup O \atop \diagdown OR}^{\displaystyle H} \quad OR$$

Thus Meyrick and Thompson [1] reported strong P=O and P–H absorptions in a number of compounds of this type, and the same effects have been noted by Bellamy and Beecher.[6] The absence of P–OH absorptions and the fact that the P–O absorption frequency corresponds to an unbonded phosphoryl group confirm that not more than a very small proportion of the whole can exist as hydrogen phosphite.

The intensity of the P=O absorption is reasonably strong, but varies somewhat with the nature of the attached groupings. The comparison of absolute intensities for different classes of materials is, however, complicated by the fact that this band very frequently occurs as a doublet. Gore [4] originally suggested that the second of these bands might possibly arise from an O-ethyl vibration in ethyl phosphates, but the fact that the doublet character persists in many wholly aromatic phosphates and phosphonates indicates that it must be associated with the P=O vibration itself. The origins of doubling have not been finally resolved, but interactions with neighbouring CH groups have been suggested,[25, 28] and there are also possibilities of rotational isomerism.

18.3. P-O-C STRETCHING VIBRATIONS

18.3(a). P-O-C (Aromatic) Vibrations. Just as there are marked differences between the absorption frequencies of C-O-C (alkyl) and C-O-C (aryl) linkages, so are there marked differences between the two types of P-O-C linkage. In the case of the phosphorus compounds the frequencies appear to be rather more consistent and less subject to variation from compound to compound, although this may only arise from the fact that the great majority of the compounds studied so far are fairly closely related types.

The differentiation between the two classes of P-O-C linkage has been clearly demonstrated by studies on related series of compounds such as triphenyl, diphenyl-ethyl, phenyl-diethyl and triethyl phosphates. Examination of these materials at the same concentration in the same cell reveals a gradual weakening and ultimate disappearance of a strong band near 1200 cm.$^{-1}$, whilst, at the same time, a band at 1030 cm.$^{-1}$ that is absent in triphenylphosphate shows a corresponding increase in strength throughout the series.[6]

On the basis of this and other related series,[6, 7] the P-O-C (aromatic) absorption has been assigned to the 1200 cm.$^{-1}$ region, and it has been shown that a band in this region is present in all the aromatic phosphates, phosphonates and phosphites so far examined, as well as in some aryl thiophosphates and similar materials, whilst no band is present in wholly aliphatic compounds.

The overall range so far found is 1240–1190 cm.$^{-1}$, and within this range we have noticed that the frequency is nearest to 1240 cm.$^{-1}$ in *para*-nitrosubstituted compounds such as certain insecticide preparations. In some additional compounds of this type studied by Thomas [28] the absorption in a few cases falls as low as 1180 cm.$^{-1}$.

A second P-O-C (Ar) absorption which is not so intense [6] has also been found near 1030 cm.$^{-1}$. This is less useful for identification purposes, as it falls in the region of the aliphatic ethers, and also of some aromatic ring vibrations. However, the intrinsic intensity of this absorption is so much less than that of the corresponding P-O-C (alkyl) band, that the latter is readily differentiated from it.

18.3(b). P-O-C (Alkyl) Vibrations. The studies described above also serve to establish the position of the P–O–C (alkyl) absorption as being near 1030 cm.$^{-1}$, whilst the same correlation had also been put forward earlier by Daasch and Smith.[5] Altogether, a very large number of alkylphosphates and similar materials have now had their spectra determined,[1, 4-10] and in all cases an extremely strong absorption is found in the range 1050–995 cm.$^{-1}$, with the great majority absorbing near 1030 cm.$^{-1}$. Bergmann *et al.*[10] describe this band as being absent in *iso*propylphosphate, and assign the 995 cm.$^{-1}$ band found to other causes. However, the spectra of other branched-chain materials described by Meyrick and Thompson [1] and by Bellamy and Beecher [6, 7] are in line with the general correlation, so that there is no reason to suppose that branched-chain materials are in any way exceptional. Recently Thomas [28] has noted that in some 300 organo-phosphorus compounds examined this absorption falls in the range 1050–1000 cm.$^{-1}$ for methyl and ethyl esters. With longer-chain alkyl groups, however, the frequency is somewhat lower, falling to 950 cm.$^{-1}$ in extreme cases unless a fluorine or other electronegative substituent is also present. This assignment is, of course, applicable only to the P–O–C vibration in phosphates, and the change in the valency state to trivalent phosphorus leads to a shift to lower frequencies.

Some workers have attempted to identify this absorption, and that near 1150 cm.$^{-1}$ described below with independent stretching motions of the P–O– and C–O– portions of this linkage. Thus Thomas [28] and McIvor *et al.*[31] assign the 1030 cm.$^{-1}$ band to the P–O–(C) vibration and the higher-frequency band to the C–O–(P) mode. Maarsen,[25] on the other hand, identifies the C–O–(P) mode with the 1030 cm.$^{-1}$ region and assigns the other at lower frequencies. If any differentiation between these modes is possible it would seem more reasonable to assign the 1030 cm.$^{-1}$ band to the C–O–(P) vibration in view of the close similarity with alkyl ethers and alcohols. Further, this band moves in aryl phosphates to a position essentially similar to aryl ethers. However, it is probably unsafe to pursue identifications of individual bands too far in view of the obvious possibilities of mass effects and of coupling between the two frequencies. There are also possibilities of the occurrences,

for example, of symmetric and anti-symmetric $-O-\overset{\overset{\displaystyle O}{\|}}{P}-O-$ stretching modes which could lead to multiple absorptions. Bergmann *et al.*[10] have suggested that the 1030 cm.$^{-1}$ band may indeed arise in this way. The precise identification of the origin of these bands is therefore doubtful, but this in no way affects their obvious utility in analytical and diagnostic work. No detailed intensity studies have been made on this band, but it can usually be recognised in trialkyl phosphates from its very strong absorption. However, it should be realised that many other skeletal absorptions can occur in the same spectral region, although few are likely to be of comparable intensity. Apart from the obvious cases of compounds, such as ethers and alcohols, containing C–O– bonds, Harvey and Mayhood [24] have noted strong absorptions in the 1000–980 cm.$^{-1}$ range in compounds such as $(CH_3)_2NPOCl_2$.

18.3(c). P–O–Ethyl Vibrations, etc. Daasch and Smith [5] have observed that ethyl phosphates and similar materials containing the P–O–Et group all give a sharp but weak absorption at 1160 cm.$^{-1}$. We have confirmed that this is so in a large number of compounds, but have also observed that a similar, but considerably stronger band appears when P–O–Aryl groups are present. In all the seventy compounds we have examined containing either of these groups a band appeared in the range 1156–1163 cm.$^{-1}$, the only exception being ethyl phosphorodichloridite, in which the band appears at 1143 cm.$^{-1}$. A band at this point is therefore indicative of the presence of one or other of these groups, and reference to the 1200 cm.$^{-1}$ and 1030 cm.$^{-1}$ regions will usually serve to indicate which is involved. Thomas [28] has recently studied this band over a larger range of alkyl compounds and shown that, within wider limits, the correlation can be applied to groups containing the $-CH_2$–O–P structure. Of 196 compounds containing this structure 185 absorbed in the range 1170–1140 cm.$^{-1}$, whilst 65 out of 69 branched-chain esters containing the $\rangle$CH–O–P– linkage absorbed between 1150 cm.$^{-1}$ and 1130 cm.$^{-1}$. This band therefore seems to be reasonably characteristic of the C–O–P link itself, and this is the basis of his assignment to the C–O–(P) vibration. As suggested above, however, in so far as any differentiation of the C–O– and –O–P– links is possible at all, it would seem more reasonable to associate the higher frequency absorption with the P–O– [91] link in analogy with the corresponding 1250 cm.$^{-1}$ absorption in esters, and the lower frequency with the C–O– residue in analogy with ethers and alcohols.

18.3(d). P–O–Methyl Vibrations. The P–O–CH_3 group absorbs at 1190 cm.$^{-1}$ as a weak but well-defined band.[5] This was shown to be the case by Daasch and Smith, and has been confirmed in a number of instances in our own laboratories. The frequencies at which the P–O–CH_3 and P–O–C_2H_5 absorptions occur in normal alkyl phosphates are reasonably precise, but wider variations are introduced with halogen and other substituents. Thomas,[28] for example, quotes the wider range 1190–1170 cm.$^{-1}$ for the CH_3–O–P absorption. Nevertheless, this is still sufficiently distinctive to enable the recognition of this structure in alkyl phosphates when taken in conjunction with the bands at 1030 cm.$^{-1}$.

18.4. PYROPHOSPHATES

A good deal of work has been carried out by different groups in an attempt to identify absorptions characteristic of the pyrophosphate P–O–P linkage. Bergmann *et al.*[10] have examined three pyrophosphates and compared their spectra with those of the original phosphates. They find that in each case the former contain one more band than the latter and that this is in the range 970–930 cm.[-1]. They point out that the data on *n*-butyl pyrophosphate given by Daasch and Smith [5] also indicate a band at 950 cm.[-1]. They have therefore assigned the asymmetric P–O–P vibration as being the origin of this absorption.

Holmstedt and Larsson,[9] on the other hand, have tentatively suggested that the P–O vibration of the pyrophosphate grouping occurs in the 710 cm.[-1] region. In organic compounds this absorption has been studied by Corbridge and Lowe.[32] In this class of compound they obtained evidence for the presence of P–O–P absorptions near 900 cm.[-1] and also near 700 cm.[-1], thus providing support for both assignments. However, much of their data related to polypyrophosphates, and it has been suggested that in organophosphorus pyrophosphates the 900 cm.[-1] band occurs at higher frequencies. Harvey and Mayhood [24] suggest the 950–910 cm.[-1] region for this absorption as a result of studies on fourteen compounds of this type, and McIvor *et al.*[31] confirm this on a further range of compounds with an extension of the upper frequency limit to 970 cm.[-1]. Thomas [28] and Simon *et al.*[33] have quoted similar data. There would therefore seem to be good grounds for the assignment of the P–O–P absorption in pyrophosphates to this frequency range. In thionopyrophosphates, however, the characteristic band is moved to lower frequencies.[31] The same workers have also studied the 700 cm.[-1] range, but no useful correlations have been found, probably due to the multiple peaks which are commonly found in this region.

However, whilst this absorption may be of value in a few specific cases, it is important to realise that it falls in a region in which many other organo-phosphorus compounds absorb. There is some degree of overlap at the higher frequencies with the P–O–C (alkyl) absorption, and with the band in the 980 cm.[-1] region discussed in Section 18.12 below. Harvey and Mayhood [24] have suggested that differentiation from P–O–C bands may be possible using measurements on the half-band widths, as the pyrophosphate absorption is appreciably broader than the other. Nevertheless, the identification of this structure in an unknown must remain a matter of considerable difficulty.

18.5. P–OH STRETCHING VIBRATION

The OH valency vibration is, of course, relatively independent of the nature of the attached group. However, in acid compounds of phosphorus containing the $P{\diagup}^{O}_{OH}$ group, hydrogen bonding effects are even greater than those of carboxylic acids, so that the OH vibrations occupy a very characteristic position. In all the acids examined by Daasch and Smith [5] and by Bellamy and Beecher [7,8] no OH bands could be found in the normal region, but, instead, a broad shallow absorption appeared in the 2700–2560 cm.$^{-1}$ range. In solutions in non-polar solvents this band persists. The band is clearly to be associated with the OH group, as it disappears on salt formation, whilst the P=O frequency also provides support for the suggestion that very strong hydrogen bonds are involved. Similar results have also been reported for synthetic kephalins [8,12] and for naphthyl acid phosphates.[13] Inorganic phosphoric acids and related compounds behave similarly,[22] and Thomas [28] has also confirmed that thiophosphorus acids absorb in this region, although he notes that in structures involving the ${\diagup}P{\diagup}^{S}{-}$ OH group the frequency is raised, reflecting the weaker association forces. On the other hand, in acids such as monosodium trifluoromethyl phosphonate the band occurs at lower frequencies [26,27] near 2350 cm.$^{-1}$, reflecting the enhanced hydrogen bonding strength resulting from the fluoromethyl substitution.

In addition, the acid phosphorus compounds show broad, shallow absorptions in the 2500–1600 cm.$^{-1}$ region which have not been fully studied. These absorptions are generally weak and broad, and are difficult to detect in many cases. Thomas [28] has assigned the 1650 cm.$^{-1}$ absorption to the OH deformation mode, but this seems high in comparison with carboxylic acids and phenols.

The P–OH deformation mode cannot be assigned with any precision and is, indeed, unlikely to have a very narrow frequency range. However, in some cases it appears to fall near 1030 cm.$^{-1}$. Diphenyl hydrogen phosphate, for example, absorbs at 1030 cm.$^{-1}$, whereas neither the silver salt nor triphenyl phosphate do so. Corbridge and Lowe [22] report similar findings, whilst Emeleus *et al.*[26,27] assign the P–OH deformation as being near 940 cm.$^{-1}$ in a number of fluorinated compounds. This would seem to be reasonable in comparison with the corresponding frequency in dimeric carboxylic acids which falls near 900 cm.$^{-1}$. However, the identification of this absorption is in any case complicated by the likely presence of other absorptions, particularly the P–O–C band in the same region. Indeed, Thomas [28] prefers to identify it with the P–O(H)

Y

stretching mode in line with his earlier assignments. It would be unwise to attempt to identify P–OH groups from absorptions in the low-frequency range, but the possibility that they may absorb near 1030 cm.$^{-1}$ should be borne in mind when P–O–C (alkyl) groups are being sought.

18.6. P–H STRETCHING VIBRATION

A limited number of inorganic and organic phosphorus compounds containing the P–H linkage have been examined by various workers,[1, 5-7, 27, 28, 32] and in these a sharp absorption band of medium intensity occurs in the range 2440–2350 cm.$^{-1}$. This is the expected region for the P–H valence vibration, and phosphine itself absorbs [14] at 2327 cm.$^{-1}$ and 2421 cm.$^{-1}$, so that the assignment can be regarded as being fully substantiated. In almost all cases the band is found to be sharp, and the fact that the P=O absorption occurs in very much the expected region for the appropriate dialkyl phosphonate suggests that the P–H link is not capable of entering into hydrogen bonding to any appreciable extent.

The overall range 2440–2350 cm.$^{-1}$ (excluding phosphine) in which the P–H absorption has been reported is rather wider than might be expected from a simple stretching mode of this type, and Thomas [28] has suggested that it may be possible to differentiate between phosphonates (2450–2400 cm.$^{-1}$) and phosphinates (2350–2325 cm.$^{-1}$) using this absorption. The P–H deformation mode has not been identified except in phosphine itself.

18.7. PHOSPHORUS–CARBON LINKS

18.7(a). Aromatic. Daasch and Smith [5] have examined a considerable series of aryl phosphorus compounds containing the P-aryl group, and have found in all cases bands in the regions 1450–1435 cm.$^{-1}$ and 1005–995 cm.$^{-1}$ which are sharp and of moderate intensity. They associate these with the P-phenyl link, but point out also that they might equally well arise from ring vibrations which have become activated in some way. There is a certain amount of evidence that this is indeed the case as regards the lower frequency band, as we have found a medium-weak absorption in this region in many compounds containing the P–O-phenyl group, and have also shown that this band shifts in compounds with substituents on the aromatic ring, in the same way as would be expected if it arose from a ring vibration. However, the 1440 cm.$^{-1}$ band is not shown in any of these spectra, and there is no reason to suppose that this is not a reliable and useful correlation for the P-phenyl group. Corbridge [23] also has confirmed that his own unpublished data supports this correlation. Compounds containing the Si-phenyl group also absorb near this point (Chapter 20), but this is not of any significance, as the two groupings are rarely, if ever, found together.

18.7(b). Aliphatic. No useful correlations for the P–C linkage have been formulated, and as the P–C stretching bands of compounds such as trimethyl phosphine oxide [15] appear to lie in the 750–650 cm.[-1] range in which many other types of organo-phosphorus compounds also absorb, it is doubtful whether any such correlations could be developed.

In the case of P–CH₃ compounds a characteristic absorption should arise due to the asymmetric CH_3 deformation mode. This has been identified as falling [22, 24, 28, 31] in the range 1320–1280 cm.[-1], where it occurs as a strong-to-medium intensity band in most cases. In pentavalent phosphorus compounds this band usually occurs in the upper half of this range, whereas it falls nearer 1285 cm.[-1] in the trivalent series.[28] This band is not, however, entirely specific for this group, despite its narrow frequency range, as $N(CH_3)_2$ groups which are commonly found in organo-phosphorus insecticides also absorb near this point. It has been suggested that differentiation between the two possibilities may be possible from measurements of the half-band widths, which are appreciably smaller in the case of the P–CH₃ bands.[24, 28]

18.8. PHOSPHORUS–SULPHUR LINKS

Infra-red spectral correlations covering the P=S and P–S– bands would be of considerable value in the organo-phosphorus insecticide field as, combined with studies on the corresponding phosphorus–oxygen links, the method might permit the study of the complex isomerisation occurring on heating thiophosphates. However, although a good deal of work has been done in this field, the characteristic absorptions appear to be very weak and are, therefore, of very limited value.

18.8(a). P=S Stretching Vibrations. The compounds $PSCl_3$ and $PSBr_3$ absorb at 753 cm.[-1] and 718 cm.[-1], and these bands are absent from the corresponding oxychlorides. This suggests that the P=S absorption should occur in the 750 cm.[-1] region, and this has been supported by Gore's calculated value of 752 cm.[-1] based on Gordy's rule. Both Daasch and Smith,[5] and Gore,[4] have examined a considerable number of thiophosphates of various types and compared the results with the spectra of corresponding phosphates. In general, the results all confirm the view that the P=S absorption occurs in the 750–600 cm.[-1] range, but the intensity shown is very variable. In a few isolated cases the P=S absorption is strong, but in the great majority of instances it is relatively weak, and in some cases cannot be detected at all. Trimethyl thiophosphate, for example, has no band of any appreciable intensity between 800 cm.[-1]

and 600 cm.$^{-1}$. Corbridge [23] confirms this general finding, but, on the other hand, McIvor *et al.*[31] and Thomas [28] propose a somewhat higher frequency range. McIvor *et al.* find a medium absorption in the 840–780 cm.$^{-1}$ region in a series of compounds they have studied which contain the P=S link. In some instances, as when SR, SH or chlorine atoms are also attached to the phosphorus, an additional strong band appears near 650 cm.$^{-1}$. These workers are unable to assign the P=S band in these latter cases, but express a preference for the 800 cm.$^{-1}$ region. Thomas is more definite in dividing the compounds of this type into different classes. He quotes $(RO)_3PS$ as absorbing between 845 cm.$^{-1}$ and 800 cm.$^{-1}$, $(RO)_2RP=S$ 805–775 cm.$^{-1}$, $(RO)R_1R_2PS$ 790–770 cm.$^{-1}$ and phosphine sulphides 770–750 cm.$^{-1}$. This is reasonably consistent in showing a trend similar to the P=O frequency and explains, for example, the previous anomaly of trimethylthiophosphate, which absorbs at 815 cm.$^{-1}$. On the other hand, it is not easy to see why $POCl_3$, for example, should absorb at higher frequencies than the $PO(OR)_3$ compounds, whereas $PSCl_3$, absorbing at 753 cm.$^{-1}$, is appreciably lower than its OR analogue. Nevertheless, these proposals provide some basis for the tentative assignment of P=S frequencies, although the presence of additional bands in this region in many cases reduces their overall value.

18.8(b). P–S– Stretching Vibrations. The positions of any P–S– frequencies are not well known and are probably variable. Gore has noted that the 1200 cm.$^{-1}$ band characteristic of the P–O– phenyl grouping is not shown by the P–S– phenyl group. If the P=S absorption occurs near 700 cm.$^{-1}$ the single-bond vibration is likely to be beyond the rock-salt range. Thomas [28] and McIvor *et al.*[31] suggest that it occurs between 575 cm.$^{-1}$ and 510 cm.$^{-1}$, depending in part on the nature of the other substituents.

18.9. PHOSPHORUS–NITROGEN LINKS

18.9(a). P–NH$_2$ and P–NH– Vibrations. Only a limited number of phosphoramidates and similar materials have been examined.[7, 9, 32] The NH stretching and deformation vibrations are very little affected by the presence of the phosphorus atom and occur at very much the same positions as in normal amines. Thus P–NH$_2$ compounds show two, and sometimes three NH stretching bands in the 3330–3150 cm.$^{-1}$ region when examined as solids. Dilute solutions in which the hydrogen bonds are broken absorb near 3400 cm.$^{-1}$. Similarly, P–NH– compounds show normal behaviour in this region. P–NH$_2$ compounds, also, exhibit their deformation absorption in the region 1570–1550 cm.$^{-1}$, except in isolated instances when, as in benzyl hydrogen phosphoramidate, a zwitterion type structure is involved.[7] In anilido-phosphorus compounds the characteristic

Ar–NH– stretching bands are shown in the usual 1280 cm.$^{-1}$ region where they may be confused with P=O vibrations.[7]

18.9(b). P–N Stretching Vibrations. Several workers have attempted to identify a characteristic P–N stretching frequency. Holmstedt and Laarsen [9] suggested that this may occur near 775 cm.$^{-1}$, and this has been supported by Harvey and Mayhood [24] and by Corbridge,[23] to the extent that they are agreed in finding a common absorption when this group is present, in the 750–680 cm.$^{-1}$ range. Laarsen [33] has also suggested a modification to include the

P–N–C structure, which he believes to absorb in the 820–780 cm.$^{-1}$ region. Any correlation for the P–N link must be expected to be mass sensitive, and therefore liable to considerable frequency shifts with minor alterations in structure. The correlation is not therefore a particularly useful one, and in a number of cases it has not proved possible to identify the band in question. Maarsen [25] confirms this and attributes it to obscuration by other absorptions, such as the C–P stretching band, but Thomas [28] has also noted a number of instances in which the P–N– link shows no absorption in the range quoted, and this is in accord with our own experience.

In cyclic structures in which the P=N link arises, absorptions are found at higher frequencies, which may be associated with this group. Daasch [34] has assigned absorptions in phosphonitrilic chlorides to the 1300–1200 cm.$^{-1}$ region, and salts of phosphonitrilic acids [22] also show strong bands in the range 1300–1100 cm.$^{-1}$.

In the absence of any very specific P–N absorption, attempts have been made to find frequencies which are characteristic of large residues, such as P–N–CH$_3$ and P–N(CH$_3$)$_2$. The attachment of a methyl group to an N–P link in this way gives rise to a characteristic CH$_3$ deformation frequency [24, 25, 28] in the range 1325–1290 cm.$^{-1}$. This overlaps the region of the corresponding P–CH$_3$ absorption, but differentiation between the two may be possible on the basis of half-band widths.[24, 28] A number of other frequencies stated to be characteristic of the N(CH$_3$)$_2$ structure have also been discussed.[24, 25] Most of them are bands of medium intensity which are very difficult to identify with certainty. It is worth noting, however, that the dimethyl amino-group directly attached to phosphorus does appear to give a strong absorption in the 1010–990 cm.$^{-1}$ region,[24, 25, 28] where it is liable to be confused with P–O–C(alkyl) frequencies.

18.10. PHOSPHORUS–HALOGEN LINKS

18.10(a). P–Cl Vibrations. Phosphorus trichloride[16] has two absorptions at 511 cm.$^{-1}$ and at 488 cm.$^{-1}$ which correspond to P–Cl stretching modes, and POCl$_3$ and PSCl$_3$ exhibit two bands in this spectral region. Daasch and Smith [5] have examined seven other compounds containing the P–Cl band, all but one of which contained more than one chlorine atom. The observed frequency ranges were 572–500 cm.$^{-1}$ and 500–433 cm.$^{-1}$. Diphenylchlorophosphine oxide showed only a single band at 521 cm.$^{-1}$, as is to be expected. These findings have been confirmed by later studies by Corbridge,[23] Thomas [28] and McIvor et al.[31] These workers are agreed in finding a strong doublet, generally in the 580–440 cm.$^{-1}$ region. McIvor et al.[31] have discussed this correlation in some detail, and divide the frequency range into various classes. Thus, in trivalent phosphorus compounds the doublet is near 500 cm.$^{-1}$, rising to 540 cm.$^{-1}$ in phosphates and falling to near 475 cm.$^{-1}$ in thionophosphates. However, they note also that the position is influenced also by such factors as the number of halogen substituents and the presence of C–P linkages, so this generalisation must be treated with caution.

18.10(b). P–F Vibrations. The position of absorption peaks from P–F bonds have also been investigated by Daasch and Smith.[5] They find that, as with C–F links, intense absorptions are produced, but that their spectral position appears to be variable between 900 cm.$^{-1}$ and 800 cm.$^{-1}$. Six compounds of this type have been examined, some of which contained more than one P–F link, and so gave multiple peaks. All showed at least one strong band in the above region, and on the basis of their findings they tentatively assigned the P–F link in pentavalent compounds to 900–850 cm.$^{-1}$ and in trivalent compounds to 900–750 cm.$^{-1}$. In PF$_3$ the first fundamental absorption occurs [16] at 890 cm.$^{-1}$. This correlation has been confirmed by Corbridge, who also quotes the general range 900–720 cm.$^{-1}$. The most detailed study is due to Thomas,[28] who has examined sixty-four compounds of this type, and his results indicate that this wide range can be effectively narrowed to 885–810 cm.$^{-1}$ with the exception of PF$_3$ and POF$_3$ themselves.

18.10(c). P–Br and P–I Linkages. Phosphorus links with bromine or iodine have been little studied. The stretching frequencies of the P–Br links in PBr$_3$ [16] are at 400 and 380 cm.$^{-1}$.

18.11. THE IONIC PHOSPHATE GROUP

In inorganic phosphates of the type M$_3$$^+PO_4$$^{---}$ a strong band is found [17] in the region 1050–1000 cm.$^{-1}$ and there is also evidence of a second absorption in the 980 cm.$^{-1}$ region [14, 10] in some cases. With the hydrogen phosphates a distinct but progressive shift is observed towards higher frequencies, and many compounds of the type HPO$_4$$^-$ absorb in the 1070–1050 cm.$^{-1}$ range and H$_2$PO$_4$$^-$ in the 1090–1030 cm.$^{-1}$ range.[17] In both cases weaker absorptions are also shown in the 1000–900 cm.$^{-1}$ region (see Chapter 21). These preliminary correlations have been confirmed and extended by detailed studies by Corbridge and Lowe [22, 23, 32] on inorganic phosphate salts. Correlations based in general on at least eight salts of any one class are now available for *ortho*-phosphates (mono-, di- and tri-basic), phosphofluoridates, methyl phosphonates, monobasic phosphoramidates, hypophosphates, pyrophosphates, etc., etc. These have been very conveniently summarised in the form of a correlation chart [23] limited to salts of phosphorus oxy-acids, and this has useful applications in analytical work.

With organophosphoric acids the position is further complicated by the fact that the electronegativity of the organic substituents may have a direct influence on the bond lengths of the resonance hybrid arising from the $P{\overset{\diagup O}{\diagdown}}O^-$ structure. Insufficient information is available at present for any precise correlation rules to be formulated, but a series of six salts of aromatic acids of the type $\left[(RO)_2P{\overset{\diagup O}{\diagdown}_O}\right]^-$ have been found to show strong absorption bands in the 1090–1040 cm.$^{-1}$ range in which the corresponding triaryl phosphates do not absorb.[7, 8] Four salts of monosubstituted aromatic acids [(RO)PO$_3$] have also been studied [7, 8] and these absorb in the 1100–1050 cm.$^{-1}$ range. The majority absorb near the top of this range, but the numbers involved are too few to indicate whether or not this is indicative of a small shift such as is shown by the corresponding inorganic compounds.

With aliphatic substituents present, the 1050 cm.$^{-1}$ region cannot be studied, as the P–O–C (aliphatic) link itself gives rise to strong absorptions, but a series of six salts of aliphatic acids (RO)$_2$PO$_2{}^-$ have been found to absorb in the 1185–1156 cm.$^{-1}$ range in which neither the corresponding aryl compounds nor the corresponding alkyl phosphates absorb.[8] This also has been associated with the ionic phosphate absorption, and later work by Maarsen [25] has correlated this band with the asymmetric PO$_2$ stretching mode, the symmetric mode occurring close to the P–O–C alkyl absorption near 1080 cm.$^{-1}$. Emeleus *et al.*[26, 27] have also studied a number of ionised salts in which the CF$_3$ group is attached to the phosphorus atom. In these materials the principal absorption assigned to the $\geqslant$PO$_2$ group falls near 1250 cm.$^{-1}$, indicating the sensitivity of this frequency to electronegativity effects.

These preliminary indications therefore suggest that the ionic-phosphate absorptions in organo-phosphorus acid salts may occur anywhere within the range 1250–1040 cm.$^{-1}$ and that their actual position will be determined more by the nature of the organic substituents than by the number of negative charges carried by the ionised grouping.

Absorptions in the 920–880 cm.$^{-1}$ range have also been found in many aromatic ionic phosphate compounds, which parallel the similar bands shown by inorganic materials.[8] They are often weak, however, and although it has been suggested that they are probably associated also with the ionic phosphate vibration,[7] no detailed comparison of aromatic and aliphatic materials in this region has been given.

18.12. OTHER CORRELATIONS FOR ORGANO-PHOSPHORUS COMPOUNDS

An extraordinarily high proportion of organo-phosphorus compounds show a very intense absorption band near 980 cm.$^{-1}$, as can be seen by reference to the numerous published spectra in this field.[1, 4, 5, 6, 8, 9, 10] This has led to several suggestions being put forward as to its origin, but the great diversity of different types of compounds in which it occurs makes it extremely difficult to correlate with any one unit of molecular structure. Holmstedt and Larsson,[9] for example, on the basis of a limited number of compounds have identified it with a C–N stretching absorption in the skeleton $\text{P–C}\underset{N}{\overset{N}{\lessgtr}}$ but this cannot be the sole origin, as it arises in most phosphates, phosphonates and phosphonites. Bergmann *et al.*[10] regard it as arising in alkyl phosphates and pyrophosphates from a symmetrical stretching of the three P–OR bonds, and therefore analagous to the 980 cm.$^{-1}$ absorption of the ionic phosphate radical. As in the case of the 1030 cm.$^{-1}$ band, however (which they assign to the corresponding asymmetric vibration), it is difficult to see why the frequency should remain unchanged through the series phosphate, phosphonate and phosphonite, as well as in the corresponding acids with organic substituents.

This band has also been discussed by Bellamy and Beecher,[8] who have very tentatively associated it with the P–O stretching vibration of pentavalent phosphorus compounds. They point out, however, that this must lead to the conclusion that the 1030 cm.$^{-1}$ band arises from the O–C portion of the P–O–C link and the 980 cm.$^{-1}$ band from the P–O portion. Maarsen[25] provides some support for this view in that he assigns this band to an asymmetric P–O stretching mode, but this is clearly a field in which more work is required before any final conclusions can be drawn. This is particularly so in view of Thomas's work,[28] which indicates that P–O–C frequencies may be expected at frequencies below 990 cm.$^{-1}$ in some circumstances. In the meantime, however, the extremely high intrinsic intensity of the absorption renders it particularly suitable for quantitative work, whilst the presence of a strong band near 980 cm.$^{-1}$ is often valuable in providing a measure of confirmation of the identification from other spectral regions of an organo-phosphorus compound.

18.13. BIBLIOGRAPHY

1. Meyrick and Thompson, *J. Chem. Soc.*, 1950, 225.
2. Yost and Anderson, *J. Chem. Phys.*, 1934, **2**, 624.
3. Arbusov, Batuev and Vinogradova, *Compt. rend. Acad. Sci. U.S.S.R.*, 1946, **54**, 599.
4. Gore, *Discuss. Faraday Soc.*, 1950, No. 9, 138.
5. Daasch and Smith, *Analyt. Chem.*, 1951, **23**, 853 and *N.R.L. Report*, 3657.
6. Bellamy and Beecher, *J. Chem. Soc.*, 1952, 475.
7. *Idem, ibid.*, p. 1701.
8. *Idem, ibid.*, 1953, 728.
9. Holmstedt and Larsson, *Acta Chem. Scand.*, 1951, **5**, 1179.
10. Bergmann, Littauer and Pinchas, *J. Chem. Soc.*, 1952, 847.
11. Kosolapoff and McCullough, *J. Amer. Chem. Soc.*, 1951, **73**, 5392.
12. Baer, Maurukas and Russell, *ibid.*, 1952, **74**, 152.
13. Friedman and Seligman, *ibid.*, 1951, **73**, 5292.
14. Herzberg, *Infra-red and Raman Spectra of Polyatomic Molecules* (Van Nostrand, 1945), p. 302.
15. Daasch and Smith, *J. Chem. Phys.*, 1951, **19**, 22.
16. Herzberg, *Infra-red and Raman Spectra of Polyatomic Molecules* (Van Nostrand, 1945), p. 164.
17. Miller and Wilkins, *Analyt. Chem.*, 1952, **24**, 1253.
18. Hanahan and Jayko, *J. Amer. Chem. Soc.*, 1952, **74**, 5070.
19. Mislow, *ibid.*, 5155.
20. Baer, *ibid.*, 1953, **75**, 621.
21. Marinetti, Berry, Rouser and Stotz, *ibid.*, 313.
22. Corbridge and Lowe, *J. Chem. Soc.*, 1954, 4555.
23. Corbridge, *J. App. Chem.*, 1956, **6**, 456.
24. Harvey and Mayhood, *Can. J. Chem.*, 1955, **33**, 1552.
25. Maarsen, *Thesis, University of Amsterdam*, 1956.
26. Emeleus, Haszeldine and Paul, *J. Chem. Soc.*, 1955, 563.
27. Bennett, Emeleus and Haszeldine, *ibid.*, 1954, 3598.
28. Thomas, *Chem. and Ind.*, 1957, 198, and private communication.
29. Gutowsky and Liehr, *J. Chem. Phys.*, 1952, **20**, 1652.
30. Bell, Heisler, Tannebaum and Goldenson, *J. Amer. Chem. Soc.*, 1954, **76**, 5185.
31. McIvor, Grant and Hubley, *Can. J. Chem.*, 1956, **39**, 1611.
32. Corbridge and Lowe, *J. Chem. Soc.*, 1954, 493.
33. Simon and Stolzer, *Chem. Ber.*, 1956, **89**, 2253.
34. Laarsen, *Acta Chem. Scand.*, 1952, **6**, 1470.
35. Daasch, *J. Amer. Chem. Soc.*, 1954, **40**, 397.

CHAPTER 19

Halogen Compounds

19.1. INTRODUCTION AND TABLE

INFRA-RED methods are not required for the detection of halogens in organic materials, as this can be more simply done by other methods. Occasionally, cases arise in which only very small or very precious samples are available, but these are rare. It is, however, desirable that the spectroscopist should have a working knowledge of the expected positions of C-halogen absorption bands and of the influence this type of substitution is likely to have on other regions of the spectrum.

The only characteristic absorptions shown by halogen compounds in the rock-salt region are those arising from the C–X stretching mode. This is a single-bond skeletal mode, and it is consequently subject to considerable frequency alterations as a result of interactions with neighbouring groups. This is especially the case with the lighter halogens, fluorine and chlorine, in which the masses involved are not very different from the rest of the carbon skeleton. The interaction effects are reduced in organic bromides in which the C–Br stretching absorption is therefore rather more stable in position. Alkyl halides studied in solution or in the liquid state show multiple C–X stretching frequencies. These arise from the co-existence of rotational isomers with different fundamental frequencies. In simple alkyl halides such forms are limited to *trans-* and *gauche-* configurations only, but in compounds such as 1 : 2-dichlorethane or in long-chain halides the number of possible isomers is increased. A substantial volume of work has been carried out on individual molecules of this type, and this provides much of the data which are available on C–X stretching modes. A variety of such cases have been reviewed by Mizushima,[12] and recent detailed studies have also been made by Brown and Sheppard.[13, 14] This work has established that in the solid states in which only one rotational form is allowed the *trans*-form is generally the more stable and has the higher C–X stretching frequency. Parallel results are found also in the axial and equatorial C–X stretching modes of chlorinated *cyclo*hexanes [15] and sterols [16] which have useful diagnostic applications.

With fluorine substitution, interaction effects are at their greatest, and C–F stretching absorptions occur anywhere within the range 1400–1000 cm.$^{-1}$, depending on the nature and degree of fluorination.

In heavily fluorinated compounds such as the fluorocarbons this results in a series of very intense absorptions appearing over the whole of this range. The intensity of the C–F absorption is exceptionally high, and fluorocarbons can be recognised as such from this property alone. Fluorine substitution results in very considerable high-frequency shifts in adjacent CH, C=C and C=O stretching vibrations, and further details of this will be found in the appropriate chapters dealing with these groupings. It is clear, therefore, that the only correlations likely to be reasonably precise and widely applicable are those which arise from some particular vibration occurring in a constant environment. Some possible correlations along these lines are suggested below for the $CF–CF_3$ grouping.

Chlorine substitution also gives rise to interaction effects, but they are relatively small, and the influence of chlorine on neighbouring C=C bonds, for example, is slight. The C–Cl stretching absorption in compounds containing only a single such link is therefore usually confined to a narrow frequency range, but its range is considerably increased in complex chlorinated products containing more than one chlorine atom.

Bromine–carbon stretching absorptions are more consistent generally, but show occasional abnormalities, as in brominated sterols, in which the frequencies are unusually high.

Carbon-iodine absorptions have been studied in only a few molecules. They occur in the long wave-length region near 500 cm.$^{-1}$.

The correlations discussed are shown in Table 19 below.

TABLE 19

Carbon–Halogen Stretching Absorptions

C–F	1400–1000 cm.$^{-1}$ (v.s.)
C–Cl	800–600 cm.$^{-1}$ (s.)
C–Br	600–500 cm.$^{-1}$ (s.)
C–I	Near 500 cm.$^{-1}$ (s.)
The Grouping $CF–CF_3$	745–730 cm.$^{-1}$ (v.s.)
,, ,,	1365–1325 cm.$^{-1}$ (m.s.)

19.2. C–F LINKAGES

In simple molecules the presence of a single fluorine atom usually results in the appearance of a moderately intense absorption in the 1100–1000 cm.$^{-1}$ region. A considerable number of simple fluorinated compounds have been fully studied,[1, 2, 4] and it is found that in general this frequency rises with further fluorine substitution and is split into two peaks arising from symmetric and asymmetric vibrations. With larger molecules containing a considerable proportion of fluorine very intense absorption occurs over the 1400–1000 cm.$^{-1}$

range. The study of individual compounds of this type has been a popular subject, and a considerable number of papers have been published in this field without, however, any general correlations being formulated.

A typical series which exhibit this frequency shift is the fluoromethane group described by Thompson and Temple.[3] Their assignment of the CF stretching mode is as follows: CCl_2FH, 1072 cm.[-1]; CCl_3F, 1102 cm.[-1]; CCl_2F_2, 1155 cm.[-1] and 1095 cm.[-1], and $CClF_3$, 1210 cm.[-1] and 1102 cm.[-1]. With even a small increase in complexity up to 1 : 1 : 1-trifluoroethane, multiple peaks appear due to interaction, and this compound shows bands at 1290 cm.[-1], 1278 cm.[-1], 1266 cm.[-1], 1230 cm.[-1] and 1135 cm.[-1] which cannot be fully assigned.

In the fully fluorinated hydrocarbons the spectra are very complex, and a whole series of very intense bands appear in the 1350–1100 cm.[-1] region, most of which are probably associated in some way with C–F stretching vibrations. The spectra of a number of such materials have been given by Thompson and Temple,[5] and a considerable number are also included in the A.P.I. series of infra-red spectra. These materials are immediately recognisable both by the extreme intensities shown and by the lack of any appreciable absorption at frequencies higher than 1350 cm.[-1], but no detailed correlation rules can be formulated, and it is clear from the evidence of interactions that it is unlikely that any simple correlations will be developed in the future. This may, however, be possible if they relate to larger molecular units in which the environment around a specific linkage is reasonably constant. Barnes *et al.*[6] have suggested that the $=CF_2$ group may have characteristic absorptions at 1340 cm.[-1] and 1200 cm.[-1], and this is supported by many of the spectra of simple fluorinated compounds in which this group is present, but its value is much reduced by the appearance of bands at these points in many saturated fluorocarbons.

19.3. C–Cl LINKAGES

The spectra of chlorinated compounds are generally more regular than those of fluorinated materials, and the C–Cl stretching band appears in a narrower, although still broad, range. There is also less interaction and interference with the characteristic absorptions of neighbouring groups such as C=O or C=C. As before, a very large number of simple chlorine-containing molecules have been examined.[1, 7, 12-14] These cannot be discussed in detail but, in general the C–Cl stretching absorption occurs in the range 750–700 cm.[-1] in compounds containing only a single chlorine atom. This is the frequency corresponding to the more stable *trans*-configuration, and in alkyl chlorides in solution it is accompanied by a second absorption due to the *gauche*-isomer, which is found near 650 cm.[-1].

In cyclic structures, such as *cyclo*hexanes, chlorine substitution can be either axial or equatorial, and the two configurations show different frequencies as before. The connection between these cases and the simple alkyl halides has been discussed by Sheppard.[17] In *cyclo*hexane the C–Cl absorptions are at 742 cm.$^{-1}$ (equatorial) and 688 cm.$^{-1}$ (axial),[15] and similar results are shown by halogenated steroids. In the latter case, however, there are also some differences which are characteristic of the position of substitution.[16] Equatorial C–Cl stretching frequencies of 2-, 3- and 7-chlorosteroids, for example, are 755 cm.$^{-1}$, 782–750 cm.$^{-1}$ and 749 cm.$^{-1}$ respectively; the corresponding axial frequencies being 693 cm.$^{-1}$, 730–617 cm.$^{-1}$ and 588 cm.$^{-1}$. Several chlorines attached to the same carbon usually lead to higher C–Cl frequencies. With carbon tetrachloride, for example, a very intense band is shown at 797 cm.$^{-1}$. When fluorine is also present the results are difficult to interpret, but there is evidence that interaction effects result in higher frequencies. Similarly in phosgene, dichloroethylene and chlorinated aromatics, interactions raise the C–Cl frequency [7] to about 845 cm.$^{-1}$. With chloroprene and some other complex compounds,[8] on the other hand, the C–Cl absorption occurs below 650 cm.$^{-1}$. Many complex chlorinated compounds exhibit a reasonably strong band in the 750–700 cm.$^{-1}$ range due to the C–Cl vibration, but the correlation is of limited value in diagnostic work, as the frequency range for this grouping is considerably wider. In compounds in which a number of chlorine atoms are present and the fundamental is consequently very intense, a medium intensity band is usually shown at 1510–1470 cm.$^{-1}$ representing the first overtone.

19.4. C–Bʀ LINKAGES

Work on simple molecules indicates that the C–Br absorption occurs in the region of 600–500 cm.$^{-1}$ but, as before, two bands are shown by alkyl bromides in solution, and in cyclic structures the frequency also varies with the orientation. The spectra of a series of alkyl bromides from ethyl to *tert.*-butyl bromide, and of various aromatic and benzyl bromides have been obtained by Mortimer, Blodgett and Daniels,[9] who have given tables of the two frequencies. The overall range for the main *trans*-band was 689–645 cm.$^{-1}$. This indicates that the interaction effects are somewhat less than those occurring with the lighter halogens, but the range is still a wide one, and the C–Br bands are difficult to identify unless several bromine atoms are present, when the C–Br absorption can be recognised by its intensity.

The general assignment of the *trans*-form to an absorption near 650 cm.$^{-1}$ has been confirmed by Brown and Sheppard,[13, 14] who have identified the C–Br *gauche* frequency near 560 cm.$^{-1}$. In the sterol series [16] a limited number of compounds have been studied, and the results indicate that equatorial substitution leads to bands in the 750–700 cm.$^{-1}$ region, whereas axial substitution results in absorption in the 590–690 cm.$^{-1}$ range. In some dibromo-steroids axial substituents show an even wider range and absorb near 550 cm.$^{-1}$. The reasons for this wide range and for the abnormally high frequencies of the equatorial form compared with alkyl bromides are not known.

19.5. C–I LINKAGES

Only a very small number of simple iodinated materials have been studied. Pentamethylene iodide and *n*-propyl iodide [14] and other simple molecules [1] show the *trans* C–I absorption near 600 cm.$^{-1}$. The *gauche* band appears at lower frequencies, near 503 cm.$^{-1}$ in the liquid. One iodosterol has been studied [16] and absorbs at 672 cm.$^{-1}$. Again, the reasons for this shift over the normal alkyl series are not known.

19.6. OTHER CORRELATIONS

It has been suggested above that in view of the considerable coupling which occurs between C–C and C–F links, the only correlations which are likely to be of any value for such bonds will be those relating to larger structural units in which these effects are stabilised. Several correlations of this type have in fact been described.

Thus in the grouping CF_3Ph the asymmetric and symmetric deformation frequencies of the CF_3 group appear at stable positions and are not much influenced by the nature or positions of other substituents in the aromatic ring. They occur at 1321 ± 9 cm.$^{-1}$ (symmetric); 1179 ± 7 cm.$^{-1}$ and 1140 ± 9 cm.$^{-1}$ (asymmetric),[11] the asymmetric frequency being split due to the influence of the aromatic ring. These values are therefore useful for the recognition of the CF_3-aryl group.

A second limited correlation of this type relates to the C–F stretching frequencies of the CF_3 group when attached to a fluoromethylene link. The structure CF_3CF_2–X has a characteristic frequency in the range 1365–1325 cm.$^{-1}$ which is reasonably strong when X is a halogen or carbonyl group.[18, 19] The CF_3CF_2– group has also a characteristic frequency,[10] which is probably a methyl deformation frequency in the range 745–730 cm.$^{-1}$.

19.7. BIBLIOGRAPHY

1. Herzberg, *Infra-red and Raman Spectra of Polyatomic Molecules* (Van Nostrand, 1945).
2. Torkington and Thompson, *Trans. Faraday Soc.*, 1945, **41**, 236.

3. Thompson and Temple, *J. Chem. Soc.*, 1948, 1422.
4. *Idem, ibid.*, p. 1428.
5. *Idem, ibid.*, p. 1432.
6. Barnes, Gore, Stafford and Williams, *Analyt. Chem.*, 1948, **20**, 402.
7. Cf. Randall, Fowler, Fuson and Dangl, *Infra-red Determination of Organic Structures* (Van Nostrand, 1949).
8. Thompson and Torkington, *Proc. Roy. Soc.*, 1945, **A184**, 21.
9. Mortimer, Blodgett and Daniels, *J. Amer. Chem. Soc.*, 1947, **69**, 822.
10. Bellamy and Branch, *Nature*, 1954, **173**, 633.
11. Randle and Whiffen, *J. Chem. Soc.*, 1955, 1311.
12. Mizushima, *Structure of Molecules and Internal Rotation* (Academic Press, New York, 1954).
13. Brown and Sheppard, *Trans. Faraday Soc.*, 1954, **50**, 1164.
14. *Idem, Proc. Roy. Soc.*, 1955, **A231**, 555.
15. Larnaudie, *Compt. Rend. Acad. Sci. (Paris)*, 1952, **235**, 154; 1953, **236**, 909.
16. Barton, Page and Shoppee, *J. Chem. Soc.*, 1956, 331.
17. Sheppard, *Chem. and Ind.*, 1957, 192.
18. Hauptschein, Stokes and Nodiff, *J. Amer. Chem. Soc.*, 1952, **74**, 4005.
19. Tiers, Brown and Reid, *ibid.*, 1953, **75**, 5978.

CHAPTER 20

Organo-silicon Compounds

20.1. INTRODUCTION AND TABLE

INFRA-RED absorption bands arising from linkages involving silicon atoms are about five times more intense than the bands from the corresponding carbon linkages. The reasons for this have been discussed by Wright and Hunter.[1] This fact is of considerable help in analytical work, and infra-red absorption spectra have been very extensively employed in the development and characterisation of organo-silicon polymers and related materials. In addition to the work of Wright and Hunter,[1] three other groups of workers—Young, Servais, Currie and Hunter,[2] Richards and Thompson,[3] and Clark, Gordon, Young and Hunter[4]—have carried out fairly extensive studies in the silicon field, and a number of valuable correlations are now available. The first two groups employed solutions in carbon disulphide or carbon tetrachloride, but Richards and Thompson worked mainly on thin liquid films. Comparison of the solution and liquid spectra indicates that in the cases examined the shifts of the main bands were small unless hydrogen bonding was occurring. Simon and McMahon[18] have confirmed this by a comparison of the spectra of some alkyl silanes and siloxanes in the gaseous, liquid and solid phases. In working in this field, however, it should be borne in mind that Hyde has shown[5] that polymorphic crystalline forms can exist, and this would be expected to have a considerable influence on the absorption pattern. Solution studies are therefore to be preferred if this is possible, especially as a number of correlations relate to invariant absorptions at a single frequency.

In addition to the correlation data mentioned, fundamental studies

TABLE 20 *

$Si(CH_3)_3$	.	.	.	.	1250 cm.$^{-1}$, 841 cm.$^{-1}$, 756–4 cm.$^{-1}$
$Si(CH_3)_2$	.	.	.	.	1259 cm.$^{-1}$, 814–800 cm.$^{-1}$
$Si(CH_3)$	.	.	.	.	1259 cm.$^{-1}$, near 800 cm.$^{-1}$
Si–Phenyl	.	.	.	.	1429 cm.$^{-1}$, 1130–1090 cm.$^{-1}$
Si–O–Si cyclic	.	.	.		Trimers 1020–1010 cm.$^{-1}$; Tetramers 1090–1080 cm.$^{-1}$; higher rings 1080–1050 cm.$^{-1}$ (s.)
Si–O–C and Si–O–Si (open chain)					1090–1020 cm.$^{-1}$
SiH	.	.	.	.	2300–2100 cm.$^{-1}$

* All the absorptions listed are very strong.

have been made on silane,[6, 7] tetramethyl silane,[8, 9] and methyl [19, 23, 24] and halogenated silanes,[10, 11, 20, 21, 23] whilst there has been a considerable volume of work on quartz.[12, 13, 17] In the following discussion no reference is made to the Si=O grouping. None of the workers in this field has found any evidence of intense bands in the 6·5 μ region, where absorption from this group would be expected to arise, and there is a good deal of chemical evidence that this group does not occur in organo-silicon compounds. Frequencies which have been suggested as being characteristic for specific groupings including silicon, are listed in Table 20, and the evidence on which they are based is discussed in the text.

20.2. Si–C LINKAGES

Vibrations involving the stretching of the Si–C link occur in the 900–700 cm.$^{-1}$ region of the spectrum, and are considerably influenced by the nature of the substituent groupings. Thus the C–Si stretching vibration in tetramethyl silane has been assigned to 860 cm.$^{-1}$, whereas that of tetraethyl silane is given at 733 cm.$^{-1}$. The only consistent bands likely to be found associated with this linkage are therefore those which arise from invariant groupings such as Si–CH$_3$, Si-phenyl, etc., whilst rocking vibrations of these groups may also be expected to give rise to characteristic absorptions at higher frequencies.

20.2(a). SiCH$_3$ Stretching Vibrations. $-Si(CH_3)_3$. In the series of open-chain compounds examined by Wright and Hunter [1] (the range from hexamethyl disiloxane to octadecamethyl octasiloxane) a strong band is shown at 841 cm.$^{-1}$ which decreases in intensity as the chain length is increased, and which is uniformly absent from the corresponding cyclic compounds (hexamethyl*cyclo*trisiloxane to hexadecamethyl*cyclo*octasiloxane). A second band whose intensity varies with chain length occurs in the same compounds at 756–754 cm.$^{-1}$. These are clearly associated with vibrations involving the Si(CH$_3$)$_3$ end-groups of the open-chain materials, and would appear to be sufficiently characteristic for the identification of this grouping. These findings were confirmed by Richards and Thompson in their series of compounds,[3] whilst twelve aryl trimethyl silanes examined in solution by Clark *et al.*[4] all show absorption close to 840 cm.$^{-1}$. In trimethylchlorosilane the first of these bands occurs at 857 cm.$^{-1}$, and has been identified as the CH$_3$ rocking mode.[19]

$-Si(CH_3)_2-$. All the compounds examined by Wright and Hunter [1] show absorption in the 800 cm.$^{-1}$ region when $-Si(CH_3)_2-$ groups are present. This is identified as the rocking mode of the methyl group by comparison with the methylchlorosilanes, in which the band occurs in the range 850–800 cm.$^{-1}$, depending on the

z

number of methyl groups present.[19]   The absorption appears to be quite characteristic for this grouping, especially as it is absent in the dimer in which only $Si(CH_3)_3$ groupings are present.   Richards and Thompson [3] have confirmed these findings and extended them to the alkoxy silanes in which the band is still present when two methyl groups are directly attached to the silicon atom.   On the other hand, Young *et al.*[2] do not show this band in the spectra of the cyclic dimethyl trimer and tetramer, although it is recorded by both the other groups for these compounds.   The band appears in the range 814–802 cm.[-1] in the cyclic polymers, and is practically invariant at 800 cm.[-1] in the open-chain materials and methyl silanes. Richards and Thompson [3] have also drawn attention to a second band near 700 cm.[-1] which occurs in both the open-chain and cyclic series.   They believe this may also be associated with $-Si(CH_3)_2-$ groupings, but this assignment is likely to be less valuable than the other, as bands very close to this region occur in the spectra of a number of ethyl- and phenyl-substituted materials given by Young *et al.*[2]

–Si(CH_3)–. In compounds containing the grouping $Si(CH_3)R_1R_2R_3$, Richards and Thompson [3] found that a band usually occurred near 800 cm.[-1], but that it varied in position with the nature of the R groups more than in the compounds in which more than one methyl group is present.   Similarly, Young *et al.*[2] found two isomeric phenylmethyl cyclic trimers to absorb at 791 cm.[-1] and 788 cm.[-1]. A band near 800 cm.[-1] can always be expected when two methyl groups are attached to a silicon atom, and its absence can be used to show the absence of this grouping.   On the other hand, the presence of this band could also be associated with only a single methyl substitution.

20.2(b). Si–CH_3 Deformation Vibrations.   All the compounds examined by Wright and Hunter exhibit a strong band at 1258 cm.[-1]. A similar band is exhibited by tetramethylsilane [8, 9] at 1250 cm.[-1], and this vibration has been attributed by these workers to the rocking mode of the methyl grouping.   Richards and Thompson agree with this but the assignment has led to a good deal of controversy. Young, Koehler and McKinney [8] have attributed it to the symmetric deformation mode and Rank *et al.* to a γ-(CH) vibration.[9]   Subsequent work on compounds such as the methylsilanes has tended to confirm the assignment of this band to the symmetric methyl deformation frequency, leaving the 800 cm.[-1] band as the rocking mode. However, the specificity of this band in silicones is not in question, and in suitable circumstances it affords a valuable means of recognition of the methyl group.   Wright and Hunter [1] point out that a second band is present in their open-chain series at 1250 cm.[-1] which decreases in intensity as the chain length is increased.   This band is absent from the cyclic series, and they therefore associate it with the $Si(CH_3)_3$ end-groups. Two branched chain polymers they have examined also show this band. Young *et al.*[2] concur in finding an absorption uniformly at 1259 cm.[-1] in all the cyclic compounds containing methyl groups which they have examined. These will not, of course, exhibit the second 1250 cm.[-1] band, as they contain no end-groups. However, they have also noted the occurrence of a band at 1241 cm.[-1] in all the ethyl derivatives which they have examined which they suggest may be a $-CH_2Si-$ deformation absorption. The precise determination of the wave-length of the band in this region is clearly essential if the $Si-CH_3$ correlation is to be employed, and for this purpose work in solution is obviously necessary. This is emphasised by the values quoted by Richards and Thompson for liquid materials in which only a single band is quoted for both the open-chain and cyclic methyl polymers in the range 1265–1260 cm.[-1]. As the compounds were the same as those of Wright and Hunter,[1] this difference must be due to the effect of change of state. Clarke *et al.*[4] do not quote precise figures for this absorption in their aryl trimethylsilanes, but all the spectra show absorption near 1256 cm.[-1].

This correlation appears to hold roughly for the siloxymethyl-silanes examined by Richards and Thompson.[3] In ten compounds examined as liquids, in which the methyl group is directly attached to silicon, they find strong bands in the range 1269–1256 cm.[-1], whereas in those containing ethyl groups the frequency falls to 1250–1239 cm.[-1]. How far the variability of position of the methylsilicon band is due to packing effects in the liquid state, and how far it may be due to the direct influence of the alkoxy-substituents cannot be determined until these materials have been examined in solution. The possibility of identifying the $-Si-C_2H_5$ group through lower-frequency absorptions has been explored by Kaye and Tannenbaum.[23] For the system $-Si-CH_2-R$ they quote frequencies of 1281 cm.[-1] (R=H), 1235–1220 cm.[-1] (R=CH₃) and 1220–1163 cm.[-1] (R>CH₃). However, Harvey *et al.*[25] have noted that although absorption in this overall region is found throughout the series methyl- to hexyl-phenylsilane, similar bands are shown by *cyclo*hexylphenylsilane and by *iso*propylphenylsilane, and they therefore conclude that this correlation is of very limited value.

20.2(c). Si-Phenyl Vibrations. Young *et al.*[2] have examined

seven cyclic silicon materials of the type $(SiO)_3$ or $(SiO)_4$ in which un-

substituted aromatic groups are attached directly to the silicon atom.

In all of these, in solution, they find two bands at 1429 cm.$^{-1}$ and near 1110 cm.$^{-1}$ which may be characteristic of the Si–Ph link, whilst the normal mono-substituted aromatic ring vibrations at 740–735 cm.$^{-1}$ and 700 cm.$^{-1}$ appear to be substantially unaffected. These authors regard the 1429 cm.$^{-1}$ band as being characteristic of the silicon-phenyl link, but it should be noted that the CH vibrations of methyl and ethyl groupings attached to silicon occur at 1412 cm.$^{-1}$, so that in this case also solution measurements are to be preferred in applying this correlation. Nevertheless, Richards and Thompson [3] find values of 1430–1425 cm.$^{-1}$ in six compounds containing this linkage, although they were examined in the solid state, and this affords further support for the correlation. This correlation has been confirmed by Harvey *et al.*,[25] who report an absorption at 1431 cm.$^{-1}$ in a considerable number of phenylalkylsilanes.

The second band of Young *et al.*[2] is described as being less constant in wave-length, but in the spectra given it is very close to 1124 cm.$^{-1}$. In the case of tetramers it falls on the side of the strong Si–O absorption at 1090–1080 cm.$^{-1}$, but is clearly differentiated from it in the trimers in which the Si–O absorption shifts to 1020–1010 cm.$^{-1}$. The association of this band with the Si–Ph link is supported by the fact that it appears as a doublet when more than one phenyl grouping is attached to the same silicon atom. A similar strong band in the region 1123–1110 cm.$^{-1}$ can be seen in the spectra of four of the aromatic silicon compounds examined by Richards and Thompson,[3] all of which show a stronger band, which can be ascribed to Si–O, at lower frequency. In triphenylhydroxysilane and diphenyldihydroxy-silane interaction or hydrogen bonding effects appear to result in a merging of the Si–O and Si–Ph bands into a single band or doublet about 1120–1111 cm.$^{-1}$. Although no precise values are given, the aryl trimethylsilanes [4] appear to show these bands over a somewhat wider range (1430–1390 cm.$^{-1}$ and 1135–1090 cm.$^{-1}$). The values for the higher frequency band relate to liquid films. Neither α nor β-naphthyltrichlorosilanes show either of these bands.[14] Absorption at 1116 cm.$^{-1}$ is, however, also a characteristic of the phenylalkyl-silanes studied by Harvey *et al.*,[25] which further supports the identification of this band with the Si–Ph group.

20.3. Si–O STRETCHING VIBRATIONS

The Si–O stretching vibration in crystalline quartz gives rise to two strong bands in the reflection spectrum [13] at 1179 cm.$^{-1}$ and 1109 cm.$^{-1}$, so that an absorption in this approximate region is to be expected in organo-silicon compounds containing the Si–O linkage. This is found to be the case but, as there are some differences between cyclic and open-chain compounds, these will be discussed separately.

20.3(a). Cyclic Siloxanes. Wright and Hunter[1] have given the spectra of the six cyclic materials from hexamethyl*cyclo*trisiloxane to hexadecamethyl*cyclo*-octasiloxane. In the trimer the Si–O band appears at 1018 cm.$^{-1}$, whilst in the remainder it falls in the range 1076–1056 cm.$^{-1}$, the frequency showing a small but steady fall throughout the series with increasing ring size. Richards and Thompson[3] confirmed these findings for the first five members of the series, and also examined two cyclic aromatic siloxanes $(SiPh_2O)_3$ and $(SPh_2O)_4$. The first of these materials gave a strong band at 1015 cm.$^{-1}$ close to that of the trimer of the methyl series, whilst the tetramer gave its strongest band in this region nearer to 1100 cm.$^{-1}$.

Young *et al.*[2] studied the trimers and tetramers only, but covered a wider range of substituents on the silicon atom. Thus, in cyclic materials $(SiR_1R_2O)_n$ they examined the trimers and tetramers of the dimethyl, diethyl, diphenyl, methyl-phenyl and ethyl-phenyl series together with a mixed diphenyl tetraethyl trimer. They found that there was remarkably little difference in the position of the Si–O–Si absorption bands with variation in the nature of the substituents, although there was a considerable shift as between the trimers and tetramers. Thus they found all the trimers to exhibit the Si–O–Si absorption band in the narrow range 1020–1010 cm.$^{-1}$, whereas all the tetramers absorbed in the range 1093–1081 cm.$^{-1}$. These values agree within the limits of experimental error with those obtained by the earlier groups for the methyl trimers and tetramers. The discrepancy of about 20 cm.$^{-1}$ between the value they obtain for this band in the diphenyl tetramer, and that given by Richards and Thompson may arise from the differences in state or from interaction in the liquid state of the Si–O and the Si–Ph absorption bands. Young *et al.*[2] point out that this clear-cut distinction is of considerable use in the differentiation of the trimeric and tetrameric forms of cyclic silicon polymers which are the ones most commonly produced by the hydrolysis of R_2SiCl_2 type materials.

There is therefore a considerable body of evidence for assigning the Si–O ether link to the range 1020–1010 cm.$^{-1}$ in cyclic trimers and to 1090–1080 cm.$^{-1}$ in cyclic tetramers, and for presuming them to be reasonably independent of the nature of the substituent groups. In larger rings the frequency falls with increase in ring size to about 1050 cm.$^{-1}$. The spectra of some organosilsesquioxacenes have also been measured by Barry *et al.*,[26] but the assignments are not discussed in detail.

20.3(b). Open-chain Polymeric and Monomeric Siloxanes.

In the series of open-chain polymethyl siloxanes from hexamethyldisiloxane, to octadecamethyloctasiloxane, Wright and Hunter[1] find the Si–O absorption band within the range 1055–1024 cm.$^{-1}$, and again there is a small fall in the frequency for each unit increase of the chain length. With two branched chain polymers they found slightly higher values (1056 cm.$^{-1}$ and 1068 cm.$^{-1}$). These results were again confirmed by Richards and Thompson for the first five members of the series, and they also examined two polymeric phenyl-substituted silanols which showed their strongest bands in this region at 1078–1076 cm.$^{-1}$. It would seem therefore that the Si–O–Si absorption in open-chain compounds occurs in the same region as in cyclic materials, but possibly with a tendency towards the lower end of the range.

Richards and Thompson have also examined ten alkoxysilanes which all have a very strong band in the range 1090–1050 cm.$^{-1}$. Triphenylhydroxysilane and diphenyldihydroxysilane absorb at slightly higher frequencies (*c*. 1100 cm.$^{-1}$), but this is probably an interaction or hydrogen bonding effect. These bands can clearly be related to the Si–O–C absorption bands. It will be noticed that the absorption has a slightly higher frequency range than the general value for open-chain Si–O–Si absorption, but too little evidence is available for any decision to be made as to whether this difference between the two types is significant. The most that can be stated at present is that the Si–O absorption in open-chain compounds appears as a very strong band in the range 1090–1020 cm.$^{-1}$, and this is supported by studies by Kreshov *et al.*,[27, 28] who have examined some simple oxygenated silicon ethers.

The occurrence of this absorption in the same region as that from C–O–C and P–O–C is remarkable in that the changes in reduced mass in this series do not appear to have influenced the band position to any extent.

In addition to the Si–O stretching vibration, a second absorption arising from the valence bending of the Si–O link would be expected in the 500–300 cm.$^{-1}$ region, corresponding to the 482 cm.$^{-1}$ reflection band in quartz.[13] Wright and Hunter [1] have examined a few compounds in this region using a potassium bromide prism. In all cases they found powerful bands in the region 450–435 cm.$^{-1}$ (end of prism range), but this vibration has not been further studied.

20.4. Si–H STRETCHING VIBRATIONS

The assignment of the Si–H frequency rests largely on numbers of alkyl and halogenated silanes, and therefore covers a relatively wide frequency range for a hydrogen stretching vibration. In silane the Si–H stretching frequency [6, 7] occurs at 2187 cm.$^{-1}$, and Richards and Thompson [3] report that trichlorosilane, dichloroethylsilane and chlorodiethylsilane all give strong bands close to 2200 cm.$^{-1}$ due to Si–H stretching vibrations. A recent value for trichlorosilane [15] is 2274 cm.$^{-1}$ for the vapour and 2258 cm.$^{-1}$ for the liquid state. These high values reflect the influence of the three chlorine atoms, and in the monohalogenosilanes the two SiH_3 stretching frequencies are almost superimposed in the region 2205–2195 cm.$^{-1}$. When alkyl groups are attached to the silicon atom the Si–H frequency falls appreciably. West and Rochester [29] suggest that dialkylsilanes (which absorb between 2096 cm.$^{-1}$ and 2083 cm.$^{-1}$) can be differentiated from diarylsilanes (2096–2111 cm.$^{-1}$), but the frequency differences are small. Further, Harvey *et al.*[25] have reported a series of alkylarylsilanes as absorbing uniformly at 2128 cm.$^{-1}$. The expected region for the Si–H band is therefore near 2100 cm.$^{-1}$ with higher frequencies when halogen atoms are attached.

20.5. Si–Cl STRETCHING VIBRATIONS

In contrast to the previous grouping, the Si–Cl absorption might be expected to be considerably influenced by the nature of the attachments to the silicon atom. No correlation work has been attempted on this grouping, but Richards and Thompson [3] noted a strong band near 810 cm.$^{-1}$ in the three chlorosilanes mentioned above, which they believe may be associated with the Si–Cl band. $SiCl_4$ [16] absorbs at 800 cm.$^{-1}$.

20.6. Si–OH STRETCHING VIBRATIONS

As is to be expected, the silicon atom has no influence on the O–H stretching vibration, except in cases where hydrogen bonding occurs. Richards and Thompson [3] have examined four silanols which, in the solid state, show strong absorption near 3250 cm.$^{-1}$. In dilute solutions in carbon tetrachloride this band gives way to the normal "free" OH absorption at 3690 cm.$^{-1}$. The OH deformation mode in these compounds has not been assigned. The authors noted a strong band in the 880–830 cm.$^{-1}$ region in all cases, which was absent from the cyclic diphenylsiloxanes, but they considered that an assignment to this mode would be speculative on the basis of the evidence so far available. The position of the free Si–OH stretching band has been confirmed in the case of silanol,[30] which absorbs at 3676 cm.$^{-1}$ in dilute solution.

20.7. THE INFLUENCE OF Si–C LINKS ON CH VIBRATIONS

The possible influence of the Si–C link on CH vibrations on the same carbon atom has been considered by Wright and Hunter [1] and by Young *et al.*[2] Wright notes that the CH stretching band in all his methyl-type polymers occurs at precisely the same point as in the methyl group of hydrocarbons, but that the intensity of this band is of the order of only one-third to one-fourth of that in corresponding C–CH_3 compounds. The CH bending vibration occurs at a very slightly lowered frequency at precisely 1412 cm.$^{-1}$ in all the compounds studied in solution. Young *et al.*[2] confirm these findings on both methyl and ethyl polymers, and comment on the invariability in both position and in relative intensity shown by both of these bands when the materials are studied in solution.

With the aromatic compounds studied by Young [2] the C=C ring stretching vibrations appear in the normal positions at 1595 cm.$^{-1}$ and 1493 cm.$^{-1}$, whilst the out-of-plane CH bending vibrations in the long wave-length region are also normal. The remainder have not been fully studied but, in addition to these bands and those at 1429 and 1124 cm.$^{-1}$ assigned to Si–Ph, Young *et al.*[2] note that in all the aromatic compounds they have studied bands at 1190 cm.$^{-1}$, 1031 cm.$^{-1}$ and 996 cm.$^{-1}$ appear consistently. These may be associated with the phenyl ring and bands close to these positions can also be traced in the four additional aromatic compounds examined by Richards and Thompson.[3]

20.8. BIBLIOGRAPHY

1. Wright and Hunter, *J. Amer. Chem. Soc.*, 1947, **69**, 803.
2. Young, Servais, Currie and Hunter, *ibid.*, 1948, **70**, 3758.
3. Richards and Thompson, *J. Chem. Soc.*, 1949, 124.
4. Clark, Gordon, Young and Hunter, *J. Amer. Chem. Soc.*, 1951, **73**, 3798.
5. Hyde, Frevel, Nutting, Petrie and Purcell, *ibid.*, 1947, **69**, 488.
6. Steward and Nielsen, *J. Chem. Phys.*, 1934, **2**, 712; *Phys. Rev.*, 1935, **47**, 828.
7. Tindal, Straley and Nielsen, *Proc. Nat. Acad. Sci. U.S.*, 1941, **27**, 208.
8. Young, Koehler and McKinney, *J. Amer. Chem. Soc.*, 1947, **69**, 1410.
9. Rank, Saksena and Shull, *Discuss. Faraday Soc.*, 1950, **9**, 187.
10. Bailey, Hale and Thompson, *Proc. Roy. Soc.*, 1938, **A167**, 555.
11. Scott and Frisch, *J. Amer. Chem. Soc.*, 1951, **73**, 2599.
12. Cf. Barnes, Gore, Liddel and Williams, *Infra-red Spectroscopy* (Reinhold, 1944).
13. Coblentz, *Investigations of Infra-red Spectra* (Carnegie Inst. of Washington, 1905).
14. Gilkey and Tyler, *J. Amer. Chem. Soc.*, 1951, **73**, 4982.
15. Gibian and McKinney, *ibid.*, p. 1431.
16. Herzberg, *Infra-red and Raman Spectra of Polyatomic Molecules* (Van Nostrand, 1945), p. 167.
17. Simon and McMahon, *J. Chem. Phys.*, 1953, **21**, 23.
18. *Idem, ibid.*, 1952, **20**, 905.
19. Smith, *J. Chem. Phys.*, 1953, **21**, 1997.
20. Newman, O'Loane, Polo and Wilson, *ibid.*, 1956, **25**, 855.
21. Andersen and Bak, *Acta Chem. Scand.*, 1954, **8**, 738.
22. Mayo, Optiz and Peake, *J. Chem. Phys.*, 1955, **23**, 1344.
23. Kaye and Tannenbaum, *J. Org. Chem.*, 1953, **18**, 1750.
24. Cerato, Lauer and Beachell, *J. Chem. Phys.*, 1954, **22**, 1.
25. Harvey, Nebergall and Peake, *J. Amer. Chem. Soc.*, 1954, **76**, 4555.
26. Barry, Daudt, Domicone and Gikey, *ibid.*, 1955, **77**, 4248.
27. Kreshov, Mikhailenkov and Yakimovich, *Zhur. Anal. Khim.*, 1954, **9**, 208.
28. *Idem, Zhur. Fiz. Khim.*, 1954, **28**, 538.
29. West and Rochester, *J. Org. Chem.*, 1953, **18**, 303.
30. Kakudo, Kasai and Watase, *J. Chem. Phys.*, 1953, **21**, 1894.

CHAPTER 21

Inorganic Ions

21.1. INTRODUCTION AND TABLE

STUDIES on the vibrational spectra of inorganic materials have, until recently, been largely confined to Raman work. A certain amount of early work in this field used infra-red reflection [1] methods, and later Lecomte [2,3] and his co-workers examined large numbers of such materials by normal infra-red absorption techniques. However, the equipment available to these workers was such that high-resolution spectra were not readily obtainable. Work in this field has been primarily limited by the difficulty in preparing specimens in a suitable state for examination, as unless a very fine particle size is obtained the scattering losses are very considerable, especially in the high-frequency region, and the spectrum shows only a series of broad rather indeterminate absorptions.

Recently, however, there has been a revival of interest following the observation that good, clear-cut spectra comparable with those given by organic compounds could be obtained from either paraffin mulls or from thin powder films, provided the particle size was sufficiently small. There have, for instance, been a number of detailed studies on individual inorganic salts, and of small groups of related materials. Thus Duval, Lecomte and Morandat [4] have examined groups of nitrites and chlorites and obtained evidence that their ions have an angular structure, whilst Duval and Lecomte [5] have also employed infra-red methods for studying the degree of polymerisation of *ortho*-borates and *meta*-borates, and for following reactions in the solid state.[10] The introduction of the pressed potassium bromide disc technique with the associated equipment for fine grinding has also led to a stimulation of interest in this field.

From the point of view of correlations for analytical and identification work, the most important and detailed recent paper is that of Miller and Wilkins,[6] who have examined and reproduced the spectra of one hundred and fifty-nine inorganic salts, and have compiled a chart showing correlations for a large number of different ionic groups. The more important of these are discussed below, but the original text should be consulted for more detailed information. Hunt, Wisherd and Bonham [7] have demonstrated the utility of infra-red spectra in the identification of complex rocks and other minerals, and they included also the spectra of fifteen inorganic materials from

343

which they were able to derive some correlations. These authors also devised a simple and efficient procedure for the preparation of sample powders under five microns in size by sedimentation methods.

The infra-red method will not of course permit the complete analysis of complex mixtures except possibly in the case of certain minerals in which matching of the whole spectrum is possible but, as Miller and Wilkins have pointed out, it affords a valuable adjunct to inorganic analysis, especially when coupled with emission analysis and X-ray diffraction data. A number of quantitative analyses of rocks and minerals have also been carried out in this way,[12] and detailed studies on silicate rocks have revealed sufficient differences between various types to enable infra-red methods to be used in their identification.

The correlations discussed are listed in Table 21 below.

TABLE 21

Carbonates (CO_3^{--}) .	1450–1410 cm.$^{-1}$ (v.s.), 880–860 cm.$^{-1}$ (m.)
Sulphates (SO_4^{--}) .	1130–1080 cm.$^{-1}$ (v.s.), 680–610 cm.$^{-1}$ (m.-w.)
Nitrates (NO_3^-) . .	1380–1350 cm.$^{-1}$ (v.s.), 840–815 cm.$^{-1}$ (m.)
Nitrites (NO_2^-) . .	1250–1230 cm.$^{-1}$ (v.s.), 840–800 cm.$^{-1}$ (w.)
Ammonium (NH_4^+) .	3300–3030 cm.$^{-1}$ (v.s.), 1430–1390 cm.$^{-1}$ (s.)
Cyanide, thiocyanates, cyanates and complex ions . . .	2200–2000 cm.$^{-1}$ (s.)
Phosphate (PO_4^{---}, HPO_4^{--}, $H_2PO_4^-$) .	1100–1000 cm.$^{-1}$ (s.)
Silicates (all types) .	1100–900 cm.$^{-1}$ (s.)

21.2. CARBONATES AND BICARBONATES

Hunt et al.,[7] and Miller and Wilkins [6] have examined the infra-red spectra of twelve different carbonates in addition to a number of basic carbonates, bicarbonates and similar materials, and Louisfert and Pobeguin [11] have examined a number of different crystal forms of calcium carbonate.

The normal carbonates are characterised by a strong band in all cases in the range 1450–1410 cm.$^{-1}$ and by a medium intensity band in the range 880–860 cm.$^{-1}$. In the last case, however, lead carbonate appears to be an exception, giving only an extremely weak absorption at 840 cm.$^{-1}$. Hunt et al.[7] have related the position of this second absorption to the atomic weight of the cation, and have found a progressive logarithmic displacement to lower frequencies with increase in atomic weight. The carbonates of Miller and Wilkins (except lithium) also follow this progression. In calcium carbonate these bands occur at 876 cm.$^{-1}$ and 1430 cm.$^{-1}$, and the former has been used for the estimation of carbonate in phosphates.[13, 14] Vibrational assignments for the individual carbonate frequencies have been given by Louisfert [15] and by Decius.[16] Studies have also been made on the nature of bone carbonates using infra-red methods.[17]

In addition, many carbonates show absorption in the 750–700 cm.$^{-1}$ region. Not all of them absorb in this region, but when they do so the observed frequencies are often useful in the identification of minerals. For calcite and dolomite, for example, the bands are 17 cm.$^{-1}$ apart.[7]

Considerable spectral changes occur with basic carbonates and with bicarbonates. In the former case the spectra are more complex and the 1430 cm.$^{-1}$ absorption is almost always doubled. In addition, the number of bands between 1110 cm.$^{-1}$ and 700 cm.$^{-1}$ increases in most cases from two to five, whilst the bonded OH groupings are evident at 3300 cm.$^{-1}$. Here also the various basic carbonates show sufficient differences amongst themselves to enable individuals to be identified in many cases.

Only a limited number of bicarbonates have been studied,[6] but they do not absorb in the 1431 cm.$^{-1}$ range. Instead two widely separated bands appear on either side. However, no definite correlations are possible at present.

21.3. SULPHATES

Miller and Wilkins [6] have examined ten different inorganic sulphates, and two others have been reported by Hunt *et al.*[7] In all cases a very strong band is shown in the range 1130–1080 cm.$^{-1}$ accompanied by a considerably weaker band, in most cases, in the region 680–610 cm.$^{-1}$. With calcium sulphate dihydrate the strong band was centred at 1140 cm.$^{-1}$, and after heating at 170° C. overnight a group of three bands was found in this region. This illustrates the influences which both hydration and crystal symmetry may have on such spectra and possible variations from such causes must be taken into account in assessing the spectra.

Unlike the carbonates, there did not appear to be any direct connection between the observed absorption frequencies and any property of the positive ion, despite the fact that the variations from one sulphate to the next were usually sufficiently large to enable any particular one to be identified. Lecomte *et al.*[18] have also studied the sulphate ion and report essentially similar conclusions. They note in particular [19] that the band near 610 cm.$^{-1}$ is single with Mg, K or Mn, but is doubled with Ca, Cu, Be or Ba.

As with bicarbonates, the bisulphates have not been fully studied, but from the three samples examined [6] it is clear that the strong 1110 cm.$^{-1}$ absorption is not shown, and there are again indications that it is replaced by a pair of widely separated medium intensity bands on either side. Sulphites do not absorb in this region.

21.4. NITRATES AND NITRITES

Ten inorganic nitrates examined by Miller and Wilkins [6] all show characteristic absorptions in the ranges 1380–1350 cm.$^{-1}$ (v.s.) and 840–815 cm.$^{-1}$ (m.). Again, no correlation could be found between the position of these bands and the nature of the positive ion. There is a good deal of support for this correlation from data on organic nitrates, such as guanidine nitrate, in which the NO_3 group exists in the ionic form. These also absorb in the given regions, although the spectral ranges in these cases are sometimes rather wider (Chapter 17). Nitrites also show a weak to medium intensity band in the 840–815 cm.$^{-1}$ region, but they can be readily differentiated from nitrates by the presence of a strong absorption [5, 6] in the region 1250–1230 cm.$^{-1}$. A vibrational assignment for sodium nitrite has been given by Tarte,[20] and Hafele [41] has discussed the spectra of some crystalline nitrates.

21.5. THE AMMONIUM ION

Eighteen different ammonium salts have been examined.[6] Two characteristic absorptions are shown, in all cases. One of these corresponds to the NH stretching vibration and occurs in the 3200 cm.$^{-1}$ region, whilst there is a second absorption, also strong, in the range 1430–1390 cm.$^{-1}$.

The number and position of bands in the NH stretching region reflects the possibilities of hydrogen bonding within the crystal, and in cases where multiple peaks are shown it may also indicate the formation of several hydrogen bonds of different strengths. In ammonium perchlorate the NH stretching frequency is as high as 3300 cm.$^{-1}$, and this indication of little or no hydrogen bonding may be correlated with the fact that this compound does not absorb water to form a hydrate. Most ammonium salts show some degree of bonding and the NH frequencies of quite a high proportion fall between 3200 cm.$^{-1}$ and 3100 cm.$^{-1}$. Ammonium nitrate is an extreme case in which strong bonds are formed, and this exhibits a triplet absorption [6] at 3160 cm.$^{-1}$, 3060 cm.$^{-1}$ and 3030 cm.$^{-1}$. The spectrum of ammonium azide has been studied by Pimentel *et al.*,[21] and Waldron and Hornig [22] have examined some crystalline ammonium hydrates.

The lower frequency absorption near 1410 cm.$^{-1}$ is reasonably strong and the band is sharp and clear-cut so that, coupled with the stretching absorption, the identification of this ion is usually relatively simple.

21.6. CYANIDES

The number of simple cyanides examined is very small, but the agreement shown with the spectra of organic nitriles and *iso-*

cyanides is sufficient to indicate that the $C \equiv N$ vibration is not greatly affected in the inorganic ion, so that it is highly probable that other simple cyanides will also be identifiable by absorption in the 2200–2000 cm.$^{-1}$ region. Sodium and potassium cyanide show a strong band between 2080 cm.$^{-1}$ and 2070 cm.$^{-1}$. In the fused state this moves to 2250 cm.$^{-1}$, and there has been some discussion [23] as to whether this represents isomerism to the *iso*cyanide. Potassium ferro- and ferri-cyanides and cobalticyanides have been studied by several workers,[6,24–27] and these also absorb between 2100 cm.$^{-1}$ and 2000 cm.$^{-1}$. The infra-red spectra of cyanide complexes of silver, copper and gold have also been studied in aqueous solutions.[28–30]

Thiocyanates (six in all) absorb in the 2090–2020 cm.$^{-1}$ range and silver cyanate [6] has a strong band at 2170 cm.$^{-1}$.

The range 2200–2000 cm.$^{-1}$ therefore can be regarded as covering all the various forms in which the $-C \equiv N$ grouping occurs in inorganic compounds.

21.7. PHOSPHATES

The ionic phosphate absorption is reported on the basis of Raman work to absorb at 1080 cm.$^{-1}$ and 980 cm.$^{-1}$.[8] However, in infra-red studies with tribasic phosphates only a single band is found in many cases. This is, however, very strong and broad, and in a series of nine orthophosphates studied by Miller and Wilkins [6] was found between 1030 cm.$^{-1}$ and 1000 cm.$^{-1}$.

More recently, the fundamental frequencies of all types of phosphate ions, such as metaphosphates, pyrophosphates, hypophosphites, etc., have been studied by several groups of workers, notably by Corbridge,[31, 32] by Lecomte [33, 34] and by Tsuboi.[42] Their findings have been condensed in the form of a correlation chart for phosphorus oxyacids by Corbridge,[32] and sufficient data are now available to enable most of the individual types to be differentiated. These absorptions have already been discussed in Chapter 18, to which further reference should be made. The spectra of some phosphate high polymers in molten, glaceous and crystalline states have been reported by Bues and Gehrke.[35]

21.8. SILICATES

Fifteen different silicates have been examined by Hunt *et al.*[7] All show very intense absorption bands in the 1100–900 cm.$^{-1}$ range. Both the numbers and positions of these bands vary considerably from one mineral to the next, but compounds in which the silicate ions are similar show related spectra. Tremolite $((OH)_2 Ca_2 Mg_5 (Si_4 O_{11})_{12})$ and actinolite $((OH)_2 Ca_2 (MgFe)_5 (Si_4 O_{11})_{12})$, for example, show very closely related spectra with several strong bands in this region, whereas hornblende, $Ca(MgFe)_3Si_4O_{12}$; $CaMg_2(AlFe)_2Si_3O_{12}$ has only one band at 1010 cm.$^{-1}$. It has been shown that these differences are sufficient to give very useful leads in mineral ore analysis, and the various classes of silicates can be identified by their characteristic band patterns.[9] Studies have also been made on the spectra of materials such as vitreous porcelain [36] and on individual crystalline silicates such as afwillite.[37]

21.9. OTHER CORRELATIONS

Miller and Wilkins [7] have examined also numbers of sulphites, chromates, borates, silicates, bromates, iodates, vanadates, manganates, etc., and have made tentative assignments of characteristic frequencies in each case. These results are not included in detail here as in many cases only three or four compounds have been examined, and whilst there is a strong presumption that others will prove to be similar, they cannot yet be regarded as established correlations. In other cases there are indications that a correlation may well exist, but one or more anomalous cases are reported. Thus five out of six sulphites absorb strongly between 960 cm.$^{-1}$ and 910 cm.$^{-1}$ but ammonium sulphite has no absorption nearer than 1105 cm.$^{-1}$.

Several studies have been made of boric esters [38, 39, 43] and of boric acid.[40] In the latter the B–O stretching frequency occurs near 1400 cm.$^{-1}$ and the deformation mode near 810 cm.$^{-1}$, but both are liable to alterations with structure. In simple borates the B–O link appears [43] at 1340 ± 10 cm.$^{-1}$, which suggests some double bond character.

Deformation frequencies of ions XO_4 have also been studied, and differences arising from alterations in the element X have been noted.[19] Data are also available on some inorganic peroxides and superoxides.[44]

21.10. BIBLIOGRAPHY

1. Schaefer and Matossi, *Das Ultrarot Spektrum* (Springer, Berlin, 1930).
2. Lecomte, *Anal. Chim. Acta*, 1948, **2**, 727.
3. *Idem*, *Cahiers Phys.*, 1943, **17**, 1.
4. Duval, Lecomte and Morandat, *Bull. Soc. chim. (France)*, 1951, **18**, 745.
5. Duval and Lecomte, *Compt. rend. Acad. Sci. (Paris)*, 1951, **232**, 2306.
6. Miller and Wilkins, *Analyt. Chem.*, 1952, **24**, 1253.
7. Hunt, Wisherd and Bonham, *ibid.*, 1950, **22**, 1478.
8. Herzberg, *Infra-red and Raman Spectra of Polyatomic Molecules* (Van Nostrand, 1945), p. 162.
9. Launer, *Amer. Mineralogist*, 1952, **37**, 764.
10. Duval and Lecomte, *Compt. Rend. Acad. Sci. (Paris)*, 1952, **234**, 2445.
11. Louisfert and Pobeguin, *ibid.*, **235**, 287.
12. Hunt and Turner, *Analyt. Chem.*, 1953, **25**, 1169.
13. Pobequin and Lecomte, *Compt. Rend. Acad. Sci. (Paris)*, 1953, **236**, 1544.
14. Pobequin, *J. Phys. Radium*, 1954, **15**, 410.
15. Louisfert, *Compt. Rend. Acad. Sci. (Paris)*, 1955, **241**, 940.
16. Decius, *J. Chem. Phys.*, 1954, **22**, 1956.

17. Underwood, Toribara and Neuman, *J. Amer. Chem. Soc.*, 1955, **77**, 317.
18. Pascal, Duval, Lecomte and Pacault, *Compt. Rend. Acad. Sci. (Paris)*, 1951, **233**, 118.
19. Duval and Lecomte, *ibid.*, 1954, **239**, 249.
20. Tarte, *Ann. Soc. Sci. Bruxelles*, 1956, **70**, 244.
21. Dows, Whittle and Pimentel, *J. Chem. Phys.*, 1955, **23**, 1475.
22. Waldron and Hornig, *J. Amer. Chem. Soc.*, 1953, **75**, 6079.
23. Brugel, Daumiller and Rommel, *Angew. Chem.*, 1956, **68**, 440.
24. Bonino and Fabbri, *Atti Accad. Naz. Lincei. Rend. Classe. Sci. Fis. mat. Nat.*, 1956, **21**, 246.
25. *Idem, ibid.*, 1955, **19**, 386; 1956, **20**, 414.
26. Bonino and Salvetti, *ibid.*, 1956, **20**, 150.
27. Emschwiller, *Compt. Rend. Acad. Sci. (Paris)*, 1954, **238**, 1414.
28. Jones and Penneman, *J. Chem. Phys.*, 1954, **22**, 965.
29. Jones, *ibid.*, 1954, **22**, 1135.
30. Penneman and Jones, *ibid.*, 1956, **24**, 293.
31. Corbridge and Lowe, *J. Chem. Soc.*, 1954, 493, 4555.
32. Corbridge, *J. App. Chem.*, 1956, **6**, 456.
33. Duval and Lecomte, *Compt. Rend. Acad. Sci. (Paris)*, 1955, **240**, 66.
34. *Idem, Mikrochim. Acta*, 1956, 454.
35. Bues and Gehrke, *Z. Anorg. Chem.*, 1956, **288**, 307.
36. Avgustinik, Setkina and Fedorova, *Zhur. Fiz. Khim.*, 1954, **28**, 637.
37. Petch, Sheppard and Megaw, *Acta cryst.*, 1956, **9**, 29.
38. Steele and Decius, *J. Chem. Phys.*, 1956, **25**, 1184.
39. Duval and Lecomte, *J. Opt. Soc. Amer.*, 1954, **44**, 261.
40. Bethell and Sheppard, *Trans. Faraday Soc.*, 1955, **51**, 9.
41. Hafele, *Z. Physik.*, 1957, **148**, 262.
42. Tsuboi, *J. Amer. Chem. Soc.*, 1957, **79**, 1351.
43. Werner and O'Brien, *Austral. J. Chem.*, 1955, **8**, 355.
44. Brame, Cohen, Margrave and Meloche, *J. Inorg. Nuclear, Chem.*, 1957, **4**, 90.

CHAPTER 22

Organo-sulphur Compounds

22.1. INTRODUCTION AND TABLE

A CONSIDERABLE number of correlations are available for absorption bands arising from sulphur linkages, but only a limited number of them are likely to find any general application in structural analysis. Linkages including sulphur and hydrogen or sulphur and oxygen have not been as fully studied as the corresponding OH and CO groups, but the absorptions arising from them are well-defined and can usually be recognised without undue difficulty. The sulphur-hydrogen bands occur in a region in which few other materials absorb, whilst the sulphur–oxygen absorptions can usually be recognised from their intensity and characteristic complex appearance. The fact that most sulphur–oxygen links give rise to more than one characteristic band is also very useful in their recognition. In the case of the sulphur–oxygen stretching modes of the group XSO_2Y it has been shown [37] that the asymmetric and symmetric frequencies are related by a simple linear function, and a cross check of an identification of this group is possible in this way.

On the other hand, the C–S, S–S and similar linkages are not readily identified because either the absorption is extremely weak or the position of the band is too variable. Usually both factors apply. However, a certain amount of useful data concerning these

TABLE 22

–S–H	. .	2600–2550 cm.$^{-1}$ (w.)
–S–S–	. .	500–400 cm.$^{-1}$ (w.)
–C–S–	. .	700–600 cm.$^{-1}$ (w.)
$C{=}S$	. .	1200–1050 cm.$^{-1}$ (s.) (Thioureas up to 1400 cm.$^{-1}$
–N–C$=$S .	.	1500–1470 cm.$^{-1}$ (s.)
–S$=$O	.	1060–1040 cm.$^{-1}$ (s.) (10–20 cm.$^{-1}$ less in solid state)
–SO–OH .	.	near 1090 cm.$^{-1}$ (s.)
–SO–OR .	.	1125–1135 cm.$^{-1}$ (s.)
–RO–SO–OR	.	1215–1150 cm.$^{-1}$ (s.)
–SO$_2$–	.	1160–1140 cm.$^{-1}$ (s.) and 1300–1350 cm.$^{-1}$ (s.)
–SO$_2$Cl	.	Slightly higher than R–SO$_2$–R
–SO$_2$–N– .	.	1180–1140 cm.$^{-1}$ (s.) and 1350–1300 cm.$^{-1}$ (s.)
–O–SO$_2$– .	.	1200–1145 cm.$^{-1}$ (s.) and 1420–1330 cm.$^{-1}$ (s.)
–O–SO$_2$–O–	.	1230–1150 cm.$^{-1}$ (s.) and 1440–1350 (s.)
SO$_3$H and SO$_3$–		1210–1150 cm.$^{-1}$ (s.) and 1060–1030 cm.$^{-1}$, near 650 cm.$^{-1}$ (s.)
P$=$S .	.	See Chapter 18

links may be obtained in certain cases and details of the correlations proposed are therefore included.

The correlations discussed are listed in Table 22.

22.2. SH STRETCHING VIBRATIONS

Several early workers studied the position of the SH stretching absorption band. Bell [1, 2] was able to show that a number of simple mercaptans such as propyl, butyl and *iso*amyl mercaptans gave a well-defined but rather weak absorption at 2650–2550 cm.[-1]. He was also able to show that the bands near 2550 cm.[-1] in thiophenol and thio-*p*-cresol were absent from the corresponding sulphides.

Confirmation of this assignment of the SH mode was forthcoming from further work by Ellis, who found the first overtone in the 5000 cm.[-1] region,[3] and from Williams,[4] who extended the series of compounds examined by Bell and showed that other mercaptans absorbed near 2630 cm.[-1].

These early assignments have been fully supported by later workers. Trotter and Thompson,[5] and Sheppard [6] have each examined numbers of simple mercaptans and compared them with the corresponding sulphides and in all cases one of the major points of difference has been the disappearance of the SH absorption, which the former workers assign as being near 2575 cm.[-1], whilst Sheppard finds a range of 2590–2560 cm.[-1] for the compounds he has examined.

Randall *et al.*[7] who have also examined a few mercaptans propose the range 2688–2560 cm.[-1], but this is clearly designed to include hydrogen sulphide which has its asymmetric SH mode at 2688 cm.[-1]. This is an exceptional case, and organic mercaptans do not appear to absorb at higher frequencies than 2600 cm.[-1]. The range 2600–2550 cm.[-1] is therefore given in Table 22. This has been confirmed by the small amount of recent work on this correlation. Haines *et al.*[38] quote three thiols as absorbing at 2564 cm.[-1], whilst Wagner, Becher and Kottenhahn [39] quote a number of similar cases. Sweeney *et al.*[40] record 1 : 2-dimercaptoethane as absorbing at 2350 cm.[-1] in the liquid state, but this appears to be wholly exceptional. Thus even thioacetic acid [8] (2550 cm.[-1]) and dithioacetic acid [41] (2481 cm.[-1]) absorb at higher frequencies, indicating that polymerisation does not occur to any extent, and indeed the SH link is not apparently capable of the extensive degree of hydrogen bonding which occurs with OH and NH groupings. There is very little change in the frequency of SH absorptions on passing from the liquid state to dilute solutions, so that any intermolecular bonding effects must be very small. On the other hand, small shifts suggestive of hydrogen bonding have been observed in solution in certain bases and other compounds, indicating the formation of weak S–H . . . N. bonds. Gordy and Stanford [9] studied the SH stretching frequencies of

A A

thiophenol, butyl and benzyl mercaptans and of thioacetic acid in a variety of different solvents. In ether and similar solvents the frequency was unaffected, but a slight fall was observed in aniline and in *iso*propyl ether, whilst the largest shifts (up to 80 cm.$^{-1}$) were observed with pyridine, α-picoline and dibenzylamine. Parallel results have been obtained by Wagner *et al.*,[39] who have shown that thiophenol is capable of hydrogen bonding to sulphoxides, to give a frequency shift of the SH vibration of 100 cm.$^{-1}$. With aryl sulphoxides the shift is somewhat smaller. These workers have also given evidence for chelation in thiosalicylic acid (2515 cm.$^{-1}$) and its ethyl ester (2542 cm.$^{-1}$). Josien *et al.*[42] have also described studies indicating hydrogen bonding by thiophenol, and similar results have been obtained with dithiophosphoric acids.[43] Plant *et al.*[69] have not found any evidence of hydrogen bonding between SH links in the liquid state.

The SH absorption is not inherently strong, and whilst it is usually well defined, it is often difficult to detect in dilute solutions or in samples examined in very thin cells. It is also obscured in compounds containing COOH groups which exhibit general absorption in this region. However, if allowance is made for these factors the presence or absence of a band in this region can afford decisive evidence for the occurrence of a mercapto-group. Studies in this region have been used, for example, to determine whether certain thiols of quinoline exist in the mercaptan or thio-keto form,[10] whilst the absence of any SH absorption from the spectrum of mercapto-benzthiazole is one of the strongest pieces of evidence for the existence of this substance as a thio-ketone under normal conditions.

22.3. S–S STRETCHING VIBRATIONS

The –S–S– linkage absorption is unlikely to be of any value in infrared analysis except in a very few special instances. It occurs as a very weak band in the 500–400 cm.$^{-1}$ region, and is identifiable only because the corresponding Raman line is very strong. Venkateswaren[11] has attributed the 470 cm.$^{-1}$ Raman line of liquid sulphur to the –S–S– stretching mode, and such infra-red and Raman studies as have been made on organic disulphides indicate that the S–S link absorbs in the same region in these compounds.

Trotter and Thompson[5] assigned weak bands at 517 cm.$^{-1}$ to the S–S stretching mode in dimethyl and diethyl disulphides respectively, but in di-*n*-propyl disulphide only a very feeble absorption near 500 cm.$^{-1}$ could be detected. Similarly Sheppard[6] assigned the 510 cm.$^{-1}$ band of di*cyclo*hexyl disulphide to this vibration, but was unable to detect corresponding bands in di-*n*-butyl or di-*tert.*-butyl disulphides. In aromatic compounds the band appears to be more readily detectable, and Cymerman and Willis[12] quote S–S values within the range 490–430 cm.$^{-1}$ for fifteen aromatic disulphides, thiol-sulphonates, etc., whilst they note its absence in corresponding compounds lacking the S–S link. Even so, they comment that the band is ill-defined and difficult to identify. They have also noted an anomaly in respect of diphenyldisulphone in which no S–S vibration could be found. This is tentatively ascribed to the fact that this molecule has a centre of symmetry and that if it exists wholly in the *trans* form the S–S vibration would be expected to be inactive in the infra-red. These authors also quote a value of 454 cm.$^{-1}$ for this vibration in cystine, whereas the mercaptan cysteine has no corresponding absorption.

The occurrence of this absorption in the 500–400 cm.$^{-1}$ region has therefore been adequately established, but in view of the low energy available in this range and the high incidence of scattered light, correlations on bands other than those which are reasonably intense can be used only with extreme caution. This absorption is therefore likely to be of value only in a limited number of cases in which small changes involving the S–S link are expected, and in which the absence of any other absorption in the region would permit the use of relatively thick cells.

22.4. C–S STRETCHING VIBRATIONS

The C–S stretching vibration normally appears in the infra-red as a weak absorption in the range 700–600 cm.$^{-1}$. This correlation applies to all types of sulphur compounds containing this link and a band in this region is found in mercaptans, sulphides, sulphoxides, sulphones, etc. The frequency appears to show some dependence on the nature of the sulphur link but the conditions under which such shifts occur have not been very fully studied. The weakness of this band and its variability in position therefore render it of very limited use in analytical work, especially as a number of skeletal vibrations occur in the same region. Identifications therefore have to be made with extreme caution, and in fundamental studies have always been accompanied by evidence from Raman spectra in which the C–S vibration appears as an intense band. Analytical studies on this band are therefore only likely to be of value in a limited number of specialised cases.

The initial study of a group of compounds containing the C–S linkage was made by Trotter and Thompson,[5] who determined the infra-red spectra of the seven simple mercaptans from methyl to *tert.*-butyl mercaptan, and correlated their findings with the published Raman data.[11, 13-15] Samples were examined in the vapour or liquid state, and they noted that considerable shifts in the C–S frequency resulted from relatively small changes in structure. The C–S frequency for methyl mercaptan, for example, was assigned at 705 cm.$^{-1}$ whilst that of ethyl mercaptan occurred at 660 cm.$^{-1}$. In the case of some of the higher homologues a number of bands were found in this region which made the assignment difficult. Three sulphides and three disulphides were also examined, and the C–S frequencies were found to lie in the same overall range 705–587 cm.$^{-1}$. In a fourth disulphide in which the C–S link was conjugated with an aromatic ring the C–S frequency was found to be lowered to 570 cm.$^{-1}$. On the basis of this work and of the earlier work of Thompson and Duprè on ethylene disulphide,[16] Thompson [17] later proposed 700–600 cm.$^{-1}$ as an approximate correlation for the C–S–C linkage.

This work was later extended by Sheppard,[6] who compared the infra-red and Raman spectra of a wider range of mercaptans, sulphides and disulphides. He noted a progressive lowering of the frequency in primary, secondary and tertiary C–S compounds, and proposed a subdivision of the 700–600 cm.$^{-1}$ range as follows:

	CH_3S- .	.	. 705–685 cm.$^{-1}$
Primary	RCH_2-S-	.	. 660–630 cm.$^{-1}$
Secondary	R′R″CH–S	.	. 630–600 cm.$^{-1}$
Tertiary	R′R″R‴C–S	.	. 600–570 cm.$^{-1}$

*cyclo*Hexyl derivatives were found to be an exception to this classification, although pentamethylene sulphide absorbs in the appropriate position for a primary sulphide (654 cm.$^{-1}$). This sub-division of the range is therefore applicable only to saturated acyclic materials and may well be applicable only to alkyl mercaptans, sulphides and disulphides similar to those on which it is based. Sheppard also noted a progressive small frequency shift throughout the series mercaptan ⟶ sulphide ⟶ disulphide. These shifts were in all cases towards lower frequencies, but were of the order of 10 cm.$^{-1}$ and did not affect the overall classification. A limited number of compounds in which the C–S linkage was conjugated with a double bond were also examined, and in these a low-frequency shift of the order of 60 cm.$^{-1}$ was found. Carbonyl sulphide appeared to be an exception to this, but the assignment in this case was in doubt. An increase in the intensity of the C–S vibration was noted following conjugation, di*cyclo*hexenyl sulphide showing a strong band at 634 cm.$^{-1}$ against a medium intensity band in *cyclo*hexyl *cyclo*hexenyl sulphide at the same point. However, the number of compounds examined is too few to enable any firm conclusions to be drawn.

Sheppard has also directed attention to the marked coincidence of corresponding C–S and C–Cl frequencies in this region. The C–Cl frequencies are known from Raman work to show a progression through the series Methyl > Et ≏ Pr > *sec.*-Pr > *tert.*-Butyl ≏ Allyl ≏ Benzyl, and the corresponding C–S compounds show not only the same progression, but almost the same frequencies. Assuming the decreasing frequency effect in C–Cl compounds corresponds to a reduction in the force constant, it would appear that the small alteration in mass in passing from Cl to S has little effect and that the same order of decrease holds for sulphur compounds.

The assignment of the C–S frequency has also been discussed by Cymerman and Willis,[12] who have worked largely with aromatic disulphides and thiol sulphonates. They found the same difficulty as earlier workers in identifying the weak C–S vibration, especially as an aromatic ring vibration occurs near 700 cm.$^{-1}$. In all the aromatic compounds in which a C–S frequency has been assigned it lies towards the top end of the range within the limits 702–673 cm.$^{-1}$, and those compounds in which a definite assignment is not possible also show a band in this region. It appears likely, therefore, that the phenyl ring attached directly to a sulphur atom results in a C–S frequency at the higher end of the range. These workers also quote C–S frequencies for a few sulphur-containing amino-acids in which the C–S absorption falls between 700 cm.$^{-1}$ and 600 cm.$^{-1}$.

This correlation has been further confirmed by studies on individual molecules such as dithioacetic acid [41] (581 cm.$^{-1}$), 1 : 2-dimercaptoethane [40] (735 cm.$^{-1}$) and various sulphones and sulphoxy compounds, but its variability in position and in intensity renders it of limited use except in special cases.

22.5. C=S STRETCHING VIBRATIONS

The identification of the position of the C=S absorption has been a matter of some difficulty. In carbon disulphide the C=S stretching modes have been assigned [19] to 1522 cm.$^{-1}$ and 650 cm.$^{-1}$, whilst in carbonyl sulphide [20] it is given at 859 cm.$^{-1}$, but these are clearly unusual cases in which the carbon is doubly unsaturated, and they do not afford any guide to the likely position of the C=S vibration in saturated thioesters and similar compounds.

Colthup [18] and Thompson *et al.*[21] initially suggested a tentative range of 1400–1300 cm.$^{-1}$ for this absorption, but Sheppard [6] was unable to find any useful correlations from the spectra of a number of simple alkyl thioketones which he examined, and we confirmed this in our own laboratories. These uncertainties may well have arisen from the choice of simple thioketones for study in the first instance, as these are now known to exist in many cases as dimers in which the thioketone structure is lost. The study of large molecules therefore offers more promise of success in this field, and this has been confirmed by the studies of Mecke [44, 45] and subsequent workers. Mecke, Mecke and Luttringhaus [44] compared the carbonyl and thioketone spectra of over seventy different compounds of various types. Preliminary calculations indicated that the ratio ν_{co}/ν_{cs} would be about 1·5 and that the C=S frequency would be found in the 1200–1050 cm.$^{-1}$ region. This was confirmed experimentally by the comparison of the spectra of the individual pairs.

Just as with the carbonyl group, the C=S absorption was found to be sensitive to the nature of the surrounding structure, but the relative effects of various substituents were not always the same. Thus halogen atoms attached to the carbon did not raise the C=S frequency as much as oxygen atoms in thioesters, whereas the reverse is true of the carbonyl series. In consequence, the ratio between the carbonyl and thiocarbonyl frequencies varies over the range 1·6–1·14. The general ranges found by these workers for various classes of thioketones are as follows: Cl_2CS 1121 cm.$^{-1}$, $(RS)_2CS$ 1058–1053 cm.$^{-1}$, $(RO)_2CS$ 1212–1234 cm.$^{-1}$, $\rangle C{=}C{-}C{=}S$ (1156–1143 cm.$^{-1}$), $(Phenyl)_2C{=}S$ 1226–1219 cm.$^{-1}$ and thioureas, which show the widest variation, 1400–1130 cm.$^{-1}$. The numbers of compounds studied in each class naturally varied, and these classifications may need adjustment as further materials are studied. The cases of the thioureas are interesting in relation to the assignment of the amide absorptions, and thioamides have been separately studied by Mecke and Mecke.[45] In a series of compounds of this type the C=S frequency was identified as falling near 1120 cm.$^{-1}$ in thiolactams and was not particularly sensitive to changes of state. Thiocaprolactam, for example, absorbs at 1121 cm.$^{-1}$ in the vapour, 1117 cm.$^{-1}$ in chloroform solution and 1113 cm.$^{-1}$ in the solid. Thioureas absorbed in general at higher frequencies near 1205 cm.$^{-1}$ with the C–N absorption (amide III) in both cases near 1300 cm.$^{-1}$.

Confirmatory evidence for these correlations is available from several sources. Hadži[46] has examined thiobenzanilide and related materials in which the C=S frequency falls near 1000 cm.$^{-1}$, and Jones *et al.*[48] have studied ethylene trithiocarbonate (C=S 1074 cm.$^{-1}$), 2 : 4-dihydroxydithiobenzoic acid (1125 cm.$^{-1}$) and similar materials. They also confirmed the variable frequencies shown by thioureas and related compounds. Thiourea itself absorbs at 1408 cm.$^{-1}$, thiocarbanilide at 1344 cm.$^{-1}$ and dithio-oxamide at 1425 cm.$^{-1}$. Marvel *et al.*[49] have also published data on a small number of thioketones and assign dithioesters to the range 1195–1170 cm.$^{-1}$. A small number of thioketones with α-trifluoromethyl groups have been reported by Haszeldine and Kidd,[47] and these show the expected rise in the C=S frequency over the original compound.

The C=S frequency in compounds other than thioamides and ureas will generally be found as an intense band in the range 1234–1053 cm.$^{-1}$, the exact position depending upon the nature of the substituents. With thioureas the frequency is usually higher, but may fall anywhere in the range 1400–1150 cm.$^{-1}$. This wide range may indicate varying degrees of coupling with other vibrations.

22.6. THIOUREIDES –N–C=S AND –NH–C=S

Randall *et al.*[7] have drawn attention to a strong band which occurs between 1613 cm.$^{-1}$ and 1471 cm.$^{-1}$ in eighteen compounds which they have examined containing the structure R–N–C=S or R–NH–C=S. They believe that this arises from the C–N vibration, the linkage being shortened from the normal length by association with the C=S linkage, as they consider the frequency is too high to be associated with the C=S linkage itself.

In the case of secondary thioamides this is probably the amide II absorption which has been identified by Mecke [45] as the NH deformation mode. Nevertheless, a strong absorption persists in this region even in *NN*-dialkyl compounds, such as dithiocarbamates. We have noted a strong band in the 1490–1470 cm.$^{-1}$ region in such materials which is absent from the corresponding xanthates, and subsequent studies by Mann [22] and by Chatt, Duncanson and Venanzi [50] have confirmed this. The latter workers assign this absorption, which they place in the wider range 1542–1480 cm.$^{-1}$ to the C–N stretching mode shortened under the influence of canonical forms such as

$$X \diagdown_{\underset{\bar{S}}{\overset{\bar{S}}{\diagup}}} C = \overset{+}{N}R$$

They have also studied the changes in this frequency which accompany alterations in the valency and geometry of the element X. The highest frequencies in solution are shown by divalent planar complexes of Pt, Ni, Pd or Cu, and there seems to be a tendency for divalent tetrahedral complexes to absorb at slightly lower frequencies. This trend is still more marked in octahedral complexes of trivalent elements such as cobalt.

It is interesting that the C–N band, which in normal thioamides absorbs near 1300 cm.$^{-1}$, should absorb at so high a frequency in these *NN*-dialkyl compounds, but this could well be due to the influence of the second sulphur atom, and suggests that ionic forms such as that shown above will play a considerable part even in compounds such as dithiodisulphides. It also suggests that caution is necessary in the application of this correlation beyond the range of the limited types of compounds on which it is based.

22.7. S=O STRETCHING VIBRATIONS

22.7(a). Sulphoxides $\overset{\text{O}}{\underset{\text{S}}{\parallel}}$. The number of sulphoxides described in the infra-red literature is relatively small, but sufficient work has been done to fix at least the approximate position of the main band arising from this grouping. Schrieber,[23] in the course of the examination of a number of sulphones, examined also the infra-red spectra of diphenylsulphoxide, di-n-butylsulphoxide and of thionyl chloride. He found some evidence of a band near 1190 cm.[-1] and, working largely by analogy with the sulphones which absorb close to this region, he made the tentative suggestion that this frequency might also be connected with the S=O vibration. However, a fuller examination of the infra-red spectra of sulphoxides was later made by Barnard, Fabian and Koch,[24] who examined seven sulphoxides, of which five were obtained in a high state of purity. In all cases they found a very strong band to occur near 1050 cm.[-1] which they ascribed to the S=O link by analogy with sulphur monoxide [25] in which the S=O stretching vibration occurs at 1124 cm.[-1].

This band was found to be not only very intense but also remarkably constant in position in dilute solution, and this is attributed to the low frequency of the adjoining C–S linkages, which are consequently unlikely to exert any marked coupling effect. Thus both *cyclo*hexylmethylsulphoxide and phenylmethylsulphoxide absorb strongly at 1055 cm.[-1] in dilute solution in carbon tetrachloride, and even in unsaturated materials such as diallyl sulphoxide (1047 cm.[-1]) the frequency is not markedly diminished. Indeed, in one case— phenyl vinyl sulphoxide—Price and Gillis [51] have found a small frequency rise in comparison with saturated materials. In this the sulphoxides appear to differ from carbonyl compounds, in which the frequency is considerably affected by conjugation with a double bond. On the other hand, shifts of the order of 10–20 cm.[-1] towards higher frequencies occur on passing from the solid state to dilute solutions, so that it would appear probable that this grouping is capable of some degree of hydrogen bonding in the solid state. Thus phenylmethyl sulphoxide absorbs at 1035 cm.[-1] in the solid state, and similar shifts are shown by the other materials examined.

The tendency to hydrogen bonding is not unexpected, as Moffit [26] has shown that the sulphoxide link is likely to have considerable double-bond character. However, there is one other difficulty with this assignment which arises from the high observed frequency of the S=O link in thionyl chloride. Schrieber [23] quotes a value of 1238 cm.[-1] for this in the infra-red, whilst the corresponding Raman band [27] is at 1229 cm.[-1]. Thionyl fluoride absorbs even higher,[52] near 1330 cm.[-1]. Barnard *et al.*[24] point out that chlorine groups directly attached to the sulphur atom would be expected to have a marked influence on the frequency of the sulphoxide link by lowering the amount of RRS[+]–O[-] in relation to RRS=O; and they point to the exactly analogous behaviour of the carbonyl grouping, for which Hartwell, Richards and Thompson [28] have suggested a similar explanation for the shift from 1718 cm.$^{-1}$ in $(CH_3)_2CO$, to 1803 cm.$^{-1}$ in Cl_2CO.

Further support for the 1050 cm.$^{-1}$ assignment is also given by Cymerman and Willis,[12] who have re-examined the two organic sulphoxides reported by Schrieber.[23] They find that the bands near 1190 cm.$^{-1}$ are relatively weak compared with the very intense one shown by both compounds near 1050 cm.$^{-1}$. Thus diphenylsulphoxide has a strong band at 1053 cm.$^{-1}$ (1042 cm.$^{-1}$ in the solid) and di-*n*-butyl-sulphoxide a strong band at 1039 cm.$^{-1}$ (1019 cm.$^{-1}$ solid). These authors also examined four disulphoxides believed to contain the grouping –SO–SO–. In none of these was any strong band found at 1050 cm.$^{-1}$, and the only bands in the 1100–1000 cm.$^{-1}$ region were also given by the corresponding sulphides. On the other hand, all these compounds showed intense bands near 1150 cm.$^{-1}$ and 1340 cm.$^{-1}$ which are characteristic of sulphones, and they therefore concluded that these compounds exist as thiol sulphonates with the structure –S–SO$_2$–.

Amstutz, Hunsberger and Chessick [29] also give some data on the infra-red spectra of two sulphoxides. The most interesting point of their findings is that *ortho*-hydroxydiphenyl-sulphoxide has only a weak band at 1034 cm.$^{-1}$ in the solid state, and a strong band at 994 cm.$^{-1}$. They attribute this to hydrogen bonding, and consider that on general grounds sulphoxides would be more susceptible to hydrogen bonding than sulphones. This shift is, however, considerably greater than those reported earlier for changes from the solid to solution state, and it may be that in this case something corresponding to the chelation effects observed with such compounds as *ortho*-hydroxyacetophenone is occurring. In the case of carbonyl compounds in which the CO grouping is separated by a conjugated double bond from a β hydroxyl grouping, very considerable CO frequency shifts are known to occur which are much greater than those associated with normal hydrogen bonding, and it is therefore possible that some similar explanation holds for the shift observed in *ortho*-hydroxydiphenylsulphoxide, although it is not so great as in the carbonyl compounds.

In the light of the above, it seems likely that most normal sulphoxides will be found to give a strong band in the range 1060–1040 cm.$^{-1}$ in solution, with a corresponding reduction of 10–20 cm.$^{-1}$ in the solid state. It should be remembered, however, that the number of compounds so far examined is small, and further work will no doubt reveal a number of cases in which the S=O frequency lies above or below this range. Colthup [18] has quoted the range 1090–1000 cm.$^{-1}$ for sulphoxides, and whilst this is a broader range than normally occurs, it probably defines roughly the extremes of frequency at which this linkage is likely to absorb. This frequency will, however, be considerably higher in compounds, such as thionyl halides or covalent sulphites, in which strongly electronegative atoms are attached to the sulphur atom.

22.7(b). Covalent Sulphites –SO–O– and –O–SO–O–. Sulphinic acids RSOOH and their esters have been examined by Detoni and Hadži,[53, 54] and Simon, Kriegsmann and Dutz [55] have studied a small number of dialkyl sulphites $(RO)_2S=O$. In the sulphinic acids a strong band is found in solution near 1090 cm.[-1] which is very little affected by deuteration, and in the corresponding esters it is at somewhat higher frequencies (1126–1136 cm.[-1]). The analogy with carboxylic acids and esters supports the assignment to the $S=O$ link, and the frequency is of the order to be expected in comparison with the sulphoxides. When a further oxygen atom is attached to the sulphur, as in dialkyl sulphites, the frequency would be expected to rise further, and in the small number of such compounds which have been studied [55] there is a strong band near 1200 cm.[-1] which is assigned to the $S=O$ frequency.

This latter assignment is based on very small numbers of compounds, but is in accord with expectation and is indirectly supported by data on comparable cyclic compounds. De la Mere *et al.*[56] have examined a number of cyclic sulphites in the solid state and find strong absorptions in the range 1213–1215 cm.[-1] for 1 : 2-compounds (five-ring) and 1195–1208 cm.[-1] for 1 : 3-compounds (six-ring). These ranges are those observed for the limited number of compounds studied, and the group frequencies will necessarily fall over a wider range. Samant and Emerson [57] have confirmed these findings, although there is some difference in the values quoted which probably arises from the fact that they were working in solution. Under these conditions they report cyclic sulphites as absorbing between 1210 cm.[-1] and 1220 cm.[-1], but they were unable to detect any differences between five- and six-membered ring systems. They have also studied the variation of the $S=O$ group frequency with electronegativity using the " group electronegativities " suggested by Kagarise, but failed to find any very satisfactory relation. This probably arises from the differences in the geometry between sulphoxides and the carbonyl compounds on which the group electronegativities are based, as the latter is planar and the group electronegativities derived from it may contain an element of mesomeric conjugation which could well be absent in the case of sulphoxides.

22.7(c). Sulphones –SO$_2$–. The basic work on the characteristic infra-red frequencies of the sulphones was carried out by Schrieber.[23] He examined the solution spectra of thirteen sulphones and compared them with the spectra of the corresponding sulphides. In every case he found two bands to be present in the sulphones which were absent from the sulphides. These were at 1160–1120 cm.$^{-1}$ and at 1350–1300 cm.$^{-1}$. These bands are very intense, and are readily identifiable by the fact that in the solid state they usually show signs of splitting into a strong group of bands of closely related frequencies. Their assignment to the S=O stretching modes is directly confirmed by the assignments for these vibrations in sulphur dioxide [30] which occur at 1151 cm.$^{-1}$ and 1361 cm.$^{-1}$. The actual ranges of Schrieber's compounds were 1159–1128 cm.$^{-1}$ and 1352–1313 cm.$^{-1}$, and he therefore proposed the ranges 1160–1120 and 1350–1300 cm.$^{-1}$ for the characterisation of normal sulphones. As with the sulphoxides, conjugation does not appear to have any marked effect on this frequency and, in fact, the majority of the aromatic sulphones examined showed the lower-frequency band towards the top of the range, usually about 1150 cm.$^{-1}$. All Schrieber's measurements were made in solution, and he did not study the effect of changes of state.

Barnard, Fabian and Koch,[24] however, have compared the spectra of seven sulphones in the solid and solution state and find that, as with the sulphoxides, the solid materials absorb at frequencies 10–20 cm.$^{-1}$ lower than the solutions in carbon tetrachloride. Otherwise their findings supplement those of Schrieber, and all their compounds absorb in the expected ranges 1160–1120 cm.$^{-1}$ and 1350–1300 cm.$^{-1}$. The shifts observed from molecular aggregation or hydrogen bonding effects appear to be a little less in the case of the lower frequency band. Thus *cyclo*hexylmethylsulphone absorbs at 1144 and 1321 cm.$^{-1}$ in solution and at 1138 and 1309 cm.$^{-1}$ in the liquid state. These authors also examined the 500 cm.$^{-1}$ region of the spectrum in search of the third band which might be expected to arise from this group in analogy with the sulphur dioxide band at 520 cm.$^{-1}$. They found, however, no regularities, and suggested that this is due to the fact that the C–S link also occurs in this region, so that interactions between the two would be expected. In this they are at variance with Colthup,[18] who assigns the 600–520 cm.$^{-1}$ region to sulphones, in addition to 1170–1110 cm.$^{-1}$ and 1350–1290 cm.$^{-1}$. The latter two are, of course, essentially in agreement with Schrieber. Support for the 600–500 cm.$^{-1}$ assignment for the SO_2 deformation mode is, however, available from the studies of Simon *et al.*[55, 60]

Amstutz, Hunsberger and Chessick [29] have also examined a number of sulphones, but they have confined their attention to the 1160–1120 cm.$^{-1}$ band. However, they have noted a number of interesting instances of hydrogen bonding effects in this region. Three sulphones containing no hydroxyl group were found to absorb in the range 1151–1146 cm.$^{-1}$, whilst a fourth with a *para*-hydroxyphenyl grouping also absorbed at 1154 cm.$^{-1}$ (1151 cm.$^{-1}$ in solution). On the other hand, two *ortho*-hydroxyphenylsulphones absorbed at 1138 cm.$^{-1}$ and 1130 cm.$^{-1}$ in the solid state, and reverted to 1145 cm.$^{-1}$ and 1148 cm.$^{-1}$ in solution. One other compound, *ortho*methoxy *para*hydroxy-phenylsulphone, also showed this hydrogen bonding effect absorbing at 1148 cm.$^{-1}$ in solution and at 1133 cm.$^{-1}$ in the solid state. Further data are also available from the work of Price *et al.*,[51, 58] who find absorption in sulphones near 1310 cm.$^{-1}$ and 1140 cm.$^{-1}$, and they have confirmed that in this case also, conjugation does not influence the –SO$_2$– frequencies. This has been interpreted as in-dicating that conjugation effects are absent in these compounds, but this has been challenged by Barrow *et al.*[59] on the basis of infra-red intensity and dipole moment data. However, these latter workers quote values for the symmetric frequency within the range 1154–1141 cm.$^{-1}$ which confirm that in any case the frequency itself is unaffected by conjugation.

The disulphoxides which Cymerman and Willis [12] have shown to be probably thiolsulphonates cannot appropriately be quoted as evi-dence for the SO$_2$ correlations, as the proposed structure rests only on the infra-red evidence. It is nevertheless interesting to note that the four aromatics examined absorbed in the solid state, in the narrow ranges 1154–1144 cm.$^{-1}$ and 1342–1333 cm.$^{-1}$. In agreement with Barnard *et al.*, they were unable to identify any band in the 520 cm.$^{-1}$ region as being due to the SO$_2$ linkage.

Other workers have also published the infra-red spectra of various sulphones in connection with structural studies. Thus Ross and Raths [31] give the infra-red spectra of 1-cyano-2-benzyl sulphonyl *cyclo*hexane and the corresponding 2-phenyl derivative. They also give the spectra of the corresponding mercapto-derivatives, and com-parison of these with the sulphones shows that in both cases the major points of difference are the two sulphone bands near 1150 cm.$^{-1}$ and 1320 cm.$^{-1}$. Cope, Morrison and Field [32] also give the spectra of a number of sulphones including carbonyl phenyl sulphone and α-methyl allyl phenylsulphone. They make no comment on the correla-tions, but again the spectra show strong bands in the appropriate regions. The spectra of two other sulphones are given by Ross, Bushey and Rolih.[35]

These correlations can therefore be regarded as being well estab-lished and, in view of the very great intensity shown and the splitting effects frequently observed, the identification of these bands can usually be made with reasonable confidence. In the great majority of the materials examined the first band falls in the narrow range 1160–1140 cm.$^{-1}$ in solution, with only very small shifts in the solid state. This may, however, be due in part to the fact that many of the materials examined have been aromatic compounds. Hydrogen bonding effects can result in somewhat larger shifts in this band, but they are still relatively small, and are not so great as in the sulphoxides. The sulphones would therefore appear to show a somewhat reduced tendency towards hydrogen bonding, and this is in accordance with theory.[29] A useful cross check on the identification of an SO_2 group is available through the work of Bellamy and Williams,[37] who have pointed out that the asymmetric and symmetric stretching frequencies of the SO_2 group are related linearly.

22.7(d). Sulphonyl Chlorides. The substitution of a halogen atom directly on to the sulphur atom of a sulphone would be expected to result in frequency shifts of both of the characteristic bands towards higher frequencies. Very little has been published on compounds of this class, but Schrieber [23] noted that in benzene sulphonyl chloride in solution the bands occurred at 1185 cm.[-1] and 1340 cm.[-1], whilst we find *para*-toluene sulphonyl chloride to give bands at 1166 cm.[-1] and 1366 cm.[-1] in the solid state. In addition, a certain amount of scattered data are available from work on single or small groups of compounds [60, 61]. Simon *et al.*,[60] for example, have found bands at 1370 cm.[-1] and 1175 cm.[-1] in the spectrum of methane sulphonyl chloride.

22.7(e). Sulphonamides. In normal amides the presence of a tertiary nitrogen atom with two spare electrons directly attached to the carbonyl group results in a lengthening of the C—O bond and a shift to lower frequencies. This shift is of the same order for primary, secondary and tertiary amides, and some similar effect might have been expected to occur with sulphonamides. The amount of published evidence available on sulphonamides is relatively small, but it is clear that low-frequency shifts do not normally occur. Indeed, the tendency is for a broadening of the range of absorption with, in some cases, the SO_2 bands appearing at higher frequencies than normal.

Adams and Tjepkema [33] have published the infra-red spectra of sixteen $N : N'$-di-substituted sulphonamides, and noted that a strong band occurs in all cases in the range 1180–1160 cm.[-1] which they ascribe to the $-SO_2-$ grouping. Schrieber [23] has pointed out that, in addition, these spectra also have a strong band in the 1360–1330 cm.[-1] region corresponding to the second sulphone band. No systematic work has been published on primary or secondary sulphonamides. Barnes *et al.*[34] give the spectra of *ortho*-, *meta*- and *para*-sulphanilamides, and all show strong bands near 1300 cm.[-1] and 1150 cm.[-1], whilst Schrieber quotes three sulphonamides absorbing at 1167–1162 cm.[-1] and 1358–1346 cm.[-1].

Further studies by Adams [63] have confirmed his earlier findings, but the most extensive study of this group is due to Baxter, Cymerman-Craig and Willis,[64] who have examined twenty-five primary, secondary and tertiary sulphonamides in dilute solutions and in the solid state. The SO_2 frequencies are the same for all three types, and occur in solution in the ranges 1370–1333 cm.[-1] and 1178–1159 cm.[-1]. As with the sulphones, the symmetric frequency is unchanged on passing over to the solid state, but the asymmetric frequencies fall by 10–20 cm.$^{-1}$. The NH_2 stretching frequencies of primary sulphonamides were very similar to those of primary amines, but in secondary compounds the NH stretch was found near 3390 cm.$^{-1}$, which is about 40 cm.$^{-1}$ lower than in the corresponding amines.

22.8. COVALENT SULPHATES AND SULPHONATES

An oxygen linkage attached to the SO_2 grouping would be expected to result in a small shift in the SO_2 bands towards higher frequencies, in the same way as the CO vibration of esters occurs at slightly higher frequencies than in ketones. A still further frequency shift would be expected when two oxygens are so linked in covalent sulphates. The amount of data available is very small, but it appears probable that these shifts occur. Schrieber [23] finds two *para*-toluene-sulphonates to absorb at 1375–1370 cm.$^{-1}$ and at 1185 cm.$^{-1}$ in solution, whilst he quotes dimethyl and diethyl sulphates as absorbing at 1193 and 1187 cm.$^{-1}$ respectively. A series of five esters of *para*-toluene sulphonic acid absorbs in the ranges [65] 1375–1350 cm.$^{-1}$ and 1192–1170 cm.$^{-1}$; very similar values are given by the sultones,[66] in which the $-SO_2-O-$ group is included in a six-membered ring system. Simon *et al.*[68] find absorption near 1350 cm.$^{-1}$ and 1176 cm.$^{-1}$ in a few alkyl esters of sulphonic acids. In agreement with the above, Colthup [18] quotes the ranges 1420–1330 cm.$^{-1}$ and 1200–1145 cm.$^{-1}$ for covalent sulphonates; and 1440–1350 cm.$^{-1}$ and 1230–1150 cm.$^{-1}$ for covalent sulphates.

22.9. SULPHONIC ACIDS AND SALTS

Only a very limited amount of data is available on sulphonic acids and their salts. Colthup [18] has suggested the ranges 1260–1150 cm.$^{-1}$, 1080–1010 cm.$^{-1}$ and 700–600 cm.$^{-1}$. Schrieber [22] reports three sulphonic acids as absorbing between 1182 cm.$^{-1}$ and 1170 cm.$^{-1}$, but does not comment on any other bands. Haszeldine and Kidd [67] have examined twelve sulphonic acids and salts, and quote strong absorptions in the ranges 1190–1170 cm.$^{-1}$ and 1064–1040 cm.$^{-1}$. Very little difference was found between the acids themselves and their salts. Although these ranges are narrower than those of Colthup, they relate to a narrower range of alkyl and fluoroalkyl sulphonic acids, so it is likely that the wider limits originally quoted will be more generally applicable.

22.10. BIBLIOGRAPHY

1. Bell, *Ber.*, 1927, **B60**, 1749.
2. *Idem., ibid.*, 1928, **B61**, 1918.
3. Ellis, *J. Amer. Chem. Soc.*, 1928, **50**, 2113.

4. Williams, *Phys. Rev.*, 1938, **54**, 504.
5. Trotter and Thompson, *J. Chem. Soc.*, 1946, 481.
6. Sheppard, *Trans. Faraday Soc.*, 1950, **46**, 429.
7. Randall, Fowler, Fuson and Dangl, *Infra-red Determination of Organic Structures* (Van Nostrand, 1949).
8. Sheppard, *Trans. Faraday Soc.*, 1949, **45**, 693.
9. Gordy and Stanford, *J. Amer. Chem. Soc.*, 1940, **62**, 497.
10. Hannan, Lieblich and Renfrew, *ibid.*, 1949, **71**, 3733.
11. Venkateswaren, *Indian J. Physics*, 1930, **5**, 219.
12. Cymerman and Willis, *J. Chem. Soc.*, 1951, 1332.
13. Kohlrausch, Dadieu and Pongratz, *Wien. Ber.*, 1932, **141**, 11a, 276.
14. Kopper, Seka and Kohlrausch, *ibid.*, p. 465.
15. Köppl and Kohlrausch, *ibid.*, 1933, **142**, 11b, 477.
16. Thompson and Duprè, *Trans. Faraday Soc.*, 1940, **36**, 805.
17. Thompson, *J. Chem. Soc.*, 1948, 328.
18. Colthup, *J. Opt. Soc. Amer.*, 1950, **40**, 397.
19. Herzberg, *Infra-red and Raman Spectra of Polyatomic Molecules* (Van Nostrand, 1945), p. 276.
20. Bailey and Cassie, *Proc. Roy. Soc.*, 1932, **A135**, 375.
21. Thompson, Nicholson and Short, *Discuss. Faraday Soc.*, 1950, **9**, 222.
22. Mann, *Trans. Inst. Rubber Ind.*, 1951, **27**, 232.
23. Schrieber, *Analyt. Chem.*, 1949, **21**, 1168.
24. Barnard, Fabian and Koch, *J. Chem. Soc.*, 1949, 2442.
25. Herzberg, *Molecular Spectra and Molecular Structure*, Vol. 1 (Van Nostrand, 1950), p. 573.
26. Moffit, *Proc. Roy. Soc.*, 1950, **A200**, 409.
27. Cabannes and Rousset, *Ann. Physique*, 1933, **19**, 229.
28. Hartwell, Richards and Thompson, *J. Chem. Soc.*, 1948, 1436.
29. Amstutz, Hunsberger and Chessick, *J. Amer. Chem. Soc.*, 1951, **73**, 1220.
30. Herzberg, *Infra-red and Raman Spectra of Polyatomic Molecules* (Van Nostrand, 1945), p. 285.
31. Ross and Raths, *J. Amer. Chem. Soc.*, 1951, **73**, 129.
32. Cope, Morrison and Field, *ibid.*, 1950, **72**, 59.
33. Adams and Tjepkema, *ibid.*, 1948, **70**, 4204.
34. Barnes, Gore, Liddel and Williams, *Infra-red Spectroscopy* (Reinhold, 1944), p. 87.
35. Ross, Bushey and Rolih, *J. Amer. Chem. Soc.*, 1951, **73**, 540.
36. Flett, *J. Chem. Soc.*, 1953, 347.
37. Bellamy and Williams, *J. Chem. Soc.*, 1957, 863.
38. Haines, Helm, Bailey and Ball, *J. Phys. Chem.*, 1954, **58**, 270.
39. Wagner, Becher and Kottenhahn, *Chem. Ber.*, 1956, **89**, 1708.
40. Sweeney, Mizushima and Quagliano, *J. Amer. Chem. Soc.*, 1955, **77**, 6521.
41. Mecke and Spiesecke, *Chem. Ber.*, 1956, **89**, 1110.
42. Josien, Dizabo and Saumagne, *Bull. Soc. Chim. France*, 1957, 423.
43. Meneefe, Alford and Scott, *J. Chem. Phys.*, 1956, **25**, 370.
44. Mecke, Mecke and Lüttringhaus, *Z. Naturforsch.*, 1955, **105B**, 367.
45. Mecke and Mecke, *Chem. Ber.*, 1956, **89**, 343.
46. Hadži, *J. Chem. Soc.*, 1957, 847.
47. Haszeldine and Kidd, *ibid.*, 1955, 3871.
48. Jones, Kynaston and Hales, *ibid.*, 1957, 614.
49. Marvel, Radzitzky and Brader, *J. Amer. Chem. Soc.*, 1955, **77**, 5997.
50. Chatt, Duncanson, and Venanzi, *Suomen. Kem.*, 1956, **29B**, 75.
51. Price and Gillis, *J. Amer. Chem. Soc.*, 1953, **75**, 4750.
52. Haszeldine and Kidd, *J. Chem. Soc.*, 1955, 2901.
53. Detoni and Hadži, *ibid.*, 3163.
54. *Idem, Bull. Sci. Yougoslavie*, 1955, **2**, 44.
55. Simon, Kriegsmann and Dutz, *Chem. Ber.*, 1956, **89**, 2390.
56. De la Mere, Klyne, Millen, Pritchard and Watson, *J. Chem. Soc.*, 1956, 1813.
57. Samant and Emerson, *J. Amer. Chem. Soc.*, 1956, **78**, 454.
58. Price and Morita, *ibid.*, 1953, **75**, 4747.
59. Rogers, Barrow and Bordwell, *ibid.*, 1956, **78**, 1790.

60. Simon, Kriegsmann and Dutz, *Chem. Ber.*, 1956, **89**, 1883.
61. Ham and Hambly, *Aust. J. Chem.*, 1953, **6**, 33.
62. Dudley, Cady and Eggers, *J. Amer. Chem. Soc.*, 1956, **78**, 2.
63. Adams and Cosgrove, *ibid.*, 1954, **76**, 3584.
64. Baxter, Cymerman-Craig and Willis, *J. Chem. Soc.*, 1955, 669.
65. Tipson, *J. Amer. Chem. Soc.*, 1952, **74**, 1354.
66. Philbin, Stuart, Timoney and Wheeler, *J. Chem. Soc.*, 1956, 4414.
67. Haszeldine and Kidd, *ibid.*, 1954, 4228.
68. Simon, Kriegsmann and Dutz, *Chem. Ber.*, 1956, **84**, 2378.
69. Plant, Tarbell, and Whiteman, *J. Amer. Chem. Soc.*, 1955, **77**, 1572.

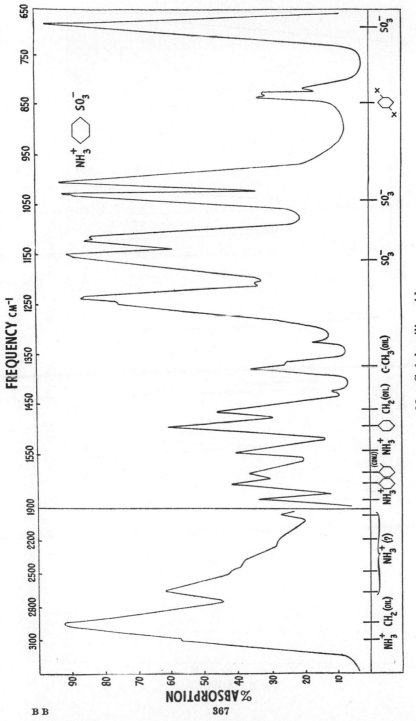

23. Sulphanilic acid

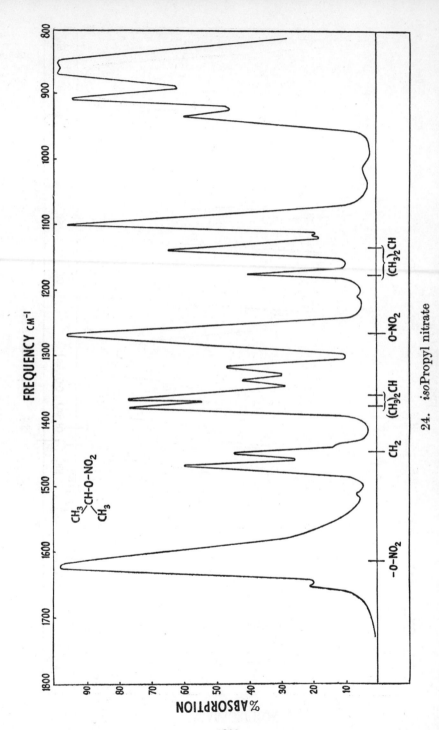

24. *iso*Propyl nitrate

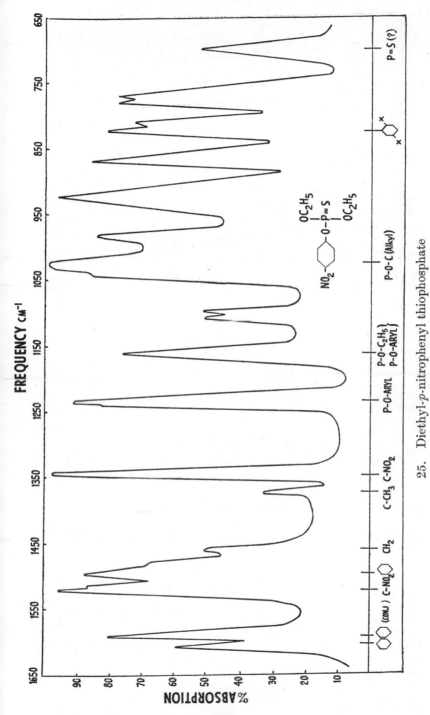

25. Diethyl-*p*-nitrophenyl thiophosphate

26. Diphenyl hydrogen phosphate

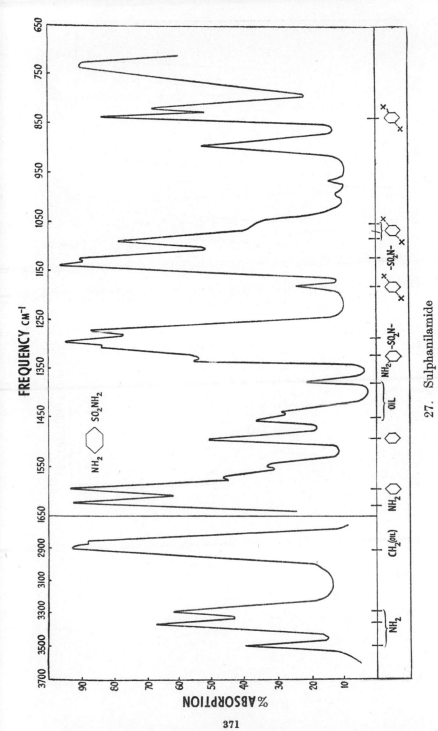

27. Sulphanilamide

371

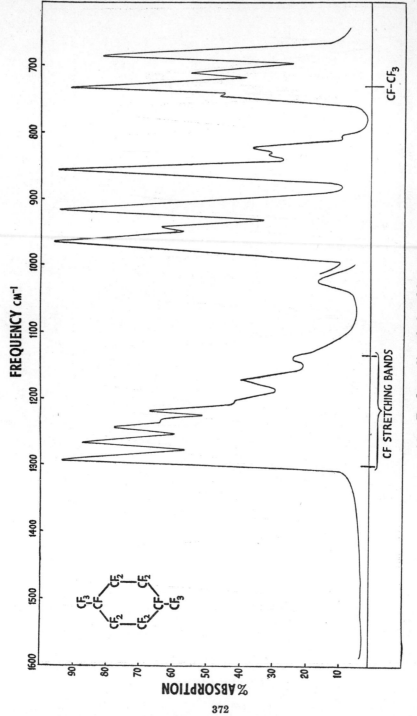

28. Perfluorodimethyl *cyclohexane*

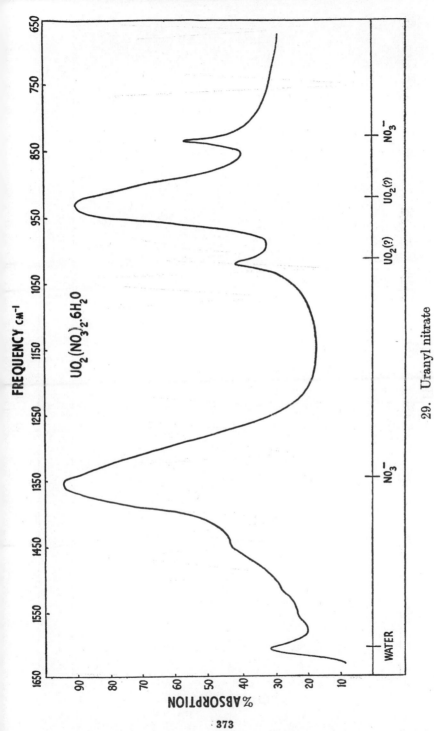

29. Uranyl nitrate

373

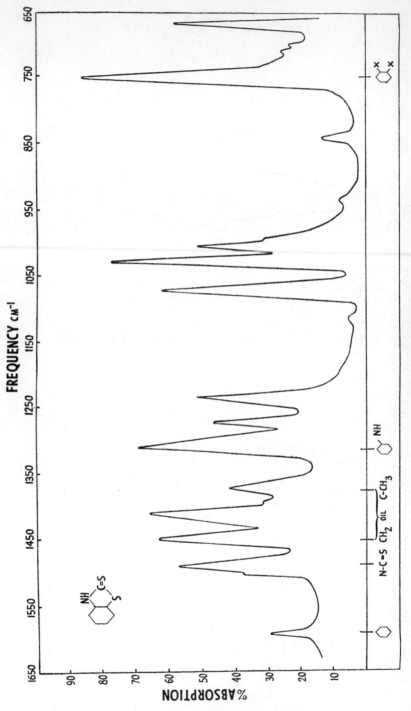

30. Mercaptobenzthiazole

374

PART V

THE ORIGINS AND SIGNIFICANCE OF GROUP FREQUENCY SHIFTS

CHAPTER 23

The Origins and Significance of Group Frequency Shifts

23.1. INTRODUCTION

THE concept of localised group frequencies is, of course, generally recognised as an over-simplification. The approximate vibrational frequency of a link AB is determined primarily by the elasticity of the bond as measured by the force constant, and by the masses of A and B. In a complex molecule this is modified by the interplay of many other factors, the resultant of which determines the precise position of the absorption band. Some of these factors are concerned with the external environment of the vibrating group, and these include such effects as changes of phase or of crystal form, the influence of solvents and the occurrence or otherwise of hydrogen bonding. Others arise internally and relate to changes in the molecular geometry, or in the masses of substituent groups, the occurrence of mechanical coupling between one vibration and another, the effects of steric strain and the electrical influences of the substituent groups operating either along the bonds or sometimes across intramolecular space.

With so many potential variables it is at first sight difficult to see why characteristic group frequencies should exist at all, but it should be remembered that many of these factors can be minimised in favourable circumstances. For example, the vibration of the carbonyl group can be shown to be almost completely independent of mass effects for all substituents of atomic weights greater than 12, and the high force constant of this bond in relation to those of adjacent links renders it relatively immune from coupling effects. The basic frequency is therefore reasonably constant and shows only minor differences under the influence of steric strain or of the electrical effects of the substituents. These minor differences, however, lead to the important distinctions between the carbonyl frequencies of ketones, esters, acid chlorides, etc., which are so valuable in correlation work. In general, it is the vibrations of multiple bonds or of hydrogen atoms which are least sensitive to mass or coupling effects, and it is for this reason that linkages of this type give rise to the most characteristic group frequencies. With linkages such as the carbon–carbon single bond, on the other hand, absorption occurs over so wide a range as to be valueless for this purpose.

377

Despite the number of separate variables which go to determine the position of an individual absorption band, it is often possible to devise conditions under which one is essentially isolated from the rest so that it can be studied separately. For example, isotopic exchange of one atom for another alters the vibrating masses without changing the chemical nature of the bond; the same substance can be studied in different solvents or phases, or the influence of strain can be explored by the comparison of similar ring systems of different sizes. Studies of this kind have led to a better understanding of the circumstances in which any one of these factors is likely to have an important influence upon a particular group frequency, and in favourable circumstances the expected direction, and sometimes even the approximate extent of the frequency shift which will result from a given change of environment, can be predicted. However, this is not to suggest that all the operative factors are known or measurable. In the discussion which follows the various factors are considered individually, and it will be seen that our understanding of them varies greatly. A good deal is known of the circumstances under which mass changes, coupling effects and hydrogen bonding can lead to any considerable frequency shifts, but our knowledge of the environmental effects of different solvents is still fragmentary. Our understanding of electrical factors, and particularly of intramolecular dipolar interactions, is also still largely in the formative stage, so that the discussion of these topics must be regarded as representing to some extent the personal views of the author. Many individual frequencies which appear to be anomalous can be satisfactorily accounted for on the basis of what is now known, but others, such as the high $C≡C$ stretching frequency of tetrafluoroethylene (Raman active), continue to defy any reasonable interpretation, and it is clear that further extensions of the theory will be required before such cases can be properly understood.

Despite these limitations, studies of the origins of group frequency shifts have led to several useful correlations between the positions of different absorptions in a single spectrum which are helpful in diagnostic work. Numbers of relationships have also been found between the quantitative extents of group frequency shifts and other physical properties, such as reactivities, acid and base strengths, bond lengths, etc., which strongly suggest the possibility of important new applications in this field. These are accordingly discussed below.

23.2. THE EFFECTS OF CHANGES OF STATE

Although there are a few instances, such as hydrogen fluoride, in which molecular association persists in the vapour state even at low pressures, this is not usual, and a molecular vibration studied in this way can be regarded as being essentially free from the influence of other molecules. In the liquid state, however, the vibrating group is surrounded by other molecules, which may influence its frequency either through the change they have produced in the dielectric constant of the medium or through molecular association. In carboxylic acids dimerisation through strong hydrogen bonds leads to carbonyl and hydroxyl frequencies as much as 50 cm.$^{-1}$ and 500 cm.$^{-1}$ lower than in the vapour state. However, the association need not always be of a kind which results in a specific molecular complex. In liquid acetone, for example, it is likely that in the attractive forces between the individual $\overset{+}{>}\!C\!=\!\overset{-}{O}$ dipoles lead to loose associations of the type $\overset{}{>}\!C\!=\!\overset{-}{O} \ldots \overset{+}{>}\!C\!=\!\overset{-}{O}$, in which the separate molecules are linked in chains by electrostatic forces. Under such conditions each positive charge will induce a small additional negative charge in the oxygen atom of the neighbouring molecule, and the polarity of the $C\!=\!O$ link is increased. This implies that there will now be an increased contribution from the resonance form involving the $\overset{+}{>}\!C\!-\!\overset{-}{O}$ structure so that the bond lengthens and the carbonyl frequency falls. It is probable that the greater part of the frequency shift shown by acetone on passing from the vapour (ν_{co} 1742 cm.$^{-1}$) to the liquid (ν_{co} 1718 cm.$^{-1}$) arises in this way.

On going over from the liquid to the crystalline solid the situation is rather different. Frequency shifts occur due to a further increase in intermolecular forces, but except in the case of links involved in hydrogen bonding, these are usually relatively small. However, owing to the increased order of the system, some bonds will often be found to have disappeared from the spectrum. In other instances additional bands will appear. The first effect arises from the fact that rotational isomerism, which can occur in liquids and vapours, is eliminated in an oriented crystal so that absorption bands due to the less-stable isomer no longer appear. In liquid ω-chloroaceto-phenone, for example, two carbonyl absorptions appear with approximately equal intensities, but only one of these remains in the spectrum of the crystal. Inversely, a valuable group of diagnostic bands which are found in the spectra of crystalline fatty acids arise primarily from the all-*trans* arrangement of the methylene groups. In the liquid state these band progressions are not shown.

The appearance of additional bands in the spectra of solids is due to a different effect. Within the rigid crystal environment strong intermolecular forces exist so that the individual group vibrations are influenced by the nature of the unit cell. In suitable circumstances in-phase and out-of-phase vibrations of the same groups in two different molecules are set up, leading to the splitting of the original single band into two.   The $-(CH_2)_n-$ rocking mode, which absorbs near 720 cm.[-1], is particularly prone to do this, and the doubling of this band in crystalline polyethylene provides a convenient route to the estimation of crystallinity in this material. In the same way alterations in the crystal lattice, such as occur on changing from one polymorphic form to another, can result in important spectral changes due to the alterations which take place in the immediate environments of the vibrating groups.   This is particularly marked in the low-frequency region, in which the differences between different crystalline forms of the same substance are often sufficiently great as to allow the estimation of the individual components of mixtures.   Crystal lattice effects of a different type are also found in some cases with samples examined in the form of pressed alkali halide discs.   It has been shown that spectral changes occur which are related to the degree of grinding to which the mixture is subjected and that in finely dispersed samples interactions occur between vibrations of the sample and the alkali halide lattice.   Spectra can then be obtained showing marked differences from those of the same substance examined in paraffin oil.   Cases of this kind have been observed in carbohydrates,[2] hydroxyl compounds and acids [3, 4] and other materials, and have been discussed by Farmer [3] and by Baker.[5]

The factors which are operative in producing spectral changes with alterations of phase are therefore understood in broad general terms, but our present state of knowledge is wholly inadequate to explain or predict all the changes which are observed.   In general, molecular association effects lead to lower stretching frequencies and higher deformation frequencies, and except in the cases of complexes with strong hydrogen bonds the overall shifts produced in this way are usually small.   With the carbonyl group, for example, the overall frequency shift on passing from the vapour to the solid is rarely more than 25 cm.[-1], although in exceptional cases involving resonance it can be as much as 100 cm.[-1].   The frequency shifts which arise from crystal packing effects are less predictable. Crystal splitting effects involve only small frequency changes, but, as indicated above, many low-frequency vibrations appear to be very sensitive to their immediate crystal environment, and these sometimes show considerable alterations.

23.3. THE EFFECTS OF SOLVENTS

The frequency shifts which occur on passing from one solvent to another are usually small unless hydrogen bonding is involved. They are imperfectly understood and have not been very intensively studied.   Usually the observed changes are explained along similar lines to those just discussed for changes of phase.   For example, when one solvent is replaced by another, the dielectric constant of the medium in which the vibration is taking place is altered. This has led to numerous attempts to relate solvent shifts with dielectric constants or refractive indices.[6-13] Kirkwood,[6] and Bauer and Magat[7] derived an expression for a simple oscillating dipole in which the frequencies in the vapour (ν_v) and in solution (ν_s) are related to the dielectric constant D by the expression

$$\frac{\nu_v - \nu_s}{\nu_v} = \frac{K(D-1)}{(2D+1)}$$

where K is a constant. These studies were carried out principally in non-polar solvents, and later work by Josien *et al.*,[8-11] and by Bayliss, Cole and Little[12] has shown that whilst most non-polar solvents obey this relation roughly, some polar solvents, including even benzene in many cases, do not. Some small improvement[11,12] has been obtained by the substitution of a term involving the square of the refractive index for D, but as the shifts shown in passing from one non-polar solvent to another are relatively small, it is clear that some additional factor or factors must be considered if the existing data are to be adequately explained. This is supported by the fact that in more concentrated solutions, in which bands due to solute–solvent interactions appear, the observed frequency is independent of the dielectric constant of the solvent[11] in some cases, although this would have been expected to be particularly sensitive to such effects.

The major cause of departures from what is termed the K.B.M. line must be association phenomena between solute and solvent. At one end of the scale will be found very strongly associated materials, such as hydrochloric acid in ether, which forms a 1 : 1 complex, and at the other very loose solvent dipole orientation effects in which a wide diversity of different solvent–solute arrangements occur but which are not completely random. Bauer and Magat[7] pointed out that the use of the static dielectric constant in the expression given above is fully justifiable only if the electronic and orientation polarisation components follow at every instant the changes in solvent dipole originating in thermal libration, vibration and vibrational transitions. As dipole orientation relaxation times are many times greater[98] than the molecular vibrational periods, this condition does not obtain in solution.

The frequency and intensity changes of C=O, C–C and C–H vibrations have been studied from these points of view by Bayliss *et al.*[12] C–C vibrations show only a very small displacements with changes of solvent, but the shifts of C=O and C–H frequencies are of the order of 10–20 cm.⁻¹, with the C=O overtones being displaced almost twice as much as the fundamentals. Their findings are in good general agreement with the theory they have outlined, but the C–H results do not fit so readily with this interpretation.

In a few exceptional instances shifts of stretching vibrations towards higher instead of lower frequency have been observed as the polarity of the solvent is increased. An outstanding case is that of nitrosyl chloride, which has been studied in our own laboratories. In the vapour this compound absorbs at 1800 cm.$^{-1}$, but in carbon tetrachloride solution this rises to 1814 cm.$^{-1}$. Further shifts towards higher frequencies occur as the polarity of the solvent is increased through benzene (1836 cm.$^{-1}$), dioxane (1859 cm.$^{-1}$) and acetonitrile (1874 cm.$^{-1}$) to nitromethane (1881 cm.$^{-1}$). This is not a case in which complex formation seems likely, as in mixtures of carbon tetrachloride and acetonitrile the observed frequency shows a steady progression towards higher frequencies as the proportion of the more polar solvent is increased. This must be some type of solvent dipolar interaction in which the more polar solvents bring about an increase in the proportion of the ionic canonical form $(O{\equiv}\overset{+}{N}){-}\overset{-}{Cl}$, thereby raising the $N{=}O$ frequency towards that of the $(N{\equiv}O)\overset{+}{}$ radical.

No theoretical treatment is yet available which can adequately explain all these observations. However, in some ways the problem is similar to that which arises in the comparison of molecular dipole moments measured in different solvents. In this field a quasi-empirical approach has led to some very successful equations, from which the changes which occur on passing from one solvent to another can often be predicted with high precision.[14-16] These equations involve arbitrary terms which take account of the shape factors, and it may well be that an approach to frequency shifts along similar lines would be very rewarding. In this connection it is perhaps worth noting that the dipole moment of nitrosyl chloride shows an anomalous behaviour similar to the observed frequencies in that the direction of shift on passing from the vapour to the liquid phase is the opposite of that which is normally found.

23.4. HYDROGEN BONDING

Hydrogen bonding is, of course, a specialised form of the molecular association phenomena discussed above. It has, however, been studied in much greater detail than other forms of association, and will be dealt with separately, because it provides the only instances in which useful quantitative data on molecular structure or properties can be derived directly from the observed frequency shifts which occur with changes of phase. The extents of shifts which occur with different types of hydrogen bonding have already been indicated in the appropriate chapters on individual linkages, and need not be further discussed here. The main shifts occur in the stretching and deformation frequencies of the X–H bonds, and the effects upon the proton acceptor group are usually small unless resonance stabilisation is involved. However, in cases in which an X–H frequency is mechanically coupled with some other vibration, as in the OH deformation and C–O stretching modes of carboxylic acids,[17] changes in hydrogen bonding naturally result in frequency changes in other regions of the spectrum.

The earliest attempts to derive quantitative data from the shifts of X–H stretching frequencies on association are due to Badger,[18] who pointed out that the frequency shifts of bonded hydroxyl groups are a good measure of the force constant of the hydrogen bonds formed. The shifts are therefore also connected with the O . . . O distances and with the energy of the hydrogen bond. An expression was derived which permitted the direct calculation of such bond energies from the observed frequency shifts.

In later studies Lord and Merrifield [19] showed that in organic acids, acetyl glycine, ice and other compounds in which strong OH . . . O bonds were formed the OH frequency shifts followed an inverse linear relationship with the oxygen–oxygen distances. This relationship has found useful applications in the differentiation of geometric isomers. In *cyclo*hexane-1 : 2-diols, for example, O–H . . . O distances obtained in this way have been used to determine the probable configurations.[20, 21] Caution is, however, required, as deviations from the original relationship can arise if the three atoms involved in the hydrogen bond are not colinear. This has become clear from further studies by Nakamoto, Margoshes and Rundle,[22] and by Pimentel and Sederholm [23] on a wider range of different hydrogen bonded materials. For OH . . . O bonds they have confirmed that, for all but the largest O . . . O distances, the OH frequency shift is a linear function of the separation of the oxygen atoms, provided the bonds are not bent. This relation is given by the expression $\Delta\nu = 4.43 \times 10^3$ $(2.84-R)$, where R is the O . . . O distance. When the oxygen atoms are widely separated the hydrogen bonds are very weak, and it is to be expected that the form of the relationship will change and the curve become asymptotic. In more detailed studies on this point Lippincott and Schroeder [100] have devised a potential function which appears to characterise the O–H . . . O system reasonably well. Some improvements in this have been suggested by Welsh.[101]

Similar relationships have been developed [22] for OH . . . N, OH . . . Cl and other types of hydrogen bonds, but the slopes of the lines obtained differ very considerably, and there is appreciably more scatter of the individual points. Cannon [24] has also discussed this type of relation in connection with the association of secondary

C C

amides, in which the very small NH frequency shifts, as compared with the considerable changes in the carbonyl frequencies, has led him to postulate a dipolar interaction mechanism for these cases, instead of the conventional type of hydrogen bond. However, it is not wholly clear how far this represents a clear break from the more usual picture, as all hydrogen bonds must contain some elements of dipolar interaction.

One other useful application of X–H frequency shift determinations is found in the determination of the heats of mixing of materials which hydrogen bond. Tamres *et al.*,[25] for example, have shown that the frequency shift of the OD stretching vibration in *d*-methanol dissolved in organic bases is a linear function of the heat of mixing and is also related to the basicity of the solvent.

23.5. MASS AND COUPLING EFFECTS

Mass effects are not easy to study in isolation other than by isotopic-techniques, as the substitution of one element for another invariably introduces other factors, which are usually electrical in character. Alterations in the substituents of a vibrating group can also alter its susceptibility to mechanical coupling effects, and so lead to larger frequency changes than would be expected from the mass effect alone. However, the probable effects of simple mass changes which do not involve coupled vibrations can be predicted in some cases from basic theory. This indicates that the vibrations which will be least sensitive to changes in the masses of substituents will be those involving the motions of hydrogen atoms or of multiple bonds which are attached to the rest of the molecule only at one end. In the cases of X–H stretching and deformation modes almost the whole of the movement is localised in the hydrogen atom and the heavier element X hardly moves at all, so that, to a first approximation, such vibrations are not sensitive to changes in the mass of any substituents at X. With multiple bonds, such as the carbonyl group, in which atoms of nearly equal mass are involved in the vibration, the situation is more complex, but a number of theoretical treatments of such cases is available. Halford [26] has discussed the case of the carbonyl group, and has been able to show that for molecules of the type COX_2 the masses of X can be altered over the range from 12 to infinity without altering the carbonyl frequency by more than 25 cm.$^{-1}$. Changes due to alterations in the masses of substituents at X are relatively trivial. With masses a little less than 12, mixed vibrations begin to occur which are discussed below. In the cases of hydrogen and deuterium substituents, however, the C–X stretching frequencies have risen above the range in which coupling is likely, and the difference between the carbonyl frequencies of formaldehyde and formaldehyde-d_2 is probably due to a real mass effect.

For practical purposes, however, as long as due caution is exercised in the case of aldehydes, the carbonyl frequency can be regarded as mass insensitive. Discussions of the X–C≡N series by Whiffen [27] and of the acetylenic bond by Lord and Miller [28] lead to a similar conclusion.

It is for these reasons that the most useful and important correlations discussed in the preceding chapters are those which involve either the motions of hydrogen atoms, in groups such as OH, CH_2, NH_2 and the phenyl ring, or the stretching vibrations of groups such as C=O, P=O, NO_2, SO_2, etc. When the multiple bond is substituted at both ends the influence of mass is appreciably greater, and although the frequency is localised to some extent by the high force constant, bonds such as $\geq$C=C$\leq$ and $\geq$C=N– tend to absorb over a wider frequency range. With single-bond vibrations which do not involve hydrogen atoms, the sensitivity to mass and coupling effects is increased to such a degree that useful correlations are made possible only by considering large molecular units in which the mass effects are effectively constant. The C–O single-bond stretching vibration, for example, occurs over a wide range of frequencies but can be recognised within the more limited environments of esters, primary, secondary and tertiary alcohols, etc., separable correlations being required for each class. In the same way the CF_3 group gives rise to constant group frequencies only when its immediate environment is kept constant. For example, when attached to a phenyl ring [29] recognisable frequencies are found and this is true also when the attachment is to another CF_2 group,[30] but the characteristic frequencies in the two cases are not the same, and they cannot be applied to any other system.

The effects of vibrational coupling on group frequencies have been very ably discussed in a recent paper by Lord and Miller.[28] Coupling occurs when two groups vibrating with reasonably high and nearly equal frequencies are situated near to each other, provided that they have the same symmetry. This explains the relative freedom of multiple bonds from these effects, as it is unusual for more than one to be joined to the same atom. When this does happen, as in allene or carbon dioxide, the resulting interaction is extremely strong and the asymmetric and symmetric stretching frequencies are very widely separated. The incidence of coupling effects is well illustrated by the X_2CO molecules discussed above. When X is hydrogen or deuterium the C–X stretching frequencies are too high to couple with the carbonyl frequency near 1700 cm.$^{-1}$, but as the mass of X increases they approach nearer this range. With masses of about 6 the coupling would be so extensive that neither the C–X nor the C=O links would have any separate identity, and two widely separated bands would appear. By the time the mass of X has risen to 12 the C–X frequency has fallen sufficiently below that of the carbonyl group for the coupling to cease, and the identity of the individual vibrations is restored.

Coupling effects of bonds involving hydrogen atoms can be very conveniently studied by deuteration methods, which produce a substantial mass change without altering the chemical character of the bonds. If neither the X–H nor the X–D frequencies are involved in coupling effects they should be inversely related to each other by the square root of two. If therefore deuteration leads to a frequency shift which is in this ratio the absorption can be identified positively as an uncoupled XH vibration. If the ratio is not $1 : 1/\sqrt{2}$ it indicates that either the X–H or X–D mode is involved in vibrational coupling. This is well illustrated by the frequencies of the molecules HCN, DCN and TCN.[77] The highest frequency in each case is 3312, 2629 and 2460 cm.$^{-1}$. This is a vibration involving primarily the C–H (D or T) stretching mode, but as these are not in the ratio $1 : 1/\sqrt{2} : 1/\sqrt{3}$, it is clear that coupling is occurring. Similarly, the vibration with the greatest C≡N character falls at 2096, 1928 and 1724 cm.$^{-1}$ over this series, and these substantial changes as compared, for example, with the value of 2267 cm.$^{-1}$ for acetonitrile also indicate that mechanical coupling is taking place to a considerable extent in the deuterated and tritiated compounds.

The possibility of coupling effects must always be borne in mind in considering the possible origins of abnormal group frequencies, but this does not preclude many such vibrations from finding useful applications in correlation work. For example, the well-known amide II and III bands are highly characteristic of open-chain secondary amides, but both arise from coupled vibrations involving the NH deformation and C–N stretching frequencies.[31] Within the constant environment RCONHR the degree of coupling is reasonably constant and characteristic frequencies result. Similarly, the C–O stretching and OH deformation vibrations of carboxylic acids are coupled,[17] but this does not prevent them from providing useful group frequencies within the constant environment of the RCOOH group. It is, however, important to remember that such correlations do not relate to vibrations of individual bonds, so that alterations in the degree of hydrogen bonding or deuteration in acids will affect not only the OH frequencies but also the C–O stretching modes. In the same way, deuteration in secondary amides alters both the amide II and amide III frequencies, whereas in thioamides only the former is affected.[32] This is because there is less mesomerism in thioamides, and the C–N mode does not then rise to a sufficiently high frequency to allow it to couple with the NH deformation mode. When these compounds are deuterated the C–N absorption therefore remains unchanged, but the NH deformation frequency is lowered by the square root of two.

23.6. THE EFFECTS OF STRAIN

The geometric arrangement of the groups about a carbon atom in a particular valency state is determined by the state of hybridisation of that atom. A saturated sp^3 carbon atom, for example, has a tetrahedral arrangement and an olefinic sp^2 carbon a planar trigonal one. Any alterations in these angles which is enforced by steric strain results in small changes in the proportions of s and p character in the individual links. s Orbitals are spherical and generally shorter than p orbitals, which are cylindrically symmetric, so that changes in the proportions in which these are mixed result in alterations in the individual bond lengths and the vibrational frequencies change. As an atom such as an olefinic carbon has only one s orbital and two p orbitals available for hybridisation, an increase in the s character of one bond must be counterbalanced by an increase in the p character of another. A simple illustration of this is given by *cyclo*propane, in which the natural tetrahedral carbon angles are reduced by ring strain. This implies an increase in the directional component of the C–C bonds, so that the C–H bonds take on more s character, become shorter and their frequencies rise to 3030 cm.$^{-1}$.

Strain effects of this kind are, however, most marked in vibrations involving double bonds. A good deal is now known of the behaviour of $>C=C<$ and $>C=O$ links under various conditions of strain, and the topic has been well reviewed by Lord and Miller.[28] When the $>C=C<$ group is part of a six-membered ring system the bond angles, and therefore the frequencies, are normal. *cyclo*Hexene [33] absorbs at 1646 cm.$^{-1}$. This is true also for larger ring systems, in which buckling of the ring allows adjustments which reduce the strain and lead to near normal valency angles. However, as the ring size is diminished, strain increases and the $>C=C<$ frequency falls. *cyclo*Pentene absorbs at 1611 cm.$^{-1}$ and *cyclo*butene at 1566 cm.$^{-1}$. For reasons which are not well understood the attachment of a second ring to the first appears to increase the strain in the system so that the vibrational frequency of the C=C bond falls further, the effect being roughly equal to that resulting from the removal of one carbon atom from the ring. Thus a double bond in a fused six-membered ring system bi*cyclo*-2-2-1-octene-2 absorbs [33] at 1614 cm.$^{-1}$, which is close to the frequency of *cyclo*pentene. Similar effects occur in bi*cyclo*-2-2-1-heptene-2, but in bi*cyclo*-2-2-1-hept-5-en-2-yl compounds the strain appears to have a marked effect upon the C=C intensities, which are reduced to a point at which the absorptions cannot be detected.[38]

Similar strain effects occur in more complex systems. The Δ^2 frequencies of steroids and triterpenes, in which strain effects are equal, are the same, but the $\Delta^{9(11)}$ bonds of sterols absorb at lower frequencies [39] (1643–1648 cm.$^{-1}$) than the corresponding bonds [40] in triterpenes (1660 cm.$^{-1}$) because of the differences in the size of the adjacent fused ring. The effect of ring fusion on the strain in the olefinic bonds is also reflected by their reactivities, which show a parallel behaviour.[34]

As is to be expected, the CH stretching frequencies rise as the C=C frequencies fall, and in *cyclo*butene [28] these occur at 3060 cm.$^{-1}$, as compared with 3017 cm.$^{-1}$ in *cyclo*hexene. The behaviour of the CH out-of-plane deformation frequencies is, however, less well known. In steroids and *cyclo*hexenes the *cis*-CH=CH deformation vibration is not readily identified as a single band, but a complex pattern of bands appears which is characteristic of the particular system.[41] In the *cyclo*hexene series the band pattern is simpler than in the steroids, and appears to move to higher frequencies if the strain is increased by ring fusion. However, in *cyclo*pentene and in the bi*cyclo*heptene series the opposite effect is found, and the absorptions occur at lower frequencies than in *cyclo*hexene itself.[38] With exocyclic methylene groups the strain is applied to different bonds, and the frequency therefore rises as the ring size diminishes. This follows from the fact that it is now the single C–C bonds which are distorted and take on additional p-character. The olefinic bond therefore has more s-character in the orbitals from the ring carbon atom, and the bond length is reduced. Methylene *cyclo*butane [28] absorbs at 1678 cm.$^{-1}$ and methylene *cyclo*hexane [35] at 1651 cm.$^{-1}$. The influence of conjugation is still apparent in 1 : 2-dimethylene*cyclo*pentane,[36] which absorbs at a lower freqency (1626 cm.$^{-1}$) than 1-methylene*cyclo*pentane [35] (1657 cm.$^{-1}$). However, in the *cyclo*butane series both 1- and 1-2-dimethylene derivatives absorb at 1650 cm.$^{-1}$, which suggests that the two exocyclic double bonds may not be able to achieve full coplanarity.

The behaviour of carbonyl absorptions in cyclic systems is essentially similar to that of exocyclic methylene groups, and details of the various frequency shifts have been given in the appropriate preceding chapters. Rings with more than six members are capable of some degree of internal adjustment to reduce the strain, and these show normal frequencies, but five-membered ring systems, such as lactones, lactams and anhydrides, all show higher frequencies than the corresponding open-chain compounds. In four-membered ring systems the effect is greater still, and in certain inorganic carbonyl compounds which include very highly strained bridges the carbonyl frequencies rise to above 1800 cm.$^{-1}$. Halford [26] has given a theoretical treatment of the variation of carbonyl frequencies to be expected with changes of bond angle which is in general accord with these observations.

Carbonyl frequencies are also sensitive to the effects of ring fusion. In early studies on the spectrum of penicillin it was observed that β-lactams which were fused to a five-membered ring system absorb at higher frequencies than those which are not. Cyclic ketones show similar effects, and Allen *et al.*[38, 39] have studied six-, seven- and eight-membered ring systems with carbonyl bridges, in all of which the additional strain is reflected in higher carbonyl frequencies.

The effects of strain arising from steric hindrances have been less fully studied, but the principal changes appear to take place in the band widths rather than in the frequencies. Orr [42] has examined *trans-ortho*-substituted stilbenes in which the substituents are sufficiently large to produce buckling, and although the CH deformation frequency is unaltered, the band width increases with the degree of strain. We have observed similar effects with the NO_2 stretching bands of some *ortho*-substituted nitro compounds. However, with aromatics large steric effects can lead to frequency and intensity changes due to the twisting of the nitro groups out of the plane of the ring when conjugation is lost. Some low OH stretching frequencies in unsaturated alcohols [43] have been associated with steric hindrance effects arising from the π electrons, but there is a possibility that some form of hydrogen bonding to the π cloud is involved in these cases.

23.7. ELECTRICAL EFFECTS

The term electrical effect is an indefinite one, but it is difficult to find any alternative which equally well comprehends the various inductive, mesomeric and dipolar field effects which operate in the local environment of a vibrating group. All these effects basically alter the state of hybridisation of the atoms on which they operate, and from this point of view the steric effects discussed above could perhaps equally well be included under this heading. The separation has, however, been made deliberately in order to emphasise the strictly local nature of the effects now to be considered.

Inductive, mesomeric and field effects are the principal factors responsible for the minor but very important differences which occur, for example, between the carbonyl frequencies of ketones, esters and acid chlorides. They can be studied effectively only in groupings which are not sensitive to mass or coupling effects, and it is particularly important to ensure that any comparison between different molecules relates to similar conditions of association, etc. For example, in carbon tetrachloride solution the carbonyl frequencies of acids are lower than those of the corresponding ketones, but this is because the acids are associated as dimers under these conditions. In the vapour phase the reverse is in fact found to be true, and a change of substituent from OR to OH raises the carbonyl frequency.

Ideally it should be possible from a quantitative study of these separate effects to predict the directions and extents of the frequency shifts a given vibration will show following specific alterations of its substituents. This stage is still very far off, and indeed, our whole understanding of the operation of these effects on vibrational frequencies is still to some extent in the field of speculation. Furthermore, these effects sometimes work in opposite directions, one tending to lower the frequency and another to raise it, so that the resultant determines the final direction and extent of the frequency shift. This is well illustrated in the different behaviour of the OH and NH_2 stretching frequencies with alterations in their substituents. Thus, in the series $CH_3OH > PhOH > CH_3COOH$ the OH frequencies fall progressively, whereas the NH_2 stretching frequencies rise in the parallel series of amines, $CH_3NH_2 < PhNH_2 < CH_3CONH_2$. In both cases the increasing inductive effects which follow increasing unsaturation of the substituent in this series would be expected to result in more polar X–H links and lower stretching frequencies. However, the same factors also influence the susceptibility of the OH or NH_2 groups to mesomerism. Both oxygen and nitrogen atoms possess lone-pair electrons with some degree of mobility. In the acids and amides therefore contributions are to be expected

from canonical forms such as $CH_3-\overset{\displaystyle -O}{\underset{|}{C}}=\overset{+}{O}H$ and $CH_3-\overset{\displaystyle -O}{\underset{|}{C}}=\overset{+}{N}H_2$. These will have higher X–H stretching frequencies, just as the corresponding CH_2 modes of vinyl groups have higher stretching frequencies than ordinary CH_2 groups. It would therefore seem that the greater mobility of the lone-pair electrons of the nitrogen atom leads to a substantial contribution from mesomeric forms in amides which outweighs the inductive effect and produces higher NH_2 stretching frequencies than in amines. In the acids, however, the mobility of the lone-pair oxygen electrons is much less, so that the inductive effect predominates and the OH frequency is lower than in alcohols. An exactly parallel behaviour occurs in the carbonyl frequencies of acids and amides, the former being higher than those of ketones and the latter lower. This has been explained on a similar basis by Thompson *et al.*[44]

23.7(a). Inductive Effects. It is now generally recognised that almost all covalent bonds have some degree of polar character, and it is only in exceptional cases, such as in the nitrogen molecule or in the central C–C bond of ethane, that pure covalent links occur. Such vibrations are inactive in the infra-red, so in practice we are always concerned with the vibrations of bonds with some degree of polarity. If a change is made in the electronegativity of a substituent of a vibrating bond the polarity, and therefore the frequency, of the bond will be altered. This is the inductive effect; it operates only along the bonds, is independent of the molecular geometry and is primarily dependent upon the electronegativities of the substituent atoms or upon the effective electronegativities of the substituent groups.

A simplified picture of the operation of inductive effects can be obtained by considering the changes in carbonyl frequency which occur on passing from acetone to acetyl chloride. In acetone the carbonyl bond has some polar character and the oxygen atom carries some negative charge. This implies that the electron cloud forming the link is displaced away from the geometric bond centre towards the oxygen atom. If now one of the methyl groups is replaced by a much more electronegative substituent, such as chlorine, the increased electron attraction will pull the electron cloud back a little nearer to the geometric centre. The polar character of the carbonyl link is therefore diminished and the vibrational frequency rises.

It is therefore to be expected that frequency shifts from induction effects will be controlled mainly by the electronegativities of the substituents, and in cases in which only induction is involved the two should be quantitatively related.

This possibility can be explored in the case of simple molecules XH_n by a direct comparison of the X–H stretching frequencies (corrected as necessary for minor mass effects), and the electronegativities of the elements X. Fig. 1 shows the result of such a comparison. The points corresponding to monovalent elements lie on a straight line and show a simple linear relationship with the Pauling electronegativities, and points from multivalent elements lie on similar lines displaced to one side, depending upon the valency state. This indicates that there is indeed a close quantitative connection between frequencies and electronegativities, but also shows that some additional factors are involved with the multivalent elements. These are not fully understood, but the X–H frequencies themselves in the latter cases are not single but composed of asymmetric and symmetric modes, and there may well be angle effects involved also.

A more direct case is found with the OH stretching frequencies of carboxylic acids, RCOOH. It has long been recognised that the relative ease of ionisation of the hydrogen atom as measured by the PK_a value of the acid is a measure of the inductive effect of the group R. In alkyl acids in which only inductive forces are involved there should accordingly be a direct relation between the OH-stretching frequencies of the monomers and the PK_a values.

Goulden [45] has shown that a simple linear relation of this type does exist. In aromatic acids inductive and mesomeric forces are both at work, and a new linear relation connects the PK_a values and OH frequencies, the difference in slope arising from the introduction of the additional effect.

The relation between electronegativity and group frequencies has also been studied in vinyl compounds of the type CH_2–CXY, in which the CH_2 deformation frequencies have been plotted against the sum

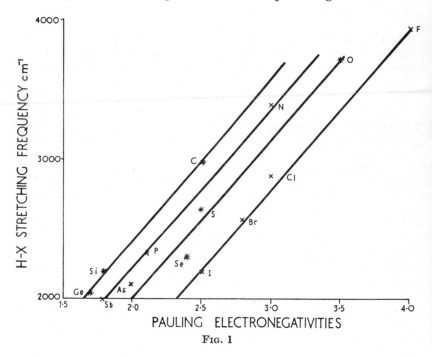

Fɪɢ. 1

of the electronegativities of the substituents.[46] A linear relation is found for substituents such as alkyl or halogen groups, which on chemical grounds are not expected to show marked mesomeric effects. With oxygen or nitrogen substituents, however, in which mesomerism is likely to be appreciable, the relation fails, as is to be expected. One requirement for the occurrence of mesomeric effects is the coplanarity of the bonds concerned, as otherwise it is not possible for suitable molecular orbitals to arise. In non-planar structures, such as pyramidal phosphates and sulphoxides, the incidence of this effect is accordingly much reduced, and this explains the comparative freedom of the P=O and S=O group frequencies from conjugation effects. Induction is therefore the main factor responsible for shifts in these frequencies with alterations in the group substituents, and Bell *et al.*[47] have shown that in phosphoryl halides the P=O frequency is a linear function of the sum of the halogen electronegativities. They have also been able to derive group electronegativities for other substituents which appear to be widely applicable over this series, although there are some irregularities with OH and NH_2 substituents which suggest that interference from hydrogen bonding effects should be allowed for. Kagarise [48] has made a similar study of the carbonyl absorption and derived other " group electronegativities ". It is interesting to find that these show distinct differences from the values of Bell *et al.*, presumably because the planar carbonyl structure permits more extensive mesomerism. For a substituent such as the OR group in esters, for example, both inductive and mesomeric effects will be taken account of in the " group electronegativity " derived from the carbonyl frequency. In the corresponding trialkyl phosphates, however, mesomerism is much reduced, as it is not possible for all the P-O bonds to lie in the same plane as the phosphoryl group. This illustrates the need for caution in the application of group electronegativities derived in this way, and in any event it is not to be expected that anything more than very approximate relationships of this type will be found, because the electronegativities of elements themselves are far from precise quantities and vary with the state of hybridisation employed.[49]

One quantitative approach to the study of induction effects which does not depend upon electronegativities is that of Bellamy and Williams,[1] and has arisen indirectly from their studies on the nature of field effects. This depends on earlier work by Smith, Ree, Magee and Eyring [51] on the quantitative aspects of inductive forces in relation to bond dipoles. These workers have evolved a semi-classical approach which permits the calculation of the residual net charges on the individual atoms of small molecules on the assumption that only inductive forces along the bonds are involved. The values so obtained can be expressed in terms of the individual bond dipoles, and they have been able to show that in the methyl halide series these can be added vectorially over the whole molecule to give molecular dipole moments in excellent agreement with the experimental values. Bellamy and Williams extended this approach to the calculation of the bond dipoles of carbonyl groups in compounds in which mesomeric effects would be low or absent. They also obtained values for molecular dipole moments in good agreement with experiment and then went on to show that the carbonyl bond dipoles obtained in this way were a simple linear function of the observed frequencies. This is illustrated in the lower line of Fig. 2. The upper line relates to the special cases of CF_3COX compounds, in which field effects are superimposed on inductive forces, and will be discussed in the appropriate section below.

It would therefore seem to be reasonably well established that in cases in which only inductive effects are operating the alterations in group frequencies provide a measure of the strength of these effects. Indeed, it is probable that they provide a much more sensitive measure than any other which is yet available, but it will be necessary to proceed very cautiously in the application of this principle because our understanding of the circumstances in which only inductive effects operate is still very incomplete. For example, it is not possible adequately to explain the observation that the $C \equiv C$ frequency of bromo- and iodo-acetylenes are about 100 cm.[-1] lower [28] than either the alkyl or chlorine substituted compounds.

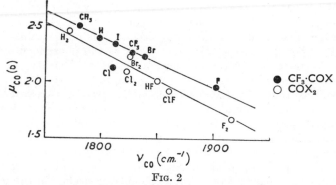

FIG. 2

[*Reproduced from J. Chem. Soc. 1957, 4294, by kind permission of the Council of the Chemical Society.*]

In these cases the physical size of the substituent appears to play some part, and this seems to be true also in certain 1 : 2-halohydrins studied by Nickson.[52] The strengths of the hydrogen bonds between neighbouring halogen and hydroxy groups might be expected to be a function of the halogen electronegativities, as the distances between the centres of the oxygen and halogen nuclei remain the same. The reverse is true in practice, and the strongest bonds are formed to iodine, which is the least electronegative of the series. This suggests that atomic volume is more important in this case and that it is the distance between the proton and the outer valency electrons of the halogen atom which determines the strength of the bond formed.

23.7(b). Conjugation and Mesomerism. The electrons which compose the π clouds of multiple bonds are to some extent polarisable and can be regarded as having some degree of mobility. In a compound such as 1 : 3-butadiene, in which all the carbon atoms lie in a common plane, this leads to the formation of molecular orbitals which encompass all the carbon atoms, with the result that the central single C–C bond acquires some degree of double bond character, whilst the multiple bonds become slightly weaker. The system as a whole gains resonance energy and has higher stability as a result. This is simple conjugation, and it is easy to see that the slight lengthening of the original double bonds which results will lead to falls in their vibrational frequencies. Many illustrations of this are given in the preceding chapters, and no further examples are necessary.

Related effects are also found when an element containing readily polarisable electrons in the form of lone pairs is attached to the multiple bond. In amides, esters and acid chlorides the carbonyl frequency is influenced not only by the electronegativities of the substituents but also by the contributions of canonical forms such as

$$\overset{\displaystyle O^-}{\underset{\displaystyle R-C=\overset{+}{N}R_2}{|}} \qquad \overset{\displaystyle O^-}{\underset{\displaystyle R-C=\overset{+}{O}R}{|}} \qquad \overset{\displaystyle O^-}{\underset{\displaystyle R-C=\overset{+}{C}l}{|}}$$

which in all cases will tend to lower the frequency due to the increased C–O bond length. This is the mesomeric effect, and the extent to which it operates depends upon the availability of the lone-pair electrons for multiple bond formation, which is determined by the polarisabilities of the elements concerned in their given environments. Usually the contribution of canonical forms of this type is low with halogen substituents, so the inductive effect outweighs the mesomerism and the carbonyl frequency is high. The effect is greater with the more polarisable oxygen atom, and is most marked with nitrogen substituents. In the last case the C–N link is shortened considerably, and the carbonyl frequency is lower than in ketones, despite the increased electronegativity of the nitrogen atom. In special cases, such as vinyl acetate, it is found that the system has no resonance energy, which implies that mesomerism has effectively been eliminated, and that there is no contribution from

$$\overset{\displaystyle O^-}{\underset{\displaystyle CH_3-C=\overset{+}{O}-CH=CH_2}{|}}$$

any resonance form such as $CH_3-C=\overset{+}{O}-CH=CH_2$. This may be due to the fact that the carbonyl and vinyl groups will both be exerting a mesomeric pull upon the oxygen lone-pair electrons. If these effectively cancel there will be no resonance, and the carbonyl frequency will then be determined only by the effective electronegativity of the OR group. It is therefore significant that the carbonyl frequencies of vinyl esters should be appreciably higher than those of normal esters and have values approaching those of acid chlorides. Mesomeric effects are therefore to be expected in systems in which an atom with available polarisable electrons is directly attached to a multiple bond, provided that the three atoms lie in a common plane. Thus in αβ-α'β' unsaturated carbonyl compounds both double bonds contribute to the lowering of the carbonyl frequency, but in a non-planar system, such as diallyl-sulphoxide, the S=O frequency is unaffected. Similarly, in aceto-phenones with large substituents at the *ortho*-position the carbonyl group can be made to rotate out of the plane of the ring, and the frequency rises.

Mesomeric effects cannot be isolated from the inductive effects of the same substituents, so it is always necessary to consider the incidence of the combined effect. The resultant is very important, not only in relations to infra-red frequencies but also because it is the controlling factor in changes in many other important physical properties. Alterations in acid and base strengths, dipole moments, bond lengths and, in suitable cases, reaction rates are all determined primarily by the resultant of the inductive (I) and mesomeric (M) effects. Many different attempts have been made to evaluate these effects in a quantitative way, but only in limited cases is this possible with any precision. It may well be that, in suitable instances, the measurement of frequency shifts in the infra-red will provide such a measure, but it is first necessary to show that the vibrations chosen for this purpose are in fact quantitatively de-pendent only on I and M effects and that they are not influenced by any other factors.

Evidence that vibrational frequencies suitable for this purpose do exist is afforded by the many studies on which group frequency shifts have been directly related to other physical properties which are dependent upon I and M effects. The case of the strengths of acids has already been noted,[45] and similar data are available relating the NH stretching frequencies of primary amines to their basic strengths.[53, 54] Carbonyl frequencies have been related to polaro-graphic half-wave potentials,[55] redox potentials,[56] bond lengths [57] and to the stabilities of chelates,[58] and relationships have also been established between the group frequency shifts of carbonyl and of CH_2 vibrations, with changes in the atomic refractivity constants which are an important measure of I and M effects.[46] However, the most important physical property which is connected with these effects is that of reactivity, and numerous studies have been made on the relation between group frequency shifts and reactivity changes.

In this field it is particularly important to distinguish clearly between the types of reaction whose rates are determined solely by I and M effects, and which may therefore be expected to relate to frequency shifts, and those which are influenced by additional factors. Induction and mesomerism can be regarded as the static factors which control reactivities, and in some instances they alone control the reaction rates. In other cases dynamic factors are also involved. For example, the electronic distribution within a molecule may be profoundly disturbed by the approach of the attacking reagent, and this introduces a new element which will not be reflected in any spectroscopic measurement made on the original molecule in the ground state. These dynamic factors have been termed electromeric effects, and have been very fully discussed by Ingold.[59, 60] It is therefore only in reactions in which dynamic effects of this type play no appreciable part that any relationships between reactivities and group frequency shifts are to be expected. Such reactions are generally found in the aromatic series, particularly in reactions involving attack on ring substituents. Hammett [61] has studied reactions of this type very extensively, and his work has been extended by Jaffe [62] and Taft.[63, 64] Hammett has been able to show that a particular group in a given position in an aromatic ring will exert a constant effect upon the reactivity of the compound, depending upon its inductive and mesomeric properties. This can be expressed in terms of a constant σ value, which is a measure of the electron donating or withdrawing powers of the substituent. These constants apply over a wide range of different types of reaction, and they are also additive, so the reactivity of a doubly substituted compound can be predicted from the arithmetic sum of the group σ values.

Hammett σ values therefore afford a convenient measure of the I and M effects of individual groups in aromatic systems, and numerous studies have been made on the relationship they may have to group frequency changes. Linear relationships between σ values and group frequency shifts have been established for the NH_2 stretching frequencies of anilines,[53, 65] the OH stretching frequencies of phenols,[66] the carbonyl frequencies of acetophenones and similar compounds [55, 68-70] and the out-of-plane CH deformation modes of aromatic rings.[71] The order of agreement found is well illustrated by this last example, which is reproduced in Fig. 3. The frequencies are the well-known strong aromatic absorptions which characterise the substitution pattern and are determined by the number of adjacent free hydrogen atoms in the ring. They are known to be mass insensitive, and it will be seen that with the exception of the halogen substituents the order of agreement found is very good. The halogen substituents all behave as though they had zero σ values, and have been plotted on this basis. This is in accord with the nuclear magnetic resonance data of Corio and Dailey,[72] who have found that chlorine and bromine substituents do not alter the electron densities of the aromatic CH groups, and they have therefore concluded that dynamic electromeric effects are important in the reactivities of such compounds. The relationship shown in Fig. 1 has also been used to derive σ values directly from the observed frequencies, the σ value of the *tert*[y].-butyl group, for example, being obtained from the appropriate absorption in the spectrum of 1 : 3 : 5-*tritert*[y]-butyl benzene. The values so obtained can then

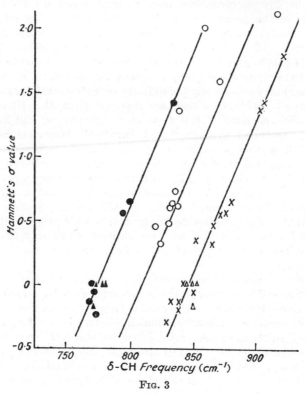

Fig. 3

δ-CH vibrations of : ● 3 adjacent ring hydrogen atoms.
                       ▲ 2   ,,   ,,   ,,   (halogen-substituted).
                       ○ 2   ,,   ,,   ,,
                       × An isolated ring hydrogen atom.
                       △   ,,   ,,   ,,   (halogen-substituted).

[*Reproduced from J. Chem. Soc., 1955, 2818, by kind permission of the Council of the Chemical Society.*]

be used to predict the absorption frequencies of other compounds containing this group, and the agreement with the experimental data is usually of the order of a few cm.[-1].

Lebas and Josien [73] have made rather similar studies on CH stretching frequencies, and have found that, with the exception of the halogen substituents as before, the observed frequency can be correlated directly with the percentages of *meta*-nitro-compounds produced when the mono-substituted compound is nitrated.

In considering the general application of these findings to the evaluation of specific properties it is essential to pay great regard to the suitability for this purpose of the group frequency selected. Ideally it should be one which is particularly sensitive to I and M effects but insensitive to all others. In some of the examples quoted above the overall frequency shifts are relatively small, so they cannot be regarded as providing a sufficiently precise measure of the changes in I and M effects concerned. In other instances, such as in the methyl halide series, there are changes of about 50 cm.$^{-1}$ in the ν_4 CH stretching frequencies on passing from methyl fluoride to methyl iodide. In the high-frequency region these can be measured with great precision, and they therefore afford a sensitive relative measure of the inductive effects of the halogen elements. The fact that the overall changes in CH bond lengths in this series is only 0·001 A is itself an indication of the sensitivity of the frequencies to electrical effects.

The above discussion has been limited to the possible uses of group frequency shifts in the assessment of I and M effects, and of the physical properties which are also dependent upon these factors. Some preliminary studies along parallel lines have also been made in the much more difficult field of intensity measurements. In many cases the intensity changes which follow small alterations in the electron distribution of a vibrating group are dramatically large compared with the corresponding changes in frequency. In so far as they depend upon the same factors, intensity measurements offer an alternative, and often preferable, approach. In some cases it would seem that the two methods give parallel results and relationships between intensities, and Hammett σ values have, for example, been described for NH_2 [75] and OH [76] stretching vibrations. In other instances the intensity changes are not parallel to the frequencies, and there is no obvious connection between the two. Thus, the intensities of carbonyl absorptions in substituted acetophenones show only small changes with alterations of the substituents, and these are not related to the Hammett σ values.[68] Similarly, Barrow [78] finds that over a fairly wide range of different carbonyl compounds the intensity changes are not related to the frequency shifts, but are a function of the resonance energies. This last factor would not at first sight appear to take much account of inductive effects, and it is possible that changes in carbonyl intensities depend primarily on the mesomeric components. There is clearly room for further work in this field, and the results of combined intensity and frequency studies probably constitute the best hope for future advances.

D D

23.7(c). Dipolar Field Effects. Until recently it was thought likely that induction and mesomerism were the only electrical factors operating on group frequencies in unstrained systems, but the more detailed study of some anomalous frequencies has brought a third effect to light. In α-halogenated keto steroids Jones *et al.*[79, 80] noted that equatorial substitution raised the carbonyl frequency by about 25 cm.[-1], but axial substitution did not. Parallel cases were noted by Page,[81] and Corey and others have also found this effect in α-halogen-substituted *cyclo*hexanones.[82-85] Mesomeric effects would be expected to be very small in these compounds, and induction is not dependent upon the molecular geometry, so the results cannot adequately be accounted for by I and M effects. The position is further complicated by the finding that the introduction of a second halogen atom at the α-carbon has little or no effect upon the carbonyl frequency, but if it is introduced at the α′-position a further frequency rise occurs. This has led Jones *et al.*[68, 86] and Bellamy and Williams[1, 50, 87, 88] to suggest that field effects may be operating in such cases and that the frequency is influenced by dipolar electrical forces operating across intermolecular space rather than along the bonds in the conventional manner.

This concept has been elaborated by Bellamy and Williams[1] in simple electrostatic terms. They suggest that the near approach of a negatively charged halogen atom to the readily polarisable negatively charged oxygen of the carbonyl group will result in a mutual induction of opposite charges. In consequence, the negative character of both the chlorine and oxygen atoms will be diminished, and the C–Cl and C=O bonds will become less polar. Their vibrational frequencies will therefore rise, as is observed experimentally. This is essentially similar to the electrostatic effects discussed earlier in relation to liquid acetone, in which the C=O dipoles align themselves preferentially so that unlike charges are brought together. In the more restricted intramolecular environment, however, it will not always be possible for bond dipoles to arrange themselves in this way, and frequency shifts in either direction are to be expected, depending upon whether the interactions occur between like or unlike charges.

This hypothesis rests in part on experimental studies on α-halogenated carbonyl compounds, and in part upon some rough calculations which suggest that frequency shifts of the observed order of magnitude would be expected to arise from such electrostatic interactions. However, its main importance is perhaps that it provides a simple unifying picture which enables a number of otherwise anomalous frequencies to be explained.

Experimental studies of field effects have concentrated primarily on α-halogenated carbonyl compounds, and in addition to the sterols and *cyclo*-hexanones a considerable number of open-chain ketones and similar compounds have been examined. These latter materials are capable of rotational isomerism in the liquid state, so that a compound such as chloroacetone then exists as a mixture of forms I and II. Two carbonyl frequencies are therefore found in the liquid or solution corresponding to the separate isomers, and by

I.
$$
\begin{array}{c}
\text{O} \\
\text{Cl} \parallel \\
\underset{\text{H}\quad\text{H}}{\overset{}{\text{C}}}\!\!-\!\!\overset{}{\text{C}}\!-\!\text{CH}_3
\end{array}
$$
II.
$$
\begin{array}{c}
\text{O} \\
\text{H} \parallel \\
\underset{\text{H}\quad\text{Cl}}{\overset{}{\text{C}}}\!\!-\!\!\overset{}{\text{C}}\!-\!\text{CH}_3
\end{array}
$$

studies on the intensity changes which they show with alterations in temperature and of the polarity of solvents it is possible to decide which corresponds to the more polar form. In some cases, such as chloroacetone itself, the results are confirmed by dipole moment studies.[89] In all the compounds examined which exhibit rotational isomerism of this type the higher carbonyl frequency has been identified with the more polar form similar to I above,[1, 50] whilst the lower frequency, corresponding to forms such as II, is usually close to that of the original ketone, which is in accordance with the suggested mechanism. This theory also offers a convenient explanation of the failure of a second α-halogen atom to result in a further frequency rise, as it is not possible for more than one of them to take up a *cis*-position with respect to the carbonyl oxygen atom. However, when halogen atoms are substituted on opposite sides of the carbonyl group it should be possible for both to exert a separate field effect. This is confirmed in the case of 1 : 3-dichloroacetone, which can exist in the isomeric forms III, IV and V below. This compound has three carbonyl frequencies in the liquid state, which can be assigned in the manner indicated by temperature dependence studies.

III. ν_{CO} 1755 cm.$^{-1}$.   IV. ν_{CO} 1742 cm.$^{-1}$.   V. ν_{CO} 1728 cm.$^{-1}$.

Similar results have been obtained in our laboratories with α-halogen-substituted aldehydes and acid chlorides, and it is also possible for a field effect to occur between the carbonyl oxygen atom of acetophenone and chlorine or nitro groups substituted in the *ortho*-position.[50, 68] Data available in the literature indicate that these effects occur also in acids, esters and amides. The case of esters is well illustrated by the data of Josien and Calas,[90] who studied methyl acetate and its chlorinated derivatives in carbon tetra-chloride solutions. Methyl acetate absorbs under these conditions at 1750 cm.$^{-1}$. Both the mono- and dichloro-derivatives absorb at this point, corresponding to isomers in which the chlorine atoms are twisted away from the carbonyl oxygen atom, but both also show an additional absorption at 1775 cm.$^{-1}$, due to isomers in which a field effect is taking place. In methyltrichloroacetate only a single band is found at 1770 cm.$^{-1}$, as is to be expected.

Halogenated amides also present an interesting anomaly, in that, unlike the corresponding ketones, the introduction of an α-halogen atom does not usually result in any appreciable frequency rise, and it is not until a second halogen is substituted on the same carbon atom that the expected upward shifts occur. Data on such compounds have been given by Letaw and Groop [91] and have been discussed by Bellamy and Williams.[1] The latter authors point out that this behaviour is to some extent to be expected from their simple picture of electrostatic interactions, as normal mesomeric forces in amides leave the nitrogen atom with some formal positive charge. The electrostatic repulsion between the negative halogen and oxygen atoms is therefore reinforced by the electrostatic attraction between the chlorine and nitrogen atoms. A marked increase in the relative stability of a *gauche* form, such as VI, is therefore to be expected. This suggestion has been fully supported by recent

$$
\begin{array}{c}
\text{O} \\
\| \\
\text{H} \quad \text{C} \qquad \text{VI.} \\
| \\
\text{C} \quad \text{NR}_2 \\
\text{H} \qquad \text{Cl}
\end{array}
$$

dipole moment studies on methyl chloroacetamide, which show that this form occurs almost exclusively in non-polar solvents.[99]

The quantitative aspects of this theory of field effects have also been explored. In the previous section a method for the calculation of the bond dipoles of carbonyl groups was discussed, and the lower line of Fig. 2 illustrates the relationship found between carbonyl frequencies and the bond dipoles in compounds in which only inductive effects along the bonds are involved. When the same treatment is applied to trifluoromethyl carbonyl compounds the upper line of Fig. 2 is obtained, and the displacement from the original is associated with the superposition of field effects which are not taken into account in the calculation. This displacement, which is of the order of 0·2 Debyes, is therefore a measure of the alteration of the C=O bond dipole under the influence of the field effect of the CF$_3$ group. It is possible to make a separate calculation of the probable magnitude of this field effect by considering the fluorine and oxygen atoms as point charges, using the individual calculated values for the C–F and C=O bond dipoles and taking reasonable values for the longitudinal bond polarisabilities. This gives a value of 0·19 Debyes for the particular series in question. The excellent agreement is almost certainly fortuitous, as many approximations are involved, but it serves to show that the observed field effects are of the order of magnitude which would be expected from the theory of simple electrostatic interactions.

It would therefore seem that field effects are the predominant cause of frequency shifts in α-halogenated carbonyl compounds. This is not to suggest, however, that inductive effects are wholly absent. The observation that halogen atoms in a *gauche* configuration to the oxygen atom do not lead to any appreciable carbonyl frequency shifts could also be due to the cancellation of the inductive effects by small residual field effects, which in this configuration would be expected to operate in the opposite direction. This may be the origin of some of the minor fluctuations of carbonyl frequencies such as occur with ethyl trifluoroacetate, which absorbs 9 cm.-1 higher than the difluoro compound,[93] and with methyl trichloroacetate, which absorbs 5 cm.-1 lower than the corresponding dichloro derivatives.[90]

Field effects have not been extensively studied in other types of compound, although they are to be expected in any molecules in which two charged atoms with polarisable electrons occur near to each other in space. It has been suggested, for example, that the abnormal carbonyl frequencies of 21-acetoxy-20-keto steroids may arise from interactions of this type between the two carbonyl oxygen atoms.[87]

Intramolecular field effects which may be of a rather different type occur in some cyclic aminoacyloins and related compounds which show abnormally low carbonyl frequencies.[94] A good deal of work on this class of compound has been carried out by Leonard and his collaborators, and full references are given in Chapter 9. The compounds concerned are cyclic ring systems such as VII and VIII below, in which the configuration is such that the nitrogen

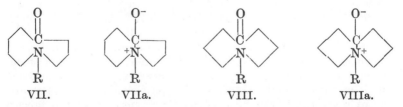

VII.   VIIa.   VIII.   VIIIa.

atom approaches very closely to the carbon of the carbonyl group. Interaction then occurs, either through a simple field effect, which in this case would involve unlike charges and lead to a frequency fall, or perhaps more probably through contributions from resonance forms such as VIIa and VIIIa. Either mechanism would result in an increase in the polarity of the C=O link and a fall in the frequency. In consequence, compounds of this type show low carbonyl frequencies similar to those of amides rather than of ketones. The close approach of the nitrogen atom to the carbonyl carbon is confirmed by the fact that on salt formation with perchloric acid bridged-ring compounds with hydroxyl groups are formed. Also it is possible to cause the interacting atoms to separate farther apart, either by adjustments in the ring size or by the use of bulky substituents on the nitrogen atom. The carbonyl frequency then reverts to the normal value for a large ring ketone and appears near 1720 cm.$^{-1}$.

23.7(d). Applications. The data presented above suggest very strongly that the study of the group frequency shifts of very carefully selected vibrations may open the way to new applications of infra-red techniques in following changes in physical properties, and of the electrical effects which are responsible for them, although for the full exploitation of these possibilities it will almost certainly be necessary for frequency studies to be supplemented by work on intensities. As has been repeatedly pointed out, however, this approach requires the greatest caution, both in the selection of suitable vibration frequencies and in the application of the data to any particular problem.

Despite these limitations, there are already a number of cases, such as those quoted in the preceding sections, in which frequency measurements can be used to supplement and extend physical data of other types, and studies in this field have also led to some useful correlations connecting the positions of two or more bands within the same spectrum. Examples of such applications are afforded by the SO_2 and the NH_2 stretching frequencies, which are essentially free from mass and coupling effects. Both of these groups give rise to asymmetric and symmetric stretching frequencies, the precise positions of which depend upon the electrical character of the substituents. In each case therefore the frequency shifts of the asymmetric and of the symmetric vibrations are dependent upon a common factor, and they should therefore be directly related to each other. Fig. 4 illustrates the results of plotting these two frequencies, one against the other, for a variety of different environments of the SO_2 group. It will be seen that a good linear relationship exists, and this is useful in correlation work, as a provisional identification of one of these bands can be confirmed by reference to the precise position of the other.[88] The two NH_2 stretching modes of primary amines behave similarly and are connected by the relation [94]

$$\nu_s = 345 \cdot 5 + 0 \cdot 876 \, \nu_{as}.$$

These relationships depend upon the equivalence of the two bonds concerned and their dependence upon the same electrical factors. If this equivalence is removed by hydrogen bonding or other association effects which influence one bond more than the other the relationship will no longer apply.   This has been found to be true in primary amines, in which one NH group is bonded and the other is not, and this indirectly provides a sensitive test for this type of association.

Another relationship of this type has been found which connects the carbonyl and C–O stretching frequencies of steroid acetates.[95]

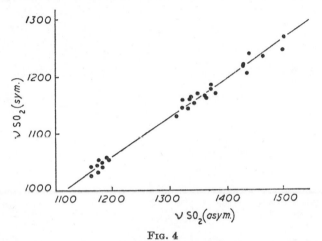

Fig. 4

[*Reproduced from J. Chem. Soc., 1957, 863, by kind permission of the Council of the Chemical Society.*]

The normal mass sensitivity of the C–O bond is minimised in these cases by its constant environment, and its frequency, like that of the carbonyl group, varies systematically with the electrical character of the substituents.   In consequence, a simple linear relationship connects the two, which is valuable for identification purposes.

An example of the need for caution in this type of approach is provided by the results obtained when the asymmetric and symmetric stretching frequencies of the nitro group are plotted, one against the other.   No smooth overall relationship is found in this case.   Brown [96] has discussed the reasons for this, and has pointed out that, although the asymmetric frequency is free from coupling effects, this is probably not the case with the symmetric vibration, which occurs near the C–N frequency and has the same symmetry. The symmetric vibration is therefore subject to an additional variable and does not follow a linear relation with the asymmetric frequency.

It is also possible to find relationships involving many bands within one spectrum, as in the case of the six fundamental methyl group vibrations.   It can be shown that each of the CH stretching, deformation and wagging modes of the methyl halide series is dependent upon the halogen electronegativities, and this is even true of the C–X stretching frequency if suitably corrected for mass. This in itself is not particularly useful, because of the lack of precision in the electronegativity values.   However, the mass corrected H–X stretching frequencies of the halogen acids also vary systematically with the electronegativities (Fig. 1), and by plotting these HX frequencies directly against the CH_3X frequencies the uncertainties

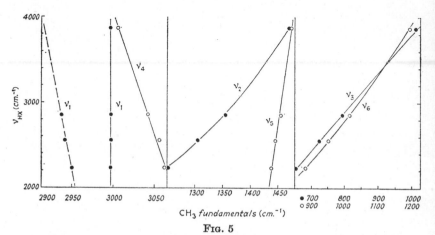

FIG. 5

[*Reproduced from J. Chem. Soc., 1956, 2753, by kind permission of the Council of the Chemical Society.*]

of electronegativities can be cancelled out.   The order of agreement found is illustrated in Fig. 5, which includes the five CH modes, a calculated line representing the correction of one of them for coupling effects and the mass corrected C–X frequencies.

Reference to Fig. 1 shows that factors other than electronegativity play a part in determining the X–H stretching frequencies of multivalent elements.   If, however it can be assumed that these same factors apply equally in the CH_3–$X(H)_n$ series it should be possible to read off from Fig. 5, using, say, the OH stretching frequency of water, the six fundamental methyl-group frequencies of methanol. It has been shown that the agreement obtained in this way is reasonably good over a fairly wide range of differently substituted methyl compounds,[74] and this has useful applications in the checking of vibrational assignments.

Studies have also been made involving the intercomparison of the vibrations of different groups with the same substituents. For example, the systematic changes in the carbonyl frequencies of compounds $RCOCH_3$ with alterations in the nature of R have been compared directly with the shifts of the $N{=}O$ stretching frequencies of compounds $R{-}N{=}O$ with the same series of substituents. Reasonably good linear relationships [88, 97] can be realised in this way, provided that the groups compared are both subject to electrical effects to a comparable degree. However, as is to be expected, discrepancies occur in circumstances in which field effects are operative, as the differences in the interatomic distances and the atomic polarisabilities result in different degrees of interaction.

One other field in which the study of the origins of group frequency shifts could well find useful application is in the more detailed examination of intramolecular field effects in relation to the intermolecular effects which accompany a change of phase. The mechanisms of interaction, in some cases at least, would seem to be very similar, and studies of intramolecular forces which operate at known angles and across known distances may well pave the way for a better understanding of the more complicated problems of intermolecular interactions.

23.8. BIBLIOGRAPHY

1. Bellamy and Williams, *J. Chem. Soc.*, 1957, 4294.
2. Barker, Bourne, Neely and Whiffen, *Chem. and Ind.*, 1954, 1418.
3. Farmer, *ibid.*, 1955, 87.
4. *Idem, Spectrochim. Acta*, 1956, **8**, 374.
5. Barker, *J. Phys. Chem.*, 1957, **61**, 450.
6. Kirkwood, cited by West and Edwards, *J. Chem. Phys.*, 1937, **5**, 14.
7. Bauer and Magat, *J. Phys. Radium*, 1938, **9**, 319.
8. Josien, Sourisseau and Castinel, *Bull. Soc. Chim. France*, 1955, 1539.
9. Josien and Sourisseau, *ibid.*, 178.
10. Josien and Saumagne, *ibid.*, 1956, 937.
11. Josien and Fuson, *J. Chem. Phys.*, 1954, **22**, 1169.
12. Bayliss, Cole and Little, *Austral. J. Chem.*, 1955, **8**, 26.
13. Hirota, *Bull. Chem. Soc., Japan*, 1954, **27**, 295.
14. Buckingham and Le Fevre, *J. Chem. Soc.*, 1952, 132.
15. Le Fevre and Le Fevre, *Austral. J. Chem.*, 1954, **7**, 33.
16. Smith, *Electric Dipole Moments* (Butterworths, London, 1955), pp. 159 *et seq.*
17. Hadži and Sheppard, *Proc. Roy. Soc.*, 1953, **A216**, 247.
18. Badger, *J. Chem. Phys.*, 1940, **8**, 288.
19. Lord and Merrifield, *ibid.*, 1953, **21**, 166.
20. Kuhn, *J. Amer. Chem. Soc.*, 1952, **74**, 2492.
21. Jones and Sandorfy, *Chemical Applications of Spectroscopy* (Interscience, 1956), p. 422.
22. Nakamoto, Margoshes and Rundle, *J. Amer. Chem. Soc.*, 1955, **77**, 6480.
23. Pimentel and Sederholm, *J. Chem. Phys.*, 1956, **24**, 639.
24. Cannon, *Mikrochem. Acta*, 1955, 555.
25. Tamres, Searles, Leighly and Mohrman, *J. Amer. Chem. Soc.*, 1954, **76**, 3984.
26. Halford, *J. Chem. Phys.*, 1956, **24**, 830.
27. Whiffen, *Chem. and Ind.*, 1957, 193.
28. Lord and Miller, *Applied Spectroscopy*, 1956, **10**, 115.

29. Randle and Whiffen, *J. Chem. Soc.*, 1955, 1311.
30. Bellamy and Branch, *Nature*, 1954, **173**, 634.
31. Frazer and Price, *ibid.*, 1952, **170**, 490.
32. Mecke and Mecke, *Chem. Ber.*, 1956, **89**, 343.
33. Lord and Walker, *J. Amer. Chem. Soc.*, 1954, **76**, 2518.
34. Traynham and Sehnert, *ibid.*, 1956, **78**, 4024.
35. Akishin and Tatevskii, *Vestnik Moscov Univ. 6 No. 2 Ser. Fiz. mat i Estestven Nauk.*, 1951, 103.
36. Blomquist, Wolinsky, Meinwald and Longone, *J. Amer. Chem. Soc.*, 1956, **78**, 6057.
37. Blomquist and Verdol, *ibid.*, 1955, **77**, 1806.
38. Henbest, Meakins, Nicholls and Wilson, *J. Chem. Soc.*, 1957, 997.
39. Jones, Humphries, Packard and Dobriner, *J. Amer. Chem. Soc.*, 1950, **72**, 86.
40. Cole and Thornton, *J. Chem. Soc.*, 1957, 1332.
41. Henbest, Meakins and Wood, *ibid.*, 1954, 800.
42. Orr, *Spectrochim. Acta*, 1956, **8**, 218.
43. Anet and Bavin, *Can. J. Chem.*, 1956, **34**, 1756.
44. Hartwell, Richards and Thompson, *J. Chem. Soc.*, 1948, 1436.
45. Goulden, *Spectrochim. Acta*, 1954, **6**, 129.
46. Bellamy, *J. Chem. Soc.*, 1955, 4221.
47. Bell, Heisler, Tannebaum and Goldenson, *J. Amer. Chem. Soc.*, 1954, **76**, 5185.
48. Kagarise, *ibid.*, 1955, **77**, 1377.
49. Skinner and Pritchard, *Trans. Faraday Soc.*, 1953, **49**, 1254.
50. Bellamy and Williams, *J. Chem. Soc.*, 1956, 3704.
51. Smith, Ree, Magee and Eyring, *J. Amer. Chem. Soc.*, 1951, **73**, 2263.
52. Nickson, *J. Amer. Chem. Soc.*, 1957, **79**, 243.
53. Flett, *Trans. Faraday Soc.*, 1948, **44**, 767.
54. Richards, *ibid.*, 40.
55. Fuson, Josien and Shelton, *J. Amer. Chem. Soc.*, 1954, **76**, 2526.
56. Josien, Fuson, Lebas and Gregory, *J. Chem. Phys.*, 1953, **21**, 331.
57. Fillwalk, Fassel and Rundle, *ibid.*, 1954, **22**, 381.
58. Bellamy and Branch, *J. Chem. Soc.*, 1954, 4491.
59. Ingold, *Chem. Reviews*, 1934, **15**, 225.
60. *Idem, Structure and Mechanism in Organic Chemistry* (Bell, London, 1954).
61. Hammett, *Physical Organic Chemistry* (McGraw Hill, New York, 1940).
62. Jaffe, *Chem. Reviews*, 1953, **53**, 191.
63. Taft, *J. Amer. Chem. Soc.*, 1953, **75**, 4231.
64. *Idem, Steric Effects in Organic Chemistry* (Wiley, New York, 1956).
65. Califano and Moccia, *Gazz. Chim.*, 1956, **86**, 1014.
66. Ingraham, Corse, Bailey and Stitt, *J. Amer. Chem. Soc.*, 1952, **74**, 2297.
67. Forbes and Müeller, *Can. J. Chem.*, 1957, **35**, 488.
68. Jones, Forbes and Müeller, *ibid.*, 504.
69. Scrocco and Liberti, *Ricerca Sci.*, 1954, **24**, 1687.
70. Davison, *J. Chem. Soc.*, 1951, 2456.
71. Bellamy, *ibid.*, 1955, 2818.
72. Corio and Dailey, *J. Amer. Chem. Soc.*, 1956, **78**, 3043.
73. Lebas and Josien, *Bull. Soc. Chim. France*, 1956, 62.
74. Bellamy and Williams, *J. Chem. Soc.*, 1956, 2753.
75. Califano and Moccia, *Gazz. Chim.*, 1957, **87**, 58.
76. Stone and Thompson, *Spectrochim. Acta*, 1957, **10**, 17.
77. Staats, Morgan and Goldstein, *J. Chem. Phys.*, 1956, **25**, 582.
78. Barrow, *ibid.*, 1953, **21**, 2008.
79. Jones, Ramsey, Herling and Dobriner, *J. Amer. Chem. Soc.*, 1952, **74**, 2828.
80. Jones, *ibid.*, 1953, **75**, 4839.
81. Dickson and Page, *J. Chem. Soc.*, 1955, 447.
82. Corey, *J. Amer. Chem. Soc.*, 1953, **75**, 2301.
83. Corey, Topie and Wozniak, *ibid.*, 1955, **77**, 5415.
84. Corey, and Burke, *ibid.*, 5418.
85. Inayama, *Pharm. Bull. Japan*, 1956, **4**, 198.
86. Jones and Sandorfy, *op. cit.*, p. 479.

87. Bellamy and Williams, *J. Chem. Soc.*, 1957, 861.
88. *Idem, ibid.*, 863.
89. Nakagawa, Ichishima, Kuratani, Miyazawa, Shimanouchi and Mizushima, *J. Chem. Phys.*, 1952, **20**, 170.
90. Josien and Calas, *Compt. Rend. Acad. Sci. (Paris)*, 1955, **247**, 1641.
91. Letaw and Groop, *J. Chem. Phys.*, 1953, **21**, 1621.
92. Bender, *J. Amer. Chem. Soc.*, 1953, **75**, 5986.
93. Leonard, Fox, Oki and Chiavarelli, *ibid.*, 1954, **76**, 630.
94. Bellamy and Williams, *Spectrochim. Acta*, 1957, **9**, 341.
95. Jones and Sandorfy, *op. cit.*, p. 482.
96. Brown, *J. Amer. Chem. Soc.*, 1955, **77**, 6341.
97. Bellamy, *Chem. and Ind.*, 1957, 26.
98. Whiffen, *Quart. Reviews, Chem. Soc.*, 1950, **4**, 131.
99. Mizushima, Shimanouchi, Ichishima, Miyazawa, Nakawaga and Arkai, *J. Amer. Chem. Soc.*, 1956, **78**, 2038.
100. Lippincott and Schroeder, *J. Chem. Phys.*, 1955, **23**, 1099.
101. Welsh, *ibid.*, 1957, **26**, 710.

SUBJECT INDEX

COMPOUND INDEX

416

	0	1	2	3	4	5	6	7	8	9	1 2 3	4 5 6	7 8 9
1·0	1·0000	·9901	·9804	·9709	·9615	·9524	·9434	·9346	·9259	·9174	9 18 27	36 45 55	64 73 82
1·1	·9091	·9009	·8929	·8850	·8772	·8696	·8621	·8547	·8475	·8403	8 15 23	30 38 45	53 61 68
1·2	·8333	·8264	·8197	·8130	·8065	·8000	·7937	·7874	·7813	·7752	6 13 19	26 32 38	45 51 58
1·3	7692	·7634	·7576	·7519	·7463	·7407	·7353	·7299	·7246	·7194	5 11 16	22 27 33	38 44 49
1·4	·7143	·7092	·7042	·6993	·6944	·6897	·6849	·6803	·6757	·6711	5 10 14	19 24 29	33 38 43
1·5	·6667	·6623	·6579	·6536	·6494	·6452	·6410	·6369	·6329	·6289	4 8 13	17 21 25	29 33 38
1·6	·6250	·6211	·6173	·6135	·6098	·6061	·6024	·5988	·5952	·5917	4 7 11	15 18 22	26 29 33
1·7	·5882	·5848	·5814	·5780	·5747	·5714	·5682	·5650	·5618	·5587	3 7 10	13 16 20	23 26 30
1·8	·5556	·5525	5495	·5464	·5435	·5405	·5376	·5348	·5319	·5291	3 6 9	12 15 18	20 23 26
1·9	·5263	·5236	·5208	·5181	·5155	·5128	·5102	·5076	·5051	·5025	3 5 8	11 13 16	18 21 24
2·0	·5000	·4975	·4950	·4926	·4902	·4878	·4854	·4831	·4808	·4785	2 5 7	10 12 14	17 19 21
2·1	4762	·4739	·4717	·4695	·4673	·4651	·4630	·4608	·4587	·4566	2 4 7	9 11 13	15 17 20
2·2	4545	·4525	·4505	·4484	·4464	·4444	·4425	·4405	·4386	·4367	2 4 6	8 10 12	14 16 18
2·3	4348	·4329	·4310	·4292	·4274	·4255	·4237	·4219	·4202	·4184	2 4 5	7 9 11	13 14 16
2·4	·4167	·4149	·4132	·4115	·4098	4082	4065	4049	·4032	·4016	2 3 5	7 8 10	12 13 15
2·5	·4000	·3984	·3968	·3953	·3937	·3922	·3906	·3891	·3876	·3861	2 3 5	6 8 9	11 12 14
2·6	·3846	·3831	·3817	·3802	·3788	3774	·3759	·3745	·3731	·3717	1 3 4	6 7 8	10 11 13
2·7	·3704	·3690	·3676	3663	·3650	·3636	·3623	·3610	·3597	·3584	1 3 4	5 7 8	9 11 12
2·8	·3571	·3559	·3546	·3534	·3521	·3509	·3497	·3484	·3472	·3460	1 2 4	5 6 7	9 10 11
2·9	·3448	·3436	·3425	·3413	·3401	·3390	·3378	·3367	·3356	·3344	1 2 3	5 6 7	8 9 10
3·0	·3333	·3322	·3311	·3300	·3289	3279	·3268	·3257	·3247	·3236	1 2 3	4 5 6	7 9 10
3·1	3226	·3215	·3205	3195	·3185	·3175	·3165	·3155	3145	·3135	1 2 3	4 5 6	7 8 9
3·2	3125	·3115	·3106	·3096	·3086	3077	·3067	·3058	·3049	·3040	1 2 3	4 5 6	7 8 9
3·3	3030	·3021	·3012	·3003	·2994	·2985	·2976	·2967	·2959	·2950	1 2 3	4 4 5	6 7 8
3·4	·2941	·2933	·2924	·2915	·2907	·2899	·2890	·2882	·2874	·2865	1 2 3	3 4 5	6 7 8
3·5	·2857	·2849	·2841	·2833	·2825	·2817	·2809	·2801	2793	·2786	1 2 2	3 4 5	6 6 7
3·6	·2778	·2770	·2762	·2755	·2747	·2740	·2732	·2725	·2717	·2710	1 2 2	3 4 5	5 6 7
3·7	·2703	·2695	·2688	·2681	·2674	·2667	·2660	·2653	·2646	·2639	1 1 2	3 4 4	5 6 6
3·8	·2632	·2625	·2618	·2611	·2604	·2597	·2591	·2584	·2577	·2571	1 1 2	3 3 4	5 5 6
3·9	·2564	·2558	·2551	·2545	·2538	·2532	·2525	·2519	·2513	·2506	1 1 2	3 3 4	4 5 6
4·0	·2500	·2494	·2488	·2481	·2475	·2469	·2463	·2457	·2451	·2445	1 1 2	2 3 4	4 5 5
4·1	·2439	·2433	·2427	·2421	·2415	·2410	·2404	·2398	·2392	·2387	1 1 2	2 3 3	4 5 5
4·2	·2381	·2375	·2370	·2364	·2358	·2353	·2347	·2342	·2336	·2331	1 1 2	2 3 3	4 4 5
4·3	·2326	·2320	·2315	·2309	·2304	·2299	·2294	·2288	·2283	·2278	1 1 2	2 3 3	4 4 5
4·4	·2273	·2268	·2262	·2257	·2252	·2247	·2242	·2237	·2232	·2227	1 1 2	2 3 3	4 4 5
4·5	·2222	·2217	·2212	·2208	·2203	·2198	·2193	·2188	·2183	·2179	0 1 1	2 2 3	3 4 4
4·6	·2174	·2169	·2165	·2160	·2155	·2151	·2146	·2141	·2137	·2132	0 1 1	2 2 3	3 4 4
4·7	·2128	·2123	·2119	·2114	·2110	·2105	·2101	·2096	·2092	·2088	0 1 1	2 2 3	3 4 4
4·8	·2083	·2079	·2075	·2070	·2066	·2062	:2058	·2053	·2049	·2045	0 1 1	2 2 3	3 3 4
4·9	·2041	·2037	·2033	·2028	·2024	·2020	·2016	·2012	·2008	·2004	0 1 1	2 2 2	3 3 4
5·0	·2000	·1996	·1992	·1988	·1984	·1980	1976	·1972	·1969	·1965	0 1 1	2 2 2	3 3 4
5·1	·1961	·1957	·1953	·1949	·1946	·1942	·1938	·1934	·1931	·1927	0 1 1	2 2 2	3 3 3
5·2	·1923	·1919	·1916	·1912	·1908	·1905	·1901	·1898	·1894	·1890	0 1 1	1 2 2	3 3 3
5·3	·1887	·1883	·1880	·1876	·1873	·1869	·1866	·1862	·1859	·1855	0 1 1	1 2 2	3 3 3
5·4	·1852	·1848	·1845	·1842	·1838	·1835	·1832	·1828	·1825	·1821	0 1 1	1 2 2	2 3 3
	0	1	2	3	4	5	6	7	8	9	1 2 3	4 5 6	7 8 9

	0	1	2	3	4	5	6	7	8	9	1 2 3	4 5 6	7 8 9
5·5	·1818	·1815	·1812	·1808	·1805	·1802	·1799	·1795	·1792	·1789	0 1 1	1 2 2	2 3 3
5·6	·1786	·1783	·1779	·1776	·1773	·1770	·1767	·1764	·1761	·1757	0 1 1	1 2 2	2 3 3
5·7	·1754	·1751	·1748	·1745	·1742	·1739	·1736	·1733	·1730	·1727	0 1 1	1 2 2	2 2 3
5·8	·1724	·1721	·1718	·1715	·1712	·1709	·1706	·1704	·1701	·1698	0 1 1	1 1 2	2 2 3
5·9	·1695	·1692	·1689	·1686	·1684	·1681	·1678	·1675	·1672	·1669	0 1 1	1 1 2	2 2 3
6·0	·1667	·1664	·1661	·1658	·1656	·1653	·1650	·1647	·1645	·1642	0 1 1	1 1 2	2 2 3
6·1	·1639	·1637	·1634	·1631	·1629	·1626	·1623	·1621	·1618	·1616	0 1 1	1 1 2	2 2 2
6·2	·1613	·1610	·1608	·1605	·1603	·1600	·1597	·1595	·1592	·1590	0 1 1	1 1 2	2 2 2
6·3	·1587	·1585	·1582	·1580	·1577	·1575	·1572	·1570	·1567	·1565	0 0 1	1 1 1	2 2 2
6·4	·1563	·1560	·1558	·1555	·1553	·1550	·1548	·1546	·1543	·1541	0 0 1	1 1 1	2 2 2
6·5	·1538	·1536	·1534	·1531	·1529	·1527	·1524	·1522	·1520	·1517	0 0 1	1 1 1	2 2 2
6·6	·1515	·1513	·1511	·1508	·1506	·1504	·1502	·1499	·1497	·1495	0 0 1	1 1 1	2 2 2
6·7	·1493	·1490	·1488	·1486	·1484	·1481	·1479	·1477	·1475	·1473	0 0 1	1 1 1	2 2 2
6·8	·1471	·1468	·1466	·1464	·1462	·1460	·1458	·1456	·1453	·1451	0 0 1	1 1 1	2 2 2
6·9	·1449	·1447	·1445	·1443	·1441	·1439	·1437	·1435	·1433	·1431	0 0 1	1 1 1	1 2 2
7·0	·1429	·1427	·1425	·1422	·1420	·1418	·1416	·1414	·1412	·1410	0 0 1	1 1 1	1 2 2
7·1	·1408	·1406	·1404	·1403	·1401	·1399	·1397	·1395	·1393	·1391	0 0 1	1 1 1	1 2 2
7·2	·1389	·1387	·1385	·1383	·1381	·1379	·1377	·1376	·1374	·1372	0 0 1	1 1 1	1 2 2
7·3	·1370	·1368	·1366	·1364	·1362	·1361	·1359	·1357	·1355	·1353	0 0 1	1 1 1	1 2 2
7·4	·1351	·1350	·1348	·1346	·1344	·1342	·1340	·1339	·1337	·1335	0 0 1	1 1 1	1 1 2
7·5	·1333	·1332	·1330	·1328	·1326	·1325	·1323	·1321	·1319	·1318	0 0 1	1 1 1	1 1 2
7·6	·1316	·1314	·1312	·1311	·1309	·1307	·1305	·1304	·1302	·1300	0 0 1	1 1 1	1 1 2
7·7	·1299	·1297	·1295	·1294	·1292	·1290	·1289	·1287	·1285	·1284	0 0 0	1 1 1	1 1 1
7·8	·1282	·1280	1279	·1277	·1276	·1274	·1272	·1271	·1269	·1267	0 0 0	1 1 1	1 1 1
7·9	·1266	·1264	·1263	·1261	·1259	·1258	·1256	·1255	·1253	·1252	0 0 0	1 1 1	1 1 1
8·0	·1250	·1248	·1247	·1245	·1244	·1242	·1241	·1239	·1238	·1236	0 0 0	1 1 1	1 1 1
8·1	·1235	·1233	1232	·1230	·1229	·1227	·1225	·1224	·1222	·1221	0 0 0	1 1 1	1 1 1
8·2	·1220	·1218	·1217	·1215	·1214	·1212	·1211	·1209	·1208	·1206	0 0 0	1 1 1	1 1 1
8·3	·1205	·1203	·1202	·1200	·1199	·1198	·1196	·1195	·1193	·1192	0 0 0	1 1 1	1 1 1
8·4	·1190	·1189	·1188	·1186	·1185	·1183	·1182	·1181	·1179	·1178	0 0 0	1 1 1	1 1 1
8·5	·1176	·1175	·1174	·1172	·1171	·1170	·1168	·1167	·1166	·1164	0 0 0	1 1 1	1 1 1
8·6	·1163	·1161	·1160	·1159	·1157	·1156	·1155	·1153	·1152	·1151	0 0 0	1 1 1	1 1 1
8·7	·1149	·1148	·1147	·1145	·1144	·1143	·1142	·1140	·1139	·1138	0 0 0	1 1 1	1 1 1
8·8	·1136	·1135	·1134	·1133	·1131	·1130	·1129	·1127	·1126	·1125	0 0 0	1 1 1	1 1 1
8·9	·1124	·1122	·1121	·1120	·1119	·1117	·1116	·1115	·1114	·1112	0 0 0	1 1 1	1 1 1
9·0	·1111	·1110	·1109	·1107	·1106	·1105	·1104	·1103	·1101	·1100	0 0 0	1 1 1	1 1 1
9·1	·1099	·1098	·1096	·1095	·1094	·1093	·1092	·1091	·1089	·1088	0 0 0	0 1 1	1 1 1
9·2	·1087	·1086	·1085	·1083	·1082	·1081	·1080	·1079	·1078	·1076	0 0 0	0 1 1	1 1 1
9·3	·1075	·1074	·1073	·1072	·1071	·1070	·1068	·1067	·1066	·1065	0 0 0	0 1 1	1 1 1
9·4	·1064	·1063	·1062	·1060	·1059	·1058	·1057	·1056	·1055	·1054	0 0 0	0 1 1	1 1 1
9·5	·1053	·1052	·1050	·1049	·1048	·1047	·1046	·1045	·1044	·1043	0 0 0	0 1 1	1 1 1
9·6	·1042	·1041	·1040	·1038	·1037	·1036	·1035	·1034	·1033	·1032	0 0 0	0 1 1	1 1 1
9·7	·1031	·1030	·1029	·1028	·1027	·1026	·1025	·1024	·1022	·1021	0 0 0	0 1 1	1 1 1
9·8	·1020	·1019	·1018	·1017	·1016	·1015	·1014	·1013	·1012	·1011	0 0 0	0 1 1	1 1 1
9·9	1010	·1009	·1008	·1007	·1006	·1005	·1004	·1003	·1002	·1001	0 0 0	0 0 1	1 1 1
	0	1	2	3	4	5	6	7	8	9	1 2 3	4 5 6	7 8 9